INVERTEBRATE ZOOLOGY

VOLUME II

INVERTEBRATE

Arthropod Relatives, Chelicerata, Myriapoda

ZOOLOGY

VOLUME II

by ALFRED KAESTNER

University of Munich and
Natural History Collections of Bavaria

translated and adapted from the
German by

HERBERT W. LEVI

Museum of Comparative Zoology,
Harvard University

and

LORNA R. LEVI

INTERSCIENCE PUBLISHERS
A Division of John Wiley & Sons, New York · London · Sydney

Translated and adapted from
Lehrbuch der Speziellen Zoologie, Band I$_1$
Copyright 1963, 1965, 1967 by VEB Gustav Fischer Verlag, Jena

SBN 470   45416
Library of Congress Catalog Card Number 67-13947
Printed in the United States of America

Foreword

This is the second volume of a translation and adaptation of Kaestner's *Lehrbuch der Speziellen Zoologie*. Unlike the first volume, which was shortened, this has been slightly expanded, particularly the sections on habits and classification, and some new illustrations are included to make an up-to-date volume on (mainly) terrestrial noninsect arthropods. It is hoped that this will fill the need for a text and reference for courses in the field, offered at many universities.

The first part of this volume, the arthropod relatives and chelicerates, was published as the first volume in the second edition (1965) in German. The chapter on mandibulates comes from the second part of the first volume, a second edition of the Crustacea (1967) in German. The section on myriapods comes from the first German edition (1963), and has been brought up-to-date.

References through 1966 are given. An attempt has been made to include some of the contents of the most important pertinent papers published in 1967 in galley proof. Not all references have been used, but they serve as a guide to recent literature of the groups of invertebrates. Most of the literature is European, much in French and German. The lack of recent taxonomic revisions and keys to the New World terrestrial invertebrates is a major bottleneck to American research in invertebrate animals. The difficulties of determination discourage research in anatomy, physiology and habits on these animals.

There is some diversity in the use of names for the taxa of higher categories. We have adopted the names in international use, those used in most of the scientific literature, in Grassé, *Traité de Zoologie* (vol. 6) or in Kükenthal *Handbuch der Zoologie*, except for the Diplopoda, for which there is a choice of numerous systems. For diplopods the names of Chamberlin and Hoffman's *Checklist of the Millipeds of North America* have been adopted, with the hope that they will become the accepted names for the orders. (These names, being based on priority, have an unfortunate, built-in lack of stability. Earlier names will no doubt be found and such older names are frequently attended by questions as to their exact date and their application, as the authors often did not designate types nor indicate the categories to which they belong.)

Some zoologists, through ignorance or perhaps gamesmanship in the guise of scholarship, have made frequent changes in generic and specific names, often in contradiction to recommendations or provisions of the *International Code on Zoological Nomenclature*. Therefore we have been prompted to indicate those names on which plenary action has been taken by the International Commission on Zoological Nomenclature and which are listed in the *Official Lists of Family, Generic and Specific Names in Zoology*. In some cases names whose protection is under consideration by the Commission have been indicated; according to Art. 80 of the Code, existing usage is to be maintained until the decision of the Commission is published.

Within each chapter we have followed the outline used in the chapters of the first volume. Perhaps phylogeny has been slighted. The recent writings by several outstanding arthropod specialists, given with rather strong conviction but sometimes opposing, have demonstrated to us the advantages of adopting a somewhat conservative view rather than taking sides in disputes.

Many colleagues have helped in a variety of ways. Several made available to us information or manuscripts in process of publication: Dr. B. J. Marples and Dr. R. Forster, University and Musuem of Otago; Dr. J. A. L. Cooke; Dr. M. Muma; Dr. P. Tongiorgi; Dr. P. Weygoldt; and Mr. P. R. San Martín of the Museo Nacional de Historia Natural, Montevideo. Dr. H. K. Wallace of the University of Florida permitted us to use unpublished information from the B. Theuer thesis. Dr. J. A. L. Cooke of Oxford University, Dr. H. Fechter, Dr. Mechthild Melchers of the University of Munich, and Dr. U. Haacker sent original illustrations from their research papers to facilitate reproduction. Dr. O. Kraus, Senckenbergische Naturforschende Gesellschaft, Frankfurt am Main, gave advice on the numbers of species and on names in some groups. Prof. G. Schneider, Medizin Akademie, Dortmund, read the German version of the physiology of compound eyes.

Many specialists have helped by reading certain chapters. In many cases the readers took issue with some points in the final draft, so acknowledgement of their help does not necessarily imply their complete approval. For reading various chapters we are obliged to: Dr. W. Newman, Scripps Institute (Onychophora); R. P. Higgins, Wake Forest College (Tardigrada); Dr. J. Teague Self, University of Oklahoma (Pentastomida); Dr. J. A. L. Cooke, Oxford Unisersity (all chelicerate chapters); Dr. C. N. Schuster (advice on Xiphosura and a gift of larvae); and Mr. William Eberhard, Harvard University (spiders). In the chapter on spiders the section on orientation was read and rewritten by Dr. P. Tongiorgi, Università di Pisa, and the systematic section was read by Dr. W. J. Gertsch of the American Museum of Natural History. The chapter on pseudoscorpions was read by and partly rewritten by Dr. P. Weygoldt of Duke University, Marine Laboratory and Zoologisches Institut, Universität Freiburg, i.B. The chapter on Solifugae was read by Dr. M. H. Muma, Citrus Experiment Station of the University of Florida. Dr. R. Mitchell, University of Florida, read the chapter on mites, and Dr. D. E. Johnston, Institute of Acarology, the systematic section of the chapter on mites. Dr. J. W. Hedgpeth, Marine Science Laboratory, Oregon State University, read the chapter on pycnogonids. Dr. R. E. Crabill, U. S. National Museum, and Dr. A. A. Weaver, College of Wooster, read the chapter on Chilopoda; and Dr. N. B. Causey, Louisiana State University, and Mr. P. M. Johns, University of Christchurch, that on Diplopoda. Dr. H. B. Boudreaux made suggestions for the introduction of the terrestrial mandibulates; Prof. V. G. Dethier, Princeton University, gave advice concerning the same chapter. Dr. C. C. Hoff, University of New Mexico, gave information on pseudoscorpions; Dr. T. A. Woolley on mites; and Dr. U. Haacker, Technische Hochschule, Darmstadt, supplied information on diplopods. Mrs. Janice Matthews should be thanked for the initial editing and typing of the manuscript.

A. Kaestner
H. W. Levi
L. R. Levi

August 1968

Contents

1.

Phylum Onychophora

The Onychophora include 70 species, the largest of which, *Peripatus torquatus,* can grow to a length of 15 cm.

Onychophora are terrestrial animals with one pair of antennae, a pair of claw-like mouthparts, and numerous unsegmented stumpy legs bearing claws. The body cavity is a mixocoel; traces of the coelom are found in the gonadal cavities and excretory organs. The heart is tube-shaped with metamerically arranged, paired ostia. The respiratory organs are bundles of long tracheae.

Although this phylum includes only few species, it is of great importance phylogenetically, consisting as it does of terrestrial animals in some ways intermediate in structure between annelids and arthropods. The wormlike body is not distinctly segmented, the head not set off. However, segmentation is indicated externally by the appendages, one pair to each metamere. The fine annulation of the skin (Figs. 1–1, 1–2) does not correspond to the true metameres, but results from the alternate bands of columnar hypodermal cells that stand four times higher than the cells of the adjacent grooves. In addition, the hypodermis has numerous small papillae, each bearing a short, fine seta, giving the animal a velvety texture. The external, flexible, chitinous cuticle is barely 1 μm thick. While many species are dark gray or brown, some have red or blue-green pigments and may be striped or speckled.

Anatomy

The musculature underlying the hypodermis is smooth, like that of annelids. From outside to inside there are circular, diagonal, and strong longitudinal muscles. There are also dorsoventrally arranged muscles that divide the inside into one median and two lateral cavities. As in annelids, the muscles are opposed by the turgor of the body fluid. There is no hard skeleton.

APPENDAGES. The anterior is an acron (prostomium) that bears eyes and lacks appendages. It is derived from the preoral lobe of the embryo. The acron

1

Fig. 1–1. *Peripatoides novaezealandiae.* (Photograph by Dr. R. R. Forster.)

is followed, without a clear boundary, by the antennal segment, which bears dorsally a pair of annulate antennae representing the first body appendage (Figs. 1–2, 1–3). The antennae and all subsequent appendages arise as postoral primordia in the embryo. The second appendage is a pair of sickle-shaped mandibles, the jaws (Fig. 1–4), which move from outside to deep inside the mouth during development. Salivary glands open behind the mandibles into the preoral cavity. The third pair of body appendages is represented by the oral papillae on each side of the mouth, through the tips of which open the adhesive or slime glands. The succeeding appendages are walking legs, 14 to 43 pairs occurring at regular intervals. The legs are hollow, conical evaginations of the body (Fig. 1–5). Distally they form wide flat pads, calling to mind those of insects, and are tipped by a pair of claws in a pocket; the claws can be lifted by two extensor muscles.

Onychophoran appendages differ from polychaete parapodia by the presence of claws and the absence of cirri, setae, and acicula. However, they are not arthropod

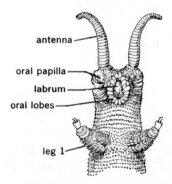

Fig. 1–2. *Peripatoides novaezealandiae,* ventral view of anterior; 0.4 cm long. (After Snodgrass.)

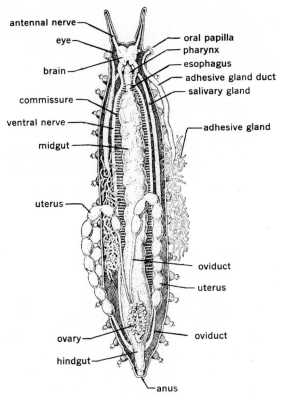

Fig. 1–3. *Peripatoides novaezealandiae,* female, dorsal view; 4 cm long. (After Snodgrass.)

legs as they lack joints. The musculature is smooth rather than striated. In some species there is a longitudinal, ventral slit in the thin cuticle, through which may be evaginated a vesicle similar to the coxal sacs of arthropods (Symphyla, Diplurida) that also live in humid areas. As a desiccated onychophoran will evert the sacs on a damp surface, they are believed to function in water absorption. The adhesive or slime glands, opening at the tips of the oral papillae, consist of an internal ectodermal tube, often longer than the body. Its wide distal portion serves as a reservoir, while the longer narrow proximal portion is lined with the secretory cells (Fig. 1–3) that produce large quantities of mucus, and there may be branches with secretory cells.

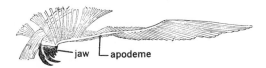

Fig. 1–4. Right mandible of *Peripatoides*. (After Snodgrass.)

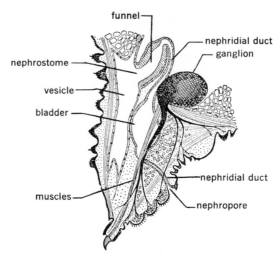

Fig. 1–5. Longitudinal section through a walking leg and a nephridium of *Peripatus.* (After Fedorow from Snodgrass.)

SENSE ORGANS. Except for the eyes, sense organs are simple, consisting of groups of sensory cells lying in the hypodermis of the numerous papillae at the bases of the setae. Similar sensory buds are found in the vicinity of the mouth, where the short, truncate setae probably have a different sensory function.

There is a pair of simple eyes, only 0.2–0.3 mm in diameter, at the base of the antennae. Each eye consists of a cup containing a thick lens, and covered by a cuticular cornea. The retina, or layer of sensory cells bearing rods directed toward the lens, is connected directly to the sides of the brain by optic nerves. As in annelids, the eye develops from an invagination or a pit in the embryonic ectoderm. As the pit closes externally, it cuts off an eyeball, from the interior of which a lens separates. The proximal part of the sphere transforms into the retina.

NERVOUS SYSTEM. The large, paired brain lying above the pharynx connects to widely separated ventral nerve cords by a pair of circumesophageal connectives. The ventral cords are connected by nine to ten fine commissures in each metamere and terminate at the anus. Though they have swellings corresponding to the segments, the cords are lined by nerve cell bodies as well as fibers, and therefore do not have segmental ganglia (Fig. 1–3).

The brain or suprapharyngeal ganglion actually consists of three parts. Anteriorly, the protocerebrum belongs to the acron; it receives the optic nerves and contains two different organs of association, a median central body and a pair of globuli. Such globuli are present also in polychaetes and arthropods, but the central body is known from arthropods only. The second part, the deutocerebrum, receives the antennal nerves and has a large antennal glomerulus. The third or posterior portion, a much smaller part, sends nerves to the area of the mouth and anterior part of the gut. It is assumed to be the tritocerebrum because in *Para-peripatus* it is derived, as are other ganglia, from a pair of ectodermal proliferations, the so-called ventral organs (see Development).

Onychophoran motor neurons are cholinergic like those of annelids but unlike those of arthropods.

DIGESTIVE SYSTEM. The mouth is ventral, just behind the oral papillae. It is surrounded by the oral or peribuccal lobes, forming the preoral cavity, which contains the paired mandibles or jaws (Fig. 1–2). Each jaw consists of a short base and a pair of large sickle-shaped, toothed claws. These are modified appendage tips, and the biting action is with their distal ends. In contrast, Crustacea, and also myriapods and insects, chew with modified limb bases. The functioning of the two types corresponds with their origins. Onychophoran jaws are directed posteriorly and move independently of each other, from anterior to posterior, while the mandibles of arthropods function as pliers, against each other.

From the base of each jaw a tubelike invagination of the hypodermis extends posteriorly as far as the segment of the second walking leg (Fig. 1–4). It secretes a chitinous rod that, as in arthropods, is called an apodeme and functions as a site for muscle attachment.

The mouth opens into an ectodermal, chitin-lined pharynx, the lumen of which is X- or Y-shaped in cross section. A thick layer of radial muscles can pull the walls outward to enlarge the lumen. When a wave of contractions of these radial muscles moves posteriorly from the mouth, followed by a wave of contraction of the circular muscles, strong suction develops. Following the pharynx there is a weakly muscular esophagus, also lined with chitinous cuticle. The esophagus leads into the straight endodermal midgut, which lacks ceca (Fig. 1–3) and is the digestive and absorptive organ. Remains of food pass into the ectodermal hindgut, chitin-lined like the foregut, and out through the anus, which opens behind the last pair of legs.

BODY CAVITY. The body cavity is a mixocoel. The embryo has typically paired coelomic or secondary body cavities derived from mesoderm. During ontogeny these remain small and parts separate to form the coelomic end sac of the nephridia (nephrocoels) and the gonads (gonocoels). The walls of the remaining parts transform into musculature and connective tissue, and their cavities unite with the blastocoel. The lining of the coelom also forms a peritoneal cover for the internal organs, just as in arthropods.

EXCRETORY SYSTEM. The excretory organs are segmentally arranged metanephridia, absent only in the antennal and mandibular segments, and in the metamere bearing the gonopores. Each nephridium consists of a long, ciliated funnel and a coiled nephridial duct leading into a contractile bladder that empties at the base of each appendage (Fig. 1–5). The funnel opens into the coelomic end sac. Funnel and labyrinth form in the embryo from the evagination of a ventromedian coelomic pouch. Those ducts are here considered nephridia that originate from paired coelom pouches, even though they originate through evagination from the coelom lining rather than from proliferation of nephroblasts. There is probably no difference, as the origin of the nephroblasts from ectoderm is doubtful.

The nephridia of the third segment, which bears the oral papillae, differentiate into salivary glands. Each nephridial canal loops from its vesicle to leg segment 10, or sometimes 36. The ducts fuse and open medially, behind the mouth, into the preoral cavity. Many species have a dorsal, bladderlike reservoir.

The nephridia resemble those of arthropods, which also may appear as antennal or maxillary glands (though in only one or two segments). Furthermore, the transformation of nephridia into salivary glands is known among insects. The nephridia differ from those of annelids in the shape of the funnel and in that they do not originate from nephroblasts.

RESPIRATORY SYSTEM. Respiration is by tracheae, which arise as ectodermal tubelike invaginations that penetrate deep into the body cavity. The tracheal epithelium secretes a fine chitinous cuticle toward the lumen.

The openings of the tracheae at first are in groups on the dorsum but in postembryonal development shift downward, the neighboring hypodermis rapidly growing and surrounding the spiracles. In half-grown animals the spiracles are deep in a tubelike respiratory atrium (Fig. 1–6).

Tracheal capillaries end directly at the cells of the organs and therefore must traverse considerable distances; they often are longer than the body. If they branch it is usually at the distal end.

This respiratory system resembles that of the tracheate arthropods, except that instead of a spiracle in each segment, there may be as many as 75 scattered on each metamere, several per mm². From the presence of the tracheae it cannot be concluded, however, that Onychophora are direct ancestors of the tracheate

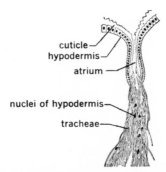

cuticle
hypodermis
atrium

nuclei of hypodermis

tracheae

Fig. 1–6. Longitudinal section through a respiratory atrium and spiracle of *Peripatopsis capensis*; diameter of atrium about 0.03 mm; capillaries 0.001–0.004 mm. (After Schneider.)

arthropods, as tracheae appear independently also in arachnids and in crustaceans (terrestrial wood-lice). The indication is rather that tracheae evolved independently, by convergent evolution.

CIRCULATORY SYSTEM. The direct supply of oxygen delivered by the tracheae frees the circulatory system of one of its functions. As one might expect the system is simple, consisting only of a heart; arteries and veins are lacking. The blood flows in the spaces between organs, and therefore is often called hemolymph. The heart consists of a median dorsal tube of circular muscles running anteriorly from the segment before the last and opening into a blood sinus in the vicinity of the first pair of legs. It has a pair of slitlike ostia in each metamere, through which blood enters from the pericardial sinus, a component of the general body cavity or hemocoel. In its shape, function, and surrounding pericardial sinus, it is similar to the corresponding organ of arthropods. Both anteriorly and posteriorly it empties blood into the hemocoel.

REPRODUCTIVE SYSTEM. The Onychophora have separate sexes, fertilization is internal, and development is ovi-, vivi-, or ovoviviparous. Males are usually smaller than females. The gonads are paired dorsal tubes in the posterior half of the body, opening through a median gonopore anterior to the anus, between the last two pairs of legs.

Each testis empties posteriorly into a wide seminal vesicle. From this there is a long, coiled duct into a median ectodermal canal, the proximal half of which forms the spermatophore, the muscular distal end serving as an ejaculatory duct.

The tubelike ovaries are fused at their anterior and posterior ends. From the seminal receptacles at their bases the oviducts loop anteriorly and finally fuse to form a short ectodermal vagina (Fig. 1–3). The posterior part of the oviduct serves as the uterus in viviparous species.

The gonads are similar to those of arthropods, but resemble those of annelids only in derivation of their walls and lumen from coelom. As in arthropods, paired gonads develop from coelomic sinuses of several posterior segments, between which the septa disappear. While the paired gonadial ducts develop from the coelomic pouches of the gonoporic metamere, the unpaired median part is formed independently from a median ectodermal invagination.

Reproduction

Mating takes place as the male crawls over the female and, holding her between his legs, deposits the spermatophore any place on her dorsum or side. There does not appear to be any courtship, and in captivity males or immatures become covered with spermatophores, even if females are present. Within 14 days one female was observed to receive 180 spermatophores, each 0.2 mm in diameter. Numerous leucocytes accumulate at the site of attachment; within 7 to 10 days they dissolve the tissues and break through the hypodermis and cuticle to the spermatophore wall. Bundles of sperm then penetrate the female and swim in the blood between tissues. On reaching the ovaries, they penetrate and fertilize the eggs in the lumen. Many are taken up and digested by immature eggs.

Development

Among the few species there is great diversity in development. Species of the genus *Ooperipatus* lay undeveloped eggs, 2 mm in diameter and rich in yolk, in moist places. Their development is unknown. All other species retain their eggs in the oviduct for 6 to 13 months while they develop to young animals. The large, yolk-rich eggs of some genera possibly supply enough nutrient for the development of the embryo. But, eggs with little or no yolk, 0.04–0.6 mm in diameter, are nourished by the mother and produce viviparous young very much larger than the eggs: *Peripatus trinitatis* has eggs 0.04 mm in diameter and the newborn young are 22 mm long. The additional nourishment, provided in the form of oviduct secretions, is taken through the egg membrane. In some species of *Peripatopsis* special extraembryonal dorsal spaces of the eggs take up such fluids. More complicated is the food supply of the small eggs of *Peripatus trinitatis*. These proliferate a tissue on the dorsum, which fuses to the uterus wall, forming a placenta that absorbs food from the mother.

The small eggs of *Peripatus trinitatis* have total cleavage while large yolk-rich eggs have superficial cleavage. The further development is described for *Peripatopsis*. These do not have a blastopore, but on the presumptive posterior of the venter, at an area of inward proliferation, blastomeres give rise to endodermal and mesodermal layers. As the number of mesodermal cells on each side of the future venter increases, they become organized into two mesoderm bands. These later become segmented, starting anteriorly, one pair of coelomic pouches for each somite. Subsequently they split internally, forming the coelomic cavities, just as do the mesodermal bands in the annelid trochophore. There are as many pairs of coelomic pouches as there are body appendages, the first belonging to the antennal segment.

The coelomic pouches grow dorsally to meet at the midline and from their walls presumably proliferate cells that give rise to heart, muscles, epithelial tissues lining organs, and connective tissues. The cavities themselves persist only as the nephridial vesicles and gonad lumen.

The pharynx and esophagus develop as ectodermal invaginations at the site of the mouth; hindgut at the site of the anus. The ectoderm also forms paired ventral spherical proliferations in each metamere, the so-called ventral organs (Fig. 1–7) which are the primordia of the ventral nerve cords. In the head lobe the ventral organs become the protocerebrum.

In *Paraperipatus amboinensis* a pair of small ectodermal proliferations anterior to the mandibular segment has been interpreted as the primordium of the tritocerebrum or the ventral organ of a premandibular segment lacking appendages. There also appears a small coelomic pouch anterior to that of the mandibular segment. There are no corresponding observations for other genera and more study is necessary to clarify the homologies of the brain and head segments. On both sides of the germ band in each segment, the ectoderm evaginates a cone-shaped appendage bud. Mesoderm drawn into the bud from the body wall forms the musculature of the limb. The most anterior pair of buds move dorsally to become the antennae, the second the mandibles, and the third the oral papillae. The remainder differentiate into walking legs.

The first ectodermal formations leading to the development of a head are regular. These are followed, however, by a number of conspicuous changes in the relative positions of parts. The mouth shifts posteriorly along the midline, so that the antennae with their ganglia come to lie in a preoral position (Fig. 1–7a). While the antennal ganglia form the deutocerebrum, they approach and fuse with the protocerebum, forming an apparently uniform brain. The two following pairs of appendages shift. Next to the anterior appendage are several lateral folds (Fig. 1–7a). The appendage and these folds move medially toward the mouth and differentiate into mandibles (Fig. 1–7b), and the lateral skin folds become the oral lobes. By continued shifting the original third pair of appendages becomes the apparent second, the oral papillae lying anterior to the mouth (Fig. 1–7b). From the tip of each papilla an ectodermal invagination deep into the body forms the adhesive gland.

Young are born after 6 to 13 months of development. In *Peripatopsis moseleyi* parturition takes 15 minutes, usually two young covered by mucus appearing

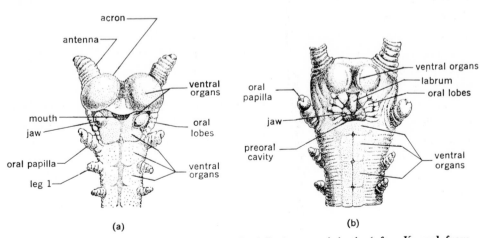

(a) (b)

Fig. 1–7. **Development of the anterior end of *Peripatus trinitatis* (after Kennel from Snodgrass): (a) the mandibles are still lateral and anterior to the oral papillae, the third pair of appendages; (b) the mandibles have shifted medially and lie at the same level as the oral papillae.**

posterior end first. A few minutes later the young molt and are free of mucus within half an hour. Though smaller than adults, they look similar and usually have the same number of metameres. *Peripatopsis moseleyi* becomes sexually mature in 9 to 11 months but does not reach maximum size of 7.5 cm for three and one-half years.

The average life span is 6 or 7 years and during this time *Peripatopsis* molts regularly every 13 to 18 days. The animal causes the cuticle to break between the antennae by bending them ventrally, and by extending and contracting the body, continues the break along the dorsal midline to the end of the body. The soft skin moves ventrally toward the legs, and finally is pushed, accordion-style, from anterior to posterior, where it shrivels up after 2 hours. The skin, which includes the jaw cuticle, the lining of the fore- and hindgut, and old attached spermatophores, is usually eaten.

Relationships

The anatomy and ontogeny of the Onychophora show clearly that the phylum had annelid-like ancestors. The most important annelid characters include:
  1. homonomous body segmentation
  2. presence of nephridia in most segments
  3. smooth musculature and muscle physiology
  4. simple spherical eye structure and photoreceptors (retinal cells)
  5. cholinergic motor neurons

At the same time the Onychophora display arthropod-like characteristics:
  1. the mixocoel
  2. the modification of a pair of appendages into mandibles
  3. claws on appendages
  4. heart with ostia and formation of a pericardial sinus
  5. the anatomy and development of the gonads
  6. transformation of a nephridium into a salivary gland
  7. tracheae
  8. coxal vesicles
  9. superficial cleavage
  10. chitinous cuticle
  11. dependency of locomotion on leg musculature rather than on serpentine or peristaltic motions
  12. lactic dehydrogenase similar to that of mandibulate arthropods

A study of the fine structure of peripatus eyes indicates that in their general organization they are similar to the eyes of polychaetes; the presence of cilia and kinetosomes is also polychaete-like. The arrangement of microvilli, in an even array of straight cylindrical projections, is arthropod-like; nereid microvilli are twisted.

Arthropods respond with convulsions and hyperexcitability to picrotoxin and glutamate injections, while onychophorans, like annelids, are insensitive to these compounds; but, eserine injections are convulsive.

From this account it may be concluded that the Onychophora represent a stage in the development from annelid to arthropod. However, some special adaptations speak against this view and preclude the possibility that onychophorans are phylogenetic missing links between annelid and arthropod organization:

1. the transformation of the claws of the second appendages into jaws and their anterior-posterior motion parallel to the body axis
2. the large number of tracheal spiracles on each segment and their distribution over the back and sides
3. the large distance between the two ventral nerve cords
4. the structure of the eyes

Considering also that the mixocoel and tracheae appear convergently in various animal groups, the Onychophora are best considered a special phylum. Probably they branched from the annelids earlier than the line that evolved into arthropods, although they certainly represent a general level of organization through which such arthropods as the Myriapoda and Insecta may have passed. Their arthropod-like specializations are clearly superimposed on an annelid-like organization. Like the Annelida, having only slight protection against desiccation, most Onychophora are limited to moist habitats.

The leaf litter and rotting wood inhabited by most Onychophora species perhaps has a parallel in the accumulated eelgrass and seaweeds along shorelines in its high humidity and temperature insulating properties. Thus the onychophoran ancestors may have invaded land via the shore line detritus, and with their changed method of locomotion came the disappearance of the large coelom spaces, a development that occurred convergently in walking arthropods, the Myzostomida, and leeches, among the annelids.

Habits

The Onychophora are denizens of humid areas. They live on the ground in litter, pieces of wood, rotting logs, between stones in forests, or near streams. Only a few times have they been collected in dry, sunny ravines under stones. They have little protection against water loss. During 30 minutes at 24° over calcium chloride, *Epiperipatus brasiliensis* loses half as much of its body weight as does an earthworm, but 22 times as much as a millipede. In contrast to the tracheate arthropods, the Onychophora have only a thin cuticle, and the spiracles of the tracheae cannot be closed. *Peripatopsis moseleyi* appears to be highly sensitive to differences in humidity. The humidity receptors seem to be scattered over the body. Experimentally, at 25°C it prefers areas with 98% humidity.

In captivity, water lost could be reabsorbed from wet cotton. Under drying conditions most species rest contracted or rolled up, reducing the surface. Some hibernate or estivate in this position.

Many species do not need a warm climate. *Symperipatus oviparus* of New Zealand lives in areas that are covered four to five months by snow.

LOCOMOTION. *Peripatopsis* walks with its legs, holding the body above the ground. The legs are lifted and moved forward without touching the ground again until the forward movement is completed. Claws are extended only on slippery surface. Once on the ground the leg pushes back, moving its proximal attachment forward. This movement is carried out by extrinsic muscles, originating in the trunk. The body muscles control the turgor, and extend and contract the body of the animal, preventing neighboring legs from obstructing locomotion. Onychophora which are only 1.5 cm when contracted may extend to 4 cm when walking.

There are various gaits, but unlike myriapod gaits, the duration of the step does not change. Sometimes the pushing phase of each leg is twice as long as the forward swinging phase, in which case many legs are on the ground pushing at the same time. The animal moves slowly but pushes with force, as between leaves and particles of litter. However, if the backward pushing to forward swinging phase is in a relation of 4 to 7, relatively few legs are pushing at the same time, and progress is twice as fast. In such rapid movement the legs are extended and their angle of movement increased. *Peripatopsis* of 5–6 cm long can reach a speed of 50–60 cm/min, but usually the pushing phase equals the phase of swinging forward, so that while one leg pushes, the one in front moves forward. Elongated, Onychophora can crawl through crevices or holes much smaller than the body diameter.

SENSES. Often the anterior three pairs of legs do not participate in walking and the head is moved rhythmically. The antennae reach forward to feel the way or locate obstacles. The setae of the abundant sense buds are tactile receptors and may recognize air currents as well. Onychophora are very sensitive to air currents and try to avoid them. However, hungry animals do not recognize sources of food from a distance. Food is located by touch of the antennae and lips, and is probably also examined by the buccal cavity, indicating that the modified sensory setae in the oral area respond to chemical stimuli. Although the organization of the eyes should permit image formation, there is little evidence that onychophorans use their eyes except simply to differentiate light and dark, and determine the direction of light. The animals move away from light.

DEFENSE. *Peripatus* hardly reacts on touching a member of its own species or a sow bug, but if disturbed, faces its antagonist and forcefully spurts mucus several times from the adhesive gland of the oral papillae. The secretion is too fast to follow by eye in detail. One sees only a stream of fluid 10–15 cm long; some species can spurt 30 or even 50 cm through the air. The secretion immediately hardens to form a very sticky web, and an adversary coming in contact with it is glued to the ground with its legs tangled up. Even large grasshoppers are immediately immobilized. The gluey threads do not stick to the skin of *Peripatus* but separate into individual droplets. The adhesive is used for defense against all kinds of enemies. Two South African species use it also to capture rapidly moving prey such as grasshoppers and centipedes. But all observations concern captive animals; in nature they rarely emerge from the litter, even at night.

FEEDING. In captivity Onychophora feed on freshly killed termites, caterpillars, apterygote insects, snails, and sow bugs, but never on animals dead for several hours. Thus it is assumed that in nature they are predacious, capturing live prey. The prey discovered by the tentacles is held tightly by the lips and pharynx suction while the jaws within the buccal cavity slit the prey open, cutting at a rate of 14 times in 10 seconds. Thus the superficial muscles of the prey are cut into small bits and sucked in. Immediately, salivary secretions containing a mixture of enzymes (amylase, glycogenase, protease, and polypeptidase) pour over the wound and dissolve all soft parts of the prey. After this nutrient fluid has been sucked up only the exoskeleton of a sow bug or termite remains.

Peristaltic waves carry the material to the midgut where digestion takes place. The midgut walls consist of secretory and absorptive columellar cells. The absorptive cells secrete a membrane within the lumen of the midgut, barely 1 μm thick, which surrounds the contents sausagelike. Enzymes penetrate this membrane and digest the enclosed food particles. Nutrient materials then diffuse out through the membrane and are absorbed. Digestion takes about 18 hours in *Peripatopsis*. Later, peristaltic waves move the membrane and indigestible materials out of the hindgut via the anus. The absorptive cells also serve as storage tissue, and in well-nourished animals, contain proteins, lipid droplets, and glycogen.

EXCRETION. Excretion is carried on by the nephridia, the midgut, and the pericardial cells. Every 3 to 4 days the nephridia of *Peripatopsis moseleyi* empty a drop of urine, altogether about 10 mm^3, containing various nitrogenous compounds but no urea. Crystalline uric acid is excreted by the absorptive cells of the midgut. The pericardial cells function as nephrocytes, storing excretory products taken from the blood.

DISTRIBUTION. Onychophora are limited to tropics and the temperate areas of the southern hemisphere. They extend north into the Caribbean, central Mexico, and in Asia they are found in southeastern islands and continentally to latitude 28° in the Himalayas. In Africa they are not found north of the equator.

Classification

Onychophora are grouped into only two families.

Peripatidae. The gonopore is between the pair of legs preceding the last. They have 22 to 43 pairs of legs, and the number may be variable within a species. Most are 1.9 to 15 cm long and have brown or red pigments. The family is tropical in distribution.

Eggs of *Eoperipatus,* 1 mm in diameter, have a large quantity of yolk, which nourishes the developing embryos. In *Peripatus* the eggs are very small (0.04-0.05 mm) and the embryo is nourished through a placenta.

Peripatopsidae. The gonopore is just anterior to the last legs. Species are small to medium in size, have 13 to 25 pairs of legs, and often have blue-green pigments. The family is confined mostly to the temperate southern hemisphere. Different species of the same genus are found on separate continents.

The embryos never have a placenta. *Peripatopsis,* limited to South Africa, has small eggs, 0.15-0.6 mm in diameter. *Paraperipatus* eggs are even smaller, 0.06-0.12 mm. In both genera the embryo derives nourishment through the egg membrane. *Ooperipatus,* except for one species, is oviparous; the eggs are 2 mm in diameter.

References

Alexander, A. J. 1957. Onychophoran behavior. *Ann. Natal Mus.* 14:35–43.

———— and Ewer, D. W. 1955. Function of the eversible sacs of *Opisthopatus. Ibid.* 13:217–222.

Anderson, D. T. 1966. Early embryology of the Oligochaeta, Hirudinea and Onychophora. *Proc. Linnean Soc. New South Wales* 91:10–43.

Brinck, P. 1956. Onychophora, *in* Hanström et al., *South African Animal Life,* Stockholm 4:1–32.

Bursell, E. and Ewer, D. W. 1950. Reaction to humidity of *Peripatopsis. J. Exp. Biol.* 26:335-353.

Clark, A. H. and Zetek, J. 1946. Onychophores of Panama. *Proc. U.S. Nat. Mus.* 96:205–213.

Cuénot, L. 1949. Onychophores, *in* Grassé, *Traité de Zoologie,* Masson et Cie, Paris, 6:3–37.

Dodds, S. E. and Ewer, D. W. 1952. Rate of water loss of *Peripatopsis. Ann. Natal Mus.* 12:275–278.

Eakin, R. M. and Westfall, J. A. 1965. Structure of eye of *Peripatus. Z. Zellforsch.* 68:278–300.

Ewer, D. W. and van den Berg, R. 1954. A note on the pharmacology of the dorsal muscula-ture of *Peripatopsis. J. Exp. Biol.* 31:497–500.

Florey, E. and E. 1965. Cholinergic neurons in the Onychophora. *Comp. Biochem. Physiol.* 15:125–136.

Lawrence, R. F. 1953. *The Biology of the Cryptic Fauna of Forests.* A. Balkema, Capetown.

Holliday, B. A. 1942. Observations on Onychophora. *Ann. Natal Mus.* 10:233–244.

Manton, S. M. 1937. Feeding, digestion and food storage of *Peripatopsis. Philos. Trans. Roy. Soc. London* (B) 227:411–464.

———— 1938. Passage of spermatozoa into the ovary in *Peripatopsis. Ibid.* 228:421–441.

———— 1938. Onychophora found in Cape Colony. *Ann. Mag. Nat. Hist.* (11) 1:476–480.

———— 1949. Early embryonic stages of *Peripatopsis. Philos. Trans. Roy. Soc. London* (B) 233:483–580.

———— 1950. The locomotion of *Peripatus. J. Linnean Soc. Zool.* 41:529–570.

———— 1952. Locomotory mechanisms of arthropods. *Ibid.* 42:93–117.

———— 1953. Locomotory habits and evolution of arthropodan groups. *Symp. Soc. Exp. Biol.* 7:339–476.

Morrison, P. R. 1946. Water loss and oxygen consumption in *Peripatus. Biol. Bull.* 91:181–188.

Pflugfelder, O. 1948. Entwicklung von *Paraperipatus. Zool. Jahrb. Abt. Anat.* 69:443–492.

Robson, E. A. 1964. The cuticle of *Peripatopsis. Quart. J. Microscop. Sci.* 105:281–299.

Wilson, A. C. and Kaplan, N. O. 1964. Enzyme structure, its relation to taxonomy, *in* Leone, C. A., *Taxonomic Biochemistry and Serology.* Ronald, New York. pp. 321–346.

Zacher, F. 1933. Onychophora, *in* Kükenthal, *Handbuch der Zoologie,* De Gruyter, Berlin, 3(2):73–138.

2.

Phylum Tardigrada, Water Bears

There are close to 350 species of Tardigrada, the largest of which, *Macrobiotus hufelandi,* can reach a length of 1.2 mm.

Tardigrades are minute, aquatic animals similar to arthropods. The short cylindrical body has four pairs of stubby legs tipped by claws and the mouth has a pair of sharp stylets used in feeding. There are no respiratory or circulatory organs.

Tardigrades are strange dwarf forms, with a preference for temporary water drops on cushion plants, often cryptogams. *Echiniscus parvulus* on hatching measures only 0.05 mm; adults are usually more than 0.1 mm long. However, body size may depend on the particular location: *Macrobiotus hufelandi* averages 0.3 mm on the island of Heligoland in the North Sea; 0.6 mm on Flores (Indonesia); 0.9 mm in Vorarlberg, Austria; and 1.2 mm at Canadian collecting sites. The animal may mature before reaching maximum size.

The body is ventrally somewhat flattened (Fig. 2–1). Four pairs of stumpy legs, five pairs of ventral ganglia, and five pairs of coelomic pouches in the embryo indicate that these are metameric animals. The epidermis secretes a nonchitinous cuticle consisting of albuminoids, which is permeable to water and swells. In marine species the cuticle is thin; in moss inhabitants (*Echiniscus*) it may have thicker areas, forming plates. These plates as well as the legs and head indicate the segmentation (Fig. 2–1). Armored species often have threads or thorns, but never movable setae.

Tardigrades exhibit constancy of cell numbers, as do the rotifers. Constancy could be demonstrated for the epidermis, muscles and fore- and midgut of several species, but does not appear to hold for the nervous system.

Some species are brightly colored. The pigments, olive green, brown, pink, and violet, may be dissolved in the cuticle, or embedded in the epidermis; they may consist of stored excretory products. The transparent epidermis may reveal blue midgut cells, colored food spheres in the mixocoel, and yellowish green intestinal contents.

Anatomy

The muscles, consisting of smooth fibers with one nucleus each, are arranged in metameres but they do not form a continuous muscular body wall. They also connect trunk and appendages. The anterior end of the Heterotardigrada has one median and a pair of lateral filiform appendages, these cirri are innervated from the brain; they are absent in the Eutardigrada. The four pairs of legs are almost equidistant, the last pair extending posteriorly (Fig. 2–2). Each leg of the Arthrotardigrada has a distinct annulate joint membrane, in other groups only indicated or missing. It permits drawing the distal segment into the proximal ones, shortening the leg. The legs are almost always tipped by claws, the number of which varies among genera. Some marine Arthrotardigrada have tubelike toes; in *Batillipes* the widened tips form attachment pads. These small animals can attach themselves to the sand grains between which they live; an ectodermal gland keeps the pads sticky.

SENSE ORGANS AND NERVOUS SYSTEM. The sense organs are the cirri and, close to the brain, cup-shaped pigment ocelli containing only one optic cell. In *Macrobiotus,* free nerve endings in the epidermis have been demonstrated to come from 19 axons from the brain and subesophageal ganglia. The nervous system consists of the dorsal brain, a pair of thick circumesophageal connectives and a ventral cord consisting of five medially fused ganglia; the most anterior is the subesophageal ganglion, the others are body ganglia that innervate legs (Fig. 2–2).

The connectives of the ventral ganglia do not bear nerve cells. The brain, which has two lateral lobes is not differentiated and lacks association centers such as globuli. But there is an unusual connective between the lateral lobe of the brain and the second ventral ganglion (Fig. 2–2).

DIGESTIVE SYSTEM. The mouth is anterior and leads into a buccal cavity, anteriorly reinforced by rings or lamellae, that can be pressed against food items (Fig. 2–3). In the back of the buccal cavity on each side is a stylet sheath, through which the tip of the stylet extends into the buccal cavity. Each calcareous stylet consists of an anteriorly pointed rod with two strong condyles at

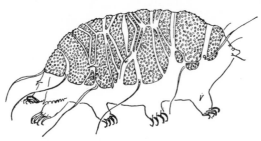

Fig. 2–1. *Echiniscus scrofa,* lateral view, anterior on right; 0.25 mm long. (After Marcus.)

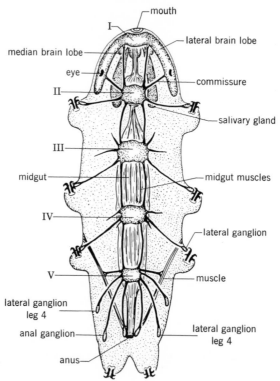

Fig. 2–2. *Macrobiotus hufelandi,* ventral view showing nervous system; 0.2 mm long. (After Marcus.)

the base. The notch between the condyles rides on a transverse chitinous support, a spring, originating from the foregut.

Each stylet is moved by two muscles attached at the base. The protractor, which originates on the wall of the buccal cavity, pulls the stylet anterior extending it out of the mouth. The retractor originates on the wall of the sucking pharynx. Transverse muscles hold the base of the stylet on its support.

The cuticular pharynx has two parts, an anterior narrow tube and a posterior muscular sucking apparatus with radial muscles. The cell number of the radial muscles, like that of the epidermal cells in this part of the gut, is constant. The muscles may widen the Y-shaped lumen, causing suction. There are no ring muscles. The cuticular esophagus carries food to the midgut, which consists of a constant number (to 40) of columnar cells. In the Eutardigrada it forms a long uniform sac (Fig. 2–4); in the Heterotardigrada it is constricted from both sides by the appendage muscles, forming five or six diverticula. The ectodermal hindgut is lined with cuticle. There are no glands along the gut except for a pair of long salivary glands situated dorsolateral to the sucking pharynx and opening into the buccal cavity.

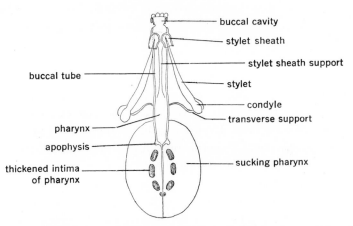

Fig. 2–3. *Macrobiotus intermedius*, mouthparts; 0.08 mm long. (After Marcus.)

BODY CAVITY. The spacious body cavity is filled with fluid, and appears to be a mixocoel. On the inside of the epidermis freshly hatched *Echiniscoides* have a layer of 143 storage cells, the cell number and position of which are constant. These all may represent the vestiges of the parietal wall of the coelom pouches. Later these cells float in the body cavity; the contained lipids and carbohydrates disappear during molting, at which time the animal does not feed.

EXCRETORY SYSTEM. Wastes are excreted by ectodermal organs, mainly the epidermis, thickenings of the hindgut wall and three short blind ducts that hang from the hindgut into the body cavity. These blind ducts, which contain strongly refractive material, might possibly be Malpighian tubules (Fig. 2–4). They are not found in Heterotardigrada, in which the salivary glands and midgut cells have an excretory function.

REPRODUCTIVE SYSTEM. Tardigrades have sexes separate. Males of some species are smaller than females. The gonads are single and of different lengths depending on their stage of maturity. Gonad walls are formed by only a few large cells. The male gonoducts are paired, the female single. In the Eutardi-

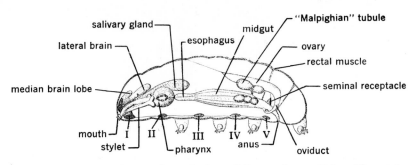

Fig. 2–4. *Macrobiotus*, lateral view; 0.3 mm long. (After Marcus.)

grada the gonoducts open ventrally into the hindgut, forming a cloaca (Fig. 2–4). But the heterotardigrades have a separate, preanal gonopore. Males of some species have never been found.

Reproduction

The males of the eutardigrades embrace the females with the forelegs and spray the sperm into the cloaca. Nevertheless, internal fertilization is known only among the moss-dwellers. During copulation the females of pond-dwelling species molt so rapidly that the sperm sprayed into the cloaca is received by the molted skin, which also contains the eggs.

The eggs, 0.04–0.17 mm in diameter, are of two types: of the smooth type, from 3 to 30 are contained in the mother's exuvium (*Echiniscus, Milnesium,* many *Hypsibius*). Others, bearing thorns or cuticularized areas, usually are free (most *Macrobiotus, Echiniscoides*). Some *Hypsibius* carry the exuvium, filled with developing eggs above the posterior end.

Development

The zygote undergoes total cleavage. Five pairs of coelomic pouches are constricted off from the archenteron (Fig. 2–5), a form of coelom formation unique among the Protostomia, found only in the Brachiopoda. It is, however, characteristic among the Deuterostomia. The anterior four coelomic pouches disintegrate, and their walls transform into muscles and storage cells. The fifth pair fuses to a single gonad from which the gonoducts grow. The nervous system originates from a thickened layer of ectoderm. After separation from the superficial cells, the two bands widen in four places to produce the posterior ganglion pairs that innervate the legs. The legs originate from evaginations of the body in the areas of coelomic pouches two to five, which at first extend into the

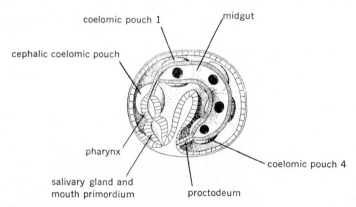

Fig. 2–5. *Hypsibius* embryo, right body half, showing formation of coelomic pouches; 0.04 mm long. (After Marcus.)

legs. The young hatch 3 to 40 days after the eggs are laid and, except for size, resemble the adults.

In cultures tardigrades may live more than a year; animals 18 months old show no loss of vitality. Most molt throughout the entire life. Six days before molting the lining of the foregut and both stylets are pushed out of the buccal cavity. Then the entire cuticle, including claws is shed. New claws develop from a thick epidermal cone on the leg tip. First, two cavities appear into which the claws are secreted; the walls later part, freeing the claws. Similarly, the stylets with their supports and the lining of the buccal cavity are renewed in a thick solid cone-shaped mass that has its base outside on the pharynx wall, its tip on the wall of the buccal cavity. The cell accumulation arises from ectodermal salivary glands moving along the midline of the body. Soon one sees the mouthparts developing in the middle, the buccal cavity behind, and at the sides of the stylets, the transverse supports that connect to the muscles.

Relationships

The appearance of five pairs of coelomic pouches, postoral ganglion pairs and four pairs of appendages tied to the four posterior ganglia and coelomic pouches, shows that the tardigrades belong to the group of phyla of segmented protostomes. They differ from the other phyla by numerous characters that might be explained as adaptations to small size: the lack of respiratory and circulatory systems and nephridia. Also the lack of teloblastic segment formation may be explained by the shortness of the body: there are only five pairs of postoral metameres. On the other hand, the very different origin of the coelomic pouches from the archenteron can not be explained as an adaptation to small size; it appears to be a specialization.

The Onychophora are closest in structure to the tardigrades, as evidenced by the appendage shape, indistinctly set off head, smooth muscles, mixocoel, and gonad formation. It is doubtful that the mouthparts of the two phyla can be compared. The tardigrade stylets originate, as do the leg claws, in an epidermal proliferation, suggesting that they represent lost appendages belonging to the first segment. They would then be homologous to the Onychophora mandibles, which are tips of appendages, but not to the mouthparts of arthropods, which are proximal parts of appendages. But their origin can only be surmised.

The tardigrades differ from arthropods by lacking a distinctly delimited head, antennae, and segmented legs, by having smooth muscles and by the mouthparts. All these characters are unrelated to small size, but might be considered primitive, possibly bringing the tardigrades close to arthropod ancestors. But there is no doubt of their specialization. They are here considered a separate phylum because, like the Onychophora, they represent a developmental level reached from annelid-like ancestors.

Traditionally, many students of phylogeny have assumed monophyletic origin of the large phyla, especially of those belonging to the segmented protostomes. In this view, the stumplike legs of the Onychophora, Tardigrada, and Pentastomida would represent modifications of arthropod ancestors. But this view does not entirely correspond with our knowledge of onychophoran anatomy. Newer investigations, especially in paleontology, force us critically to question the monophyletic origin of the large groups. For instance, recent paleontological research has shown that the gymnosperms and the mammals may not be monophyletic. With groups such as the Onychophora, Tardigrada, and Pentastomida, which lack fossils, the specializations make us assume separate lines of evolution and force us to place them in separate phyla.

The opinion that the tardigrades are reduced arthropods can be dismissed. The habit of climbing would not force reduction of leg segmentation, as is demonstrated by mites, even though the legs are much shortened in some mites (Tetrapodili) as an adaptation to life in narrow tunnels.

Habits

The majority of tardigrades inhabit freshwater, both ponds and lakes to a depth of 150 m, but mainly temporary water drops on lichens and moss cushions, especially those of moist trees, walls, on straw roofs, or in gutters. The easiest way to collect tardigrades is to cover dried mosses with a little water in a watch glass. Examine the water a few hours later under a magnification of 20 to 50 times. In Japan tardigrades have been found on dead bamboo leaves. Above timberline in high mountains they are found in cushion plants such as moss campion, *Silene acaulis;* purple saxifrage, *Saxifraga oppositifolia; Cerastium* and *Sedum.* Nearly two dozen species, all but one belonging to the Heterotardigrada, are marine.

It is possible that the marine shores were the primary habitat of the tardigrades, as the Arthrotardigrada found here display certain primitive features. From the shore they may have colonized the dryer tide zones where the Echiniscida, related to the Arthrotardigrada, are represented by the primitive *Echiniscoides* (Fig. 2–7). Species that adapted to temporary dryness and freshwater could invade the moist cushions of terrestrial plants where many Eutardigrada and relatives of the large genus *Echiniscus* are found. The Eutardigrada alone show a tendency to live permanently in ponds and lakes. These probably arrived there via freshwater beach mosses covered by water. Many tardigrades that otherwise are found in dry places inhabit mosses that may sometimes be covered by water.

The distribution of lichen- and moss-dwellers is effected by wind, small animals, and raindrops that carry the eggs and tuns (Fig. 2–6). A city monument erected in 1904 and standing free was soon covered by moss cushions. Two years later two tardigrade species lived in the moss; in 1927, after 23 years, five species were found. This fauna could only have arrived by air.

Tardigrades live in all climates, including the Arctic and Antarctic, and in mountains to 6600 m (21,000 ft) elevation. *Macrobiotus hufelandi* and *Milnesium tardigradum* are cosmopolitan. Often their populations are high: 500 have been found in one gram of air-dried moss, and once even 22,000 were found. In 15 g of dry moss from Colorado, 1131 *Macrobiotus islandicus* have been found.

TUNS AND CYSTS. All species living on plant cushions are endangered by drought and cold. They have evolved adaptations for survival in the extreme conditions of these habitats. In the dried state, tuns, the animals contract and lose water, becoming resistant to drought, cold, and heat. The little water remaining is highly saturated or in swollen albumin that cannot freeze or evaporate. Similar adaptations, removal of surplus water and reduction of metabolism, are found in encysted protozoa, rotifers, and many overwintering plant seeds.

The stimulus to change to the dry state is lack of oxygen. If the moisture film shrinks smaller than the diameter of the animals, they stop movement and shorten the body, reducing the surface. About 45 minutes later, head and appendages are pulled in and the tardigrades have become egg-shaped and immobile (Fig. 2–6). *Macrobiotus hufelandi* can shorten 60% and increase its thickness 10%. The volume is reduced by water loss. The musculature shortens, the internal fluid thickens, the animal loses its transparency. Oxygen consumption is reduced to one six-hundredth.

If rain moistens the moss, the tuns rapidly swell. One can see that as water penetrates the cuticle the animal again becomes transparent. If dried for only 3 days they will begin to move after only 14 minutes, and within half an hour have reached original size.

Dried *Macrobiotus* survives at 15°C for at least 6 years; other species survive at least 2½ years, but will not recover after 3 years. In the course of their lives they may become desiccated more than 12 times.

The resistance of the dried animals is surprising. Dried *Macrobiotus* survived 20 months in liquid air (between −190 and −200°C), but died after 22 months

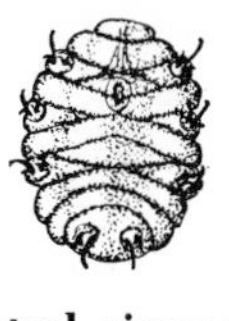

Fig. 2–6. *Hypsibius* tun, ventral view; 0.2 mm long. (After Marcus.)

at this temperature. After 8½ hours in liquid helium ($-272°C$) they survived without damage. After 10 hours at 60° to 65°C, and 1 hour at 92°C, a slower "awakening," 15 minutes, was the only observed adverse consequence. (The lower the water content, the higher the coagulation temperature of proteins.) At 100°C animals survived only 15 minutes with 30% mortality; 103°C was lethal. In 8% humidity, most tuns survive 60 days in a desiccator. But moistened animals may take 3 hours to extend and some die with the first movements. Whether metabolism stops at such extremes is not proved, even by their survival in pure H, N, He, CO_2, and H_2S.

Not all species can tolerate drying and freezing; chiefly resistant are the moss-inhabiting Eutardigrada and Echiniscida and their eggs, even if partly developed.

Macrobiotus and *Hypsibius* not only form tuns but can also encyst. The epidermis withdraws from the cuticle and the spherical body, legs pulled in, lies motionless in its molt. Soon the new cuticle thickens to form a thick cyst within the old cuticle. The cyst survives for months, its rate of O_2 use only one-fourth that of active individuals. As water droplets remain in the body, the cyst is more sensitive than the tuns. Even 3 hours at 60°C is fatal. Before crawling out of its cyst, the body withdraws from its walls and secretes a new cuticle.

LOCOMOTION. Tardigrades move with their legs, usually climbing among plant parts or sand grains. Therefore the gait rhythm is only an artifact of the flat experimental situation: *Batillipes, Macrobiotus,* and *Hypsibius* use only the anterior three leg pairs, pulling the fourth along. In backing up and climbing the fourth leg is used. *Echiniscoides* has a different gait, using all legs (Fig. 2–7). *Batillipes,* 0.6 mm long, covers 1 mm in 10 seconds on flat surfaces. Tardigrades cannot swim.

SENSES. Little is known about senses. *Batillipes* is sensitive to currents, and responds by attaching to a sand grain with all 48 attachment discs. Pond-dwellers are phototactic and gather on the light side of an aquarium, the area providing most plants and food.

FEEDING. Tardigrades are mainly vegetarians, though Eutardigrades may be found on remains of other tardigrades, nematodes, and rotifers. *Macrobiotus* and *Milnesium* have been seen to overpower live rotifers. Usually tardigrades drill a hole into a plant cell, desmid, moss, or phanerogam, and with mouth appressed, suck out the contents of the cell. *Macrobiotus furciger,* using this method, can empty 10 cells of the moss, *Hypnum,* in 24 hours. With each thrust of the stylets the musculature of the sucking pharynx contracts twice and one can see plasma and chloroplasts move from the pharynx into the midgut. The stylets are used to attack the cell walls, but sometimes chloroplasts are penetrated.

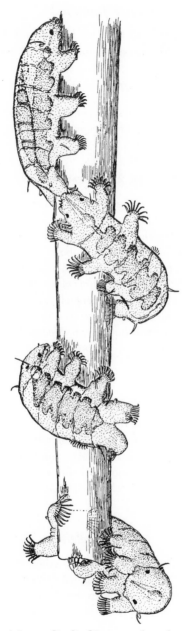

Fig. 2–7. *Echiniscoides sigismundi* climbing on threads of the alga *Enteromorpha;* 0.2 mm long. (After Marcus.)

Classification

The tardigrades are grouped into three orders. Many North American species appear to be holarctic or perhaps cosmopolitan in distribution.

Order Heterotardigrada

The head has cirri. The toes or claws are similar, and each is completely separated from the next. "Malpighian tubules" are lacking. The gonopore is separate from the anus.

SUBORDER ARTHROTARDIGRADA

At the end of the appendages there are toelike structures with wide pads or claws. About two dozen species are known, all marine. Among sand grains are found several species of *Batillipes*, 0.4–0.7 mm; *Stygarctus bradypus*, 0.09–0.15 mm; *Actinarctus doryphorus*, 0.17 mm; and *Orzeliscus*, about 0.2 mm long. Other species are *Tanarctus tauricus*, 0.1 mm; *Florarctus heimi*, 0.4 mm; *F. salvati*, 0.25 mm; *Parastygarctus higginsi*, 0.25 mm; *Halechiniscus subterraneus*, 0.13 mm; *H. remanei*, 1.2 mm; *Bathyechiniscus tetronyx*, 0.19 mm. The tentacles of the Atlantic sea cucumber, *Leptosynapta inhaerens*, are inhabited by *Tetrakentron synaptae*, 0.2 mm long, which has the body flattened; how it feeds is not known. *Pleocola limnoriae*, 0.13 mm, lives on the pleotelson of the isopod *Limnoria lignorum*. *Styraconyx sargassi*, 0.15 mm, is associated with *Sargassum*.

SUBORDER ECHINISCIDA

The claws tip the appendages, not the toes. Soft *Echiniscoides*, 0.2–0.3 mm, found on pilings, stones and among algae (especially *Enteromorpha*) in the ocean surf, may survive for 10 days as a tun. *Echiniscoides sigismundi* is found in a few freshwater lakes, but otherwise is marine. Armored *Echiniscus* inhabit mosses and lichens (Fig. 2-1). Several other genera are: *Oreelia, Archechiniscus, Parechiniscus, Pseudechiniscus, Mopsechiniscus*.

Order Eutardigrada

The head lacks cirri. The claws differ from each other, each consisting of two basally fused branches. The hindgut has three "Malpighian tubules" and the gonopores are in the hindgut. With one exception, all inhabit freshwater or terrestrial plants. *Macrobiotus, Hypsibius, Milnesium, Haplomacrobiotus, Itaquascon* are common genera.

Order Mesotardigrada

The head has cirri. Each leg has 6 to 10 almost equal claws. Lateral "Malpighian tubules" are present but middorsal tubule is lacking. There is only one known species, which may belong to Heterotardigrada. *Thermozodium esakii*, 0.4 mm, occurs in algae on the borders of Japanese sulfur hot springs at 40–41°C.

References

Crowe, J. H. and Higgins, R. P. 1967. Revival of *Macrobiotus areolatus* from the cryptobiotic state. *Trans. Amer. Microscop. Soc.* 86:286–294.

Cuénot, L. 1949. Tardigrades, *in* Grassé, *Traité de Zoologie,* Masson et Cie, Paris, 6:39–50.

Hatai, S. 1956. On Japanese Tardigrada. *Sci. Rep. Yokosuka City Mus.* 1:1–12.

Higgins, R. P. 1959. Life history of *Macrobiotus. Trans. Amer. Microscop. Soc.* 78:137–154.

_____ 1960. Tardigrades from North Carolina. *J. Elisha Mitchell Sci. Soc.* 76:29–35.

Marcus, E. 1929. Tardigrada *in* Bronn's *Klassen und Ordnungen des Tierreichs,* Akad. Verlagsges., Leipzig, (5) 4(3):1–608.

_____ 1936. Tardigrada *in* Schulze & Kükenthal, *Das Tierreich,* De Gruyter, Berlin, 66:1–340.

_____ 1959. Tardigrada *in* Edmondson, *Ward and Whipple's Freshwater Biology,* Wiley, New York. pp. 508–521.

Müller, J. 1935. Myologie der Tardigraden. *Z. Wiss. Zool.* 147:171–204.

Petersen, B. 1951. Tardigrade fauna of Greenland. *Medd. Grønland* 150:1–94.

Pigón, A. and Weglarska, B. 1953. Respiration of Tardigrada. *Bull. Acad. Polonaise Sci.* (2) 1:69–72.

Rahm, G. 1937. Eine neue Tardigraden Ordnung. *Zool. Anz.* 120:65–71.

Ramazzotti, G. 1962. Phylum Tardigrada. *Mem. Ist. Italiano Idrobiol. Dott. Marco de Marchi, Pallanza* 14:1–595.

_____ 1965. Phylum Tardigrada, 1° Suppl. *Ibid.* 19:101–212.

Riggin, T. G. 1962. Tardigrada of southwest Virginia. *Virginia Agr. Exp. Sta. Tech. Bull.* 152:1–145.

Schulz, E. 1951. *Stygarctus* ein Tardigrad aus dem Küstengrundwasser. *Kieler Meeresforsch.* 8:86–97.

_____ 1953. *Orzeliscus* ein mariner Tardigrad. *Ibid.* 9:288–292.

_____ 1955. Studien an marinen Tardigraden. *Ibid.* 11:74–79.

_____ 1963. Über Tardigraden. *Zool. Anz.* 171:1–12.

Schuster, R. O. and Grigarick, A. A. 1965. Tardigrada from western North America. *Univ. California Publ. Zool.* 76:1–67.

3.

Phylum Pentastomida,
Tongue Worms

About 65 species are included in this parasitic group, sometimes called Lingua-tulida. The largest is *Armillifer armillatus,* to 16 cm long, found in African snakes.

Pentastomida are endoparasitic and are usually considered related to arthro-pods. The long body is superficially annulate with two anterior pairs of hooks; some embryos in addition have sensory prominences which have been considered primordia of another postoral pair and an oral appendage pair.

Anatomy

Almost all pentastomids are worm-shaped; some are dorsoventrally flattened. The paired retractile hooks, on the stump tips in the Cephalobaenida, are parts of unsegmented appendages. While these are very unlike appendages of arthro-pods, there is the possibility that they evolved by reduction of segmented legs, as all pentastomids live as parasites in narrow body spaces. Recent research lends strong support for an arthropod affinity.

Two body parts can be recognized: the anterior, with mouth and two pairs of hooks, is already formed in the embryo; the much longer annulate trunk de-velops postembryonically (Fig. 3–1). The two parts are joined without sharp demarcation. Rarely are they divided by a constriction (Fig. 3–2), an adaptation to the habitat exhibited by a few species living in the lungs of snakes. Such species push into an alveolus, the narrow entrance to the cavity tightly enclosing and constricting the anterior part of the parasite.

There may be more than 100 trunk annuli. In *Armillifer* they are swollen and divided by deep grooves (Fig. 3–2). It is not completely clear whether these are true segments. However, true metamerism is indicated by corresponding division of longitudinal muscle and by the arrangement of dorsoventral muscles,

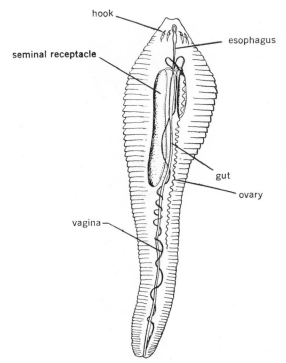

Fig. 3–1. *Linguatula serrata,* female, ventral view; 10 cm long. (After Leuckart.)

structures usually derived from the walls of embryonic coelomic pouches, and indicating their embryonic extent. But relatively little is known of the embryonic development and the adult has neither coelomic pouches nor pairs of ganglia in the trunk.

BODY WALL. The hypodermis secretes a chitinous cuticle consisting of three layers, pigmented only in the area of the hooks. Nevertheless various species appear to be lemon yellow, reddish or even red, as the color of the blood in the gut shows through the transparent tissues. *Linguatula* is colorless, transparent, and glassy, making it difficult to find on the glistening nasal membranes of a dog.

Into the cuticle open many epidermal glands, each consisting of 10–20 cells, but nothing is known of their secretion. It is thought that they might have an excretory function. In addition there often are large paired head glands and hook glands.

The fibers of the body muscles, unlike those of other parasitic worms and those of annelids, are striated. They form thin circular muscles under which there are much stronger longitudinal muscles.

APPENDAGES. Appendages are present in the form of two pairs of hooks, one behind and lateral to the other in primitive forms, side by side in the Poro-cephalida (Figs. 3–1, 3–2). In *Cephalobaena* the hooks often terminate long,

Fig. 3–2.   Anterior of *Armillifer annulatus*, female; diameter at anterior, 3 mm.

unsegmented appendages and can be folded back into pouches. The frontal papillae around the mouth of *Cephalobaena* may be derived from appendages (Fig. 3–3).

NERVOUS SYSTEM. Corresponding to the parasitic habits, there are no complicated sense organs, but only integumentary sense cells, or clusters of them, often forming a projecting cone. These sense cells are found on the frontal papillae and on other small paired papillae on the anterior body or metamerically covering the whole body. They may be everted by blood pressure and withdrawn by muscles. There is a sensory lateral line in some species.

The nervous system has ganglia only anteriorly; the last pair sends a pair of fibers into the long trunk. In the *Raillietiella* (Cephalobaenida) the preoral part of the nervous system is only a commissure. The surrounding ganglion cells may be considered remains of the protocerebrum. Under the preoral commissure lies the first pair of postoral ganglia with its commissure and with nerves to the first pairs of hooks. Caudally there are at least four ganglia marked by commissures, of which the first innervates the second pair of hooks. The ganglia of the first pair of hooks continues anteriorly in a large wide ganglionic mass, difficult to homologize. It innervates frontal and dorsal papillae, but it is not known whether the preoral commissure belongs to it.

The nervous system of adult Porocephalida is still further reduced. A single unsegmented ganglion, it consists of the postoral part of the circumesophageal connectives, and its preoral commissure lacks ganglion cells. In the larva of the Porocephalida the subesophageal ganglion, representing the whole nerve cord still extends through half the body and contains six to eight transverse bundles of fibers, possibly the commissures of fused ventral ganglion pairs. During growth the nervous system increases only slightly so that in *Linguatula* it occupies only one-eightieth of the venter of a pregnant female.

DIGESTIVE SYSTEM. The mouth is close to the anterior end at the bottom of a deep circular pit. It leads into a chitinized foregut. In cross section the foregut is sickle-shaped and it functions as a sucking organ, the lumen of which may be widened by muscles attached to a chitinous ring or support near the mouth. The adjoining midgut lacks ceca and is usually straight. Its columnar epithelial cells serve digestion and absorption. Electron micrographs show microvilli. The hindgut, like the foregut, is lined by chitinous cuticle and opens through the anus near the end of the body.

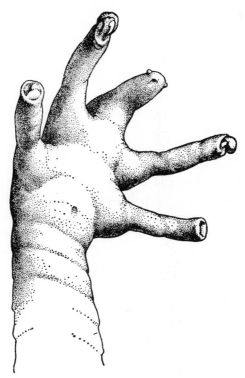

Fig. 3–3. Anterior of *Cephalobaena tetrapoda*, female; part shown, 5 mm long.

BODY CAVITY. The wide, unlined body cavity between gut and body wall contains fluid with floating cells; in the anterior of the body it must be considered a hemocoel derived as a mixocoel from various structures. The lateral mesenteries of the gut divide the cavity into a ventral space and a dorsal space, which contains the gonad, attached also to the dorsum by connective tissue.

There are no respiratory, circulatory, or excretory organs, except that perhaps the integumentary glands function in excretion.

REPRODUCTIVE SYSTEM. Sexes are separate, males usually smaller than females. While the male gonopore is far anterior, between the two body parts, the female gonopore is near the posterior end in the Porocephalida, or at least behind the middle of the body.

Linguatula has two large testes that may fill the trunk when mature. Anterior each continues into a slender vas efferens. Both vasa efferentia open into a thick, median seminal vesicle, a posteriorly directed loop that forks anteriorly into two posteriorly directed ejaculatory ducts. With longitudinal muscles both ducts pump sperm through a short vas deferens in each of two penis-like, chitinized cirri, coiled up in the atrium. The sperm extends the coiled cirrus and projects it into the female gonopore and the long vagina.

The ovary of *Linguatula* is median. Anteriorly it opens into a pair of oviducts, which join into a median duct continuing as a long posteriorly directed vagina, near the mouth of which lies a pair of large seminal receptacles. These are lined by chitin and are filled during insemination (Fig. 3–1).

Development

Pentastomids, like other parasites, produce a large number of eggs with only little yolk. As many as one-half million fertilized eggs may remain for some time in the vagina, which thus functions as a uterus. As it stretches to 100 times its original size, it completely fills the body cavity. In the course of its life, *Linguatula serrata* produces several million eggs, each 0.07 by 0.09 mm. Their minute size and thick shells make the study of embryonic development within the uterus difficult. After an early blastula the endoderm seems to form by lamination and a dorsal organ appears. We know only the first stages of the total cleavage. The embryo of *Reighardia sternae* is equipped with four pairs of appendage primordia. This is a typical short embryo with an acron, one adoral and three postoral segments, and a short trunk primordium (Fig. 3–4). Proximal to each of the postoral appendage primordia is a neuromere and a pair of coelomic pouches. The two posterior coelomic pouch pairs contain primordial reproductive cells. The dorsolateral, anterior appendage buds rise above the ectoderm which is proliferating into the anterior of the embryo, an ectodermal mass that has to be considered a ganglion adjacent to a coelomic pouch. Its position indicates with some certainty that the appendages with ganglia and coelomic pouches are homologous to the same parts of segments 1 to 4 that bear

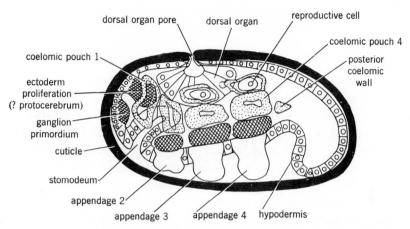

Fig. 3–4. Embryo of *Reighardia sternae.* Lateral view of cleared embryo; light stipples, coelom pouches; dark stipples, reproductive cells; 0.22 mm long. (After Osche.)

the two pairs of antennae, mandibles, and first maxillae in arthropods. Of course, their fate is different. Both posterior primordia become paired hooks in the adult, the anterior two presumably become the two pairs of frontal papillae of the Cephalobaenida. Though this has not been directly observed, an almost ready-to-hatch stage of *Reighardia* has been seen, and supports this conclusion for the third and fourth appendages. This embryo has many features of primitive arthropods, such as a large dorsal organ that functions as a gland, its secretions covering the rapidly growing embryo, which has shed its membranes.

The primary larva possesses an anterior and a posterior pair of hooks (Fig. 3–5) and a small short trunk forked at its tip. The anterior drilling apparatus has three chitinous spines, used to penetrate the gut wall of a host that has swallowed the egg. After leaving the mother's uterus, the larvae may remain alive inside their undisturbed shells for a long time before hatching.

The primary larva of *Porocephalus,* which has an especially short trunk, has been seen to move about. It hooks the posterior legs into the intestinal wall of the host and rams its short tail against the wall. Extending, it pushes its boring apparatus into the host tissue. When fully extended, the anterior legs move forward and hook into tissues while the posterior legs let go and the body is contracted. As this sequence is repeated, the larva slowly forces itself into the tissue. The postembryonal development is not the same in all families and in *Linguatula* and *Porocephalus* is characterized by the disappearance, on molting, of appendage stumps except for the hooks. How much of the trunk growth is due to teloblastic growth of the embryo is unknown.

In general three larval stages can be separated. The primary larva (embryo), after hatching and molting several times, encysts as a secondary larva in the inter-

mediate host. The third larval stage, an infective larva, is migratory and becomes adult after being ingested by the appropriate final host. Adults molt
periodically.

Relationships

The appearance of coelomic pouches, distinct neuromeres, and appendage
primordia leaves no doubt about the close relationship of pentastomids to annelids and arthropods. Whether they are true arthropods, secondarily reduced,
cannot be ascertained. The appendage primordia remain less differentiated than
the Onychophora leg; it cannot be said whether their simplicity is primitive or
derived. We can only compare the position of the appendages, neuromeres, and
coelomic pouches with those of *Peripatus* and arthropods. But this says nothing
about their differentiation. For instance, the second postoral appendage of
Onychophora is not an arthropod appendage, and the fate of the same structure
in different groups of arthropods is very different. Nor is the number of appendage primordia a key to relationships. As in Onychophora, the enzymes studied,
lactic dehydrogenases, resemble those of mandibulate arthropods. Similar
longitudinal anastomoses between lateral nerves to the sense organs and parietal
musculature are seen in some annelids.

Habits

Adult pentastomids parasitize almost exclusively the respiratory organs of
predatory terrestrial vertebrates; 42% of the species are from snakes, 28% from
crocodiles, 18% from lizards, and the rest from turtles, birds, and mammals. The
reptile parasites almost all are found in lungs. *Reighardia* has been found in the
air sacs of gulls, its larvae in the gut. It may not have an intermediate host.
Linguatula lives in the nostrils or forehead sinuses of carnivores. The larvae are
found in diverse organs of all vertebrate classes, including vegetarians that fall
prey to hosts of the adult parasites. Only a few times have adult pentastomids

Fig. 3–5.   First larva of *Linguatula serrata,* showing short body and large anterior;
0.13 mm long. (After Leuckart.)

(*Linguatula*) been found in man, but quite commonly the larvae of *Linguatula*, and *Armillifer* are found in man. The Cephalobaenida that parasitize the lungs of insectivorous lizards may have only one host, as larvae for only one species have been found in invertebrates. Other species may have facultative intermediate hosts: a freshwater fish, amphibian, or almost any terrestrial vertebrate. A regular change of hosts has been shown in *Linguatula serrata*, one of the few species whose habits are known. The adult female *Linguatula* rarely leaves its place, keeping its anterior end imbedded in nasal tissue. Mature females often settle in the posterior of the nostril, the body hanging into the lumen. Males, however, move about.

Those species living in the lung feed on blood: *Linguatula* feeds on mucus, epithelial cells and lymph. Otherwise little is known about their habits.

Classification

Order Cephalobaenida

The hooks lie in two pairs, one behind and lateral to the other, posterior to the mouth. Sometimes, as in larvae they support themselves on stumpy legs (Fig. 3-3). The nervous system has a pair of ganglia on the sides of the foregut, and posteriorly, some paired ganglia connected by commissures. The gonopore in both sexes is far anterior at the base of the trunk. *Cephalobaena* have stumpy legs and two pairs of frontal papillae; *Cephalobaena tetrapoda*, females 1.9–3.3 cm, males 0.8 cm long (Fig. 3-3), live in the lungs of South American snakes. There are no legs but the hooks are surrounded by lobes in *Raillietiella* and *Reighardia*. *Reighardia sternae*, 3 cm long, lives in air sacs of terns and gulls. *Raillietiella hemidactyli* of the Malay Peninsula live in geckos (*Hemidactylus*). The eggs are believed to pass through the pharynx, be swallowed and to pass out with feces. Cockroaches (*Periplaneta americana*) ingest the feces and eggs. The larvae hatch in the midgut of the cockroach and penetrate the wall into the mixocoel where one molt takes place. The final host is infected by feeding on a cockroach. As none has ever been found in the postpharyngeal gut, it is believed that they leave the cockroach in the lizard's mouth and migrate to the lungs.

Order Porocephalida

The mouth sometimes lies between the hooks, which are in pairs, one behind the other, or all four in a transverse row (Fig. 3-1). Leg stumps are lacking. The deep hook receptacles have an apodeme. The nervous system consists of a uniform subesophageal ganglion. The male gonopore is at the anterior, the female posterior. There are about 42 species.

Sebekia is included, as is *Kiricephalus,* found in American as well as Asian and African colubrid snakes. *Porocephalus crotali* is found principally in lung cavities of American rattlesnakes (*Crotalus*) and moccasins (*Agkistrodon*). The eggs are ingested by small mammals, hatch in the intestine and encapsulate in the viscera where they develop into nymphs. If ingested by a snake they migrate up the esophagus and down the trachea. *Armillifer* has thick annuli. The head of the female in one species is large and connected by a neck to the trunk (Fig. 3-2). *Armillifer* is found in African snakes. *Linguatula* has a flattened body; *L. serrata* (Fig. 3-1), the tongue worm, males are 1.8–2 cm long, females with eggs to 13 cm long. Orginally the final hosts were foxes and wolves, but adults are found in the head sinuses of dogs, rarely in horses, goats, and sheep, and rarely in man. The eggs pass from host dogs to plants, and larvae are found in vegetarians: rodents and ungulates.

In the intermediate host the eggs of *L. serrata* reach the small intestine where the shell breaks. On hatching the primary larva, 0.13 mm long, penetrates the intestinal wall and within seven hours all larvae occupy small hemorrhagic areas in the mucosa and submucosa. They then enter blood and lymph vessels and are carried by the fluid or move under their own power to various organs. Those in the lymph may attach to mesenteries; most others migrate via the heart to the lung where they lodge in capillaries; still others settle in the liver. Only 7 days after infection the larva reaches its new habitat, to remain as a parasite. After 15–28 days the primary larva molts into a secondary larva. The spherical secondary larva lacks hooks and appendages. Apparently it feeds, as it contains blood corpuscles in its gut, and in 6 months grows from 0.13 mm to 5 mm. The larva is enclosed by host tissues within a connective tissue cyst, forcing the larva to double up. Growth is accompanied by molting; in 8 weeks the larva has molted a second time, and after the ninth molt the body flattens and the trunk becomes annulate. In the rabbit as intermediate host, after about 6 months and the tenth molt, the larva transforms to a terminal stage, 4–5 mm long, that resembles the adult in body shape and in having four hooks. But unlike the adult, its hooks are double, and it has rows of posteriorly directed spines on the posterior borders of the annuli. Seven months after infection of the intermediate host, the parasites break their cysts and move about in the thoracic or abdominal cavity. It is not known definitely whether the cyst opens only on the death of the intermediate host, nor is it known whether the parasite normally occupies the cyst for several years.

While the encysted resting larvae rarely damage the intermediate host, the migration into the body cavity may cause pleuritis. In case the host is not eaten and survives, the larvae eventually die without reproducing. The final host may be a dog that feeds on the intermediate host. The larva moves, using its spines, from the throat or stomach toward the nostrils of the dog. Larvae artificially placed in the dog's stomach were soon found in the esophagus. From the throat they enter the nostril where they molt after 3 weeks, bcome adult and lose their spiny exterior. *Linguatula* harms the natural host only slightly during migration but the migrating nymphs cause halzoans disease in man; the adult may cause bleeding from the hook attachments as the worm feeds on mucus. After 4 months in the final host, the females are 3 cm long. They mate, after which the males die, while the females live at least 11 months more and may become 13 cm long.

References

Baer, J. G. 1951. *Ecology of Animal Parasites*. Univ. Illinois Press, Urbana.

Doucet, J. 1965. L'étude anatomique, histologique et histochimique des Pentastomes. *Mem. Office Recherche Sci. Tech. d'Outre-Mer*, Paris, 14:1–150.

Esslinger. J. H. 1962. Development of *Porocephalus*. *J. Parasitol*. 48:452–458.

Fain, A. 1961. Les Pentastomides. *Ann. Mus. Roy. Afrique Centr. Tervuren* (8)92:1-115.

_____ 1964. Le cycle évolutif du *Raillietiella*. *Bull. Acad. Roy. Belgique, Sci.* (5) 50 (9):1036–1060.

Haffner, K. von. 1967. Organisation von *Reighardia*. *Zool. Jahrb. Abt. Anat.* 83 (in press).

_____ and Rack, G. 1965. Die Entwicklung der Pentastomide *Reighardia*. *Ibid.* 82:419–444.

Heymons, R. 1926. Pentastomida *in* Kükenthal, *Handbuch der Zoologie*, de Gruyter, Berlin, 3(1):69–131.

_____ 1935. Pentastomida *in* Bronn's, *Klassen und Ordnungen des Tierreichs*, Akad. Verlagsges., Leipzig, (5)4(1):1–268.

_____ 1941. Lebensweise der in Krokodilien vorkommenden Pentastomida. *Sitzungsber. Ges. Naturforsch. Freunde* pp. 253-269.

_____ 1942. Systematik der Pentastomiden. *Z. Parasitenk*. 12:419–432.

Hobmaier, A. and Hobmaier, M. 1940. Life cycle of *Linguatula*. *Amer. J. Trop. Med*. 20:199–210.

Lavoipierre, M. M. J. and M. 1966. An arthropod intermediate host of a pentastomid. *Nature* 210:845–846.

Osche, G. 1963. Systematische Stellung und Phylogenie der Pentastomida. *Z. Morphol. Ökol.* 52:487–596.

Wilson, A. C. and Kaplan, N. O. 1964. Enzyme structure, its relation to taxonomy, *in* Leone, C. A., *Taxonomic Biochemistry and Serology*. Ronald, New York. pp. 321–346.

4.

Phylum Arthropoda, Introduction

The number of species of arthropods is probably over 850,000. The largest fossil species is the eurypterid, *Pterygotus rhenaniae*, 1.8 m long; the largest living species are crabs: *Jasus huegeli*, 60 cm long, *Pseudocarcinus gigas*, 40 cm wide, and *Macrocheira kaempferi*, with a leg spread of 3 m.

Arthropods have a chitinous exoskeleton. Their segments, at least in the anterior third of the body, have appendages consisting of jointed, stiff articles, at least one pair of which is specialized as antennae or mouth parts. The walls of the embryonic coelomic pouches disappear in organ formation. The body cavity of the adult is not a true coelom, but a mixocoel formed by fusion of the blastocoel with parts of the secondary body cavity. There are no cilia on the body or on internal organs.

Not only are arthropods rich in species, but they represent the culmination of protostome evolution, especially of the nervous system. Though of corresponding complexity, the cephalopods are limited to the ocean and lack diversity. Arthropods, on the other hand, like vertebrates, live on all continents, adapted to all possible habitats, often represented by large numbers of individuals. The adaptations that make this possible are the exoskeleton, which protects against desiccation, and the jointed appendages, which permit rapid locomotion on land. The insects, furthermore, have been able to increase their speed and radius of activity by the acquisition of wings. Along with rapid movement, the majority of arthropods have evolved good vision with corresponding brain centers. And in connection with the complicated appendages the nerve centers have become more centralized (Fig. 11–7).

Most arthropods have the anterior appendages modified as mouthparts, or into cutting, biting, or sucking tools, increasing the possibilities for obtaining food and permitting them, despite their small size, to utilize large organisms, such as herbs and trees, for nourishment.

But in contrast to vertebrates and marine invertebrates, terrestrial arthropods are subject to size limitations, probably due to stiffness, lack of permeability, and difficulty of growth resulting from the exoskeleton. The largest arachnids (scorpions) are 18 cm long; scolopendrid centipedes, 26 cm long; and walking-stick insects, 33 cm long. The last two are very slim, as were the giant dragonflies of the Carboniferous, with their wingspread of 60 cm.

Anatomy

INTEGUMENT. A chitinous cuticle is secreted by the hypodermis even in the ectodermal stomodeum and proctodeum, the tracheae, and genital atria. Except at joints it consists of several layers, providing thick protection against mechanical and chemical injury. The cuticle has two layers, the thick basal procuticle and, outside, a very thin (0.004 mm) epicuticle (Fig. 4–1). Only the procuticle contains chitin, a polysaccharide demonstrated by X-ray examination to be analogous in structure to cellulose, except that the −OH groups attached to the C in the second position have been replaced by an acetylamine group; long chains are hydrolyzed by enzymes to N-acetylglucosamine. Chitin is very resistant to pressure, tearing, and chemicals (it can even withstand boiling in KOH). It also is very light, having a specific weight of 1.3, of importance for terrestrial life.

The procuticle has been most intensively studied in insects, but is similar in other arthropods. It consists of an inner flexible layer, the endocuticle, made up of numerous layers. Outside is the exocuticle, stiff and hard as the result of impregnation by quinone-tanned proteins. Crustacea and diplopods may have calcareous substances incorporated into the exocuticle.

The thin epicuticle consists of coagulated secretions and has little or no chitin (except in pycnogonids and scolopendrid centipedes). In insects the epicuticle consists of cement, a waxy and a lipid layer, and a lower lamella made up of proteins and steroids. The wax and lipid layers are of importance in making the exoskeleton impenetrable to water; the procuticle is permeable.

The importance of the epicuticle in the water economy of terrestrial animals has been demonstrated for spiders and ticks, which have an increased water loss after removal of large areas of epicuticle by abrasion with aluminium powder.

The funnel web spider *Agelena labyrinthica* loses almost twice as much water in 48 hours after being rubbed with aluminum powder as without treatment (Nemenz, 1955; Lees, 1947). (It would have been better to experiment with quartz dust, as the experiment did not take into account possible chemical effects of aluminum; water loss through respiration also was not taken into account.) Transpiration increased four times in *Pardosa amentata* living 12 hours in Neosyl dust (an inert chemical, aluminum silicate), when the spiracles of book lungs and tracheae were closed with colloidin (Davies and Edney, 1952).

Because the exoskeleton covers the body completely, it cannot grow in area as does a mollusk shell, but must be removed periodically to permit growth. The process of molting is critical in the life of an arthropod; its control is by endocrine glands.

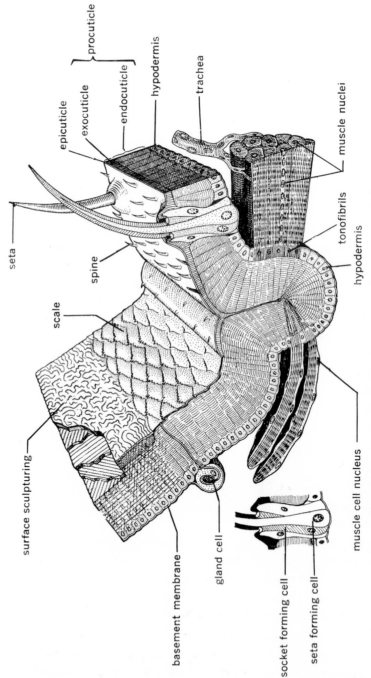

Fig. 4–1. Section through insect integument. (After Weber.)

In insects the molt proceeds as follows: first the hypodermis undergoes a period of mitosis during which the cells increase in depth. The cells separate from the procuticle and secrete exuvial fluid into the space between. Enzymes (chitinase and proteinase) contained in the fluid dissolve the basal layer the endocuticle; epicuticle and exocuticle are not affected. The digested materials, up to 80% of the old endocuticle, are resorbed, and thus are not lost to the body. Now, underneath the old exocuticle, a new layer of epicuticle is produced, then a new procuticle. The formation of the thick endocuticle and sclerotization of the outer layer, the exocuticle, are completed only after the molt. The secretions that form the outer layers of the epicuticle also are produced after the molt through pores.

Chitin is formed by the hypodermis by two simultaneous processes: secretion at the outer cell surface and transformation of the distal plasma edge. All spines, setae, and hairs are formed from plasma extensions. Both ends of the gut, the tracheal systems, and the ectodermal gland ducts are molted along with the body surface.

The surface of the integument is often sculptured by fine grooves and depressions (Fig. 4–1), or drawn out into thorns or micotrichia. There are also large numbers of setae connected at the base to the hypodermis (Fig. 4–1) and surrounded by a flexible membrane to the exoskeleton.

The integument serves as an exoskeleton for muscle attachment; inside there may be thickenings, solid apodemes that serve as a skeleton for muscle attachments (Figs. 4–1, 8–14).

MUSCULATURE. The muscles are striated. The longitudinal thoracic muscles usually do not form a body wall, but lie in two dorsal and two ventral bundles (Fig. 4–6). The metameric dorsoventral muscles may enter appendages.

APPENDAGES. The tube-shaped articles of appendages are connected by flexible articular membranes, most of them wider on one side than on the other (Fig. 4–2), permitting movement in one direction. Condyles of the proximal segment may further restrict direction of movement. The axes of successive appendage segments may move in different directions, permitting movement of the whole appendage in various directions. The number of articles is variable, as is their shape, especially of the most anterior ones, the antennae and those

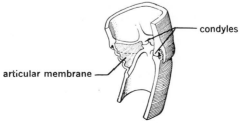

Fig. 4–2. Longitudinal section through a leg joint. (After Weber.)

differentiated into mouthparts. The first appendage is usually a segmented antenna (except in Chelicerata), while the oral appendages have been modified as mouthparts (except in Trilobitomorpha), and sometimes only parts of a segment remain (mandibles of insects). Trunk appendages, instead of walking legs may be swimmerets or raptorial legs; others may be transformed into gonopods used in sperm transfer.

According to differentiation of the anterior appendages, arthropods can be separated into several groups or phylogenetic lines.

1. The first appendage forms an antenna; others are similar and without specialization as mouthparts (Trilobites).

2. The first pair of appendages forms mouthparts, the chelicerae; the coxae of successive tube-shaped appendages, by forming endites, may have become mouthparts but do not chew or work against each other (Chelicerata).

3. The first appendage forms an antenna; behind the mouth at least two appendage pairs move against each other in chewing, as mandibles or maxillae (Mandibulata).

    a. The first two may be antennae, and respiration is through gills (Crustacea).

    b. The first appendage is an antenna, the second reduced; respiration is through tracheae (Myriapoda and Insecta).

Some biologists have tried to homologize the appendage articles of the unspecialized and specialized appendages not only within orders but throughout the arthropods and give them uniform names. But the results have been very divergent, as has their nomenclature. Possibly the problem is only apparent, as the arthropods may be polyphyletic, and their appendages convergently evolved. Thus we will continue to use the nomenclature generally used in the literature of the different groups.

Arachnid embryology indicates that the base and tip of each appendage, with its musculature, develop before the intermediate articles. Later the appendage becomes segmented: first a few grooves separating larger parts (Fig. 4–6), and later these develop new grooves or joints of the final articles.

In some groups the basal article, the precoxa, fragments; thus the coxa is usually the first proximal tube-shaped segment. At the leg tip is the pretarsus bearing one to three claws and sometimes also attachment discs. On its proximal tip insert one or two muscles that move the claws (Fig. 4–3).

BODY SEGMENTATION. The body consists of an acron (prostomium, or cephalic lobes) and the pygidium (telson) with a number of intermediate somites produced by a posterior teloblastic growth zone anterior to the pygidium. In groups having direct development the individual somites develop similarly on the germ disc (Fig. 4–11). Initially each somite consists of a sternite, paired primordia of ganglia, a pair of coelom pouches, and in the anterior germ band at

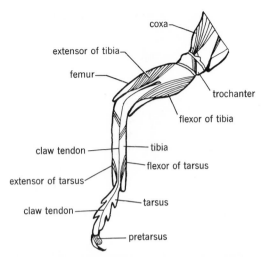

Fig. 4–3. Insect leg with muscles. (After Weber.)

least, a pair of appendage primordia (Fig. 4–11). In development the appendages differentiate, or in some somites may not grow at all, and at the same time there appear differences in somite formation so that different regions (tagmata) develop. These regions may consist of a number of distinct somites or of a uniform capsule resulting from fusion of the exoskeleton of several metameres. All arthropods have at least one anterior tagma, the head, proterosoma, prosoma, or cephalothorax. Following it there may be a homonomous body, with or without appendages (Myriapoda, many arachnids; Fig. 4–4). But in many cases two additional tagmata develop, the thorax and abdomen (Fig. 4–5).

In general each somite consists of a ventral sternite, a dorsal tergite, a pair of soft, flexible pleura, a pair of ventrolateral appendages, and a pair of ventral ganglia (Fig. 4–6). In addition, the embryo has a pair of coelomic pouches, which disappear rapidly as their walls form muscles, fat bodies and peritoneum. After feeding or during egg development the pleura permit expansion of the body (Fig. 4–7), as do the intersegmental membranes, which join successive tergites and sternites. The intersegmental membranes also permit body movement (Fig. 9–1). The short pygidium does not constitute a segment: it is the unsegmented anal end of the germ band.

SENSE ORGANS. The sense organs are highly developed. Integumental setae connected below with sensory cells serve as mechanical receptors. Some thin-walled setae, possibly chemoreceptors, may be found in large numbers on the appendages, especially the antennae and oral appendages. Of the two forms of eyes, median and lateral, the laterals usually are complicated compound eyes (except in Arachnida and most Myriapoda).

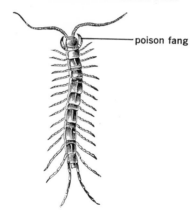

Fig. 4–4. Arthropod with body consisting of two tagmata, the centipede *Lithobius forficatus*; 25 mm long. (After C. L. Koch, from Claus–Grobben.)

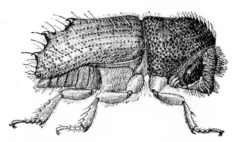

Fig. 4–5. Arthropod with body consisting of three tagmata, the bark beetle *Pityogenes chalcographus*; 2 mm long. (After Nüsslin–Rhumbler.)

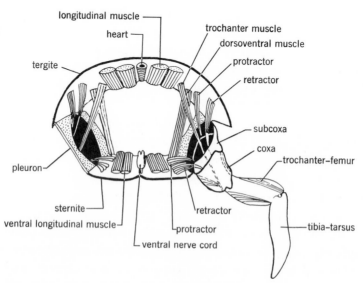

Fig. 4–6. Cross section through an arthropod. (After Weber.)

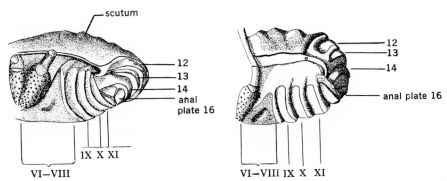

Fig. 4–7. Expansibility of the arthropod abdomen: the abdomen of the harvestman *Nemastoma quadripunctatum*; **left, a starving animal; right, a well fed female with intersegmental membranes and pleura stretched; Roman numerals indicate sternites, Arabic numerals, tergites; about 3–4 mm long. (After Kaestner.)**

NERVOUS SYSTEMS. The central nervous system consists of a suprapharyngeal brain and a ventral ganglionated chain (Fig. 4–8). The brain consists of the protocerebrum, which has association organs (globuli and the central body), and optic centers. The brain also includes the first two appendage ganglia, the deuto- and tritocerebrum, which have shifted secondarily to the front of the mouth.

In the lower Crustacea (Branchiopoda), only the first appendage ganglion, which innervates the first antennae, is fused with the protocerebrum to form the brain (Fig. 4–9). The second neuromere, which innervates the second antennae, lies some distance behind and below the pharynx and forms the anterior end of the ventral chain of ganglia. In most Crustacea this ganglion moves anterior to the pharynx and connects with the tritocerebrum above the pharynx, but its commissure remains behind the mouth (Fig. 4–10).

Similarly in the myriapods and insects, the appendages (the second antennae) of the tritocerebrum have been lost, appearing only embryonically as buds in a few species of Symphyla (Fig. 4–8). The brain of the chelicerates appears to be simpler, consisting only of the protocerebrum and the ganglion of the first appendage (chelicerae) (Figs. 4–16, 6–2). The cheliceral ganglion is in the position of the tritocerebrum of mandibulates, and is connected with a sympathetic system of the anterior gut.

The ontogeny of the arthropod brain shows clearly that the deuto- and tritocerebrum have secondarily joined the protocerebrum. They originate as metameric ganglia, as does the cheliceral ganglion, and each of the three belongs to a segment that has a pair of coelomic pouches and a pair of appendage buds. The deutocerebrum lies next to the stomodeum; the tritocerebrum and cheliceral ganglion are posterior to it (Fig. 4–11a, b). In the course of development they come to lie in front of or to the side of the esophagus, but it is uncertain whether they move anteriorly or the foregut shifts posteriorly.

The ontogeny of the protocerebrum is still incompletely known. Some invaginations of the cephalic lobes may take part in its formation, in close connection with the eye primordia (Fig. 4–11b, c). One would not expect a ganglion containing association and sensory centers to form simply from a paired invagination as a somatic ganglion. Furthermore, the complicated brains of polychaetes, related to the arthropods, without doubt develop from the small apical ganglion of the trochophore. Certain events in development suggest that a pair of somatic ganglia, prosocerebrum, is incorporated into the protocerebrum. For instance, traces of an anterior somite show up in representatives of all subphyla, coelomic pouches appear below the cephalic lobes anterior to the first appendages. In some genera (e.g., *Limulus*) this cavity is a diverticulum of the coelom of the

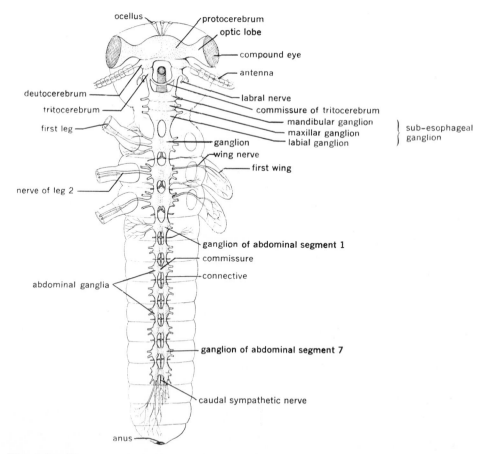

Fig. 4–8. **Nervous system of an insect having three specialized tagmata, ventral view.** (After Weber.)

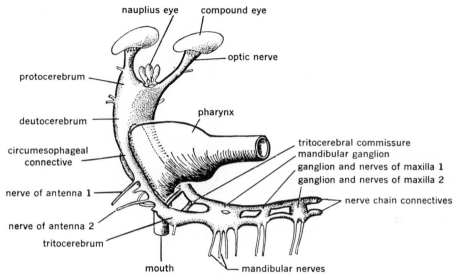

Fig. 4–9. **Lateral view of the anterior nervous system of the crustacean *Triops*. (After Henry.)**

first appendage segment. Its walls may form parts of the anterior aorta or foregut musculature. But in other arthropods it is possible that the coelomic pouches under the cephalic lobes are separate. There is no doubt about it in some Crustacea (*Nebalia, Squilla, Hemimysis, Gammarus*) as they arise independently in front of the first antennal segment from an invagination of the blastoderm. That these pouches are the vestige of a segment is clear, and it also clear that the coelomic pouches of the cephalic lobes of other Crustacea correspond.

In *Scolopendra* preantennal appendage buds have been described; these (unlike similar structures reported for insects and arachnids) can not be explained as accidental bulges of the cephalic lobes, common in the formation of the brain. A reexamination would be desirable.

The presence of the coelomic pouches under the cephalic lobes of the preantennal appendage buds of *Scolopendra* supports the assumption of a rudimentary preantennal (or precheliceral) segment. Furthermore, one can consider that to these appendages and coelom belong a pair of the neural invaginations of the cephalic lobes as prosocerebrum and that these three primordia are the rest of a preantennal segment.

Usually some postoral ganglia fuse as a subpharyngeal ganglion; sometimes all ganglia move forward and form a large subesophageal center, from which the whole body is innervated (Fig. 4–12). Shortening the distances between ganglia permits an increased number of longitudinal and transverse connectives.

DIGESTIVE SYSTEM. The mouth lies behind the labrum and anterior to the labium (Figs. 4–11c, 11–1). Laterally the mouth is framed by various lateral

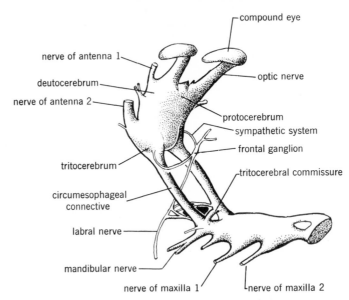

Fig. 4–10. Lateral view of the nervous system of a crustacean, a side swimmer, Amphipoda. (After Henry.)

appendages, used to hold or chew food, and in some myriapods and insects and arachnids, these may be substituted for the labium. The mouth leads into the foregut (stomodeum), an ectodermal invagination usually specialized into pharynx and esophagus; its lining is shed with the molt of the exoskeleton. It serves to transport or filter food, or to predigest. The endodermal midgut (mesenteron) digests and absorbs; it may be a straight tube, or among Crustacea or Chelicerata it may have very large diverticula, but these are lacking in the myriapods and insects. The midgut leads into the ectodermal hindgut (procto-deum), which may be very long in the higher Crustacea, and opens through the anus.

BODY CAVITY. The body cavity is a mixocoel formed by fusion of the blastocoel and coelomic pouches after their walls have been used up in organo-genesis.

EXCRETORY SYSTEMS. Despite their significance to annelids, mesodermal nephridia are of little importance to arthropods; their vestiges (except in Xiphosura) are two pairs of antennal and maxillary glands (Crustacea), max-illary and labial glands (myriapods and insects), or coxal glands (chelicerates). These structures all incorporate remnants of the coelom of their own segments. Terrestrial arthropods, which can not give off ammonia through thin parts of the integument, as do aquatic arthropods, have developed another excretory organ, the Malpighian tubules. These long fine diverticula extend from the border of the midgut and hindgut into the abdomen; the substances they excrete are in-soluble (guanin, uric acid), and thereby conserve water. Excretory products are probably also taken up by large nephrocytes along the wide blood channels, and some may be transformed into pigments.

RESPIRATORY SYSTEMS. Except in some minute, soft-bodied arthropods, respiratory organs are present, the need for them resulting from the thick exoskeleton. Aquatic and marine representatives, the Crustacea and Merostomata, have transparent, vascular evaginations, the gills, attached to appendages (Fig. 7–3). Terrestrial arthropods, however, as an adaptation against desiccation, have internal respiratory organs: ectodermal invaginations covered by a soft chitinous layer, the intima (tracheae and book lungs).

CIRCULATORY SYSTEM. An open circulatory system contains the blood, called hemolymph. Identical with tissue fluids, the hemolymph serum contains respiratory pigments, usually dissolved hemocyanin, and several kinds of nucleated blood cells. The heart is a median dorsal tube that passes through most segments in some primitive groups, but usually is limited to a few segments (Fig. 6–1). There are no veins, but in each segment the heart has a pair of buttonhole-shaped ostia, the borders of which hang into the lumen as valves (Fig. 7–5). Anterior and posterior the heart continues as an aorta. In orders having localized respiratory organs, the heart usually has lateral arteries. Arising under the ostia, these arteries are variously branched before they allow the blood to escape (Fig. 6–1). In orders having an extensive, branched tracheal system, lateral arteries usually are not developed except possibly in the head or tail regions. A notable exception to this generalization is found in the Chilopoda.

The blood collects in the mixocoel and in longitudinal ventral lacunae from which it flows through the pericardial septa, perforated connective tissue septa with some muscle, into the pericardial sinus surrounding the heart. The pericardial sinus is a dorsal level of the trunk mixocoel (Figs. 4–18, 6–1). From it the heart pumps blood in diastole. In systole the ostia valves close so that the hemolymph is forced out through a head or tail aorta, and often through lateral arteries. The heart beat, unlike that of vertebrates, is neurogenic with ganglionic pacemakers.

The pericardial sinus part of the mixocoel is very different from the pericardium of the mollusks. In mollusks it is a coelom space lined by peritoneum toward the blastocoel and impermeable to blood; thus true veins bring blood to it.

REPRODUCTIVE ORGANS. With only few exceptions the arthropods have separate sexes. The paired gonads have mesodermal walls and ducts, but the gonoducts join paired or single ectodermal invaginations that lead to the outside. In both sexes numerous glands may be present along the ducts.

In chilopods, the gonad walls develop directly from constricted-off dorsal parts of several successive coelomic pouches, the lumens of which become continuous (Fig. 4–18). The efferent ducts in chilopods and spiders are also formed from coelomic parts.

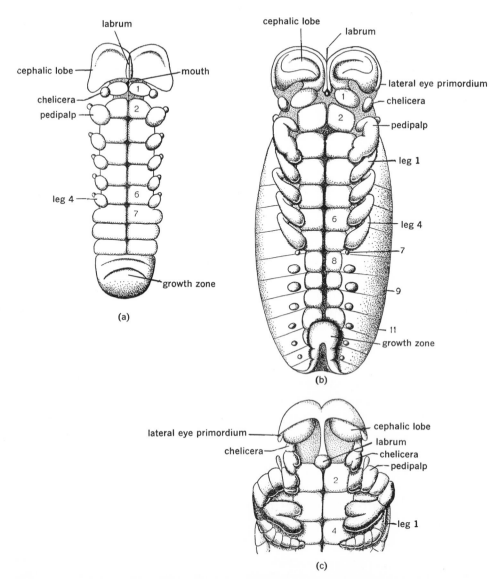

Fig. 4–11.   Shift of the mouth and development of the ganglia and appendages in the scorpion *Euscorpius carpathicus*; the numbers are those of segments, in the middle are the pillow-shaped primordia of ganglia (after Brauer); (a) showing mouth anterior to the chelicerae; length about 2.3 mm; (b) later stage, the labrum is growing posteriorly between the chelicerae, carrying the mouth with it; length about 3 mm; (c) still later, mouth has moved posterior to chelicerae and the cephalic lobes move dorsoposteriorly covering the acron, their ectoderm producing the protocerebrum; length about 1.5 mm.

Development

Superficial cleavage is characteristic of arthropod eggs, usually rich in yolk. Among all groups, however, especially in the Crustacea, a few species have eggs with little yolk, very early determination and total cleavage that resembles the spiral cleavage of annelids. Even in some Crustacea (e.g., Isopoda) that have superficial cleavage there may be mesodermal teloblast cells resembling those of oligochaetes.

Superficial cleavage results in formation of a germ band on the side of the embryo that is going to be its venter. The germ band may produce a posterior teloblastic budding zone of segments (Fig. 4–11). Every segment consists of a sternite, a pair of ganglionic primordia, a pair of appendage buds, and a pair of coelomic pouches (Figs. 4–13, 4–14). Later the germ band widens, its lateral borders and coelomic sacs grow over the sides of the egg, finally meeting to fuse and form the dorsal tergites (Figs. 4–13, 4–14).

The anterior of the germ band, the cephalic lobes (acron, prostomium), does not widen, but in the course of development grows dorsally and is bent back (Figs. 4–14, 4–15). Thus it does not take part in the formation of the venter, but forms only parts of the anterior of the dorsum. The protocerebrum formed from the cephalic lobes finally comes to lie above the succeeding ganglia (Figs. 4–9, 4–10, 4–16). For this reason the anterior end of the germ band (acron) does not correspond with the anterior end of the arthropod body, which is formed by the first segments. This can be seen externally, the position of the antennae (Fig. 4–4) or chelicerae (Fig. 4–16) being anterior of the eyes, which are innervated by the prostomium. The details of the process have been studied only in the whipscorpion *Thelyphonus,* in which the cephalic lobe finally forms the anterior

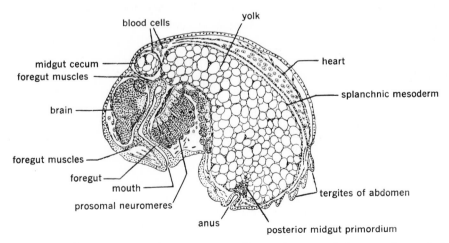

Fig. 4–12. The migration of posterior ganglion pairs toward the anterior and their fusion to form a subesophageal mass; longitudinal section of spider embryo, *Theridion;* 0.6 mm long. (After Morin from Korschelt and Heider.)

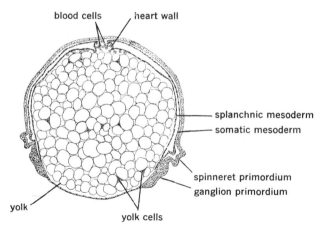

blood cells   heart wall

splanchnic mesoderm
somatic mesoderm

spinneret primordium
ganglion primordium

yolk

yolk cells

Fig. 4–13. The lateral growth of the germ band and dorsal fusion; cross section of abdominal segment 10 of the spider *Pholcus*; 0.6 mm long. (After Morin, from Korschelt and Heider.)

and middle portions of the anterior dorsum, carrying the eyes as ectodermal growths. The first to fourth metameres, then, do not grow around to meet at the dorsomedian line, but meet the cephalic lobes (Fig. 4–15), and form only the lateral parts of the anterior regions.

The ectoderm, besides producing body wall, gives rise to the nervous system and sense organs (Figs. 4–13, 4–14). Paired median growths of the germ band, ganglionic primordia, separate from the outer layer and sink in, and from their cells are derived the neuroblasts that form the ventral cord and innervate motor organs. The cephalic lobes form protocerebrum and eyes (Figs. 4–12, 4–15).

There is a pair of coelomic pouches in each segment but none in the telson. Unlike annelids, arthropods have preantennal coelomic pouches. Spiders (*Pardosa hortensis*) have a precheliceral pair and a pair still further anterior, reaching to the anterior edge of the cephalic lobes. Only in arachnids, chilopods, and Symphyla do the coelomic sacs become as extensive as in the annelids, but they remain narrow and compressed because of the yolk (Fig. 4–13). They reach into the appendage primordia and later grow laterally toward the dorsum (Figs. 4–13 to 4–15). As the cells of the coelom wall proliferate toward the integument they give rise to the dorsal and ventral longitudinal muscle layers. The septa (dissepiments) give rise to dorsoventral muscles, and the growth in the appendage buds gives rise to appendage muscles (Fig. 4–17). The edges reaching the dorsum become corresponding halves of the muscular heart, enclosing an area of primary body cavity, the blastocoel (Figs. 4–13, 4–18). The ventral edges similarly form the ventral artery; the adjoining septa form lateral arteries. The vessels are surrounded by coelom; although their walls are derived from coelom walls, their lumen is that of the blastocoel.

The muscles and vessels originating from the peritoneum retain their segmental arrangement more or less, even when other segmentation disappears, as in the spider abdomen (Figs. 4–17, 11–2, 11–13).

The splanchnic layer of the coelomic pouch surrounds the gut, forming gut musculature and peritoneum. After giving rise to some connective tissue membranes of other organs, walls and ducts of gonads, and fat body, the remainder of the coelom wall disintegrates and the coelom fuses with the primary body cavity, the blastocoel, to form the mixocoel (Figs. 4–19, 4–20). Among insects, especially of the higher orders (Coleoptera, Lepidoptera, Hymenoptera, and Diptera), the coelomic pouches are smaller (Figs. 4–19, 4–20), and they remain ventral; by the time of dorsal fusion the coelom walls have disappeared in the formation of longitudinal muscles, connective tissues, fat bodies, etc. The organ formation nevertheless resembles that of the arachnids and chilopods.

Most crustacean and many myriapod embryos at hatching have fewer segments than the adults. This is especially true of the crustacean nauplius larva, which, besides the acron, has only the three segments bearing the antennae and mandibles. A budding area gives rise to additional segments with appendages, which appear one after another at regular intervals after molts, often in a very long postembryonal development. In contrast, in many chelicerates and insects most segments are formed within the egg; nevertheless the young animals go through a long postembryonal development with a more or less fixed number of molts before they mature sexually. Some molt after maturity. Among many crustaceans and insects the newly hatched young is very different in appearance from the adult; it is a larva, and not only differs in mouthparts and lack of gonads, but also usually has habits very different from those of the adult. The postembryonal development is then a metamorphosis.

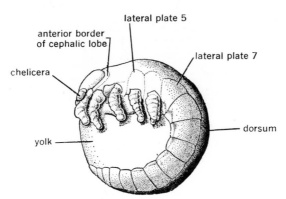

Fig. 4–14. The growth of the germ band in the whipscorpion, *Thelyphonus caudatus*; dorsum not yet overgrown by cells; lateral plates consist of ectoderm and coelomic pouches; 3 mm long. (After Kaestner.)

Relationships

There is no doubt of the annelid origin of arthropods. Unfortunately paleontology offers little evidence for phylogeny; arthropods are known from the Cambrian, and must have evolved during the Precambrian, which is represented by only a few fossils. However, many Cambrian arthropods differ from recent ones. Unfortunately most of these fossils are not well preserved in the important anterior region. The fossils therefore do not answer some of the most intriguing questions: Did the ancestors of the chelicerates have antennae? Are the arthropods monophyletic or polyphylectic? The treatment given here of fossil arthropods is necessarily limited.

Habits

While most Crustacea inhabit salt or freshwater with only few exceptions (woodlice, land crabs), the recent chelicerates have become terrestrial except for four species of horseshoe crabs and the pycnogonids, and some mites that have returned to water secondarily. The myriapods and insects have no recent primarily aquatic representatives. Terrestrial arthropods differ in few respects, other than respiratory system and insect wings, from their aquatic or marine relatives, an indication of how well preadapted the arthropods were for terrestrial habits. It might be worthwhile to cite the habitat differences, shallow water and shores not considered.

1. The factors limiting life in the ocean are salt content, oxygen, and light. On land the first two are replaced by lack of moisture and extremes of temperature.

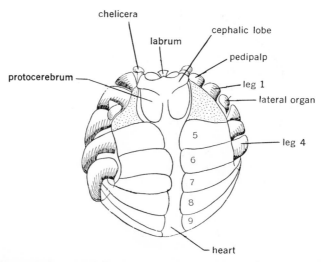

Fig. 4–15. Part of the cephalic lobes and the anterior segments in formation of the dorsum, in the whipscorpion _Thelyphonus caudatus_; function of lateral organ unknown; 3 mm long. (After Kaestner.)

2. Annual and daily temperature change in the ocean is small. On land, soil surface especially shows drastic seasonal and daily differences, especially where there is no shade (tropical rain forests and tropical coasts excepted).

In subtropical deserts the nocturnal temperature near the soil may approach freezing. In West Greenland, lat 76° 50′, in August sunshine with air temperature 15.5°C, the soil temperature reached 42°C at noon on a south slope of 20°, despite the presence of permanent frost at 30–35 cm depth (Sørensen, 1941).

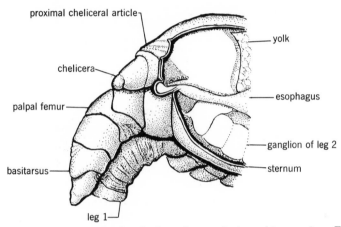

Fig. 4–16. **Head end of newly hatched embryo of the whipscorpion *Thelyphonus caudatus*; the protocerebrum with the yolk behind it was once the anterior edge of the germ band; 1.1 mm long. (After Kaestner.)**

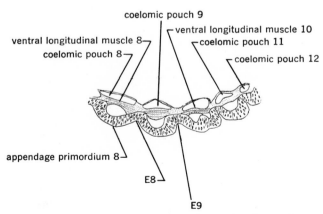

Fig. 4–17. **Formation of the ventral longitudinal muscles from the somatic wall of successive coelomic pouches, as shown by sections through somites 7 to 10 of the germ band of the spider *Sitticus floricola*. The segmental arrangement of the muscles is retained throughout life (compare to Fig. 11–13). The ectoderm (E) sinks in and later forms apodemes; 0.4 mm long. (After Purcell from Kaestner.)**

Among mosses, in forest litter, or in crevices between stones the differences between aquatic and terrestrial conditions are reduced, and such places, where temperature and humidity are relatively constant, probably typify habitats in which evolution toward terrestrial life took place.

Humidity and temperature among moss plants may be of importance to their inhabitants. The wolf spider *Pirata piraticus*, which lives among stalks of *Sphagnum* moss, has a temperature preference of 18–24°C, with heat death

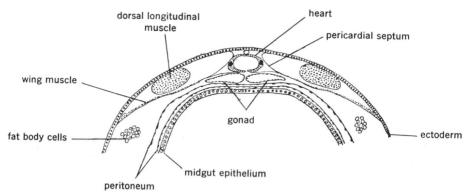

Fig. 4–18. **Heart and gonad formation of the dorsal borders of the coelomic pouches; cross section through dorsum of embryo of chilopod, *Scolopendra*; heart diameter 0.06 mm. (After Heymons.)**

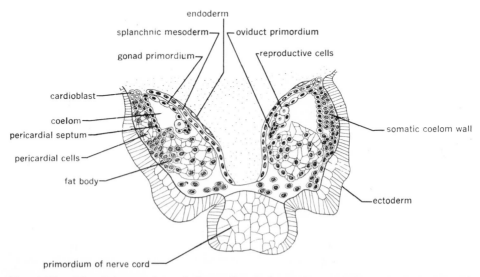

Fig. 4–19. **The disintegration of the walls of the coelom pouches and formation of mesodermal organs; cross section through the abdomen of the cockroach *Blattella germanica* embryo; only the germ band is shown, diameter 3 mm. (After Heymons.)**

occurring at 36°C. The related wolf spider *Pardosa pullata* prefers the surface and has a temperature preference of 28–36°C, with heat death at 43°C. *Pirata piraticus* carrying an egg sac with the abdomen holds it above the moss surface in the sun; the temperature preference is now 26–32°C. Actually, neither species requires sphagnum moss, but both find required conditions there: *Pardosa pullata* prefers a sunny area with little grass and mesic humidity, while *Pirata piraticus* prefers areas near open water, sun, and high humidity. Both species are also found in far different habitats (Nørgaard, 1951).

3. Terrestrial habitats separated by distances as short as a few centimeters may have different microclimates. The shadow of a stone or the southern exposure of a slope have microclimates sharply different from their surroundings. Water, in contrast, especially ocean, has layered temperature zones that may include large areas; microclimates may be present only in shallow waters.

4. Most terrestrial animals live at the border between ground and air, on rooted plants, or in the upper aerated soil layers. With the exception of small spiders and insects, which may float free in the air for some days, no terrestrial arthropod spends a portion of its life cycle floating, as do the many planktonic animals. The absence of airborne plankton results from the lower density of

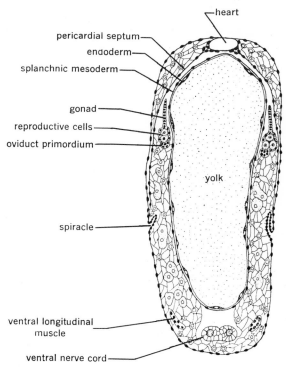

Fig. 4–20. **Growth around the yolk, dorsal fusion, and heart formation in the cockroach** *Blattella germanica;* **cross section through the abdomen, diameter 0.34 mm. (After Heymons.)**

air, demanding greater energy output or extremely light weight and help of air currents to overcome gravity.

On the other hand, the low density of air is of advantage to rapid movement, and is made use of by many insects, birds and some mammals, permitting even the development of flying predators, such as dragonflies (Odonata), robberflies (Asilidae), bats, and many birds including swifts and swallows. Filter feeders, common in water, are found only among spiders. Among both spiders and insects there are tube-dwellers analogous to marine tube-dwelling polychaetes.

The greater density of water provides support, permitting larger size; thus, the largest chelicerates, the horseshoe crabs, as well as the largest mandibulates, the spider crabs, occur in marine habitats.

Classification

A rough outline of the classification system followed is given below. Details are to be found in the appropriate chapters.

Phylum Arthropoda
  Subphylum Trilobitomorpha
    Class Trilobita
  Subphylum Chelicerata
    Class Merostomata
    Class Arachnida
    Class Pycnogonida
  Subphylum Mandibulata
    Class Crustacea
    Group Myriapoda
      Class Chilopoda
      Class Diplopoda
      Class Pauropoda
      Class Symphyla
    Group Hexapoda
      Class Insecta

References

Beament, J. W. L. 1961. Water relations of insect cuticle. *Biol. Rev.* 36:281–320.

Butt, F. H. 1960. Head development of arthropods. *Ibid.* 35:43–91.

Davies, M. E. and Edney, E. B. 1952. Evaporation of water from spiders. *J. Exp. Biol.* 29:571–582.

Gilbert, L. *et. al.* 1965. Lipolytic activity of insect tissues. *J. Insect Physiol.* 11:1057–1070.

Hackman, R. H. 1954. Studies on chitin. *Australian J. Biol. Sci.* 7:168–178.

Hansen, H. J. 1925-1930. *Studies on Arthropoda.* Copenhagen. Vols. 2, 3.

Kaestner, A. 1948-1950. Entwicklungsgeschichte von *Thelyphonus. Zool. Jahrb. Abt. Anat.* 69:493–506; 70:169–197; 71:1–55.

Lees, A. D. 1947. Transpiration and the structure of the epicuticle in ticks. *J. Exp. Biol.* 23:379–410.

Locke, M. 1961. Pore canals and related structures in insect cuticle. *J. Biophys. Biochem. Cytol.* 10:589–618.

———— 1965. Permeability of insect cuticle. *Science* 147:295–298.

Manton, S. M. 1949. Early embryonic stages of *Peripatopsis*. *Philos. Trans. Roy. Soc. London* (B) 233:483–580.

———— 1960. Head development in arthropods. *Biol. Rev.* 35:265–282.

———— 1964. Mandibular mechanisms and evolution in arthropods. *Philos. Trans. Roy. Soc. London* (B) 247:1–183.

Nemenz, H. 1955. Bau der Kutikula und dessen Einfluss auf die Wasserabgabe bei Spinnen. *Sitzungsber. Österreichischen Akad. Wiss. Math. Naturwiss. Kl.* (1) 164:65–76.

Nørgaard, E. 1951. Ecology of two lycosid spiders. *Oikos* 3:1–21.

Richards, A. G. 1958. Cuticle of arthropods. *Ergebn. Biol.* 20:1–26.

Rockstein, M., Ed. 1964-1965. *The Physiology of Insects*. 3 vol. Academic Press, New York.

Russo' Caia, S. 1964. Incorporazione dei precurseri marcati degli acidi nucleici e delle proteine nei corpi grasso dei *Musca*. *Atti Accad. Naz. Lincei* (8) 37:518–520.

Sharov, A. G. 1966. *Basic Arthropod Stock*. Pergamon Press, London.

Snodgrass, R. E. 1948. Feeding organs of Arachnida. *Smithsonian Misc. Coll.* 110 (10):1–93.

———— 1950. Jaws of mandibulate arthropods. *Ibid.* 116(1):1–85.

———— 1951. *Comparative Studies on the Head of Mandibulate Arthropods*, Comstock Publ., Ithaca.

———— 1952. *A Textbook of Arthropod Anatomy*. Comstock Publ., Ithaca.

Sørensen, T. 1941. Temperature relationships and phenology of northeast Greenland flowering plants. *Medd. Grønland* 125 (9):1–305.

Strørmer, L. 1944. Relationships and phylogeny of fossil and recent Arachnomorpha. *Skrift. Norske Vidensk. Akad. Oslo, Math. Naturv. Kl.* (5):1–158.

———— 1949. Trilobitomorphes *in* Grassé, *Traité de Zoologie*, Masson et Cie, Paris, 6:159–210.

Tiegs, O. W. 1940. Embryology and affinities of the Symphyla. *Quart. J. Microscop. Sci.* 82:1–225.

———— and Manton, S. M. 1958. Evolution of the arthropoda. *Biol. Rev.* 33:255–337.

Vachon, M. 1947. L'arthrogenèse des appendices. *Bull. Biol. France Belgique* 81:177–194.

Vandel, A. 1949. Arthropodes *in* Grassé, *Traité de Zoologie*, Masson et Cie, Paris, 6:79–158.

Weber, H. 1952. Morphologie, Histologie und Entwicklungsgeschichte der Articulaten. *Fortschr. Zool.* 9:18–231.

Wessing, A. 1966. Exkretion der Insekten. *Naturwiss. Rundschau* 19:139–147.

5.

Subphylum Trilobitomorpha: Class Trilobita, Trilobites

In addition to the Recent amandibulate chelicerates, there are a number of interesting fossil representatives. Only for the trilobites is our understanding of the morphology sufficient to be useful in comparative studies of invertebrate anatomy.

CLASS TRILOBITA, THE TRILOBITES

The trilobites include over 4000 fossil species of which the largest is *Uralichas riberoi*, 75 cm long.

Trilobites were marine arthropods. Present in the Cambrian, they have been extinct since the Permian. Structurally they are the most primitive arthropods of which we know. Their appendages, one pair of preoral antennae and a series of similar legs, display a homonomy unique among arthropods; in all others some appendages are modified as mouthparts, raptorial structures or gills.

The three-part body consists of head or cephalon, thorax or trunk, and a posterior pygidium. Judging by the appendages, the cephalon, like the proterosoma of chelicerates, has four postoral segments. But anteriorly, between the postoral segments and the acron, the trilobites have a preoral antennal segment that is lacking in the chelicerates (Fig. 5–1). The mouth, therefore, is a considerable distance from the anterior margin.

The body is longitudinally divided into three parts, suggesting the name, trilobites. The median raised area of the head is called the glabella; the lateral lobes, the cheeks, bear compound eyes. The parts of the cephalon are covered by a common carapace; the many segments of the trunk, however, are separate. Each somite has a raised median area and, laterally, pleural lobes that cover the appendages. The pygidium, like the cephalon, consists of a number of fused segments. The pygidium of trilobites is not homologous with the pygidium of annelids.

The two-branched appendages are attached to the domed middle zone of the body (Fig. 5–1). The main branch, the telopodite (= endopodite), consists of eight articles; it is the walking leg. The other branch, the preepipodite, is softer, its article number varies in different genera, and the articles have numerous filamentous posterior attachments, probably gills. This preepipodite inserts at the base of the coxa, dorsal to the endopodite. The coxae do not meet medially and thus could not have been used as jaws. Nothing is known about feeding habits. All trilobites were marine, most of them bottom-dwelling. They were once very abundant, especially during the Cambrian and Ordovician.

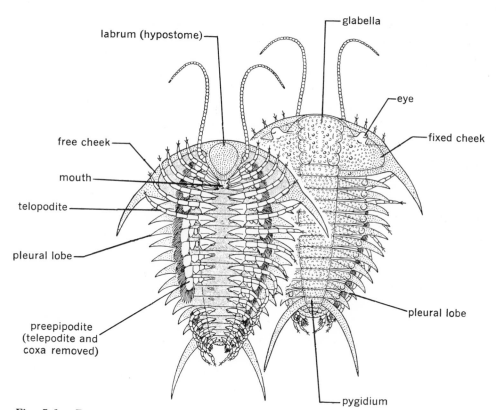

Fig. 5–1. Reconstruction of *Ceraurus pleurexanthemus*, of the Middle Ordovician: left, ventral view; right, dorsal view. Sternites are densely stippled, lateral lobes and labrum lightly stippled, appendages white. Some appendages have been removed, others have parts removed; 2.6 cm long. (After Størmer.)

References

Harrington, H. J. *et al.* 1959. Trilobitomorpha, *in* Moore, R. C. *Treatise on Invertebrate Paleontology*, Part O, Geol. Soc. Amer., Univ. Kansas Press, Lawrence, Kansas.

Hupé, P. 1953. Trilobites, *in* J. Piveteau, *Traité de Paléontologie*, Masson et Cie, Paris, 3:44–246.

Palmer, A. R. 1957. Ontogenetic development of two olenellid trilobites. *J. Paleontol.* 31:105–128.

Størmer, L. 1939, 1942, 1951. Studies on trilobite morphology. *Norsk Geol. Tidsskr.* 19:143–277; 21:50–164; 29:108–158.

_____ 1944. On the relationships and phylogeny of fossil and recent Arachnomorpha. *Videns. Akad. Oslo Skrift. 1, Math.-Nat. Klasse* 5:1–158.

_____ 1949. Sous-embranchement des Trilobitomorphes *in* Grassé, *Traité de Zoologie*, Masson et Cie, Paris, 6:159–216.

Whittington, H. B. 1957. Ontogeny of trilobites. *Biol. Rev.* 32:421–469.

6.

Subphylum Chelicerata

The chelicerates include approximately 60,000 Recent species. The largest chelicerate known is the extinct eurypterid, *Pterygotus rhenaniae*, which was 1.8 m long. Among Recent species the largest is the horseshoe crab, *Limulus polyphemus*, up to 60 cm long. Though surpassed in size by the marine eurypterids and xiphosurans, the mainly terrestrial Arachnida display greater diversity and include greater numbers of species. The aberrant sea spiders, the Pycnogonida (see Chapter 15) will not be considered in the introduction.

The amandibulate chelicerates lack antennae and usually have the first pair of appendages, the chelicerae, chelate or pincerlike. In some groups the chelicerae are modified and may even take the form of stylets. Furthermore, the chelicerates lack jawlike mandibles although in horseshoe crabs the coxae (gnathobases) of the legs move against each other to crush prey (such as mollusks) and carry food to the mouth. But they are less specialized for feeding than the mandibles of the mandibulates. In most spiders, the basal segments of the chelicerae have been rotated so that they work against each other as pliers; however, there are no chewing surfaces.

Anatomy

The chelicerate body is divided into two parts, the cephalothorax (prosoma) and abdomen (opisthosoma). The prosoma is specialized for locomotion, the abdomen for digestion and reproduction. The abdomen may have a postanal extension (Fig. 7–1), the telson of the Xiphosura and Eurypterida, the stinger of scorpions, or the flagellum of Palpigradi (Fig. 10–8).

The prosoma includes the acron and six appendage-bearing segments. Usually the entire prosoma is covered by a shield, the carapace, hiding the ancestral segmentation that persists in some arachnids and is readily seen in the development of horseshoe crabs. In others (Figs. 10–3, 12–9) the carapace covers the proterosoma, a combination of a preoral segment, and four postoral appendage-bearing segments and forms a tagma present also in the trilobites. However, in these chelicerates, unlike trilobites, the fifth and sixth segments also bear walking legs and succeeding segments may have lamellate appendages, or just vestiges of them, or may lack appendages altogether (Figs. 7–2, 8–3, 10–3).

The seventh segment forms the joint between the prosoma and opisthosoma, and it may be reduced to a stalk (pedicel) (Fig. 8–3), may be ventrally reduced, or may be completely lost.

The abdomen is sometimes segmented externally; the number of somites is variable, their reduction occurring posteriorly (in addition to any reduction of the 7th segment). Horseshoe crabs have serial abdominal appendages, while the abdominal appendages of arachnids may be lacking in adults or specialized (as pectines of scorpions, spinnerets of spiders). In most orders whose development has been studied, the gonopores are on the venter of the eighth segment. This sternite may be pushed anteriorly, to lie between the coxae of the last pairs of legs, in which case the seventh, or pregenital, sternite may completely disappear (Fig. 8–3).

The midventral position of the gonopores complicates fertilization, necessarily internal in terrestrial animals. In some chelicerates, a spermatophore deposited by the male is picked up by the gonopore of the female. In others gonopods or intromittent organs may be used to transfer the sperm.

SKELETON. In addition to the ectodermal exoskeleton with its apodemes that serve as points for muscle attachment, a mesodermal internal skeleton is present. Usually platelike, it lies above the subesophageal ganglion and provides attachment sites for the appendage muscles (Fig. 11–3).

APPENDAGES. Except for chelicerae, palpi and the feelerlike first legs of the Amblypygi, the prosomal appendages are used for locomotion. The chelicerae are used by most chelicerates to tear up prey but they cannot chew. In horseshoe crabs the function of crushing prey has been taken over by the gnathobases, the endites of the leg coxae (Fig. 7–2). Arachnids use their endites only to spoon liquid nutrient into the mouth. Usually only the second pair of appendages, the pedipalps, have such endites (Fig. 11–1), but other appendages may. The pedipalps help to hold prey; in many arachnids they are specialized for this function and may be chelate (Figs. 8–2, 10–1).

The leaf-shaped abdominal appendages of horseshoe crabs can be used for swimming. Embryonic arachnids, scorpions and spiders have abdominal appendage primordia, but these disappear or persist only as combs (pectines) or spinnerets (Figs. 7–2, 8–3, 8–11).

NERVOUS SYSTEM. The brain consists of the protocerebrum, derived from the ectoderm of the cephalic lobes, optic centers and association centers (globuli and central bodies), and the ganglion of the first postoral (cheliceral) segment. The commissures of this ganglion, which has secondarily moved anterior to the mouth, lie behind the esophagus; because it is connected to the sympathetic stomatogastric nerves, this ganglion is usually considered homologous to the tritocerebrum of mandibulates. Only in horseshoe crabs does the front ganglion (belonging to the sympathetic nerves of the digestive system), with its paired connectives, lie free in front of the brain. In arachnids, both connectives are fused with the tritocerebrum. The deutocerebrum and antennal primordia are believed absent even from the embryo.

Some students consider the absence of antennae secondary, believing that antennae and deutocerebrum were present in the ancestors of the chelicerates. As vestiges they cite a zone of glomerulus-like, dense masses in the brain of *Limulus,* anterior to the tritocerebrum, and a precheliceral coelomic pouch found in *Limulus* and some arachnids. Several pairs of coelomic pouches have recently been found anterior of the cheliceral coelom in *Pardosa.* Only further research can clarify this problem.

The ganglia posterior to the tritocerebrum are ladder-like only in the embryo. Later, ganglia two to eight, and sometimes others, move anteriorly and form a subesophageal mass, the origin of which can be deduced from the lateral nerves as well as from the number of serially arranged commissures (Figs. 6–1, 6–2). This cephalization has progressed furthest in spiders, amblypygids, pseudoscorpions, and mites, where all ganglia have migrated into the prosoma to form a uniform subesophageal mass (Figs. 4–12, 6–2). As in many other arthropods, there may be median and lateral eyes, often different in structure. Only *Limulus* has compound lateral eyes.

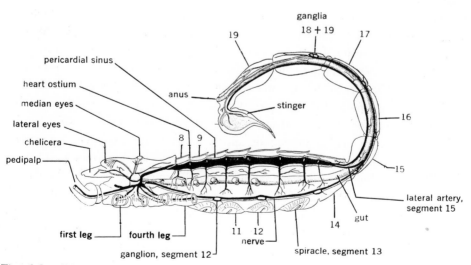

Fig. 6–1. Diagram of the structure of a scorpion in lateral view; the ganglion of segment 12 has moved forward to segment 11; about 10 cm long. (After Newton and Kaestner.)

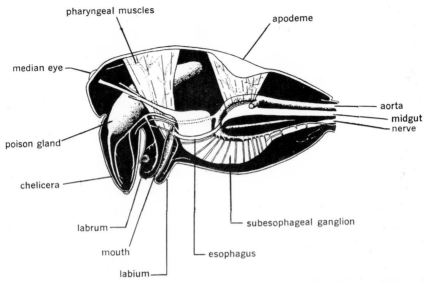

Fig. 6–2. **Vascular and nervous systems of a spider. Longitudinal section of the prosoma of** *Tegenaria*, **5 mm long. (Composite from Causard, Schneider, and Kaestner.)**

DIGESTIVE SYSTEM. The location of the mouth varies in different orders. In Palpigradi, for example, it is in the pedipalpal segment; in horseshoe crabs it lies between the coxae of the walking legs. Despite such diversity in adults, the primary invagination of the stomodeum always takes place at the posterior border of the cephalic lobes (Fig. 4–11). Behind the stomodeum, adjoining the sternites or the following segments, in *Limulus* and the collembolan *Orchesella* a median longitudinal groove forms the posterior of the pharynx. At the same time from the anterior, from the cephalic lobes, the clypeus-labrum grows over the stomodeum, forming the anterior pharynx wall. As shown in Fig. 4–11, even in arachnids the clypeus-labrum moves posteriorly over the germ band and, depending on the length of the primary stomodeum, pharynx and mouth, is pushed posteriorly. The chelicerae and appendages thus do not move forward.

The gut, unlike that of myriapods and insects, always has ceca, segmentally arranged during embryonic stages. The large ceca develop from partition of yolk masses rather than as evaginations from the gut (Fig. 4–12). Both endoderm and mesoderm, folding into the yolk, form walls that later separate and become ceca. The remaining free axial canal later becomes the gut. The glandular cells of the ceca secrete enzymes. Nutrient cells take up the breakdown products and complete their digestion (an exception is found among mites). The nutrient materials move to connective tissues derived from the coelom, which fuses and surrounds the ceca (Fig. 7–5).

EXCRETORY SYSTEM. In the prosoma, transformed nephridia form excretory organs, which develop on the walls of one or several coelomic pouches and are called coxal glands because they open on the bases of the coxae. Often primordia of two or more of these fuse, thereby forming a joined canal.

The abdomen, as in other terrestrial arthropods, has tubelike, branched gut diverticula, the Malpighian tubules, formed from endoderm.

RESPIRATORY SYSTEM. The marine Xiphosura have five pairs of lamellate abdominal appendages, each posteriorly edged by a row of gills derived from ectodermal evaginations (Figs. 7–3, 7–4). In some arachnids (scorpions, spiders) corresponding respiratory organs form, but develop as invaginations at the posterior side of the abdominal leg primordia (Fig. 8–11). Thus a row of respiratory pockets or leaves, the sclerotized book lungs, hang into a blood sinus (Fig. 8–12). They are the negative of the *Limulus* gills and their relationship to terrestrial habits demonstrates nicely that lungs invaginate as an adaptation against desiccation. After the egg hatches the abdominal leg primordia sink into the body, leaving only the spiracles to indicate the location of the posterior appendage primordia (Fig. 8–3).

Besides these localized metamerically arranged respiratory organs, there are also those that penetrate the whole body as tube tracheae. Some can be derived from book lungs, others must be considered new structures.

CIRCULATORY SYSTEM. In arachnid orders with a localized respiratory system, the heart is larger than in orders with an extensive tracheal system. In the latter there is a heart and unbranched anterior and posterior arteries (Fig. 7–5). In arachnid groups with book lungs the circulatory system is surprisingly similar to that of horseshoe crabs (Fig. 7–5). The heart is generally limited to the abdomen (except in Xiphosura, Uropygi and Solifugae). It extends through a variable number of segments and in each has a pair of ostia. In animals with localized respiratory organs the heart has pairs of lateral arteries as well as pairs of lateral and ventral ligaments (Fig. 11–13). The tail and lateral arteries branch between gut ceca and gonads. The appendages and nervous system are supplied by branches of the cephalic artery.

Both forks of the cephalic artery move ventrally and widen near their ends above the subesophagal ganglion. From each widening arteries extend to the eyes, the anterior ganglionic mass and one chelicera; laterally five branches go to the postoral appendages (Fig. 6–1). Medially the two distended areas are bridged by several connections, and from the middle of each connection descends a median artery into the subesophagal ganglion, between two ganglia, still indicating the metameric structure of the ganglion (Fig. 6–2). Also a thick spinal artery from this connection runs posteriorly on the ventral nerve and sends branches to the ganglia, lateral muscles and other ventral organs.

From the open ends of the arteries the blood reaches lacunae and collects in a ventral median sinus of the abdomen. In those animals with localized respiratory organs (gills or lungs) the blood passes from the median side, between the respiratory lamellae, to the lateral walls of the body from which it rises to the pericardial sinus (Fig. 9–4). The ascending sinus functionally resembles a lung vein, but is not lined by endothelium. Nor does it enter the heart as a vein but is enclosed in a connective tissue membrane and empties into the pericardial sinus from which the heart takes the oxygenated blood.

REPRODUCTIVE SYSTEM. The gonads consist of simple paired or branched tubes in the abdomen, between the midgut ceca and below the gut (except in the Xiphosura). The gonad walls are mesodermal; the paired efferent ducts are derived in spiders and scorpions from evaginations of the coelomic pouch of the eighth segment and open posteriorly on the eighth sternite, usually with a distal ectodermal portion (Figs. 11–8, 11–10). The ova develop in grapelike clusters on the outer wall of the ovaries (Fig. 11–8).

Relationships

Even though the chelicerates appear diverse they have a large number of characters in common, and form a uniform group. In the oldest group, the Merostomata, the respiratory organs and appendages are closely associated. From the Merostomata it is easy to derive the scorpions, which resemble the Eurypterida in number and distribution of segments and tagmata, and also in the narrow postabdomen that characterizes all eurypterids, many of which are strikingly scorpionlike (Figs. 7–7, 8–3). Nothing is known of the relationship of the Pycnogonida.

The body organization of the chelicerates is surprisingly persistent, not having changed in the millions of years since the Paleozoic. Silurian scorpions resemble present species, whipscorpions and spiders are also like Recent representatives, and Jurassic *Limulus* differs hardly at all from Recent species.

References

Kaestner, A. 1940. Arachnida, *in* Kükenthal, *Handbuch der Zoologie*, De Gruyter, Berlin, 3(2):97–116.

Størmer, L. 1944. Relationships and phylogeny of fossil and recent Arachnomorpha. *Skrift. Norske Videnskaps-Akad. Oslo*, I Kl. (5):1–158.

Snodgrass, R. E. 1952. *A Textbook of Arthropod Anatomy.* Comstock Publ., Ithaca.

Schulze, P. 1937. Trilobita, Xiphosura, Acarina; eine morphologische Untersuchung über Trilobiten und Spinnentieren. *Z. Morphol. Ökol.* 32:181–223.

7.

Class Merostomata

The Merostomata are large marine chelicerates having gills. The body is divided into a prosoma (covered completely by a carapace) and an abdomen bearing a large tail spine. Of the two orders included, only the Xiphosura have Recent representatives.

ORDER XIPHOSURA, HORSESHOE CRABS

The Xiphosura include four species, the largest of which is *Limulus polyphemus*, to 60 cm long including the tail spine.

Horseshoe crabs are marine bottom-dwellers, as were the trilobites. The body is scoop-shaped, the dorsum of the prosoma and abdomen unsegmented. The abdomen bears a long arrow-shaped caudal spine and has six flat, medially fused appendages, of which five bear gills.

Anatomy

The appendages, which cannot be autotomized, are attached along the midline of the venter, rather than along the sides (Fig. 7–2). They are thus concealed and protected by the semicircular carapace edge, which is used also for digging (Fig. 7–1).

The body organization has not changed since the Silurian. That it develops secondarily is apparent during ontogeny. The germ band barely overhangs the appendage primordia laterally. Only after 11 segments have appeared does the large plate that forms the carapace develop from a great ectodermal fold of the germ band periphery.

The horseshoe-shaped body is divided into two unsegmented, broadly joined parts, the prosoma and abdomen (Fig. 7–1). The abdomen extends beyond the anal opening into the caudal spine. Though jointed proximally, this is not a true telson (pygidium), but can be considered an appendage of the pygidium, as is the posterior spine of many trilobites. The acron and six appendage-bearing segments belong to the prosoma, segments VIII to XIV to the opisthosoma. The pregenital 7th segment is fused with the prosoma. The joint between the body parts does not correspond with the border between the 7th and 8th segments; a transverse section along this joint shows that the appendages of the 8th segment, the genital operculum, along with the gonopores, remain with the anterior body part. As in scorpions and Opiliones, the gonopores have moved anteriorly with only the median part of the 7th segment surviving. Short appendages of the 7th segment, the chilaria, are found between the posterior gnathobases (coxae) (Fig. 7–2), and dorsally the 7th segment persists as the median lens-shaped hinge fused to the prosoma. The ganglia of the 7th and 8th segments have also moved into the prosoma.

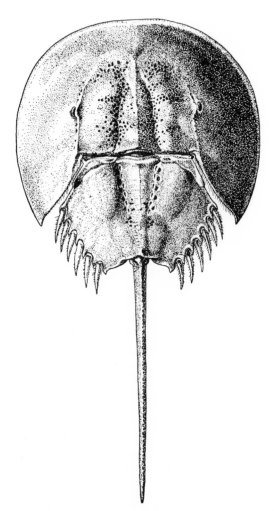

Fig. 7–1. *Tachypleus gigas*, dorsal view, 40 cm long including spine. (After Van der Hoeven from Fage.)

In contrast to the broad back, the sternites are represented only by narrow sclerites between appendage attachments. There are two groups of appendages: six tube-shaped prosomal appendages and the flat lamellate abdominal appendages of somites VIII to XIII. The rudimentary chilaria (of segment VII) resemble

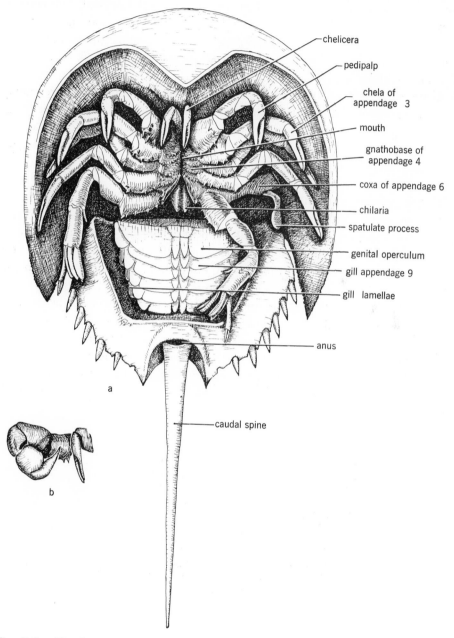

chelicera

pedipalp

chela of
appendage 3

mouth

gnathobase of
appendage 4

coxa of appendage 6

chilaria

spatulate process

genital operculum

gill appendage 9

gill lamellae

anus

a

b

caudal spine

Fig. 7–2. *Limulus polyphemus*, **venter: (a) female, about 34 cm long including spine;**
(b) right chelicera and palpus of male; width of parts about 3 cm.

the prosomal coxae. The preoral chelicerae have three articles, the distal one
chelate. The spined gnathobases of the five pairs of legs are arranged almost
radially around the mouth (Fig. 7–2). The abdominal appendages are plates;
those of the 8th segment lack gills and are grown together, forming a genital
operculum (Fig. 7–2) bearing gonopores on its posterior wall. Abdominal
appendages 9 to 13 are connected by a median membrane and each supports
about 150 gill lamellae (Fig. 7–3). Strong muscles can move these appendages,
which are attached by a transverse hinge. All six pairs have a weak beat most of
the time, a strong beat when swimming.

As the early embryonal primordia of these abdominal appendages are similar
to those of the 5th and 6th leg pairs, there can be no doubt about their being
homologous to legs. However, homologizing the individual articles has not
been successful. Currently attempts are being made to relate the median portion with the trilobite legs and the many-articled lateral portions bearing gills
with the trilobite preepipodite.

The thick exoskeleton has an epicuticle but the chitinous cuticle lacks calcareous material. Posteriorly six pairs of dorsal depressions (Fig. 7–1) mark the
location of apodemes that serve as attachment points for appendage muscles.
Leg muscles are attached to a prosomal mesodermal endosternite. In the
abdomen, however, there are six median ventral and six paired dorsal mesodermal endosternites between apodemes and muscles.

NERVOUS SYSTEM AND SENSE ORGANS. It is characteristic of the nervous
system that the suprapharyngeal ganglion lies anterior to (instead of above) the
subpharyngeal portion, as a result of the anterior esophagus loop (Fig. 7–4).
The brain receives nerves from two pairs of eyes as well as from the frontal
organ. It has a central body and a pair of large globuli, making up almost 80%
of the brain volume. The tritocerebrum (cheliceral ganglion) has fused with

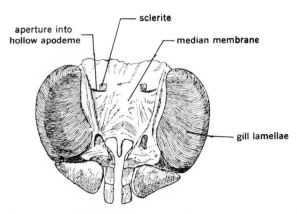

Fig. 7–3.   Gill flap of *Limulus*, posterior view, 7 cm wide. (After Lankester.)

the posterior part of the brain. In ontogeny the mouth moves back so far that it comes to lie between the ganglia of the first two walking legs (Fig. 7–4). Ganglia II to VIII have moved forward and fused to a large subpharyngeal mass, serving not only the prosoma but also abdominal segments VII and VIII. Abdominal ganglia IX to XIV stay in their segments and form a nerve chain, the anterior ones close to the appendages, the last three in one mass, possibly a vestige of the 15th ganglion.

The sensory equipment includes eyes, frontal organ and sensory hairs, the function of which has never been investigated. There is one pair of small simple median eyes at the anterior end of the carapace ridge, as well as two much larger compound eyes lateral to the lateral ridges (Fig. 7–1). The median eyes each have a large spherical cuticular lens and below it a thin epithelium of corneagen cells formed by the hypodermis. The retina consists of groups of six to eight irregular sensory cells surrounding a rhabdom. The compound lateral eyes also have lenses of thickened cuticle. To each lens belongs an ommatidium, a group of 10–15 retina cells, in the center of which is a rhabdom. The ommatidia, separated by hypodermis cells, lie in the thick hypodermis. Thus the eye has the appearance of an aggregation of ocelli. The eyes have been used extensively in physiological investigations because they are relatively uncomplicated and impulses can be recorded from a single axon. Two to three centimeters in front of the mouth is the wartlike frontal organ, 5–8 mm in diameter, of unknown function in the adult, but a light receptor in the larva.

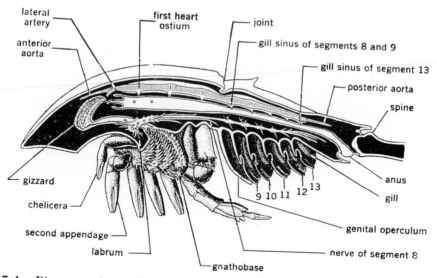

Fig. 7–4. Diagrammatic median section of *Limulus*; 20 cm long. (Adapted from Patten and Redenbaugh.)

DIGESTIVE SYSTEM. The mouth is a slit between the second and fifth gnathobases; it opens anteriorly into a narrow sclerotized pharynx that loops back into a gizzard with hard, muscular, folded walls bearing denticles (Fig. 7–4). The gizzard leads through a funnel-shaped valve into the midgut, which in turn leads into a short sclerotized hindgut. The anus opens underneath the joint of the spine. The midgut has two pairs of much-branched lateral diverticula forming glandular ceca that fill a large portion of the prosoma. In arachnids this gland is always found in the abdomen.

EXCRETORY SYSTEM. A pair of structurally complicated red coxal glands on the endosternite serve an excretory function. Having four lateral lobes (arising from metameres of appendages II to V; those of I and VI disappear), the glands consist of twisted nephridial canals, which connect with one another and lead to a vesicle (sacculus) of the fifth metamere, into a loop of the common excretory canal, and out through a short ectodermal canal that opens between the 5th and 6th appendage coxae.

RESPIRATORY SYSTEM. About 150 soft gills arise from the posterior border of each gill flap. They consist of ectodermal folds, held apart by epidermal columns (Fig. 7–3). Blood, containing dissolved hemocyanin, circulates within the cavities of the gills. Corresponding with the localized respiratory organs, the circulatory system is complex with a strong heart and widely branched arteries that empty blood into the hemocoel. The heart, hanging in the pericardial sinus, extends almost the length of the body. It has eight pairs of ostia (Figs. 7–4, 7–5). Anteriorly there is a median aorta, which supplies the dorsal portion of the prosoma, the hepatic ceca and gonads, and two lateral arteries, which turn to supply the venter. The laterals combine above the subesophageal ganglion, surrounding it and the brain, which thus lies in a blood sinus. Also, the large blood sinus has a posterior extension within which the nerve cord and ganglia lie. From the ends of arteries the blood flows into sinuses and finally collects in three longitudinal sinuses with membranous walls. One of these sinuses surrounds the intestine. The other two are on the venter, the blood within them moving posteriorly and entering the gills through openings. From the gills, lateral dorsoventral sinuses, erroneously called veins, take the blood to the pericardial cavity and return it to the heart through ostia (Fig. 7–5).

Adjacent to each of the four anterior pairs of ostia, there is a pair of lateral arteries, supplying the dorsal half of the body (Figs. 7–4, 7–5). On each side the four arteries connect to form a lateral vessel that passes posteriorly to the end of the heart. From this lateral vessel, at the level of each ostium, arise a lateral and a median branch (Fig. 7–5). These posterior lateral vessels may have been derived from lateral branches of the heart that secondarily have lost the connection.

In classic experiments at the turn of the century, the heart was shown to stop contracting when the ganglion above it is removed. The embryonic heart, however, beats before it is innervated, the embryonic beat originating within muscle tissue, while the adult beat depends upon nerve impulses. Acetylcholine accelerates the heart beat, while its action on the myogenic vertebrate heart is inhibitory.

REPRODUCTIVE SYSTEM. The paired gonads, unlike those of arachnids, lie in the very large prosoma; they are anastomosing tubes that open through gonopores on the posterior wall of the genital operculum. In the males the gonadal network is formed by the ducts, the testes being attached as small alveoli. In the females the ovary forms all of the branches. Males are smaller than females and have the tarsus of the second appendage, and sometimes the third also, modified (Fig. 7–2).

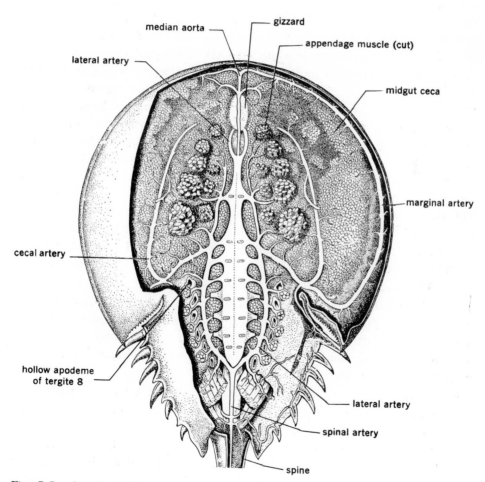

Fig. 7–5. *Limulus* **with carapace and pericardial membrane removed; 20 cm long.** (After Milne–Edwards.)

Reproduction

In spring large numbers of horseshoe crabs come to mate in shallow coastal water. The male perches on the back of the female, holding on with his modified second appendages, and may be carried around for weeks. The female finally digs a hole 15 cm deep in the intertidal zone, and deposits 200–1000 eggs, depending on the species. These are covered with sperm by the pick-a-back male, in the manner of frog egg fertilization. The female moves forward and digs a new hole every 10–15 cm so that 10 to 15 nests, each about 30 cm in diameter, form a row 2–4 m long. Females of some species cover the holes.

Development

The diameter of the eggs is 1.7–3.3 mm, depending on the species. They are deep in the sand, above the low tide mark. Despite some excellent investigations, the embryology is still not completely known. Cleavage is total and results in a morula of 120–130 yolk-filled blastomeres. In *Tachypleus gigas* segments I to IV appear anteriorly while V to XIV develop one after another from the posterior mesoderm primordia. The first four segments differ from the others in three respects: (*1*) They appear simultaneously from anterior mesoderm. (2) The coelomic pouch walls degenerate early into mesenchyme, thus the pouches never grow to the midline. Only later, after the yolk has been reduced pouches never grow to the midline. Only later, after the yolk has been reduced, can the remains form the anterior dorsal circulatory system. The posterior midline and form the heart (Figs. 4–13, 4–15). (*3*) Appendages 1 to 4 are formed by a transverse anterior ectodermal groove that cuts anteriorly into the embryo, cutting the appendage out. First the distal articles are formed. Later the proximal ones are produced by transverse ectodermal proliferation. In contrast appendages of teloblastic segments V to XIII are formed in the usual way as evaginations from the ectoderm, forming the proximal part first, the distal later.

The differences in development of the anterior (deutometameres, see Chapter. 18, Vol. I), and the posterior parts (tritometameres) make the anterior, together with the acron, a special body portion, the proterosoma, still present in some adult arachnids, but in xiphosurans grown together with the next two segments to form a uniform prosoma. The joint between prosoma and abdomen is formed by partial reduction of segment 7.

In the larva of *Tachypleus gigas* the borders of the coelomic pouches show through the unsegmented integument. There are only the nine anterior appendages, that is, only one pair of gill flaps, each with about four gill lamellae. The telson is very short. Because yolk is still present in the gut the larva does not feed, but runs around and can swim, venter up, propelled by the two genital opercula and gill flaps (Fig. 7–6). After a molt the telson and full complement of appendages appear.

Young animals undergo several annual molts, while older animals 9 cm in length or more, molt only once a year, the body length each time increasing by one-fourth. The hypodermis is wrinkled underneath the old molt, permitting this large increase. *Limulus polyphemus* matures in nine to twelve years, or at least 16 molts. After reaching adulthood it probably stops molting. The total life span is about 14–19 years.

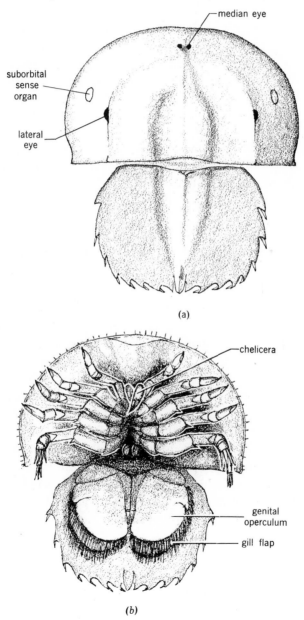

(a)

(b)

Fig. 7–6.   Trilobite larva of *Limulus*; 3.5 mm wide.

Molting commences as the anterior edge of the prosoma tears; the tear continues laterally, freeing the margin of the prosoma. Every 3 to 15 minutes the animal arches by pushing its anterior edge and the spine into the ground. In this way it gets out of the old skin in about 8 hours.

Habits

LOCOMOTION. Horseshoe crabs are marine coastal dwellers, searching at night for food in sand and mud bottoms. Individuals of *Limulus polyphemus* marked with colored celluloid bands and released were recovered at distances of 12 km (after 32 days), 19 km (after 32 days), and once even 33 km (after 56 days). The usual mode of locomotion is by walking, with little difference of phase among the five legs. The last pair, the fifth legs, are of special importance; their distal lamellae spread and can push against loose sand without sinking in (Fig. 7–4). All species dig by pushing the prosoma into sand or mud, bending the prosoma-abdomen joint and caudal spine before straightening. The animal may completely bury itself. If turned upside-down, it pushes the caudal spine into the sand, arches up supported by the carapace edge in front, and beating its legs, turns over. Small horseshoe crabs swim upside down, beating their abdominal appendages.

SENSES. Receptors located on the two distal walking leg segments and the gnathobases are sensitive to chemicals. If *Limulus* is turned over and, after quieting down, is touched with a piece of glass or wood, it does not react. However, if touched with mollusk juice on the gnathobases, there are immediate regular movements: first the chelicerae make grasping movements while the gnathobases first turn and push toward the mouth, then turn back. Finally the last pair come together with force. These responses occur only if the meat extract touches the exoskeleton directly, not if it is 1–2 mm away. However, food dropped into the aquarium causes buried animals to search within ten minutes. The sensory organs are bipolar sensory cells in coxal spines. If the gnathobases are shaved of their spines on the right side, meat extract dripped on the right side elicits no response, though extract dripped on the left side does.

A temperature sense has been demonstrated: the animals will dig themselves into sand if the temperature drops 5°C in 24 hours.

The compound eye has been used in physiological research for studying the relationship between light stimulation and electrical discharge into axons leading from the eye. In the uncomplicated eye, single axon discharge can be measured.

FEEDING. *Limulus polyphemus* feeds on worms and soft mollusks, especially large species of *Nereis, Cerebratulus, Macoma, Ensis,* and *Mya,* caught by digging through mud and sand. The chela take prey to the gnathobases which push food into the mouth, but do not chew it up. The last gnathobases can break shells and the fragments are pushed forward by the chilaria. *Limulus* killed an hour after feeding has undigested meat in the gizzard; 24 hours after feeding the meat has disappeared but bones remain, clumped together. Probably bones and shells are later removed through the mouth, as they are never found in the alkaline intestine.

The intestine has a pH of 8; active proteinase, carboxypolypeptidase, amylase, and lipase from the ceca digest the food. Peristaltic movement brings the partly digested material into blind channels of the ceca and glands secrete peptidases while other cells absorb food material for intracellular digestion. Excretory products go back into the gland lumen, the nutrient substances into the connective tissues. Fecal material consists of columns 5–10 cm long. Malpighian tubules are absent.

Respiration takes place by constant beating of the large abdominal appendages. The oxygen is taken up by the blood and brought to organs.

SYMBIONTS. The turbellarian *Bdelloura* is a common commensal among the gills of *Limulus polyphemus*.

Classification

The only Recent representatives belongs to the suborder Limulida and family Limulidae. The four species belong to three genera. *Limulus** polyphemus* (Fig. 7-2), reaching up to 60 cm in total length, lives on the Atlantic coast of North America from Nova Scotia to Yucatan. *Tachypleus* includes two southeast Asiatic species: *T. gigas* (=*T. moluccanus, T. hoeveni*) (Fig. 7-1) and *T. tridentatus* (=*T. longispina*). Carcinoscorpius lives in the Gulf of Bengal, Siam and on the Malay and Philippine coasts.

Jurassic and Oligocene Xiphosura from Europe and the near East connect the Recent distributions of the species. Fossil species of the European Devonian and Carboniferous had nine external segments on the abdomen, permitting comparison with the metamerism of the coelom of Recent larvae and the embryo of *T. gigas*, which, behind the eighth abdominal segment (metamere 14), has primordia of two small coelomic pouches.

ORDER EURYPTERIDA

Eurypterida (or Gigantostraca) includes 200 fossil species, the largest being *Pterygotus rhenaniae*, 1.8 m long.

These fossil chelicerates had the opisthosoma clearly divided into meso- and metasoma. They lived in salt- and freshwater.

In eurypterids the body is slimmer than in the horseshoe crabs, especially in the posterior abdominal segments, which were probably scorpionlike with rings, each consisting of fused tergite, sternite, and two pleura. In some species of the Upper Silurian this posterior part is very distinct, like that of scorpions and may have had a poison stinger at the tip (Fig. 7–7).

---

* Opinion 320 of the International Commission on Zoological Nomenclature (1954) placed the generic name *Limulus* on the list of Nomina Conservanda and has suppressed the generic name *Xiphosura*.

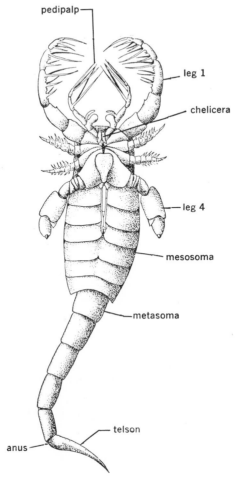

Fig. 7–7. *Mixopterus kiaeri*, ventral view of a scorpionlike eurypterid from Upper Silurian. The preabdomen, the mesosoma, has seven tergites, and if we assume the median structure to be a genital appendage, it would be the 8th segment, and thus the mesosoma would consist of segments 8 to 14.

Pterygotus has long, three-articled chelicerae; in other genera the first or second pairs of legs are raptorial. Only rarely are all legs long as in some spiders. In many genera the last pair is flat and oarlike, probably used for paddling. The abdomen, as in the Xiphosura, carries five pairs of wide appendages bearing posterior gills. *Pterygotus rhenaniae* of the Lower Devonian had long chelicerae and fin-like appendages. Eurypterida, which evolved from marine Cambrian ancestors, lived in brackish or freshwater from the Ordovician until the Permian. Some had compound lateral eyes and simple median eyes as does *Limulus*. Effective protection of the gills may have permitted excursions onto land. Most lived on the bottom; probably some swam upside-down.

References

Ankel, W. E. 1958. Begegnung mit *Limulus*. *Natur Volk* 88:101–110.

Barber, S. B. 1956. Chemoreceptors in *Limulus*. *J. Exp. Zool.* 131:51–73.

———— 1960. *Limulus* proprioceptors. *Ibid.* 143:283–321.

———— and Hayes, W. F. 1964. Tendon receptor in *Limulus*. *Comp. Biochem. Physiol.* 11:193–198.

Buhk, F. 1941. Der amerikanische *Limulus*. *Zool. Garten* 13:248-251.

Fage, L. 1949. Mérostomacés *in* Grassé, *Traité de Zoologie*, Masson et Cie, Paris, 6:219–262.

Gerhardt, U. 1932–1935. Merostomata, *in* Kükenthal, *Handbuch der Zoologie*, De Gruyter, Berlin, 3(2):1–96.

Henry, L. M. 1950. Cephalic nervous system of *Limulus*. *Microentomology* 15:129–139.

Ivanoff, P. P. 1933. Embryonale Entwicklung von *Limulus moluccanus*. *Zool. Jahrb. Abt. Anat.* 56:163–348.

Johansson, G. 1933. Morphologie und Entwicklung des Gehirns von *Limulus*. *Acta Zool.* 14:1–100.

Lochhead, J. H. 1950. *Xiphosura, in* F. A. Brown, *Selected Invertebrate Types*. Wiley, New York. pp. 360–381.

Manton, S. M. 1963. Jaw mechanisms of Arthropoda, *in* Whittington, H. B. and Rolfe, W. D. I., *Phylogeny and Evolution of Crustacea*. Mus. Comp. Zool., Harvard Univ., Cambridge, Mass.

———— 1964. Mandibular mechanisms and evolution of arthropods. *Philos. Trans. Roy. Soc. London* (B) 247 (737):1–183.

Milne, L. J. and Milne, M. J. 1956. Electrical events in vision. *Sci. Amer.* 195 (6):113–122.

———— 1965. *The Crab that Crawled out of the Past*. Atheneum, New York.

Reichardt, W. 1961. Das optische Auflösungsvermögen der Facettenaugen von *Limulus*. *Kybernetik* 1:57–69.

Richards, A. G. 1949. Chitin of *Limulus*. *Science* 109 (2841):591–592.

Richter, I. E. 1964. Bewegungsstudien an *Limulus*. *Verh. Deutschen Zool. Ges.* 27:491–497.

Ropes, J. W. 1961. Longevity in a horseshoe crab. *Trans. Amer. Fish. Soc.* 90:79–80.

Shuster, C. N. 1950. Natural history of *Limulus*. *Contrib. Woods Hole Oceanogr. Inst.* 564:18–23.

———— 1953. Odyssey of the horseshoe crab. *Audubon Mag.* 55:162–163.

———— 1955. Morphometric and serological relationships within the Limulidae. Ph.D. Dissertation, New York Univ. (unpubl.)

———— 1960. Xiphosura, *in Encyclopedia of Science and Technology*, McGraw-Hill, New York.

———— 1962. Serological correspondence among Limulidae. *Zoologica* 47:1–8.

Størmer, L. 1934. Merostomata from Downtonian sandstone. *Skrift. Norske Videnskaps Akad. Oslo* 1 Klasse 1933 (10):1–125.

———— 1944. On relationship and phylogeny of fossil and recent Arachnomorpha. *Ibid.* 1 Klasse (5):1–158.

———— 1949. Merostomoidea *in* Grassé, *Traité de Zoologie*, Masson et Cie, Paris, 6:198–210.

———— 1952. Phylogeny and taxonomy of fossil horseshoe crabs. *J. Paleontol.* 26:630–640.

———— 1955. Merostomata *in* Moore, *Treatise on Invertebrate Paleontology*, Geol. Soc. Amer., Univ. Kansas Press, Lawrence, Kansas, P:4–41.

Waterman, T. H. 1954. Directional sensitivity of single ommatidia of *Limulus*. *Proc. Nat. Acad. Sci.* 40:252–257.

————— 1954. Polarized light and angle of stimulus in the compound eye of *Limulus*. *Ibid*. 258–262.

————— 1954. Relative growth and the compound eye in Xiphosura. *J. Morphol*. 95:125–158.

————— 1958. On the doubtful validity of *Tachypleus hoeveni*. *Postilla, Yale Peabody Mus*. 36:1–17.

————— and Travis, D. F. 1953. Respiratory reflexes and flabellum of *Limulus*. *J. Cell. Comp. Physiol*. 41:261–289.

8.

Class Arachnida

The Arachnida include almost 60,000 species of scorpions, whipscorpions, pseudoscorpions, spiders, opilionids, mites and such less familiar relatives as the ricinuleids and Palpigradi. The largest is the African scorpion, *Pandinus imperator*, which may reach a length of 18 cm.

Terrestrial chelicerates, usually having book lungs or tracheae, the Arachnida have the opisthosoma (abdomen) either segmented or unsegmented and lacking appendages (or at least with only rudimentary or transformed appendages). Malpighian tubules are usually present as the excretory organs.

Of Recent terrestrial animals, the Arachnida probably are the oldest class. Scorpions are known from the Silurian. The structure of the abdominal book lungs indicates their derivation from gills of aquatic or marine animals. Some arachnid orders are rich in species and individuals. Especially abundant are spiders and mites. Not only have they invaded most terrestrial habitats but have secondarily invaded aquatic habitats: there are 2800 aquatic mites out of 20 thousand species; one aquatic spider out of 30 thousand. Except for many animal or plant parasites among the mites and possibly some scavengers among the opilionids, arachnids are predators.

In appearance the arachnids are diverse. Besides the elongate scorpions and whipscorpions, there are short, almost spherical mites; besides flattened amblypygids and pseudoscorpions there are thick-bodied spiders and wind scorpions.

Anatomy

BODY. Except in mites, in which the abdomen is secondarily much modified, the arachnids always have the prosoma, with mouthparts and legs, distinct from the opisthosoma. The abdomen (opisthosoma) contains the ceca and gonads. The two tagmata may be broadly joined or the seventh segment may be narrowed to a stalklike pedicel as in spiders, uropygids, amblypygids and Palpigradi (Figs. 8–1 to 8–3). The prosoma usually has a uniform cover, the carapace. It consists of an acron and six segments, indicated by the appendages. During development their coxae may move to the midline and may displace or replace sternites (except in Araneae, Palpigradi) (Fig. 8–3). In pseudoscorpions and opilionids, the carapace may have one or two transverse grooves, in opilionids doubtless the anterior borders of segments V and VI. In Solifugae, Palpigradi, and schizomids this division of the prosoma has given rise to a proterosoma (the acron and the anterior four appendage-carrying metameres) and separate segments V and VI. Here the proterosoma has a rigid dorsal cover, but the last two

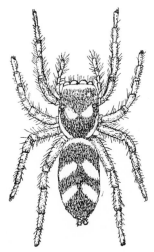

Fig. 8–1. Arachnid having unsegmented abdomen connected to the cephalothorax by a pedicel, the jumping spider *Salticus scenicus.* 6 mm long. (After Dahl.)

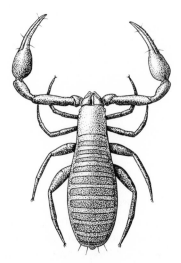

Fig. 8–2. Arachnid with segmented abdomen, pseudoscorpion *Neobisium muscorum,* 2.5 mm long. (After Kew.)

segments of the prosoma are weakly sclerotized tergites (Fig. 12–9). Internally this division of the prosoma is visible only in the Solifugae and Uropygi. In these groups the heart moves anteriorly into prosomal metameres V and VI and, as in *Limulus,* has two pairs of ostia there.

Embryological studies on the whipscorpion, *Thelyphonus,* has shown that the lack of segmentation of the proterosoma is due to the formation of its dorsum from the cephalic lobes (acron). The anterior of the germ band folds dorsally, then posteriorly to form the carapace (Fig. 4–15) as is apparent from the position of the eyes, which are derived from the cephalic lobes. The result is that the four most anterior metameres cannot, in the manner of the more posterior ones, grow dorsally to the midline and give rise to dorsal segmentation (Fig. 4–15). The first segment, with the chelicerae, grows to the fold of the germ band, thereby attaining its anterior position (Fig. 4–16).

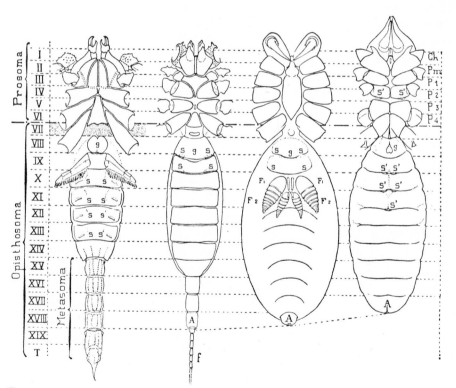

Fig. 8–3. Ventral view of some arachnids. From left to right, scorpion, whipscorpion, segmented spider (*Liphistius*) and a windscorpion. The spider abdomen is exaggerated posteriorly. *A,* anus; *Ch,* chelicera; *f,* flagellum; *F1, F2,* anterior and posterior spinnerets; *g,* gonopores, *P,* walking leg; *Pm,* pedipalp; *S,* spiracle; *T,* telson. The shaded portion in the scorpion shows the position of the reduced seventh segment. Natural size. (After Millot.)

In most orders the opisthosoma (abdomen) is divided into tergites, sternites, and pleural membranes or plates. In almost all spiders and mites the abdomen has lost its segmentation and has become a soft extensible sac (Fig. 8–1). In the groups having abdominal somites the number varies even within the suborder, the more specialized families having a reduced number of segments at the posterior end. But even at the anterior of the abdomen there is a zone in which reduction may take place. In scorpions, harvestmen, ricinuleids, and mites, sternite VII and sometimes VIII and IX are pushed forward between the posterior leg coxae. Sternite VII may disappear completely, VIII may become narrow (Fig. 8–3). Even tergite VII may become reduced.

The changes in the regular abdominal segmentation reflect adaptations to habits. The constriction of the 7th segment to a pedicel permits lifting and turning the abdomen, of importance to uropygids for using their defensive spray. In spiders it is of importance in drawing out silk, and makes possible the exact guidance of the spinnerets. In spiders, usually some posterior abdominal sternites have been lost, resulting in the location of the spinnerets at the posterior tip of the abdomen (Figs. 8–11, 11–1). Scorpions have the abdomen flat and almost immovably attached to the prosoma, but the narrow postabdomen has a series of jointed rings that make movement of the stinger possible (Fig. 9–1). This narrowing of the abdomen is found also in the whipscorpions, at least for metameres XVI to XVIII (Fig. 8–3), facilitating aiming the poison spray. The forward shift of opilionid gonopores facilitates copulation by reducing the distance between the mating animals, which face each other (Fig. 13–12).

Segmentation of the prosoma in the Solifugae makes it possible to raise the huge chelicerae (Fig. 12–9). In the Palpigradi the free segments permit lifting the abdomen, possibly of advantage in moving through narrow spaces and crevices.

In orders that have many branched intestinal ceca in the abdomen, the interior of the prosoma and abdomen are clearly separated, in spiders, Uropygi and Amblypygi by the pedicel formed from metamere VII, in scorpions and windscorpions by a diaphragm that has openings for gut, nerves and tracheae (Fig. 9–4). Whether these partitions permit the internal pressure of the two body parts to be independently raised is being investigated.

APPENDAGES. The prosoma has six pairs of appendages. The embryos of scorpions and spiders have abdominal appendage buds, which may completely disappear or may transform into pectines (scorpions) or spinnerets (spiders) (Figs. 4–11, 8–11).

The first pair of appendages, the chelicerae, appears in the embryo behind the stomodeum. Because the pharynx is directed posteriorly, the first appendage primordia finally come to lie anterior to or above the mouth (Figs. 4–16, 6–2). Chelicerae have no more than three articles; in most orders the distal article is chelate or pincerlike. In spiders, and Amblypygi it is subchelate (Figs. 8–2,

8–3, 8–5). Major transformations occur in mites, especially parasites, where the chelicerae may become narrowed, lose the chelate finger (distal article), and become a piercing structure (Fig. 8–4). The chelicerae are generally parallel to the body, directed anteriorly, and work independently and alternately. An exception is seen in most "higher" spiders (Fig. 8–5). If large (as in spiders, Solifugae and Opiliones), the chelicerae serve as a prehensile organ to handle and kill prey, to squeeze out nutrient juices, as a defensive weapon, or for digging. Scorpions, Opiliones, pseudoscorpions and many mites use them to tear food; Solifugae and some mites use them as gonopods. In spiders a poison gland opens at the tip of the distal cheliceral article; in pseudoscorpions, a silk gland opens there.

The pedipalp, the second appendage, has become a walking leg, or a palp in those arachnids that have large chelicerae (spiders, Solifugae, Palpigradi, many Opiliones, and mites). In orders with relatively small chelicerae, the pedipalp has been modified into a large raptorial organ, usually tipped by chelae (scorpions, Uropygi, Amblypygi, pseudoscorpions; Fig. 8–2), a universal tool for manipulating and killing prey, for defense and for digging. In all arachnids it functions also as an organ of touch, and perhaps as an olfactory organ. In Solifugae, Palpigradi, and primitive spiders, the pedipalpi may have the appearance of the walking legs and may be used for walking. At the tip of the pedipalp, pseudoscorpions have the opening of a poison gland. In spiders the coxae of the pedipalpi may have endites used to guide liquefied food into the mouth, and in male spiders the pedipalpal tarsus has become a copulatory apparatus.

There usually are four pairs of walking legs. Exceptions are seen only in the young stages of Ricinulei and larvae of mites, which have only the anterior three. Adults in some groups of parasitic mites may have only two (gall mites; Fig. 14–29) or only one pair (Podapolipodidae). However, it has been shown in mites that the embryo has primordia of all four and that the last ones become

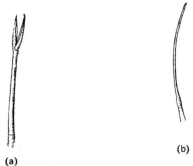

(a)

(b)

Fig. 8–4. (a) Stylet chelicera of the mite *Liponyssus bacoti*; (b) pointed chelicera of the bird mite *Dermanyssus gallinae*; the movable finger has disappeared; 0.45 mm long. (After Martini.)

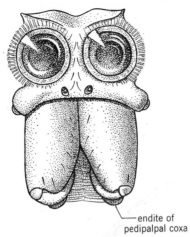

endite of
pedipalpal coxa

Fig. 8–5.   Chelicerae of the ogre-faced spider *Dinopis*, frontal view showing chelicerae moving laterally against each other, 4.5 mm wide. (After Kaestner.)

reduced only late in embryonic development. The number of leg articles differs in the various orders. The legs often are equipped with sensory hairs and substitute for antennae. In spiders, harvestmen and mites, the first or second pair of legs may be especially long and used as feelers. Still more specialized in Solifugae, Palpigradi, Uropygi, and Amblypygi, the first legs are used only as feelers. The leg is slender and often lacks claws in Solifugae, always in Uropygi and Amblypygi. In Palpigradi, Uropygi, and especially in the Amblypygi, it has become elongate and whiplike with numerous distal articles (Fig. 10–5). Legs are used not only for walking and as organs of touch, but also for swimming, digging, drawing out silk, holding the female in mating, and as gonopods (as the third leg of Ricinulei and many water mites). Endites that form part of the preoral chamber are found only on the first walking legs of Opiliones and the first and second of scorpions.

   SENSE ORGANS. In addition to the innervated sensory setae, there are trichobothria and slit sense organs. Trichobothria are long, delicate, movable hairs inserted in the center of a circular joint membrane of large diameter (Fig. 8–6). In scorpions they are innervated by the dendrite of one nerve and move in one plane. In the spider *Tegenaria*, they are innervated by the dendrites of three sense cells and can move in various directions. Each hair passes through a sclerotized flask, the bothrium. The hair base has a complicated structure (Fig. 8–6). Entering the bothrium, the hair bends slightly and the diameter tapers before penetrating a membrane stretched across a fluid-filled cylinder. Beneath the membrane it is convex on one side and ends in a helmetlike structure. Within the helmet several neurons end. The hairs, which are sensitive to air currents and vibrations, pivot at the membrane; bending the hair activates receptor cells.

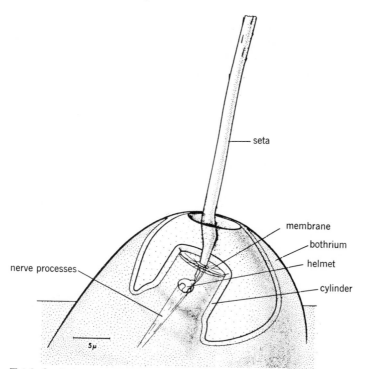

seta

membrane

bothrium

helmet

nerve processes

cylinder

5μ

Fig. 8–6. Trichobothrium of *Tegenaria*. (From Görner, courtesy Cold Spring Harbor Laboratory.)

Slit sense organs are narrow crevices, 0.005–0.16 mm long and 0.002–0.003 mm wide, in the cuticle (Fig. 8–7). Toward the outside the slit is closed by a thin membrane, probably corresponding to the epicuticle. Only at the middle portion does the slit penetrate the procuticle completely and it is closed by a fine membrane toward the hypodermis. The middle of the slit is widened to a channel into which the sensory end of a subhypodermal nerve cell penetrates, to attach in *Achaearanea* finally to cuticle (Fig. 8–7). In some orders the slits are scattered over the body and appendages. In others they are limited to appendages and may form small clusters, called lyriform organs because of their parallel arrangement. Such structures are often close to joints and react strongly to joint movement, probably due to stress in the cuticle. In addition to their propriosensory function they serve also as vibration receptors.

The eyes are always simple ocelli. Usually there are both median and lateral eyes, different in structure. In spiders differences in function have been investigated. Opiliones lack lateral eyes; pseudoscorpions and many mites have no median eyes.

The function of the sense organs is discussed in detail in Chapter 11 under senses of spiders, the group most investigated.

NERVOUS SYSTEM. The central nervous system in most orders becomes concentrated by migration of most ganglia (Uropygi, Palpigradi, Solifugae, Opiliones) or all of them (Araneae, Amblypygi, Pseudoscorpiones, Ricinulei, Acari) into the prosoma, where they are fused into a compact subpharyngeal (thoracic) ganglion (Figs. 4–12, 11–7). Only scorpions have the long double nerve cord with connectives, in which the eight posterior pairs of ganglia remain in their segments, XII to XVIII (Fig. 6–1).

The only association center is the central body, present in all orders. Globuli are found only in scorpions, Pedipalpi, Solifugae, and Opiliones, and in those spiders that are mainly visual hunters.

Neurosecretory cells have been demonstrated in several orders, in the suprapharyngeal and subpharyngeal ganglia, but little is known about the function of the secretions. Also, nothing is known about the probably neurosecretory Schneider's organs in spiders. Composed of two pairs of glands, it lies behind the suprapharyngeal ganglion; the glands are connected to each other and to the protocerebrum and cheliceral ganglion by nerves. One pair is near the aortic

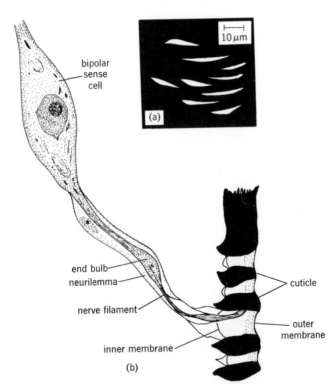

Fig. 8–7. Metatarsal lyriform organ of *Achaearanea tepidariorum*: (a) surface view showing slits at right angle to long axis of the leg, total width of section 0.05 mm; (b) cross section of lyriform organ showing nerve attached to side of slit, cuticle about 0.01 mm thick. (After Salpeter and Walcott.)

branching and the other near the pumping stomach. Both become active only after the subadult molt; the first secretes into the hemolymph.

DIGESTIVE SYSTEM. In all arachnids the mouth is narrow, as are the intestinal ceca. Therefore arachnids can not swallow prey whole, and most do not swallow large pieces. Instead their food is dissolved before reaching the mouth, by enzymes from the midgut. There is always a preoral chamber (camerostome) where digestion takes place, if it has not already been accomplished by enzymes injected into the prey. In Palpigradi the preoral chamber is a slit between labrum and labium. In most arachnids the endites of the pedipalpal coxae form the walls of the preoral chamber; in harvestmen and scorpions, the endites of walking legs also. Within the orders Araneae and Opiliones there is a progressive increase in specialization of the preoral chamber and endites, indicating their parallel evolution (Figs. 11–1, 11–7, 13–6, 13–7).

The preoral chambers are very different in the various orders. Only in spiders, Uropygi, Amblypygi, Ricinulei, and mites do they have similar structure, which can be understood by studying mygalomorph spiders. The venter of the pedipalpal coxa is widened and expanded toward the anterior, and is elongated as an endite (Fig. 8–8), resulting, in the mygalomorphs, in a V-shaped open space below the chelicerae. Dense setae converge toward the labium, preventing the liquefied food from dripping or running onto the sternum (Fig. 11–1a). If the

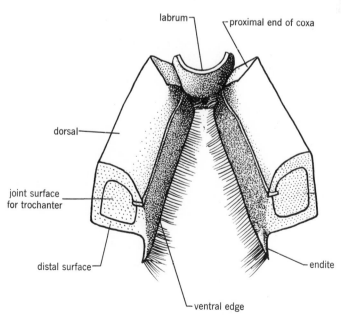

Fig. 8–8. Labrum and pedipalpal coxae of a primitive mygalomorph spider, anterior dorsal view.

two pedipalpal coxae are widened so much ventrally that they meet in the middle, the floor of the preoral chamber is closed (Amblypygi and Pseudoscorpiones) (Fig. 12–3). In a further development, seen in the Uropygi and Ricinulei, the anterior edges of the coxae and their endites fuse, forming a trough (Fig. 8–9) that substitutes for the short labium, which may disappear. In mites the fused coxae of the pedipalpi become united with part of the sternum.

Dense setae permit only liquid or very small particles to enter the pharynx, preventing the plugging of digestive ceca.

The ectodermal anterior gut is always modified as a pumping organ. Usually this is just the precerebral part, the pharynx. The postcerebral esophagus forms a pumping stomach only in Araneae (Fig. 6–2) and Amblypygi. The pumping part may have convex walls, the lumen being X- or Y-shaped in cross section. The lumen is expanded by dilator muscles attached to the outside of the walls,

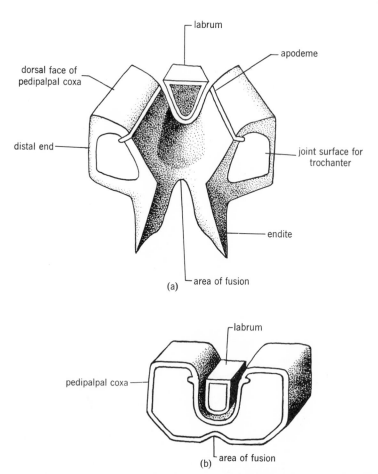

Fig. 8–9.   Preoral chamber of a whipscorpion: (a) anterior-dorsal view; (b) cross section.

and is contracted by circular muscles between the dilators (Fig. 8–10). Peristaltic waves pump in the digested liquid.

The straight midgut of the prosoma or abdomen continues with paired, segmentally arranged ceca in which digestion and absorption takes place. There are two kinds of ceca: tube-like ceca that are unbranched or have a few branches (Fig. 13–9), and much-branched diverticula with numerous alveoli connected into lobes by connective tissue (Fig. 9–2). Only simple tube-shaped ceca are found in Opiliones, Ricinulei and Acari; only branched ones in scorpions and Uropygi. Both types are found in Araneae, Amblypygi and Solifugae, simple ones in the prosoma, branched ones in the abdomen (Fig. 11–8). Corresponding with their small size, the palpigradi and pseudoscorpions and most mites, have the ceca unbranched (Fig. 14–10). The abdomen may be completely filled with ceca, the posterior anastomosing with the anterior and connected with the gut in the anterior metameres (Fig. 9–2).

EXCRETORY SYSTEM. The organs of excretion are coxal glands and paired Malpighian tubules. In addition there are large nephrocytes, 0.03–0.05 mm in diameter, of mesodermal origin. These, often found clumped together in blood sinuses, store excretory products. Scorpions and opilionids have lymph tissue organs in addition.

Coxal glands are found in one, or less often in two, segments of the prosoma. The excretory duct usually opens posteriorly on the coxa of the third or fifth appendage. In specialized arachnids the coxal glands are of little importance. In web spiders the duct is very short; probably many nitrogenous excretory products are used for silk production. In many mites excretion is taken over by the Malpighian tubules, or sometimes by a dorsomedian duct, and the coxal glands are absent.

The paired Malpighian tubules open into the posterior end of the midgut and are branched among the midgut glands (Fig. 11–8). In only a few orders (Scorpiones, Ricinulei, Acari) do they enter the prosoma. They usually excrete

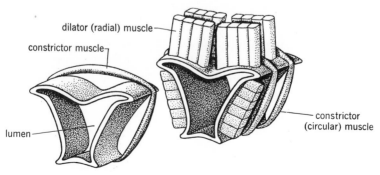

Fig. 8–10. Two diagrammatic sections through the pumping stomach of a spider.

guanin into the gut. In mites they are unbranched, sometimes reduced (Fig. 14–27).

RESPIRATORY SYSTEM. The organs of respiration arise from invaginations of the ectoderm, and therefore have a chitinous lining. They are absent in some minute forms and in all Palpigradi and many mites. In other arachnids they appear in two forms: as book lungs and as tube tracheae. Spiders may have both (Fig. 8–14). There appears to be a definite relationship between habits and type of respiratory organs. Small spiders having a proportionately large surface area tend to lose their book lungs and have tracheae instead, or very small arachnids of humid habitats sometimes may lack both lungs and tracheae and respire through the body surface. The aquatic spider *Argyroneta* has the tracheal system elaborately developed.

Book lungs must have been the ancestral arachnid respiratory organs. In both spiders and scorpions the primordia of the book lungs develop posteriorly on the abdominal appendage buds (Fig. 8–11a). This relationship between respiratory organs and appendages can only be considered a primitive character inherited from aquatic ancestors resembling the Merostomata, and is not found in other land arthropods. The primordia, unlike those of horseshoe crabs, invaginate into the appendage and grow into flat triangular pockets (Fig. 8–11). When the appendage bud sinks into the body, a slitlike depression forms posterior to it and grows deeper into the body to become the atrium. With its development complete, the opening of the book lung is a slit-shaped spiracle, leading into the atrium. From the atrium open the "leaves" of the lung books, flat pockets with their closed ends hanging into a blood sinus. These leaves, or lamellae, have many complicated sclerotized columns that prevent their collapse (Fig. 8–12). While muscles that attach to the posterior of the atrium can widen it and open the spiracle, the lamellae lack muscles and have no means of ventilation. Gas exchange, then, must be by diffusion. Of such localized book lungs (a better term would be book tracheae), four pairs are found in scorpions (Fig. 9–4), two pairs in Uropygi, Amblypygi, mygalomorphs and some other spiders (Fig. 8–3), but only one pair in most spiders (Fig. 8–14).

The more common tracheae, which usually traverse several segments, are of two types: sieve tracheae and tube tracheae. Sieve tracheae, which are book lungs that have an atrium and tube-shaped "lamellae", are found in some spiders (Fig. 8–13), most pseudoscorpions, and Ricinulei. Tube tracheae may be simple unbranched tubes, as found in most spiders and mites, or may be much branched as in Opiliones, solifuges, and some spiders and mites. The much branched tube tracheae usually start in the abdomen, from spiracles (one to three pairs) in the intersegmental membranes of sternites. Only occasionally (in Solifugae, Ricinulei, and many Acari) are there prosomal spiracles, probably secondary structures, as are the spiracles on the tibiae of walking legs of many Opiliones. The presence of both book lungs and tracheae as in many spiders can be ex-

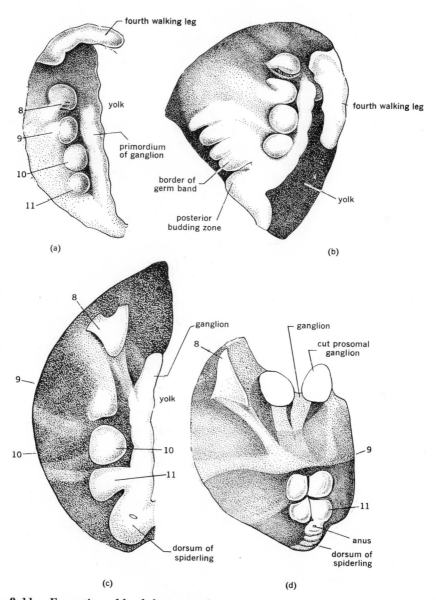

Fig. 8–11. Formation of book lungs, tracheae, and spinnerets on appendage primordia of segments VIII–XI of the spider embryo of *Agelena labyrinthica*; (a–c) has only left half of opisthosomal germ band, about 0.8 mm long. (After Kautzsch.) (a) Button-shaped primordia of appendages VIII–XI, equidistant, the posterior border of the 8th has 3 grooves, the beginnings of book lung pockets; (b) the 9th appendage is flattening; the germ band grows dorsally with irregular border; (c) the 8th and 9th appendage primordia sink in, behind them a slit appears (the spiracle) leading into the atrium; the 9th segment stretches, while the distance between the 11th and the budding zone shortens; (d) the 8th and 9th appendage primordia are completely invaginated; the 9th–11th appendage primordia are shifted toward the median line while the 9th sternite elongates.

plained. The book lungs open on the posterior of the 8th sternite, tube tracheae always on the 9th (Figs. 8–13, 8–14). Embryonically only the posterior border of appendage VIII has primordia of book lungs. Appendage bud IX does not (Fig. 8–11), but posteriorly on appendage primordium IX there develops a deep pit, an atrium, which later grows into a tracheal tube and may even enter the prosoma.

But most spiders, as shown in Fig. 8–14, have a paired median tube trachea and in addition a pair of tracheae originating from the same atrium. These paired median tracheae have no relationship to appendage bud IX, but develop from pointed, paired, median invaginations that provide an attachment point for ventral longitudinal muscles of segments VIII and IX, thus from a hollow apodeme (Fig. 4–17). These tracheal apodemes lengthen in metamere IX as sternite IX elongates (Fig. 8–11c). But the apodeme grows beyond the muscle insertion into a long hollow tube that may branch and penetrate into the prosoma. Such double function as endoskeleton and respiratory system is otherwise known only for the tracheal apodemes of millipedes. In spiders, then, tracheae develop from two origins: on the posterior of appendages, homologous to book lungs, and from tracheal apodemes. In appearance they may be similar, either unbranched or arborescent, and one can determine the type of trachea only by studying their origin.

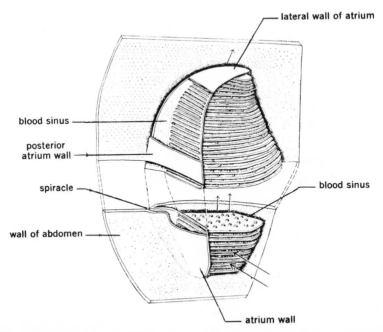

Fig. 8–12. Diagrammatic structure of a spider book lung viewed from posterior-medially and cut transversely. The dorsal portion has the posterior of the atrium removed to show the entrance to the leaves. The distance between leaf columns is exaggerated. Arrows show direction of blood flow. (After Kaestner.)

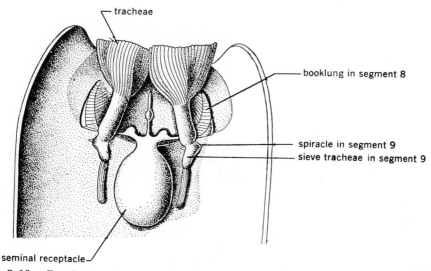

tracheae

booklung in segment 8

spiracle in segment 9
sieve tracheae in segment 9

seminal receptacle

Fig. 8–13. **Respiratory organs of the spider *Harpactes rubicundus*, showing the similar structure of book lungs and sieve tracheae. Dorsal view of a KOH treated preparation, 3 mm wide. (After Kaestner.)**

Whether the tracheae from the lateral spiracles of Opiliones, pseudoscorpions, and Ricinulei are homologous to book lungs is not known, as in these groups (at least in the representatives examined) no abdominal appendage primordia appear. The lateral position and the absence of relationship to ventral musculature exclude their origin from tracheal apodemes, but they could be of secondary origin. Solifugae have a median tracheal system that develops independently of appendage primordia. The tracheae of mites are probably new, secondary structures.

Paired, soft vesicles that can be evaginated are found on the posterior borders of abdominal sternites in Palpigradi and some Amblypygi; possibly they function as gills in highly humid air.

CIRCULATORY SYSTEM. The blood contains hemocyanin as a respiratory pigment, and numerous corpuscles of four types, derived from one another and variable in ratio during the period of molt. In spiders the corpuscles are formed by the circular heart muscle layer, in scorpions by the median lymphatic tissues, close to the posterior artery.

The dorsal heart, lying within a pericardial sinus, consists of a tube of circular muscles, a thin layer of longitudinal muscles outside, and some connective tissue. The length and segmental position vary in different orders, indicating that primitively it extended through all metameres, in each having a pair of ostia, a pair of lateral arteries, and a pair of ligaments. Only in Uropygi and Solifugae does it extend into the prosoma, reaching segments V and VI. In all other groups it is limited to the abdomen (Figs. 6–1, 11–8, 11–13). Palpigradi and most mites lack a heart, a secondary loss probably related to the small size of the animals.

REPRODUCTIVE SYSTEMS. Arachnids are dioecious. Only the harvestmen and some mites have ectodermal male copulatory structures derived from the genital atrium. Other arachnids, depending on the position of the gonopores, cannot directly transmit the sperm into the female genitalia, but produce a spermatophore (Fig. 12–6), or the sperm is picked up by the male and transferred into the female genitalia. The chelicerae may serve as gonopods in Solifugae and some mites, the pedipalpi in spiders (Fig. 11–14), and a walking leg in Ricinulei (Fig. 12–2) and some mites.

Most arachnids deposit eggs, and in Solifugae and many scorpions these may hatch immediately. Some scorpions and mites are viviparous or ovoviviparous.

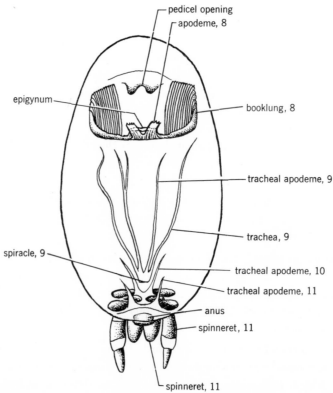

Fig. 8–14. The three kinds of respiratory organs in the funnel web spider Tegenaria. Dorsum of abdomen removed and macerated with KOH. The numbers refer to segments; abdomen 5 mm long. (After Purcell.)

Development

Cleavage of the yolk-rich eggs is superficial; only rarely is there a tendency toward total cleavage. The embryonic germ band is segmented, even though the adults have lost the segmentation (Figs. 4–15, 11–19a).

Many species construct a cocoon for the protection of the eggs; many take care of their young. The female may carry her eggs or young with her, and some share food with the young.

Relationships

The relationships among the orders are not clear. Presumably those having book lungs (scorpions, Uropygi, Amblypygi, spiders) can be grouped together, scorpions being the most primitive. Scorpions have retained the segmentation and the division of the abdomen into pre- and postabdomen (mesosoma and metasoma) as in the Merostomata. The Uropygi are close to the scorpions. The Amblypygi resemble spiders in body shape, segmentation of organs, and in having two pumping stomachs. Though the evolution may be convergent, the organization of the Amblypygi could lead to that of the spiders and the groups thus appear to be related. Palpigradi, in their segmentation and appendage structure, resemble Uropygi and may represent dwarfed forms. Of the other orders, the Ricinulei, Pseudoscorpiones and Acari in their transformation of pedipalpal coxae and formation of a preoral chamber resemble the Uropygi and Amblypygi. In body shape and external genitalia, harvestmen resemble some groups of mites. Nothing can be said about the Solifugae. All efforts to subdivide the Arachnida into subclasses have remained unconvincing, as have the associated phylogenetic speculations.

Classification of Recent Orders

Order Scorpiones, scorpions
Order Uropygi
    Suborder Holopeltidia, whipscorpions, vinegaroons
    Suborder Schizopeltidia, schizomids
Order Amblypygi, tailless whipscorpions, whipspiders
Order Palpigradi
Order Araneae, spiders
Order Ricinulei
Order Pseudoscorpiones, pseudoscorpions
Order Solifugae, solpugids, windscorpions
Order Opiliones, harvestmen
Order Acari, mites

References

Babu, K. S. 1965. Anatomy of the central nervous system of arachnids. *Zool. Jahrb. Abt. Anat.* 82:1–154.

Görner, P. 1965. Mehrfach innervierte Mechanorezeptoren bei Spinnen. *Naturwissenschaften* 52:437.

———— 1966. Transducing mechanism for a multiply innervated mechanoreceptor (trichobothrium) in spiders. *Cold Spring Harbor Symp. Quant. Biol.* 30:69–73 (1965).

Haggag, G. and Fouad, Y. 1965. Nitrogenous excretion in arachnids. *Nature* 207:1003–1004.

Hoffman, C. 1965. Trichobothrien der Skorpione. *Naturwissenschaften* 52:436.

———— 1967. Bau und Funktion der Trichobothrien von *Euscorpius*. *Z. Vergl. Physiol.* 54:290–352.

Kaestner, A. 1940. Arachnida *in* Kükenthal, *Handbuch der Zoologie*, De Gruyter, Berlin 3(2):97–116.

———— 1948. Entwicklungsgeschichte von *Thelyphonus*. *Zool. Jahrb. Abt. Anat.* 69:435–558.

———— 1952. Entwicklungsgeschichte des Prosoma der Solifugen. *Zool. Anz.* 148:156–168.

Krishnakumaran, A. A. 1961. Comparative study of the arachnid cuticle. *Z. Vergl. Physiol.* 44:478–486.

Levi, H. W. 1967. Adaptations of respiratory systems of spiders. *Evolution* 21:571–583.

Millot, J. 1949. Arachnides *in* Grassé, *Traité de Zoologie*, Masson et Cie, Paris, 6:263–385.

Petrunkevitch, A. 1953. Paleozoic and Mesozoic Arachnida. *Mem. Geol. Soc. Amer.* 53:1–128.

———— 1955. Arachnida *in* Moore, *Treatise on Invertebrate Paleontology*, Geol. Soc. Amer., Univ. Kansas Press, Lawrence, Kansas, P:42–162.

Pringle, J. W. S. 1955. Function of lyriform organs. *J. Exp. Biol.* 32:270–278.

Rao, K. P. and Gopalakrishnareddy, T. 1962. Nitrogen excretion in arachnids. *Comp. Biochem. Physiol.* 7:175–178.

Salpeter, M. M. and Walcott, C. 1960. Electron microscopical study of a vibration receptor in the spider. *Exp. Neurol.* 2:232–250.

Snodgrass, R. E. 1948. Feeding organs of Arachnida. *Smithsonian Misc. Coll.* 110 (10):1–93.

Streble, H. 1966. Das hormonale System der Spinnentiere. *Zool. Jahrb. Abt. Physiol.* 72:157–234.

Walcott, C. and Van der Kloot, W. G. 1959. Physiology of the spider vibration receptor. *J. Exp. Zool.* 141:191–244.

9.

Order Scorpiones, Scorpions

Nearly 700 species of scorpions are known, the largest of which is the African *Pandinus imperator*, 18 cm long.

Scorpions have the abdomen divided into a wide anterior mesosoma (preabdomen) and a long posterior metasoma (postabdomen). The postabdomen consists of series of ring-shaped segments and bears at its end a telson transformed into a stinger with a poison gland. The chelicerae are small; the pedipalpi are armed with very large pincers. The preoral chamber is enclosed by the endites of the pedipalpi and the first two pairs of legs. The embryonic abdominal appendages are transformed into one pair of combs (pectines) and four pairs of book lungs.

Anatomy

The body form of this order has barely changed since the Silurian. In their body segmentation scorpions resemble the eurypterids, especially *Mixopterus* (Fig. 7–7). The prosoma is covered by a carapace and broadly joins the segmented abdomen. The pleura of segments XV to IXX have fused with the tergites and sternites to form a series of strong rings (Figs. 8–3, 9–1). This construction of the metasoma permits it a wide range of movements. On the venter one can see that the anterior sternites have moved between the last coxae. Reduction of sternite VII is complete, VIII and IX are narrowed (Fig. 8–3). Chelicerae, pedipalpi and walking legs are illustrated in Figs. 8–3 and 9–1.

Scorpions are usually yellow to brown or black and more rarely orange, greenish or bluish. The integument is brown; other colors may be due to pigments in the hypodermis. All scorpions fluoresce in ultraviolet light.

Coxal apodemes and a large endosternite provide attachment sites for muscles. Between prosoma and abdomen a diaphragm attaches dorsally to the intersegmental membrane between carapace and tergite VIII, ventrally to the posterior border of the fourth leg coxa (Fig. 9–4). (Tergite VII has disappeared.)

NERVOUS SYSTEM. The nervous system consists of a supraesophageal brain and a subesophageal ganglion containing the fused ganglia 2 to 11. The remaining ganglia form a ventral abdominal chain, only the last two, the 18th and the 19th, being fused (Fig. 6–1). Giant fibers control the movements of the stinger and seem to connect with a syncytium of giant fibers to pedipalps and legs, coordinating the leap and thrust of the attack.

SENSE ORGANS. As in other arachnids, there are sensory setae, trichobothria and slit sense organs. The trichobothria on the chelae of *Euscorpius* vibrate at intermediate sound frequencies (e.g., human speech) at high intensities. But they mainly function in response to slow air movements, a deflection of 0°30′ being sufficient to make the unit fire. The basal structure of the trichobothrium allows it to move in only one plane, although the 66–68 trichobothria on each chela have different orientations. In addition to the usual arachnid sensory equipment, scorpions also have pectines (Figs. 8–3, 9–7a). The cuticle at the tip of each comb tooth is penetrated by numerous sclerotized pores. Through the pores pass the axons of sensory cells, to end in an outer membrane covering the comb tooth.

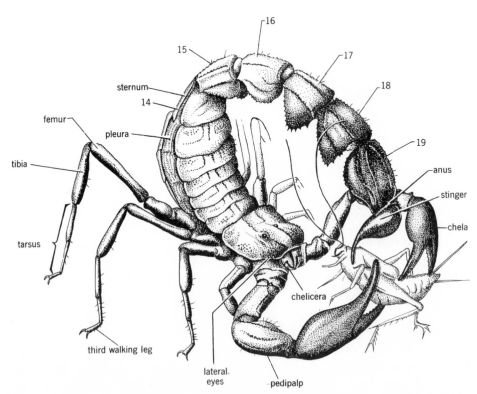

Fig. 9–1.   The scorpion *Androctonus australis* killing prey; numbers indicate segments; 9.5 cm long. (After Vachon.)

Recent electrophysiological investigations have shown that the cells are mechano-receptors sensitive to vibrations at frequencies above 100 Hz. In other studies, peglike structures on the pectines of *Leiurus quinquestriatus* were found to have a complex, pleated internal structure and to respond to touch. Electrophysiological evidence seems to rule out the possibility of a chemosensory role for the pectines, but observations on the behavior suggest that they are important in selection and preparation of a site for spermatophore deposition.

With the exception of some secondarily blind cave-dwelling species, all scorpions have a pair of median and 2–5 pairs of lateral simple eyes on the edge of the carapace (Fig. 9–1). The eyes of scorpions have a lens. In the median eyes the hypodermal cells underneath the lens are transformed into a vitreous body. In *Euscorpius carpathicus* the retinal unit is not represented by one retinal cell as in other arachnids but by a group of cells, 5 in the median eyes, 2–10 in lateral eyes, similar to the retinula of compound eyes. The rhabdom of the retinulae is made up of 5 rhabdomeres in the median eye, while those of the lateral eyes are irregular. The rhabdomeres are made up of closely packed tubular units that open into the adjacent cells. This structure resembles that of the arthropod compound eyes discussed in Chapter 16.

DIGESTIVE SYSTEM. The mouth lies deep in a preoral cavity, which opens anteriorly, beneath the chelicerae and carapace (Fig. 8–3), and runs posteriorly, bordered by the large coxae of the pedipalps and the endites of walking legs 1 and 2. Into the preoral cavity hangs a club-shaped labrum, at the ventral end of which is the entrance to the pharynx. In the anterior, pharyngeal region, the digestive tract is sclerotized and forms a pumping stomach. Posteriorly it passes between the subesophageal ganglion and the tritocerebrum to continue as the midgut. The midgut has two prosomal and five paired abdominal ceca connecting to large, much-branched digestive glands that fill most of the prosoma and mesosoma (Fig. 9–2). In the narrow postabdomen the midgut lacks ceca. The anus, at the end of a short sclerotized hindgut, is in the ventral membrane between the last metasomal segment (XIX) and the bulb of the stinger (Fig. 9–1).

EXCRETORY SYSTEM. The excretory organs are the nephrocytes, lymph tissue, coxal glands and two pairs of Malpighian tubules, one of which penetrates the prosomal digestive glands, the other ending between the diverticula of the abdominal digestive glands. The coxal glands are derived from the coelomic sacs of segment V and open posteriorly on the coxae of the third legs. The median lymph tissue, taking various shapes, lies on the ventral median of the mesosoma, and functions in the production of blood corpuscles and in phagocytosis of bacteria. One pair of lateral lymph organs arises from posteriorly directed invaginations of the diaphragm; these are absent in the family Buthidae.

POISON GLANDS. Paired poison glands open on each side of the stinger below its tip (Fig. 9–3). Each gland is emptied by a muscle that arises on its lateral wall, surrounds the gland, and inserts on the ventral wall of the bulb.

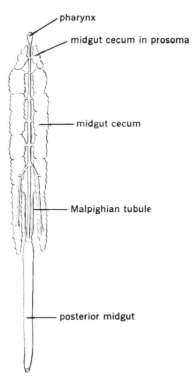

Fig. 9–2. Digestive system of a scorpion; 7 cm long. (After Newport.)

RESPIRATORY AND CIRCULATORY SYSTEMS. Four pairs of book lungs with spiracles in the middle of sternites X to XIII are the respiratory organs (Figs. 8–3, 9–4). Corresponding with the localized respiratory system, the circulatory system is very elaborate. The heart extends through the diaphragm from segment VIII to XIV (Fig. 9–4). It has seven pairs of ostia, at each of which arises a pair of lateral arteries and a pair of lateral and ventral ligaments. An additional pair of arteries arises anterior to the first and posterior to the last ostia; these arteries are probably associated with metameres VII and XV (Fig. 6–1).

REPRODUCTIVE SYSTEM. Males are more slender, have longer appendages than females, and may have a larger number of teeth on the pectines. The ovaries are unpaired tubes, or sometimes paired or partially paired, that may be connected by four or five transverse lateral tubes (Fig. 9–5). The structure of the testes is similar. The vas deferens continues as the paraxial organ (Fig. 9–6).

Reproduction

The spermatophore is formed in the paraxial organs (Fig. 9–7). The sclerotized inside of the paraxial organs provides a useful systematic character, as it differs in males of different species. During preliminary courtship the precursors of

Fig. 9–3. Poison sting opened showing left gland (a), right gland (b); 6 mm long. (After Joyeux–Laffuie.)

the spermatophore lie within the paraxial organ. Just before the male produces the spermatophore the sperm is emptied from the vesicles into the stalk part of the spermatophore, and a cement is secreted that attaches the spermatophore stalk to the substrate as it emerges. The cement also joins the two halves of the spermatophore, which are pressed tightly together as they emerge from the gonopore. The spermatophore (Fig. 9–8) consists of a stalk, an ejection apparatus, and a lever. Contact presses the lever down, shooting the sperm through the female gonopore. A new spermatophore is made in 3–4 days.

The efforts of the male to find a suitably firm surface, probably detected with the pectines, on which to deposit the spermatophore, and to maneuver the female into position to pick it up, result in behavior only recently understood and formerly interpreted in the literature as a courtship dance (Fig. 9–9). If no suitable substrate is available, the searching may go on for hours. A male scorpion whose pectines had been amputated nevertheless took a female, but the spermatophore was never deposited, despite presence of a suitable surface.

The details of courtship differ in various genera. The male of *Euscorpius* approaches the female, postabdomen vertical, jerking. The female responds by jerking her postabdomen. The male grasps the female with both pedipalpi and, moving backwards, stings the female in the pedipalpal joints while pulling her

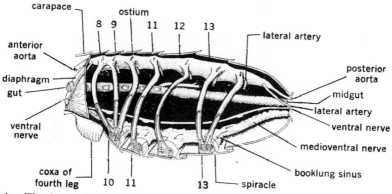

Fig. 9–4. The lung sinuses of a scorpion, left body wall removed; numbers indicate segments. (After Kaestner.)

along in a straight path. Later the male flexes his pedipalps and moves closer to the female. Moving his body above hers he touches the combs and genital area of the female with one or both of his anterior legs. He then jerks his body to the ground and makes scratching movements with the hind legs, combs touching the ground, and deposits a spermatophore on the ground. The spermatophore, 6 mm long, stands at an angle. The male, waving his postabdomen, now pulls the female over the spermatophore, which she touches with her combs while her genital operculum opens (Fig. 9–9). When the tip of the spermatophore extends into the gonopore the female walks back jerkily, and the male lets go of her. The female feeds on the remaining spermatophore stalk. The male of *Opisthophthalmus latimanus*, soon after the pair starts walking, pulls the female toward himself and takes her chelicerae with his. The male then lets go of the female pedipalpi and leads the female by the chelicerae. In some species the male holds the female by one pedipalp and they face in the same direction.

Tityus serrulatus is parthenogenetic and males are unknown.

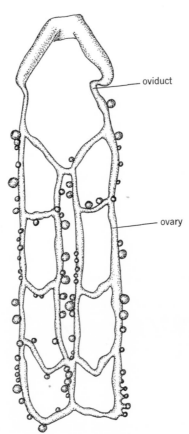

oviduct

ovary

Fig. 9–5. **Female gonads of a *Parabuthus*. (From Vachon after Pavlovsky.)**

Development

Members of the family Scorpionidae are viviparous. The fertilized eggs, which have little yolk, develop within the follicles of the ovary. While the follicle expands, the embryo receives nourishment via a tubular extension, a kind of umbilical cord, that extends to the mother's intestine, and through which nutritive material is conducted to the mouth of the embryo. In other families of scorpions yolk-rich eggs fall into the ovarian tube and develop there; the membranes break immediately after birth, freeing the young scorpions. The just-born scorpions climb on the back of their mother. The young of the Philippine forest scorpion, *Heterometrus longimanus,* leave the mother before the second molt, between the 15th and 18th days. But even then the mother may share food with them. After three molts, in 40–63 days, the young scorpions become independent and hunt for cockroach-nymphs. They mature after seven molts, or slightly more than a year.

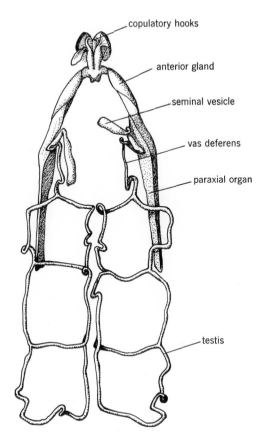

copulatory hooks

anterior gland

seminal vesicle

vas deferens

paraxial organ

testis

Fig. 9–6. Male gonad of a *Heterometrus*. (From Vachon after Pavlovsky.)

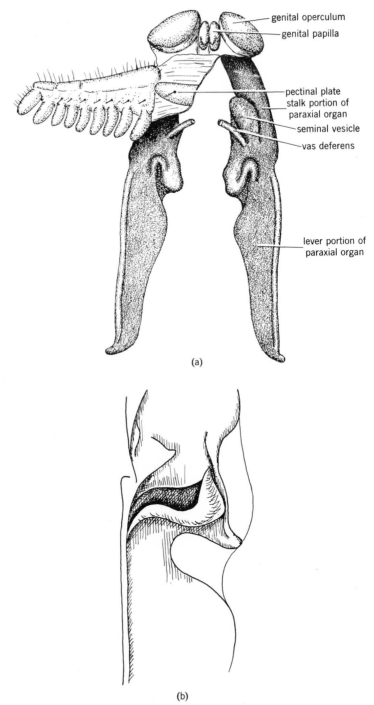

genital operculum

genital papilla

pectinal plate
stalk portion of
paraxial organ

seminal vesicle

vas deferens

lever portion of
paraxial organ

(a)

(b)

Fig. 9–7. Paraxial organs of *Euscorpius carpathicus*: (a) glands dissected out with right pectine, pectinal plate and genital opercula; preparation 5 mm long; (b) internal (ventral) view of sclerotized middle portion of right paraxial organ.

Habits

Most species inhabit deserts or dry mountainous areas; some prefer moisture, forests and cold climates. The flat body permits large species to crawl under stones, bark, into rock crevices and between palm fronds. Bark scorpions may carry the postabdomen curled to one side. Some species, such as the European *Euscorpius*, invade houses and hide behind furniture and in clothing. Many species, by supporting themselves on pedipalpi and fourth legs, can dig with the tarsi of the first three pairs of walking legs, throwing sand posteriorly. The North African *Androctonus australis* makes runways 20 cm long in sand, below the surface. *Scorpio maurus* digs 40–80 cm into hard soil. *Anuroctonus phaeodactylus* of southern California occurs in scattered but dense colonies on slopes in burrows 18–42 cm long. The animal digs 2.5 cm in half an hour, but continues digging 5–6 hours at a time. The soil is first loosened by chewing it with the chelicerae, then is pushed back and dragged out by the first pairs of legs. Holding its first femora and tarsi horizontal, its tibiae vertical, the scorpion backs out, dragging the intact mound of loose soil as far as 7 cm beyond the burrow. *Liobuthus*, which lives in the sand of Asiatic deserts, has flat, widened tarsi, adapted for digging. The flat body, digging ability and ability to close the spiracles (some can withstand blocking of seven of their eight lungs while at rest), are protective adaptations against heat and desiccation. Many scorpions show marked resistance to climatic extremes. Not only do desert species withstand water loss to a remarkable degree, but they also appear to have a striking immunity to irradiation.

DEFENSE. Most scorpions sting only in defense, when stepped on or trapped in clothing, or when excited. If it struggles, prey is stung, the stinger first searching out a soft membrane to penetrate. The poison may rapidly kill prey and may also be effective against vertebrates. Chloroformed animals wave the

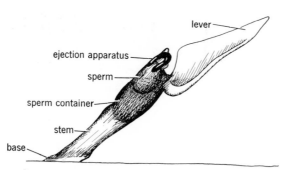

Fig. 9–8. Spermatophore of *Euscorpius carpathicus*; about 5 mm long. (After Anger-mann.)

stinger in various directions, and may sting themselves; they are immune against
their own poison. Excessive heat produces similar behavior, but that scorpions
surrounded by fire commit suicide is, of course, a superstition.

The sting of the southern European *Buthus occitanus* produces strong temporary
pain in man. The Arizona scorpion *Centruroides sculpturatus* and some Mexican
species of *Centruroides* may be dangerous. *Tityus,* the sting of which is extremely painful, is considered very dangerous in southeastern Brazil. *Androctonus
australis* is much feared in North Africa. The scorpions dangerous to man are
usually not large species; most belong to the family Buthidae, characterized also
by weak and slender pincers, suggesting that the weak pedipalpi might be correlated with the rather toxic stings. The poison is an extremely painful neurotoxin, but antivenins are available in the few areas where dangerous scorpions
occur.

SENSES. We know little about the senses of scorpions. When running they
always hold the pedipalpi ahead, suggesting that they orient by touch and with
the aid of trichobothria sensitive to air currents such as those close to obstacles.
The function of the eyes remains unknown; they are probably not important in
finding prey as most scorpions are nocturnal. Blinded *Euscorpius* can still find
prey. In an area with two equal light sources *Euscorpius* will stay in the middle,
equidistant from the two sources. That they seek dark areas for their hiding
places has been shown experimentally by placing them in an evenly illuminated
circular container with broad black and white vertical stripes on the walls. They
walked toward the black areas, even in light intensities as low as 5 lux.

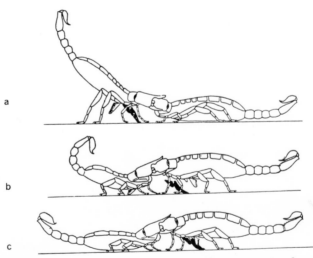

Fig. 9–9. Pairing of *Euscorpius italicus,* female right; animals about 4.5 cm: (a)
after depositing spermatophore; (b) pulling female to spermatophore; (c) female pick-
ing up spermatophore. (From Angermann.)

Temperature sensitivity has been demonstrated experimentally in scorpions, but the responsible sense organs still are not known. That the stinger is most heat sensitive can be demonstrated by approaching *Opisthophthalmus* with a hot needle; next in sensitivity are the pedipalpi and then the legs. The dorsum seems insensitive. A rise to 20–28°C in the air temperature causes the scorpion to extend its legs and lift its body high above the ground, presumably permitting cooling by convection currents. Forced to keep its body in contact with the hot ground, the body temperature of the scorpion rises rapidly.

Many species by stridulation produce a sound resembling that of a stiff brush going over a comb. *Opisthophthalmus latimanus* stridulates by extending and retracting the chelicerae, forcing medial bristles to rub against a ventral keel of the preoral cavity roof. Though they produce sound in a similar way, by rubbing posterior bristles of the pedipalpal coxa against a granular anterior area of the first coxa, *Heterometrus* stridulates offensively and *Pandinus*, defensively. *Parabuthus* stridulates by rubbing its stinger against grooves in a posterior mesosomal or anterior metasomal tergite. In intraspecific relationships stridulation of *Opisthophthalmus* seems of no importance; it occurs only when the scorpion encounters a large moving object such as a grasshopper, snake or human hand.

Males of *Scorpio maurus* do not stridulate but drum the ground with the mesosoma after a threat or after missing prey.

FEEDING. Prey is found by contact with legs or pedipalpi. The pedipalpal pincers grab quickly; if they miss their mark on the first try, they grab into space, but scorpions usually do not run after lost prey. *Leiurus* may move after a cockroach brushes past (Cooke, letter). In captivity various insects, centipedes and spiders serve as food; remains of beetles and cockroaches have been found in scorpion retreats. Certain species of *Pandinus* and *Heterometrus* feed on large juliform millipedes (Cooke, letter). The rare buthid scorpion *Isometroides vescus* of Western Australia is found in the burrows of trapdoor spiders, which it overpowers. In scorpions generally, the pincers hold the prey, which may be stung if it struggles (Fig. 9–1). The chelicerae then tear the food apart, one holding while the other pinches and pulls; then the roles are reversed.

DIGESTION. Fragments of the prey are placed in the preoral cavity, which rhythmically fills with digestive juice containing amylases, proteases and lipases. The partly digested food is sucked in. It takes 2½ hours for the little *Euscorpius carpathicus* to feed on a bluebottle fly. Undigestible parts are held back by setae of the preoral cavity, balled together with the empty exoskeleton, and discarded. Intracellular digestion continues in the midgut ceca of the digestive gland. The membranes that join parts of the exoskeleton allow extension so that considerable amounts of food may be taken up, permitting intermittent long periods of starvation; some can starve for over a year.

EXCRETION. Excretory material in the cloaca, including material from Malpighian tubules, consists mainly of guanin, but also of uric acid, both of them water-conserving products. Also excretion takes place after the gut is empty, 12–15 days after feeding. The coxal glands contain mostly uric acid.

DISTRIBUTION. Although most scorpions are tropical or subtropical, the European *Euscorpius germanus* is found in the southern Alps to 1800 m (6000 ft) elevation, the North American *Vejovis boreus* as far north as British Columbia and Alberta, and other species are found in the southwestern and southeastern United States. In South America scorpions are found in wet southern Chile to lat 52° south, and to elevations of 4000–5500 m in areas of permanent snow in the Andes.

Classification

The systematics of scorpions is difficult, and only in some Mediterranean countries are the species well known. Careful systematic work is urgently needed.

Buthidae. This is the largest scorpion family, with representatives on all continents. The sternum is triangular in front. They usually have three to five lateral eyes. Most species have slender, long pincers and many species have a tubercle under the stinger. Buthidae includes the several species poisonous to man, a few of them dangerous, while others are harmless. *Buthus* is Mediterranean, African and Asian (to Mongolia) in distribution. *Androctonus australis* occurs in North Africa. *Centruroides* includes several species of the southern United States, of which *C. sculpturatus* of Arizona is considered poisonous; *C. hentzi* is the Florida scorpion; *C. gracilis*, a large brown species of southern Florida, can produce a temporary painful sting; *C. vittatus* is the small striped centruroides of the Southeast. The dangerous *Tityus* is found in southeastern Brazil. *Leiurus* is found in the eastern Sahara and Arabia. The pantropical *Isometrus maculatus* is the only scorpion species having a wide distribution. *Isometroides* is found in Australia and *Parabuthus* in Africa. *Liobuthus* is found in Turkistan.

*Scorpionidae.** The sides of the sternum are parallel. The last two leg segments have only one spur on the outside; there is no tubercle under the stinger. Though most representatives are Old World or Australian in distribution, *Opisthacanthus* occurs in the West Indies and Central America. The giant, almost black *Pandinus imperator*, to 18 cm long, is found in tropical West Africa. *Heterometrus* occurs in southeastern Asia. Other genera are *Opisthophthalmus* and *Scorpio.*†

Diplocentridae. The sides of the sternum are parallel. The last two leg segments have only one outer spur; all species have a tubercle under the stinger. The family includes the largest scorpion in the Near East, *Nebo,* and several West Indian species of the genus *Diplocentrus.*

Chactidae. The sternum is almost square or wider than long. Between the last two leg segments, on the inside, there may be one or two spurs. There usually are only two lateral eyes. Chactidae contains the commonest scorpions of southern Europe, several

---

* The family name Scorpionidae has been placed on the Official List of Family Group Names in Zoology.

† The generic name *Scorpio* has been placed on the Official List of Generic Names in Zoology.

species of the genus *Euscorpius*. The sting is only slightly painful. *Superstitiona* is found in the southwestern United States.

Vejovidae. The sternum is broad, as in Chactidae. There are usually three to five lateral eyes and one or two spurs at base of the last tarsal segment. The family includes the commonest North American scorpions, belonging to the genus *Vejovis*. *Hadrurus hirsutus*, found in Arizona, is the largest North American species, up to 11 cm long; its color is variable, often bluish. *Anuroctonus* is found in southern California.

Bothriuridae. The sternum consists of two transverse plates much wider than long. The family is mostly South American south of the Amazon, with one genus, *Cercophonius*, occurring in Australia. *Bothriurus* and *Urophonius* are South American genera.

References

Abdel-Wahab, A. 1954. Development of the digestive system in the scorpion *Buthus*. *Bull. Zool. Soc. Egypt* 12:13–22.

Abushama, F. T. 1964. Behaviour and sensory physiology of the scorpion *Leiurus*. *Anim. Behav.* 12:140–153.

Alexander, A. J. 1956. Mating in scorpions. *Nature* 178:867–868.

———— 1957. Courtship and mating in the scorpion *Opisthophthalmus*. *Proc. Zool. Soc. London* 128:529–544.

———— 1958. Stridulation in scorpions. *Behaviour* 7:339–352.

———— 1959. Courtship and mating in buthid scorpions. *Proc. Zool. Soc. London* 133:145–169.

———— and Ewer, D. W. 1957. A chemoreceptor in the scorpion *Opisthophthalmus*. *South African J. Sci.* 53:421–422.

———— 1958. Temperature adaptive behavior in the scorpion *Opisthophthalmus*. *J. Exp. Biol.* 35:349–359.

Angermann, H. 1957. Spermatophorenbildung und Sinnesphysiologie von *Euscorpius*. *Z. Tierpsychol.* 14:276–302.

———— and Schaller, F. 1956. Spermatophore von *Euscorpius* und ihre Übertragung. *Verh. Deutschen Zool. Ges.* 19:456–462.

Auber, M. 1960. Les glandes gnathocoxales des scorpions. *Bull. Soc. Zool. France* 85:67–89.

Babu, K. S. 1965. Anatomy of the central nervous system of arachnids. *Zool. Jahrb. Abt. Anat.* 82:1–154.

Bedini, C. 1967. The fine structure of the eyes of *Euscorpius*. *Arch. Italiano Biol.* 105:361–378.

Carthy, J. D. 1966. Fine structure and function of sensory pegs on the scorpion pectine. *Experientia* 22:89.

Cloudsley-Thompson, J. L. 1956. Studies in diurnal rhythms. *Ann. Mag. Natur. Hist.* (12)9:305–329.

Ewing, H. E. 1928. Scorpions of the western United States. *Proc. U.S. Nat. Mus.* 73(9):1–24.

Guénin, H. A. 1961. Les chromosomes de *Buthus*. *Vie Milieu* 12:89–96.

Hoffmann, C. 1964. Funktion der kammförmigen Organe von Skorpionen. *Naturwissenschaften* 51(7):172.

———— 1965. Trichobothrien der Skorpione. *Ibid.* 52:436–437.

———— 1967. Bau und Funktion der Trichobothrien von *Euscorpius*. *Z. Vergl. Physiol.* 54:290–352.

Kaestner, A. 1940. Scorpiones, *in* Kükenthal, *Handbuch der Zoologie*, De Gruyter, Berlin, 3(2):117–240.

Kanungo, M. S. 1957. Cardiac physiology of *Palamnaeus*. *Biol. Bull.* 113:135–140.

———— et al. 1962. Excretion in *Palamnaeus*. *Physiol. Zool.* 35:201–203.

Kennaugh, J. 1959. Cuticle of two scorpions *Pandinus* and *Scorpiops*. *Quart. J. Microscop. Sci.* 100:41–50.

Krishnakumaran, A. 1960. Early post-molt cuticle in *Buthus*. *Ibid.* 101:433–438.

Laverack, M. S. 1966. Proprioceptive system in the legs of *Hadrurus*. *Comp. Biochem. Physiol.* 19:241–251.

Levi, H. W. and Levi, L. R. 1968. *Spiders and Their Kin*. Golden Press, New York.

McAlister, W. H. 1965. Mating behavior of *Centruroides vittatus*. *Texas J. Sci*, 17:307–312.

———— 1966. Aggregating tendency of *Centruroides vittatus*. *Ibid.* 18:80–84.

Main, B. Y. 1956. Biology of *Isometroides vescus*. *Australian J. Zool.* 4:158–164.

Mathew, A. P. 1956. Embryology of *Heterometrus*. *Zool. Mem. Univ. Travancore Res. Inst.* 1:1–96.

———— 1962. *Proc. First All India Congr. Zool.* 1959 (2):100–111.

Matthiesen, F. A. 1962. Parthenogenesis in scorpions. *Evolution* 16:255.

Millot, J. and Vachon, M. 1949. Scorpions, *in* Grassé, *Traité de Zoologie*, Masson et Cie, Paris, 6:386–436.

Muma, M. H. 1967. Scorpions, whipscorpions and wind scorpions of Florida. *Arthropods of Florida, Florida Dept. Agric.* 4:1–28.

Rao, K. P. and Gopalakrishnareddy, T. 1962. Nitrogen excretion in arachnids. *Comp. Biochem. Physiol.* 7:175–178.

Rasmont, R. 1960. Ultrastructure de la glande coxale d'un scorpion. *Ann. Soc. Roy. Zool. Belgique* 89:239–268.

Rosin, R. and Shulov, A. 1961. Sound production in scorpions. *Science* 133:1918–1919.

San Martín, P. 1961. Ecología y distribución geografica de tres especie de escorpiones en el Uruguay. *Facult. Humanid. Cienc., Dept. Entomol., Univ. Montevideo* 1–42.

———— 1963. Una nueva especie de *Bothriurus*. *Bull. Mus. Nat. Hist. Natur. Paris* 35:400–418 .

———— 1965. Escorpiofauna Uruguaya. *Com. Zool. Mus. Hist. Natur. Montevideo* 8 (106):1–22.

———— Grupo *Araguagae* del genero *Bothriurus* y la Floresta Amazonica como causa del limite septentrional de la Bothriuridae. *Papeís Avulsos Dept. Zool. São Paulo* (in press).

———— and Cekalovic, K. T. Una nueva especie de *Urophonius* para Chile. *Invest. Zool. Santiago* (in press).

———— and Gambardella, L. A. de. 1967. Ecología de tres especies de *Bothriurus* del Uruguay. *Bull. Mus. Nat. Hist. Natur. Paris* 39:188–196.

———— 1967. Nueva comprobacion de la partenogenesis en *Tityus serrulatus*. *Rev. Soc. Entomol. Argentina.* 28:79–84.

———— Descripción del espermatoforo de *Bothriurus*. *Rev. Soc. Entomol. Argentina* 29:17–20.

Shulov, A. et al. 1960. Parturition in scorpions. *Bull. Res. Council Israel* (B. Zool.) 9B:65–69.

Smith, G. T. 1966. Life history of *Urodacus abruptus* (Scorpionidae). *Australian J. Zool.* 14:383–398.

Vachon, M. 1952. *Études sur les scorpions*. Inst. Pasteur d'Algérie, Algier.

———— 1953. The biology of scorpions. *Endeavour* 12(46):80–89.

Werner, F. 1934. Skorpione, *in* Bronn's, *Klassen und Ordnungen des Tierreichs*, Akad. Verlagsges., Leipzig, 5(4)8:1–160.

Williams, S. C. 1966. Burrowing of *Anuroctonus phaeodactylus* (Vejovidae). *Proc. California Acad. Sci.* (4) 34:419–428.

10.

Orders Uropygi, Whipscorpions; Amblypygi, Tailless Whipscorpions; and Palpigradi, Microwhipscorpions

THE PEDIPALPI

The Uropygi (including Schizomida) and Amblypygi,* because of their many similarities, are often combined as suborders within the order Pedipalpi. In both groups the first walking leg is modified as a long, slender whip with numerous distal divisions, the 7th body segment is constricted into a pedicel, and there are two pairs (rarely one pair) of book lungs. Furthermore, both groups are strikingly flattened, an adaptation for living in confined spaces. Nevertheless, they form two distinct morphological groups. The somewhat scorpion-like whipscorpions (Uropygi) have a long abdomen, which ends with a flagellum (Fig. 10–1). The tailless whipscorpions (Amblypygi) are more spiderlike (Fig. 10–5).

General Description

The internal structure corresponds with the external differences. In the whipscorpions, ganglia XIV to XVIII are fused in the 14th metamere in the abdomen, the heart is segmented and in large species extends into the prosoma, and the last metamere has a pair of anal glands. In the amblypygids, as in spiders, all abdominal ganglia are fused in a large subesophageal ganglion, the heart is limited to the abdomen, and the gut resembles that of spiders, having a postcerebral pumping stomach in addition to a pumping pharynx, and finger-like prosomal ceca (in contrast to much-branched abdominal ceca); there are no anal glands.

---

* Some authors use the terms Thelyphonida for Uropygi, and Phrynichida for Amblypygi, but these names are not in accord with general usage.

In both groups the pedipalpal coxae have large endites, medially fused in the Uropygi to form a trough (Fig. 8–9). The coxae are illustrated in Fig. 8–3. The sensory equipment usually includes a pair of median eyes and three pairs of lateral eyes, trichobothria, and slit sense organs. The excretory system consists of nephrocytes, Malpighian tubules, and usually two pairs of prosomal coxal glands that open through a pore on the coxae of the first and third legs. The book lungs, as in mygalomorph spiders, are in the 8th and 9th segments, but in dwarf forms, the schizomids, the second pair is missing. Corresponding with the localized respiratory organs, the circulatory system is elaborate, having branched arteries, several heart ostia, and paired lateral arteries. The reproductive system in both sexes has glands that open into a large genital atrium.

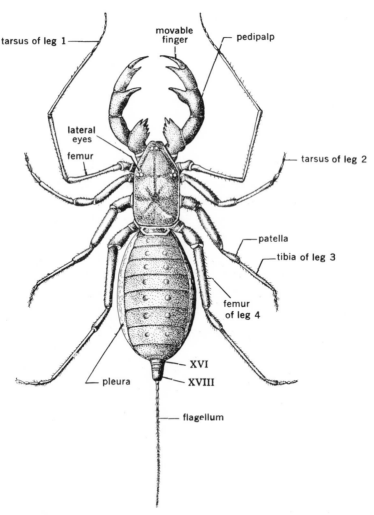

Fig. 10–1.   Vinegaroon, *Mastigoproctus giganteus*; 6.5 cm long, excluding flagellum. (After Pocock.)

ORDER UROPYGI, WHIPSCORPIONS AND SCHIZOMIDS

About 130 species of Uropygi are known.

The Uropygi have the abdomen divided into a long, wide mesosoma and a short metasoma consisting of three rings with a telson (flagellum). Next to the anus opens a pair of spray glands that extend anteriorly as far as the book lungs. The pedipalpal coxae are medially fused. In the Schizopeltidia the prosoma is externally divided, in the Holopeltidia it is internally divided into a proterosoma and two additional segments with walking legs.

SUBORDER HOLOPELTIDIA, WHIPSCORPIONS

There are about 75 species of whipscorpions, the largest being the North American vinegaroon, *Mastigoproctus giganteus,* which may reach a length of 7.5 cm.

In whipscorpions, the prosoma is not divided dorsally. The massive pedipalpi are held flexed, parallel to the ground. The last abdominal segment has a long telson, the flagellum, consisting of many divisions.

Anatomy

Body segmentation is illustrated by Figs. 8–3 and 10–1. The immovable finger of each small chelicera is reduced. The preoral cavity has been described above (Fig. 8–9). While ganglia of segments II to XIII are fused to form a prosomal subesophageal ganglion, ganglia XIV to XVIII remain in the abdomen, fused together in the 14th metamere. The large, much-branched prosomal ceca extend anteriorly and also into the coxae of the three pairs of legs used for walking. The numerous abdominal ceca form a uniform mass that fills the space between segments VIII to XV and opens through four pairs of ducts into the gut. The heart, which extends from segment XIV to the level of the next to the last coxae, has two pairs of ostia in the prosoma, and thereby divides the prosoma internally into a proterosoma and two segments. In the abdomen, at each segment from the 8th to 14th, the heart has a pair of ostia and a pair of lateral arteries. The two pairs of coxal glands have coiled ducts that fuse and open posteriorly on the coxae of the first pair of legs.

Reproduction

Mating of *Thelyphonus caudatus* is quite similar to that of scorpions. The male, using his long sensitive first legs, strokes the female and she then extends her first legs, crossed over. The male takes them with his pedipalpi and holds them with his chelicerae while the couple move to and fro, face to face, for 10 hours to several days. Throughout, the male taps the female with his first legs. Finally the male lets go of the female, steps over her prosoma, taps her genital region and turns 180°. The female then embraces the abdomen of the male with her pedipalpi (Fig. 10–2), and after walking a few minutes in embrace, jerking and stroking, he deposists a spermatophore. The female moves forward slightly, and with the genital sternite lifts and tears the spermatophore. After about 20 minutes the partners separate.

The female *Thelyphonus* digs a tunnel, ending with an enlarged chamber, about 40 cm deep into a slope. In the chamber she remains motionless for weeks, with her sac of eggs attached to her gonopore. The sac and adhesive are secreted when the eggs are laid, and subsequently harden.

The large eggs (to 3 mm in diameter) hatch after 4–5 weeks. Two broods of *T. caudatus* had 12 and 17 young. In the young the pedipalpi and first legs resemble the walking legs and the preoral cavity is not yet formed. Aided by suction cups at the ends of the tarsi in place of claws, the young keep themselves on their mother's back. Only after a molt do they take on the appearance of a diminutive adult.

In the Japanese *Typopeltis stimpsoni* the 30–40 young hatch and undergo their first molt at the same time. The larvae, which cannot feed, climb on the mother's back for three to four days, and later drop off to hide in the soil for two weeks before molting again. They can spray and feed after several days, but stay together in the nest.

Habits

Whipscorpions inhabit tropics and warm, mainly humid areas. In arid regions they may appear during the rainy season. The flat brown animals live in litter, under stones, loose bark of tree stumps, boards, and rubbish on moist earth. From their hiding places, many excavate tunnels as long as 10 cm. Digging with their strong pedipalps, they first scratch and then carry the soil back and throw it aside. *Labochirus* builds U-shaped tubes. At dusk they emerge, running rapidly forward, backward or sideways on three pairs of legs, and investigating the surroundings with their sensitive first legs.

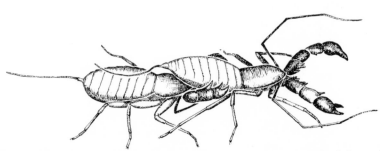

Fig. 10–2. Mating of the uropygid *Thelyphonus caudatus*; female left, male right, each about 3 cm long. (After Klingel.)

SENSES. The long telson is light sensitive. The venter of most divisions of the *Typopeltis* telson is transparent and it may be the ventral nerve that is light sensitive. Possibly this is an adaptation to living in U-shaped tubes.

PROTECTION. In addition to the protection derived from nocturnal habits, Holopeltidia use secretions of the large anal glands to spray potential attackers. The irritating spray, a cloud of fine droplets, is aimed by turning the short metasoma or the whole abdomen. The flagellum is bent forward during spraying, but the aim is accurate even if the flagellum has been removed. The spray is not used to kill or immobilize prey. The secretion of *Mastigoproctus*, consisting of 84% acetic acid, 5% caprylic acid and 11% water, is squirted 80 cm. Caprylic acid reduces the surface tension on the lipid epicuticle, spreading and permitting penetration of the acetic acid into an arthropod. This can be demonstrated by imbedding pieces of arthropod exoskeleton in gelatin impregnated with indicator dye and applying drops of the acids to be tested. What protects the vinegaroon itself is not known.

The spray of *Thelyphonus* smells of formic acid, that of an Indian species smells like chlorine.

Small vinegaroons successfully defend themselves in a terrarium by spraying attacking ants and solifugids (*Eremobates*). Two species of lizards (*Anolis*) that had picked up vinegaroons dropped their prey, closed their eyes and wiped their mouths. A similar response was given by an attacking southern grasshopper mouse (*Onychomys torridus*) and an armadillo. After eight to ten shots the supply is exhausted. In a terrarium the vinegaroon may be attacked again, but outside he would have had a chance to escape. The poison burns human skin and smarts the eyes.

Thelyphonus caudatus attacks members of its own species with the pedipalpi, pinching and tearing out appendages. Vinegaroons can pinch when handled and cause bleeding.

FEEDING. It is not known what whipscorpions feed on in nature. In the terrarium they take woodlice, centipedes, cockroaches and other small insects. *Mastigoproctus* also takes toads up to 7 mm long, and cricket frogs (*Acris gryllus*). Rapid movements of the pedipalp crush and kill the prey, and the other pedipalp may tear pieces off before it is taken by the chelicerae, which only hook into the prey. The preoral cavity fills with digestive juice that dissolves the food.

Classification

Thelyphonidae. This is the only family. *Thelyphonus caudatus* is found in southern Asia. *Typopeltis* occurs from Mongolia to Japan and Thailand. *Mastigoproctus giganteus,* 7.5 cm, is found in the southern United States from coast to coast. *Labochirus* is found in Ceylon and India. There are no representatives in Europe, Africa or Australia.

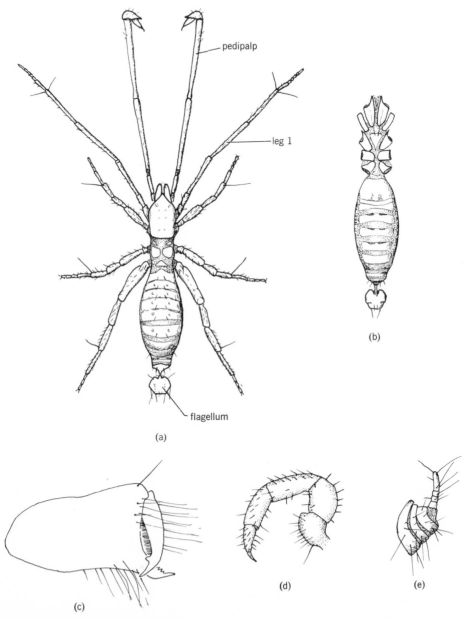

pedipalp

leg 1

flagellum

(a)

(b)

(c)

(d)

(e)

Fig. 10–3. The schizomid, *Trithyreus belkini*; 5.5 mm long: **(a) male, dorsal, with
long pedipalps and broad flagellum; (b) male, venter; (c) right male chelicera, lateral
view; (d) short left female pedipalp (coxa omitted); (e) female flagellum.** (After
McDonald and Hogue.)

SUBORDER SCHIZOPELTIDIA, SCHIZOMIDS

Of over 50 species of schizomids, the largest is *Trithyreus cambridgei,* up to 7 mm long.

The minute schizomids are sometimes placed in a separate order, Schizomida, characterized by the external division of the dorsum of the prosoma into a propeltidium and two free tergites (Fig. 10–3a). The last abdominal segment has a short flagellum consisting of three divisions at most. The pedipalpi are leglike, not chelate, but raptorial; they flex parallel to the sagittal plane (Fig. 10–3a, d). As in the Holopeltidia, there are anal glands.

Anatomy

The small, two-segmented chelicerae are tipped by small pincers and are held parallel to the walking surface (Fig. 10–3c). The ganglia of segments II to X are fused to form a subesophageal ganglion; those of segments XI to XVIII are fused to form one small ganglion in the anterior part of the abdomen.

There are no eyes. *Trithyreus* has various sense organs, but they have not been studied. There are trichobothria on the tibiae, slit sense organs on the first metatarsus, and pits, probably sensory, on the flagellum of the female.

The midgut has a pair of pear-shaped ceca in the prosoma, and five pairs of much-branched ceca in the abdomen. The eighth segment has a single pair of book lungs. The heart reaches from segment VIII to XIV and has five pairs of ostia. The arterial system has not been studied.

Reproduction

The male of *Trithyreus sturmi* follows the female until she stops. Then he stops at a distance of several millimeters, moves his body and vibrates his long first legs back and forth. The female turns, then the male, so that they face in the same direction. The female then hooks her distal cheliceral segments into two dilations on the base of the male's telson. The male moves forward, followed by the female (Fig. 10–4). They stop and the male, as in scorpions, deposits a spermatophore, then pulls the female forward, enabling her to lift the

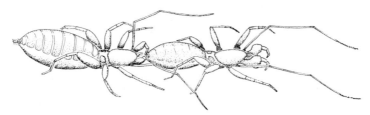

Fig. 10–4. The schizomid *Trithyreus sturmi* before depositing a spermatophore; female left, male right, each 5 mm. (After Sturm from Schaller.)

tip of the spermatophore off. The female lets go of the male's telson and they separate.

A pregnant female digs a cavity 1.5 cm deep into soil and closes herself inside. She then produces 6–7 eggs that are glued together by a secretion and remain stuck to the gonopore.

Habits

Schizomids live in tropics and subtropics under stones or layers of leaf litter. Often transported to temperate climates, they have turned up in greenhouses in England (Cooke, letter). Schizomids may dig tunnels in the soil. Feeding has been observed only once: a *Scutigerella* was grabbed with the pedipalpi. *Trithyreus belkini* has been obtained from moist logs harboring termites.

Classification

Schizomidae. The single family is represented in Africa, Asia and Americas by several species of the genus *Schizomus*, up to 3 mm found in Florida. *Trithyreus*, to 6 mm, occurs in Texas, California and south to South America, Africa and Indoaustralian region. *Stenochrus* has just one species in Puerto Rico.

ORDER AMBLYPYGI, TAILLESS WHIPSCORPIONS OR WHIPSPIDERS

There are about 60 species of tailless whipscorpions, the largest of which is the American *Acanthophrynus coronatus,* to 4.5 cm long.

Amblypygids are dark colored; the flat oval abdomen lacks a telson and spray glands. The chelicerae are subchelate (Fig. 10–6). The pedipalpal endites are not fused. The raptorial pedipalpi are held flexed, parallel to the walking surface, and their two last articles may be almost chelate.

The amblypygids (Fig. 10–5) resemble spiders in many features, but differ by the long whiplike first legs, the strong pedipalpi, and the absence of spinnerets. The whiplike tibial and tarsal articles of the first legs have numerous (false) articulations and these legs, in some species, may spread 25 cm.

Anatomy

The internal organs resemble those of spiders. All 12 abdominal ganglia have moved into the prosoma and have fused with the large subesophageal ganglion. The anterior gut has a precerebral pumping pharynx and a postcerebral pumping stomach, and in the prosoma there are four pairs of unbranched digestive ceca directed toward the coxae. In contrast, the ceca of the abdomen are much-branched and open into the midgut through four pairs of openings. At the posterior of the 8th and 9th segments there are paired book lung spiracles. The heart extends from the 8th to the beginning of the 14th metamere. Posteriorly its six pairs of ostia are situated below the posterior edge of tergites VIII to XIII and have paired lateral arteries. There is also a pair of large coxal glands; these open posteriorly on the coxae of the first legs. *Charon* has an additional small pair opening posteriorly on the last coxa.

Unlike spiders, some whipspider genera have a pair of median, thin-walled, chitinous sacs in the intersegmental membrane between the 9th and 10th sternites that can be everted by blood pressure and pulled back by muscles. They are thought to be respiratory structures. By lifting the genital operculum one can distinguish the sexes: males have two cones, females may have two slits and a single opening at the base of the operculum. The male opening is on the venter of the cones. On electrical stimulation there appears a median, lobed structure and a sticky material is secreted. From between the lobes, the spermatophore is produced.

Reproduction

Mating has been observed in the West Indian *Admetus barbadensis*, the South African *Damon variegatus*, and the southeast Asian *Sarax sarawakensis*. Courtship takes place at night and can be watched under dim or red light. In all

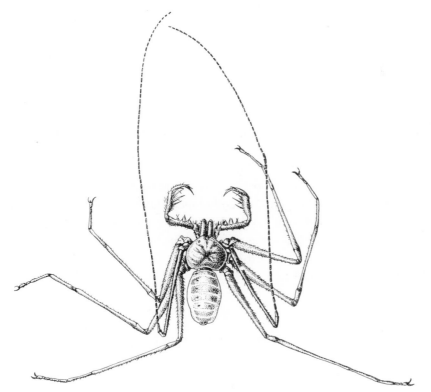

Fig. 10–5. The tailless whipscorpion, *Charinus milloti*, 12 mm long. (After Millot.)

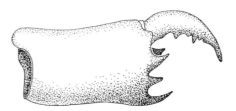

Fig. 10–6. Lateral view of left chelicera of the amblypygid *Admetus barbadensis*;
basal segment 2 mm long. (After Alexander.)

three species, the male and female only touch each other with the whiplike first
legs and do not hold one another (Fig. 10–7). The male is more active. After
several hours of stroking and tapping with his first legs and walking back and
forth, the male finally stands facing the female. The male turns 180° (*Sarax*
bends the long first legs back toward the female), and lowers its abdomen
several times to the ground, finally depositing a spermatophore without sperm;
he then turns back and faces the motionless female (Fig. 10–7). In *Admetus*
and *Damon* the male now deposits two masses of sperm side by side on the
spermatophore stalk cemented to the ground minutes before. Finally the male
slowly walks back vibrating the first legs. The female follows, guided by her
first legs, and picks up the masses of sperm with the gonopore. The male becomes active again and taps the female. In *Damon* and *Admetus*, after the
female moves away, the male eats the spermatophore stalk.

As in whipscorpions, the female amblypygid carries the eggs on her concave
venter in a tough sac of mucus. In some species the cavity of the sac is continuous with the gonopore. The young stay at least a month in the sac. They
molt while leaving the sac, and climb on the back of the female. The 15 to 50
young are carried 4–6 days on or below their mother's abdomen, their long first
legs folded up. If one falls off, the mother may eat it, unlike wolf spiders carrying young. The second molt takes place on the posterior of the mother's abdomen, and the young leave the mother immediately afterward (unlike scorpions), leaving a place for the next one to molt. They run off, first legs unfolded,
and will feed within two days.

Habits

Amblypygids live in tropics and subtropics, in humid sites under stones, logs,
loose bark and litter. Some inhabit caves and some enter houses. They are not
known to burrow. At dusk they run about on the three last pairs of legs, moving forward when stalking prey. But if disturbed they move sideways, then
stop suddenly under cover.

PROTECTION. Lacking spray glands they defend themselves by pinching with the pedipalps. If two animals of the same species meet, they touch with the first legs and the smaller one moves off sideways. If evenly matched, there may be side tapping with the whips or, rarely, fights with the pedipalpi in which one combatant may be injured.

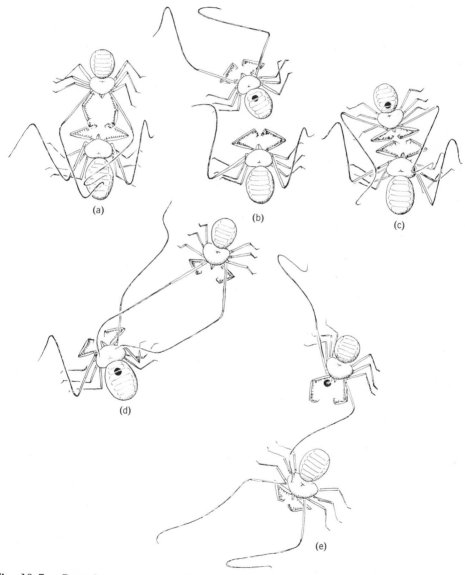

Fig. 10–7. Courtship and mating of the amblypygid *Admetus barbadensis*; **schematic; each animal about 3.5 cm long. The female is below, the male above; the black dot indicates the position of the spermatophore underneath the animals: (a) male strokes female with first legs; (b) male deposits spermatophore; (c) male deposits sperm on spermatophore; (d) female gathers sperm from spermatophore; (e) male eats empty spermatophore stalk. (After Alexander.)**

FEEDING. In terraria, they feed on cockroaches, crickets, grasshoppers, beetles, butterflies, or other small insects and also on arachnids. The prey is touched with the tips of the long first legs and is then snatched up, at a distance of several centimeters, with both pedipalpi. If it is large, the prey is attacked several times, the amblypygid withdrawing between attacks. The prey is impaled on the spines of the pedipalpi and is taken by the chelicerae, which alternately move back and forth and up and down, digging into the prey. Preoral liquefication of the food has not been demonstrated but must occur, judging by the narrow foregut. The food remains may be completely mangled, or may hardly show damage. The whips are also used to find water, which amblypygids drink readily. Like spiders, whipspiders clean themselves by running appendages through their chelicerae, the limb pulled toward the mouth by the pedipalpi. Pedipalpi clean each other of food remains and have special brushes for this purpose on the distal digit. These brushes are cleaned by the chelicerae.

Classification

There are only two families.

Charonidae. Members of this family have tarsi with pulvilli (pads) and are mostly cave inhabitants. They occur from tropical Africa to the Pacific Ocean. *Sarax* occurs in southern and eastern Asia. Other genera are *Charon, Charinus, Stygophrynus* and *Phrynicosarax. Lindosiella* has been found on Rhodes.

Tarantulidae. These lack pulvilli on the tarsi. *Phrynichus* and *Damon* have small pincers at the ends of long pedipalpi; inhabitants of the Old World, some have been carried to South America. *Myodalis* is African and Indian. *Acanthophrynus coronatus* has pedipalpi lacking pincers; it lives in Mexico and California but has been carried to Uruguay. *Tarantula* (=*Phrynus*) has pedipalpi that form a basket for capturing prey; they are found in tropical America. *Tarantula fuscimana*, to 28 mm long, is found on the Florida keys; *T. marginemaculata*, to 17 mm long, in southern Florida. *Trichodamon* is found in Brazil; *Admetus* (Fig. 10–6), is another American genus.

ORDER PALPIGRADI, MICROWHIPSCORPIONS

There are fewer than 50 species of microwhipscorpions, the largest being *Eukoenenia draco*, 2.8 mm long.

Palpigradids are minute arachnids that have the prosoma covered by a propeltidium and two tergites (Fig. 10–8). The abdomen is attached by a pedicel and divided into a large mesosoma and a short metasoma with a telson, a long many-jointed flagellum. The chelicerae are thin, long, three-jointed and chelate, the movable finger lateral. All other coxae are similar and simple, and the pedipalpal coxae do not form a part of the preoral cavity (Fig. 10–9). The first walking leg, distally many-jointed, is used as a feeler. There are no circulatory or typical respiratory systems.

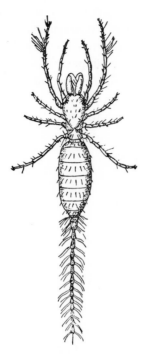

Fig. 10–8. The microwhipscorpion, *Eukoenenia mirabilis*; 1.2 mm long, excluding flagellum. (After Hansen.)

Anatomy

The minute, colorless, thin-skinned Palpigradi are probably very closely related to the uropygids and amblypygids. Except for the chelicerae, the appendages resemble those of *Thelyphonus* (Uropygi) larvae. The coxae, along the edge of the prosoma, are similar (Fig. 10–9). The preoral cavity consists of a slit between labrum and labium. Even the distal leg joints, despite the first leg being somewhat specialized as a feeler, are quite similar (Fig. 10–8).

The prosoma contains a mesodermal endosternite. Underneath it, all postoral ganglia are fused into a long subesophageal ganglion that extends from the pharynx to the 8th segment and, like the suprapharyngeal ganglion, is very large compared to other organs. Such adaptations are well known among other minute animals and the young stages of other groups. Sense organs include only innervated setae and trichobothria. The midgut in the prosoma forms one pair of ceca and in the abdomen five pairs, the last being branched into two. Other ceca are simple and unbranched; corresponding to the size of the animal, they have only a small surface. There are no Malpighian tubules; the only excretory organ is the paired coxal gland, which opens into the posterior wall of the first leg coxa. Corresponding with the soft integument and proportionately large surface, the usual types of respiratory organs are missing. But some species have ventral sacs on the 10th, 11th and 12th sternites, believed to have respiratory function. There is no circulatory system. The female gonads resemble those of uropygids and amblypygids but are simpler. The ova found in the ovary have a diameter of 0.1–0.12 mm. They occupy the entire width of the abdomen, and only a few eggs are produced at one time, as in many very small spiders. The male gonads have not been adequately studied.

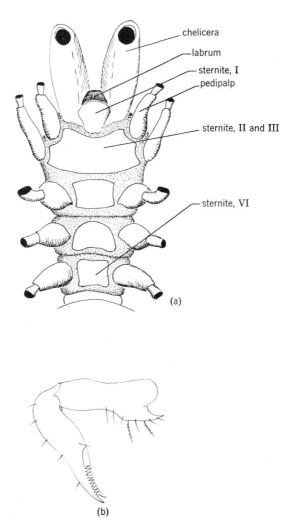

Fig. 10–9. *Eukoenenia mirabilis:* (a) venter of prosoma, 0.4 mm long; (b) left chelicera, lateral view; basal segment, 0.2 mm long. (After Hansen and Sörensen from Snodgrass.)

Reproduction

Nothing is known about mating or embryology. Only two males have been found of *Eukoenenia mirabilis*, while at different seasons 400–500 females were collected. The males of the American *Prokoenenia wheeleri* also appear to be uncommon.

Habits

Palpigradi have a worldwide distribution, most occurring in southern Europe, southern United States and South America. All prefer high humidity, under half-buried stones in soil, where they are found together with Symphyla and Pauropoda that have similar requirements. During drought they go deep into the soil. One has been found on the sand of an ocean beach. They run rapidly with their pedipalpi and last three pairs of legs, waving their feeler-legs. The flagellum may be raised, sometimes with the abdomen, compressing the posterior parts of the prosoma together. All avoid light. Two animals meeting will stop though they have not touched.

Classification

Eukoeneniidae. This is the only family. *Eukoenenia mirabilis* is found in southern Italy and North Africa. *E. austriaca* is found in Istria and in Austrian caves as far north as Innsbruck. Several species are known from California. *Prokoenenia* is found in Texas. *Leptokoenenia gerlachi* is found in the beach sand of an island in the Red Sea; *L. scurra* is found in the bank of subterranean waters in the Congo. Other genera are *Allokoenenia* and *Koeneniodes.*

References

PEDIPALPI

Babu, K. S. 1965. Anatomy of the central nervous system of arachnids. *Zool. Jahrb. Abt. Anat.* 82:1–154.

Beck, L. 1968. Aus den Regenwäldern des Amazonas. *Nat. Museum* 98:71–80.

Henry, L. M. 1954. Cephalic nervous system and segmentation in Pedipalpida and Solpugida. *Microentomology* 19:2–13.

Kaestner, A. 1932. Pedipalpi *in* Kükenthal, *Handbuch der Zoologie,* De Gruyter, Berlin, 3(2):1–76.

Krishnakumaran, A. 1962. A comparative study of the cuticle in Arachnida. *Zool. Jahrb. Abt. Anat.* 80:49–64.

Muma, M. H. 1967. Scorpions, whip scorpions and wind scorpions of Florida. *Arthropods of Florida,* Florida Dept. Agric. 4:1–28.

Pringle, J. W. S. 1955. Function of lyriform organs of arachnids. *J. Exp. Biol.* 32:270–278.

Werner, F. 1935. Pedipalpi *in* Bronn's *Klassen und Ordnungen des Tierreichs,* Akad. Verlagsges., Leipzig, 5(4)8:317–490.

UROPYGI

Eisner, T. 1962. Survival by acid defense. *Natur. Hist.* 71:10–19.

_____ et al. 1961. Composition and function of the spray of the whip scorpion. *J. Insect Physiol.* 6:272–298.

Kaestner, A. 1948–1950. Entwicklungsgeschichte von *Thelyphonus*. *Zool. Jahrb. Abt. Anat.* 69:493–506; 70:169–197; 71:1–55.

Klingel, H. 1963. Paarungsweise bei *Telyphonus* und *Sarax*. *Verh. Deutschen Zool. Ges.* 26:452–459.

_____ 1963. Mating and maternal behaviour in *Telyphonus*. *Treubia*, Bogor 26:65–69.

McDonald, W. A. and Hogue, C. L. 1957. *Trithyreus* from southern California. *Amer. Mus. Novitates* 1834:1–7.

Millot, J. 1949. Uropyges in Grassé, *Traité de Zoologie*, Masson et Cie, Paris 6:533–562.

Modder, W. 1960. The male genital system of *Schizomus crassicaudatus*. *Ceylon J. Sci. Biol.* 3:173–189.

Rao, K. P. and Gopalakrishnareddy, T. 1962. Nitrogen excretion in arachnids. *Comp. Biochem. Physiol.* 7:175–178.

Rémy, P. A. 1961. L'écologie des schizomides. *Bull. Mus. Nat. Hist. Natur. Paris* (2)33:406–414.

Sturm, H. 1958. Indirekte Spermatophorenübertragung bei dem Geisselskorpion. *Naturwissenschaften* 45:142–143.

Yoshikura, M. 1961. Development of a whip scorpion *Typopeltis*. *Acta Arachnol.* 17:19–24.

_____ 1965. Postembryonic development of a whip scorpion, *Typopeltis stimpsonii*. *Kumamoto J. Sci.* (B)7:21–50.

AMBLYPYGI

Alexander, A. J. 1962. Biology and behavior of *Damon* of South Africa and *Admetus* of Trinidad. *Zoologica*, New York, 47:25–37.

_____ 1962. Courtship and mating in amblypygids. *Proc. Zool. Soc. London* 138:379–383.

Klingel, H. 1963. Paarungsweise bei *Telyphonus* und *Sarax*. *Verh. Deutschen Zool. Ges.* 26:452–459.

Millot, J. 1949. Amblypyges, *in* Grassé, *Traité de Zoologie*, Masson et Cie, Paris, 6:563–588.

PALPIGRADI

Condé, B. 1965. Palpigrades dans le milieu interstitiel littoral. *Compte Rend. Acad. Sci. Paris* 261:1898–1900.

Kaestner, A. 1932. Palpigradi, *in* Kükenthal, *Handbuch der Zoologie*, De Gruyter, Berlin, 3(2):77–98.

Millot, J. 1943. L'anatomie et l'histophysiologie de *Koenenia*. *Rev. Française Entomol.* 9:33–51.

_____ 1949. Palpigrades, *in* Grassé, *Traité de Zoologie*, Masson et Cie, Paris, 6:520–532.

Monniot, F. 1966. Un Palpigrade interstitiel, *Leptokoenenia scurra*. *Rev. Ecol. Biol. Sol* 3:41–64.

Roewer, C. F. 1934. Palpigradi, *in* Bronn's *Klassen und Ordnungen des Tierreichs*, Akad. Verlagsges., Leipzig, 5(4)4:640–723.

11.

Order Araneae, Spiders

About 30,000 species of spiders are known, of which the largest is *Theraphosa leblondi* from Guyana, growing to 9 cm in body length.

The abdomen (opisthosoma) is almost always unsegmented in spiders, and is attached to the prosoma by a narrow stalk, the pedicel. The chelicerae are large and have a fang but no pincers. The pedipalpi are leglike, and usually have an endite on the coxa. The abdomen almost always has 2 pairs of respiratory organs, the anterior usually book lungs, the posterior usually tracheae. The abdominal appendages of segments X and XI are retained as spinnerets.

The spiders, possibly through exploiting the usefulness of silk, have evolved many species, more than any other group of arachnids except possibly the mites. Spiders are found in diverse habitats on all continents (except Antarctica) as well as in all climates, but only one species is completely aquatic.

Anatomy

The prosoma has a uniform dorsal carapace and a wide strong unsegmented sternum ventrally. An anterior lobe of the sternum, usually indicated by a groove, serves as a labium (Fig. 11–1). The narrow pedicel, segment VII, permits complete movement of the abdomen.

Only in the Mesothelae is the abdomen segmented as in amblypygids, metameres VII to XVIII having true dorsal tergites. Ventrally there are only sternites VII to IX and a soft area with the posterior metameres indicated by grooves (Figs. 8–3, 11–1a). The external segmentation corresponds to the internal arrangements of metameric trunk muscles, the heart and its ligaments (attachments) (Fig. 11–13). In other spiders the abdomen is a more or less uniform sac although some of the segmentation of the embryo may persist.

The segmentation can be recognized externally in the arrangement of the spiracles of the respiratory organs (corresponding with the posterior border of sternites VIII and IX), in the spinnerets, and in the distribution of pigment or of the sclerites that are sometimes present (Fig. 11–2). Internally in the em-

131

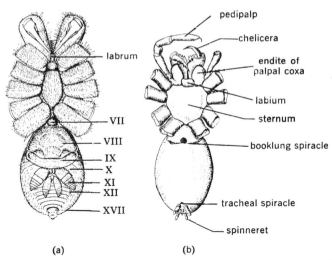

pedipalp

chelicera

labrum

endite of
palpal coxa

labium

VII

sternum

VIII

IX

booklung spiracle

X

XI

XII

XVII

tracheal spiracle

spinneret

(a)   (b)

Fig. 11–1.   (a) Ventral view of the segmented spider, *Heptathela kimurai*, 15 mm long
(after Kishida); (b) unsegmented spider.

bryos the segmentation is always present in the coelom pouches (Fig. 4–17),
and in the adults vestiges of segmentation are seen in the divisions of the ventral
longitudinal muscles (VIII to XI) and their apodemes (Fig. 8–14), the heart
ostia and lateral arteries of the heart, sometimes also in the dorsoventral muscles
and the dorsal longitudinal muscles of the metameres VIII to XV or even XVII
(Fig. 11–2).

During embryonic development the 9th and rarely the 10th sternites elongate,
bringing the spinnerets to the posterior end of the abdomen; simultaneously
sternites XIII to XVIII become reduced (Figs. 8–11, 11–1b). The spinnerets are
now at the posterior end of the abdomen and the attachment of the abdomen by
a narrow pedicel makes possible its free movement and the accurate movement
of the spinnerets.

EXOSKELETON. Most spiders are gray or brown, but there are numerous
colorful species, particularly in the subtropics and tropics, fewer in temperate
regions. The color may be due to phenolic tanning of the structural protein, or
to pigment dissolved in the exoskeleton or as granules stored in hypodermal cells.
Some species have colorful scales and ornamentation, and some coloring may be
structural (interference). In the jumping spiders, which have excellent vision,
the males are often more brightly colored than females. In many groups, particularly the Linyphiidae and Theridiidae, the abdomen is colored by white
guanin stored at the distal ends of the digestive ceca. Color change to match
the surroundings has been reported in spiders of several families. The pattern
of dorsal abdominal pigmentation often reflects the original segmentation; there

is often a direct relationship between pattern and longitudinal muscles and heart (Fig. 11–2).

The strong prosomal exoskeleton and the mesodermal endosternite serve as attachment points for the appendage musculature (Fig. 11–3). A thoracic depression of the carapace serves as an attachment for the muscles of the pumping stomach. Posterior invaginations on sternites VIII to XI form hollow apodemes for attachment of the ventral muscles, as well as for dorsoventral muscles (Figs. 4–17, 8–14).

APPENDAGES. The oral appendages have become specialized. In the primitive Mesothelae and Orthognatha the basal segment of each two-segmented chelicera is inserted laterally, as are the leg coxae (Figs. 11–1a, 11–4a). The chelicerae open forward and close down. However, in the Labidognatha the insertion has rotated 90° and the chelicerae are bent ventrally so that they are in a vertical position with their basal segments against each other (Figs. 8–5, 11–4b, 11–5). The span between fangs in the Labidognatha has been substantially increased because in biting not only the fang but also the basal segment can be spread (Fig.

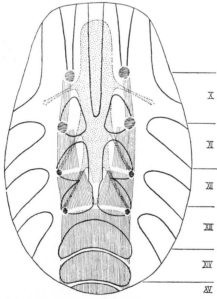

Fig. 11–2. Dorsum of abdomen of female *Ctenus*; relationship of white pattern to internal, metamerically arranged organs. Patterned areas are white with heavy outlines; dorsal longitudinal muscles of segments X to XVI have longitudinal lines; the heart and its 3 pairs of lateral attachment ligaments, reaching to the posterior border of each segment, are stippled; sclerotized discs of the integument that serve as muscle attachments have transverse lines. United muscles of somites VIII and IX are attached anteriorly; on the following 3 pairs (9th to 11th segment) the insertion of the dorsoventral muscles has moved posteriorly one segment (compare *Liphistius*, Fig. 11–13). (After Crome.)

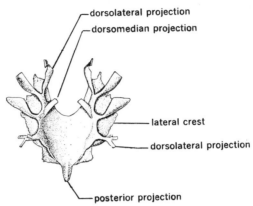

dorsolateral projection

dorsomedian projection

lateral crest

dorsolateral projection

posterior projection

Fig. 11–3.   Endosternite of the orb weaver, *Araneus quadratus*; 2 mm long. (After Kaestner.)

11–5). Another advantage of the rotation is that it permits shortening of the fang. A muscle of equal cross section can produce greater force on the shorter fang.

Because of the large span of their chelicerae, small sized Labidognatha with small jaws can handle very large prey. For an orthognath spider of similar size to manage the same prey, its fangs would have to be three times as long. Thus while a small labidognath can feed easily, an orthognath spider has to be much larger to be able to catch the same sized prey, as its cheliceral span is only one-third that of the labidognath. The abundance of small labidognaths and the relatively large size and small number of orthognaths probably reflect the evolutionary advantages. And as small spiders can reach final size and mature faster than large ones they can colonize areas with short periods of vegetation growth and insect abundance.

Modifications of the chelicerae and their teeth and fangs are common and may be correlated with the mode of life and food habits of the spider.

The pedipalpi of the primitive Mesothelae and most Orthognatha are leglike, while in the Labidognatha they are reduced, antennae-like, and are not used for walking (Fig. 11–10). In the Mesothelae the coxae of the pedipalpi are like those of the walking legs (Fig. 11–1a). The pedipalpal coxae are widened ventrally in the Orthognatha, covered with hairs, and with the chelicerae enclose a preoral chamber used for digestion (Fig. 8–8). The Labidognatha have the coxae further modified as endites forming flat plates close behind the chelicerae (Figs. 11–1b, 11–7, 11–10).

The walking legs have 8 articles. A small distal article, the pretarsus, has 2 comblike claws and often a hooklike middle claw used to manipulate silk (Fig. 11–25a).

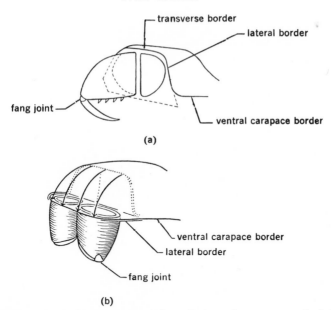

Fig. 11–4. Cheliceral attachments; anteriolateral view of carapace and chelicerae: (a) orthognath chelicera, left chelicera removed; (b) labidognath chelicerae; the arrows indicate how the insertion has moved from anterior to ventral. (After Kaestner.)

SENSE ORGANS. Most spiders are covered by setae, many of them sensory, and the legs and palpi may bear long sensory trichobothria. Slit sense organs, distributed on the integument, are thought to serve as proprioceptors sensing stresses in the cuticle and vibration detectors. There are usually 8 eyes, sometimes 6, rarely 4 or 2. In cave dwelling species they may be reduced in size or lost completely. They are always simple ocelli, variously directed (Figs. 8–5, 11–8). The anterior median eyes, sometimes called the main eyes (or direct eyes), are characterized by having rhabdoms facing the lenses while in the other eyes the rhabdoms turn inward (Fig. 11–6). The structure of the lateral eyes and also the arrangement of the eyes are characteristic in different families and are useful taxonomically. Chemoreceptors have not been identified with certainty, but they must be widespread.

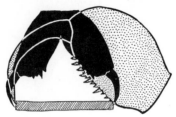

Fig. 11–5. Comparison of equal cheliceral span (lined) of large orthognath and small labidognath chelicerae. (After Kaestner.)

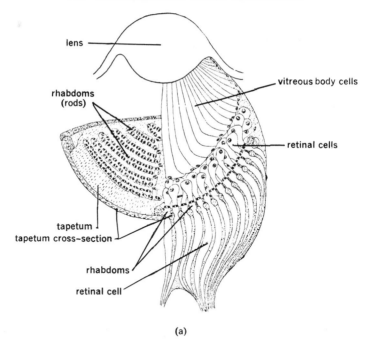

lens

vitreous body cells

rhabdoms
(rods)

retinal cells

tapetum

tapetum cross–section

rhabdoms

retinal cell

(a)

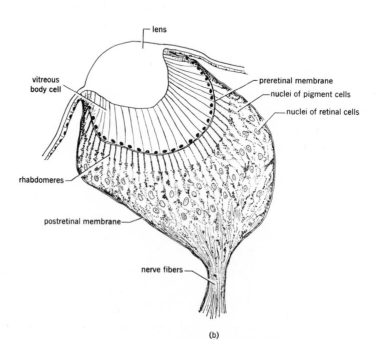

lens

vitreous
body cell

preretinal membrane

nuclei of pigment cells

nuclei of retinal cells

rhabdomeres

postretinal membrane

nerve fibers

(b)

(See page 139 for caption.)

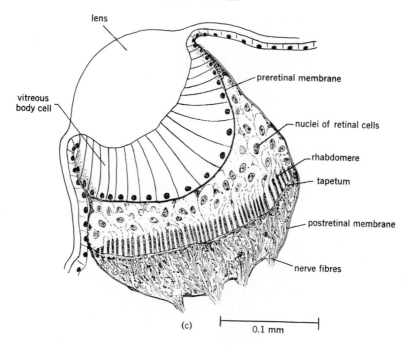

lens

preretinal membrane

nuclei of retinal cells

rhabdomere

tapetum

vitreous body cell

postretinal membrane

nerve fibres

(c)

0.1 mm

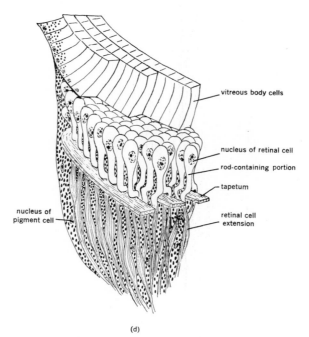

vitreous body cells

nucleus of retinal cell

rod-containing portion

tapetum

nucleus of pigment cell

retinal cell extension

(d)

(See page 139 for caption.)

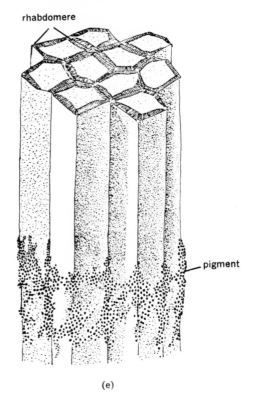

(e)

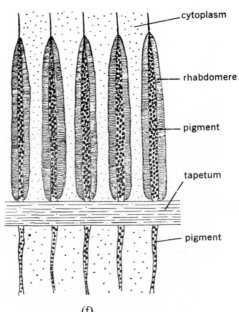

(f)

(See page 139 for caption.)

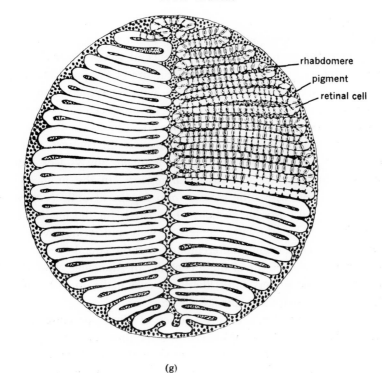

(g)

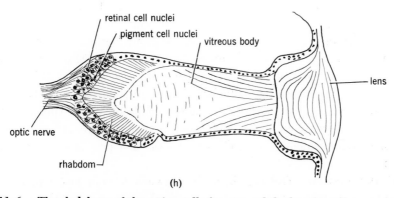

(h)

Fig. 11–6. The rhabdoms of the retina cells face toward the lens in main eyes (anterior medians), toward the back of the eye in laterals and posterior median eyes; (a) posterior median eye of wolf spider, *Lycosa*; right, cross section; left, looking down on concave surface of tapetum and rods (from Homann); (b–g) eyes of wolf spider, *Arctosa varians* (after electron micrographs, from Baccetti and Bedini); (b) section through main (anterior median) eye; (c) section through posterior lateral eye; (d) section of a lateral eye without lens (cornea); (e) distal portion of a group of retinal cells of main eyes; (f) arrangement of rhabdomeres in a lateral eye; (g) arrangement of retinal cells in a section transverse to optic axis of lateral eye; (h) main eye of the jumping spider *Salticus scenicus* (after Scheuring).

NERVOUS SYSTEM. The nervous system is highly condensed and the brain consists of supraesophageal and subesophageal ganglia. The supraesophageal ganglion contains the protocerebrum and cheliceral ganglion. Both lie in front of or above the pharynx (Fig. 11–7). The structure of the protocerebrum varies with the spider's habits. Visual spiders (e.g., jumping spiders, Salticidae; wolf spiders, Lycosidae; crab spiders, Thomisidae) have the central body with small cells, the globuli (corpora pedunculata), believed to be association centers, and also have an anterior optic glomerular commissure. In contrast, web spiders, which rely mainly on the sense of vibration or touch, always lack globuli and sometimes lack the anterior glomerular commissure. In the protocerebrum of the visual spiders, cells with little plasma form 2 pairs of optic centers consisting of an anterior and posterior portion. One pair is for the median eyes, one set each for the laterals. The optic centers of web spiders, however, are made up of ordinary optic cells, slightly differentiated, and the lateral eyes and posterior median eyes have just one pair of optic centers. In Araneidae, Dysderidae and *Tegenaria*, and all web spiders, optic fibers and cells make up 3–5% of the total brain volume; in the visual Salticidae it is 25%.

The large subesophageal ganglion is a fusion of all the posterior ganglia, the neuromeres of the abdomen having moved into the prosoma in a late embryonic stage. But the segmental origins are reflected in the blood vessels and sometimes in tracheae that run between ganglia (Fig. 6–2). The Mesothelae thus have 5 prosomal ganglia and 12 abdominal ganglia, while other spiders have only 7 abdominal ganglia.

Our knowledge about neurosecretion is quite limited. In the supraesophageal ganglion are two pairs of anterior, one pair of lateral (in *Araneus*) and one pair of posterior neurosecretory cells. The posterior group becomes active before the last molt and remains active (in *Araneus, Meta, Coelotes*). Most neurosecretory cells are in the subesophageal ganglion, some of these (of type B) are mesodermal, derived from coelomic epithelium. Their secretory activity starts before the first molt and activity continues during the whole life of the spider. Cyclical changes in *Pardosa* suggest that they control molt. There are two pairs of Schneider's organs (mentioned in Chapter 8), the first pair is very large in the Theraphosidae.

DIGESTIVE SYSTEM. The mouth, a slit between labrum and labium (Figs. 6–2, 11–1), leads into a broad and flattened pharynx, a precerebral pumping stomach, the anterior and posterior walls of which are formed by sclerotized plates. Behind the pharynx the esophagus turns and continues as a narrow passage between the brain and subesophageal ganglion, and above the endosternite it forms a large postcerebral pumping stomach with its walls folded inward. The midgut has ceca in the prosoma that differ in the various families; usually there are 4 pairs extending into the coxae and a single median anterior one (Fig. 11–8). In the anterior part of the abdomen the gut has more ceca, much-branched to form the digestive gland that fills most of the abdomen (Figs. 11–8, 11–10). The gut widens posteriorly as a cloaca (Fig. 11–8) containing the openings of the Malpighian tubules; a short sclerotized section connects the cloaca to the anus.

EXCRETORY SYSTEM. The various organs that perform excretory functions include the large nephrocytes of the prosoma; the pigment-storing hypodermis; the distal ends of the abdominal gut ceca, which store guanine; the walls of the cloaca; the Malpighian tubules, limited to the abdomen; and the coxal glands, limited to the prosoma. In the Mesothelae and Orthognatha there are 2 pairs of sacculi, as well as 2 pairs of excretory canals opening posteriorly of the first and third walking legs. Labidognatha have only one pair of sacculi, opening posteriorly on the coxa of the first leg. The canal is very short in those orb weaving spiders (Araneidae) that have large spinning glands; possibly the nitrogenous wastes are used in making silk. The Malpighian vessels excrete guanine, adenine, hypoxanthine and uric acid into the cloaca, all relatively insoluble and hence water-conserving. In different spiders examined, 34–76% of the excretory material is guanine; neither urea nor amino acids could be detected.

POISON GLANDS. At the tip of the convex side of the cheliceral fang is the opening of the poison gland. The gland lies entirely in the chelicerae in most primitive orthognath families, while in labidognaths it extends into the prosoma (Figs. 6–2, 11–8). Spiral muscles surround the cylindrical gland. In black widows (*Latrodectus;* Theridiidae) secretions are formed from vacuolate cells that disintegrate in the lumen of the gland. Smaller glands, probably digestive, for cleaning the appendages, or for breaking silk strands, open anteriorly on the endites.

SILK. The very large silk glands of the 10th and 11th appendages arise as ectodermal invaginations (as do the poison glands), and have a glandular epithelium one cell layer thick. From these cells the silk is secreted into the lumen of the gland which leads the secretion into a tubule that opens through the spinneret spigot.

The glands lack muscles but are emptied by hydrostatic pressures of 3–5 cm Hg generated within the abdomen apparently by the cuticular muscle layer. Muscular valves controlling the flow of silk have been found in ducts of *Araneus.* The form of the glands differs in various families. Mesothelae have only 2 types of glands, while some orb weaving spiders (Araneidae), have at least 6 kinds, each producing a particular kind of silk (Figs. 11–9, 11–10). The spinnerets, movable sclerotized tubes of several joints, are long in some species, short and conical in most web spiders (Fig. 11–10). In the Mesothelae they divide post-embryonically into 2 pairs; in other spiders this division occurs during embryonic development. Thus spiders have 4 pairs of spinnerets, 2 pairs on segment X and 2 pairs on segment XI. Only *Liphistius* (Mesothelae) retains the maximum of 4 pairs of spinnerets, in the adult, and these are on the venter of the abdomen

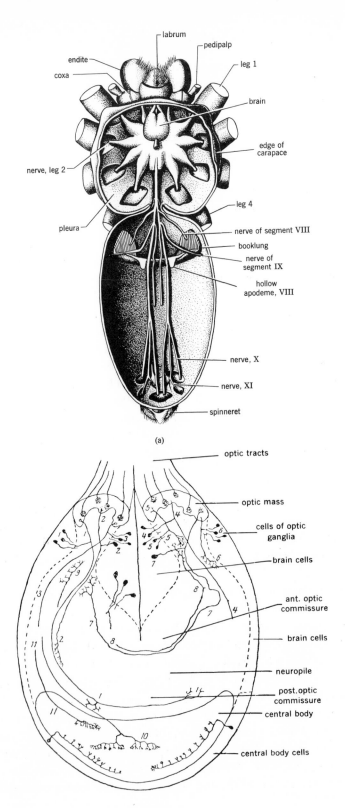

(a)

(b)

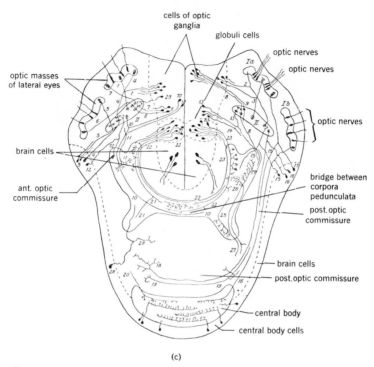

cells of optic ganglia

globuli cells

optic nerves

optic nerves

optic masses of lateral eyes

optic nerves

brain cells

bridge between corpora pedunculata

ant. optic commissure

post. optic commissure

brain cells

post. optic commissure

central body

central body cells

(c)

Fig. 11–7. Brains of web spiders have a large central body, varying with the complexity of the web; those of hunting spiders have a pair of large anterior corpora pedunculata with globuli cells, and a small central body. (a) nervous system of *Tegenaria*, 10 mm long (after Kaestner); (b) reconstruction in dorsal section of the brain of an orb weaver (Araneidae) indicating centers and pathways; numbers refer to neurones (from Hanström); (c) dorsal section of brain of a visual jumping spider (Salticidae) (from Hanström). In both (b) and (c) the optic nerve and optic masses of the main eyes are removed; in (c) also the optic mass of the posterior median eyes.

(Fig. 11–1). In the related *Heptathela* the posterior medians are united without spigots into a posterior colulus. The anterior and posterior laterals may consist of many joints in the Mesothelae. In all other spiders the spinnerets are generally at the end of the abdomen and it is usually the anterior median pair that is lost first. Sometimes remnants may be seen as a median cone, the colulus (Fig. 11–10) whose function is unknown; at other times, in the Cribellatae the anterior median pair fuse during embryonic development and form an oval plate sometimes divided, the cribellum (Fig. 11–11), covered by thousands of minute spigots. In *Hypochilus* the plate is still on the distal surface of a blunt, appendage-like cone. Some orthognath spiders have only two pairs of spinnerets, hav-

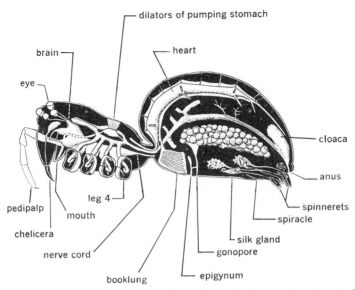

Fig. 11–8. Internal organs of a spider in lateral view. (After Comstock.)

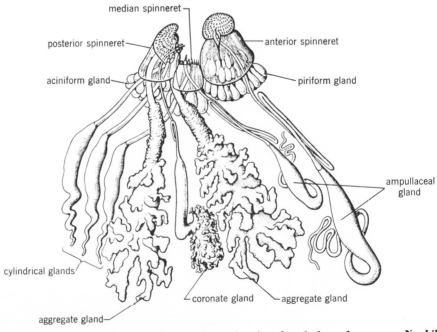

Fig. 11–9. Right silk glands and spinnerets of a female of the orb weaver, *Nephila*, in mesal view; 2.5 cm long. (After Peters.)

ing lost the anterior median and the posterior lateral pairs. In one species of *Palpimanus* (Labidognatha, Palpimanidae) which has only a single pair of spinnerets, there is a "posterior cribellum," a membraneous area bearing spigots between the spinnerets and the anal tubercle. Silk glands are also found anteriorly on the abdomen of most male spiders (Fig. 11–16), their isolated spigots lying between the anterior book lungs.

Spider silk has the highest tensile strength of any natural fiber known. This tensile strength combined with its great elasticity makes it an ideal material for the many uses spiders have evolved for it. The silk is a protein (fibroin) that polymerizes on being pulled. Probably the usual site of the conversion from solid to liquid is close to the tip of the spigot, but the conversion may not always be complete. The hardening is a direct result of tension, not of oxidation or evaporation. At least some of the silk is probably "wet" (unpolymerized) on the outside surface when it emerges from the spigot. The diameter of different silk strands varies but it is quite uniform for a given strand. The threads may be either flattened or cylindrical.

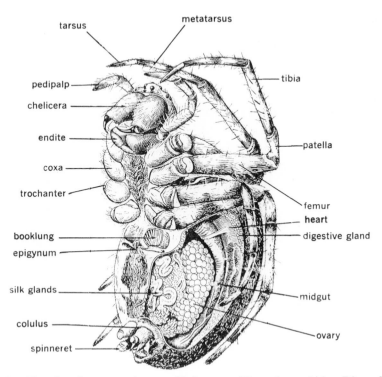

Fig. 11–10. Female orb weaver, *Araneus diadematus*, 13 mm long. (After Pfurtscheller.)

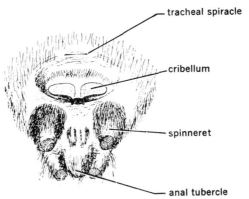

tracheal spiracle

cribellum

spinneret

anal tubercle

Fig. 11–11.   Spinnerets of *Amaurobius fenestralis*; cribellum, 0.48 mm wide. (After Nielsen.)

There are at most six different types of silk glands. They are believed to produce distinct types of silk. Aciniform glands produce silk used in wrapping prey. By sectioning orb-weaving spiders after they had constructed certain web parts, it has been demonstrated that ampullate glands produce the dragline and scaffolding, aggregate glands probably produce the sticky globules of glue on the spiral, and that in the production of the egg cocoon, the contents of the cylindrical glands are used up. Cholinergic agents stimulate the incorporation of amino acids into the ampullate and aggregate glands, as can be demonstrated by using alanine labeled with C^{14}. The incorporation of alanine is reduced by atropine. These investigations have been carried out on *Araneus sericatus.*

RESPIRATORY ORGANS. Because of their diversity, the respiratory organs are of interest. Mesothelae, Orthognatha and some Hypochilidae have two pairs of book lungs that open posteriorly on sternites VIII and IX, a primitive condition. In most Labidognatha the posterior pair and sometimes also the anterior pair are replaced by tube tracheae, demonstrating that they are homologous with book lungs. Spiders may be equipped with either of the following combinations of respiratory organs:

A. Segment VIII: a pair of book lungs
    Segment IX: (1) a pair of book lungs
                  (2) a pair of sieve tracheae (e.g., Dysderidae, Fig. 8–13)
                  (3) a pair of simple tube tracheae
                  (4) vestiges of an atrium (e.g., Pholcidae)
                  (5) a pair of simple tube tracheae opening jointly with a pair of tracheal apophyses (the most common form in Labidognatha) (Figs. 8–14, 11–8)
                  (6) a pair of branched tracheal apophyses that may penetrate the prosoma

B. Segment VIII: a pair of sieve tracheae (rare and found mainly in dwarf spiders, 1–1.5 mm long, except for the Caponiidae). Often the tracheae may be limited to the 8th metamere (Fig. 11–12); only rarely do they penetrate into the prosoma

Segment IX: (*1*) a pair of tube tracheae that may enter the prosoma
(*2*) no respiratory organs

Sieve tracheae are large tracheal trunks from the ends of which originate numerous individual tracheae (Fig. 11–12). Tracheal apodemes, otherwise found only in diplopods, are tracheae derived from hollow muscle attachments.

Tracheae are best developed in small spiders (regardless of family), some of which may lack book lungs, and also in the superfamily Dysderoidea and in the Eurasian water spider, *Argyroneta*. Some evidence suggests that the development of tracheae and the replacement of book lungs by tracheae are adaptations for the conservation of water in small spiders having high surface to volume ratios. In the Dysderoidea, which are larger, it may be a phylogenetic character inherited from smaller ancestors. The value of this adaptation in *Argyroneta* is not understood. In *Argyroneta* the large tracheae are derived from apodemes. In young instars the spiracle is posterior, close to the spinnerets, but in later instars the tracheal spiracle moves anteriorly.

CIRCULATORY SYSTEM. The complexity of the circulatory system is correlated with the type of respiratory organs. In those spiders in which the respiratory organs are localized, the heart is large, the arterial system branched and complex. However, if tracheae reach into all parts of the body, the heart is usually short and the arterial branching reduced. In the Mesothelae there is little reduction of the heart: five pairs of ostia and as many lateral arteries and ventral ligaments in metameres VIII to XII (Fig. 11–13). Orthognatha usually

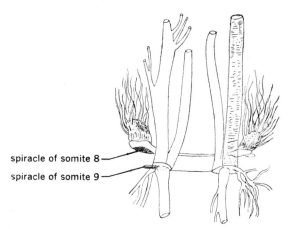

spiracle of somite 8

spiracle of somite 9

Fig. 11–12. Respiratory organs of *Nops coccineus*, Caponiidae. (After Bertkau.)

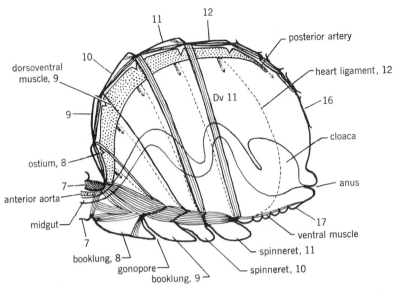

Fig. 11–13.   Longitudinal section of the abdomen of *Liphistius desultor*; Dv, dorso-ventral muscle, 2 cm long. (After Millot from Kaestner.)

lack the last (5th) pair of ostia and lateral arteries are present only in segments IX to XI. In Labidognatha there are only three pairs of ostia (VIII to X) with corresponding ligaments and lateral arteries in metameres IX to XI (Fig. 11–8). Those Labidognatha having many tracheae in the prosoma (Dysderoidea and the water spider *Argyroneta*) have only two pairs of ostia, the heart being further shortened posteriorly.

That a dorsal cardiac nerve controls the coordination of the heart beat, as in *Limulus* and scorpions, can be shown by careful sectioning of *Heteropoda venatoria*. Minor sensory stimulations cause changes in rhythm.

REPRODUCTIVE SYSTEM. In all spiders the sexes are separate. Usually males are smaller and have longer legs than females, the long legs apparently being an adaptation associated with their active role in searching for mates. The extreme of sexual dimorphism is found in the orb weaver *Nephila*, in which the female may reach 6 cm in length and the male is only 4–10 mm long. The much smaller males go through fewer molts than do the females, mature earlier, and often many more survive to maturity. More efficient maturation may be necessary to counteract the hazards entailed in searching for a mate.

Each of the paired, tube-shaped testes lying ventrally in the abdomen continues forward into a sperm duct that opens into a median ectodermal atrium in segment VIII; the gonopore is on the posterior border of the segment. The ovaries fuse in segment VIII to form a single oviduct that enlarges to form an atrium, the distal sclerotized part of which opens on the posterior border of the 8th segment in the epigastric furrow (Figs. 11–1b, 11–8, 11–10). Mesothelae,

Orthognatha, and haplogyne spiders have seminal receptacles only opening into the atrium inside the gonopore. However, in other spiders separate copulatory pores open into the seminal receptacles on the venter of a strongly sclerotized and sculptured plate, the epigynum (Figs. 11–1, 11–10, 11–15).

Reproduction

Sperm transfer is carried out by the complex organs of the male pedipalp (Fig. 11–14). It has been shown that the palpal organ is an elaboration of the pretarsus and is thus homologous with the claw of the female pedipalp, although in higher spiders the tarsal segment (cymbium) is hollowed out ventrally to accommodate the functional components. Usually the male spins a web, the sperm web, on which to deposit a droplet of sperm. Theraphosids, before depositing the droplet of sperm, have been observed to make a substrate with fine threads emanating from spigots between the anterior book lungs, from glands in segment VIII (Fig. 11–16). The theraphosid *Pamphobeteus* took 2 hours to make the web, 50 minutes to strengthen the anterior border, 20 minutes to make the substrate web, 1–2 seconds to deposit the sperm, and 12 minutes to climb around to stand on the web again and turn facing the border. Then the spider dips the palps alternately into the drop of sperm 120 times a minute for more than 90 minutes. The sperm web may then be destroyed. The silk glands at the anterior end of the abdomen are also found in most other spiders. (They may be lacking in Amaurobiidae, Dictynidae, Leptonetidae and *Ariadna*.)

The method of sperm induction is somewhat different in different families. The mechanism of uptake is not known, but the most likely hypothesis is that the reservoir is filled by secretions and the seminal fluid is drawn up by resorption of the secretions.

After the pedipalpi are filled, the male goes in search of a mate. In some families he recognizes the female by means of chemoreceptors on touching her or her silk dragline. Araneid males search among plants while the females remain in their webs; the male recognizes the web of a female of his own species, and often can tell whether she is mature. The male orb weaver may court at the web of an adult of his own species although the female inhabitant has been removed. Male wolf spiders of the genus *Trochosa*, when running on the ground, will stop at a female's dragline, first run one way, then the other, but will ignore the dragline of other species of *Trochosa*. As juveniles often do not have a dragline in *Trochosa*, the main adaptation of the dragline on level ground seems to be to facilitate meeting of adults of opposite sex. The highly visual and colorful jumping spiders probably recognize potential mates by sight.

The hazard of being treated as prey by the female is minimized by elaborate courtship. In the visual hunting spiders the darker male may wave his dark or brightly colored palpi or legs and the motion seems to inhibit the female. In the visual jumping spiders, males of congeneric species have different displays,

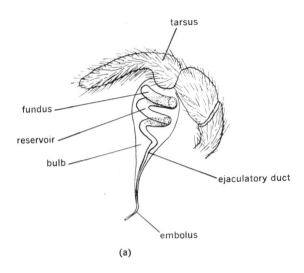

tarsus

fundus

reservoir

bulb

ejaculatory duct

embolus

(a)

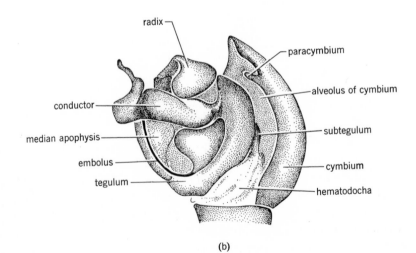

radix

paracymbium

conductor

alveolus of cymbium

median apophysis

subtegulum

embolus

cymbium

tegulum

hematodocha

(b)

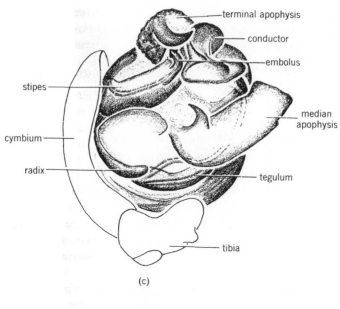

(c)

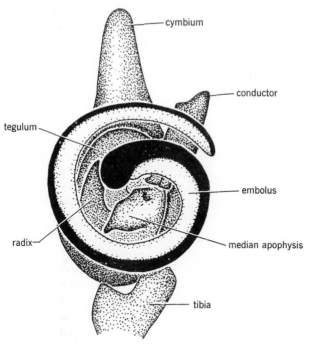

(d)

Fig. 11–14. Tips of male pedipalpi: (a) simple pedipalp of *Segestria senoculata*, bulb 2 mm long (after Gerhardt); (b) left pedipalp of theridiid *Enoplognatha ovata*, bulb pulled out of cymbium (from Levi); (c) left pedipalp of orb weaver, *Araneus diadematus*; (d) left pedipalp of funnel weaver *Agelenopsis aperta*. (After Gering.)

motions of pedipalpi and abdomen, and may be differently colored (Fig. 11–17). Other spiders pluck rhythmically on the threads of the female's web, or approach the female with jerking movements, or stroking or patting her abdomen or whole body. Some wrap the female in threads or hold her with long, specially modified chelicerae. Others (*Pisaura*) present a fly to the female before mating. After courtship, the male finally succeeds in inserting the tip of one pedipalp into the epigynum and injecting the sperm. In haplogyne spiders, both palpi are introduced at the same time. Mating position and behavior differ among the families (Fig. 11–18); sometimes they differ among or within species (*Scytodes*). The complex structure of the palpus (Fig. 11–14) and epigynum (Fig. 11–15) often provide the best character of systematic value, particularly at the species level.

It is not completely understood how the complicated palpus works, and how their sometimes spiralled tips are inserted into the epigynum and penetrate the twisted connecting canals leading to the seminal receptacles. In the entelegyne spiders, the palpus is expanded during mating by the hemolymph which extends the hematodocha, soft folded tissue between the sclerites. In many relatively small males of the Theridiidae and Araneidae, the tip of the sclerite (embolus) containing the duct breaks off, preventing the male from mating again. In *Dysdera* secretions from the palpal gland at the base of the palpal bulb force sperm out of the palpus. That it is an endocrine factor controlling the secretions can be demonstrated by injecting hemolymph from copulating males into males not mating.

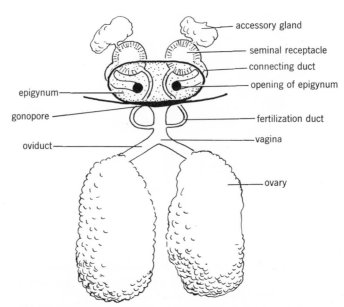

Fig. 11–15. Female genital system of a spider; cleared preparation in ventral view.

After copulation, the males of many species hurry off. In other species they die soon after or during mating, and may even be killed and eaten by females (*Argiope lobata, Cyrtophora citricola;* but this is the exception in the black widow, *Latrodectus mactans*).

The sperm remains in the seminal receptacles (spermathecae) of the female until the eggs are laid, at which time it passes into the fertilization ducts which open into the female genital atrium (Fig. 11–15). Most species enclose their eggs in a silken sac, often made of thick layers of various types of silk that may differ in color. The egg sac may be hung up by tube-dwelling spiders or by those having orb webs. Huntsman spiders, Heteropodidae, and nursery web spiders, Pisauridae, carry it in their chelicerae, while the wolf spiders, Lycosidae, attach it to the spinnerets and expose it to sun at regular intervals. Many species guard their eggs or young.

The European theridiid *Achaearanea saxatile* (=*Theridion saxatile*) keeps its eggs in a thimble-shaped retreat hung in the middle of the web. At temperatures of 30–35°C the female carries the eggs outside into the cooler web. On cooling they are placed back into the retreat. That temperature is the controlling factor and that the spider does not sun the eggs has been demonstrated in the laboratory using an incubator with dim light. A female wolf spider, *Pardosa*, if her egg sac is removed, will make searching movements. Failing to recover the egg sac, she will pick up a similar or heavier object in its place. Wolf spiders, like scorpions, carry their young for a short period on their backs, while the young of some cobweb spiders, *Theridion*, and the agelenid, *Coelotes*, live with the mother and may share her prey. The young of *Coelotes*, after their mother dies of old age, feed on her body. In many species the young leave the egg sac in spring, long after the mother has died.

Females of the wolf spider *Pirata piraticus*, which inhabit sphagnum moss and have a temperature preference of 18–24°C, change their temperature preference to 26–32°C when carrying egg sacs, bringing their temperature preference close to their thermal death point of 35°C.

It has been observed that female wolf spiders of the genus *Trochosa* must bite the egg sac open to permit the young to escape, whereupon they climb up her legs and are carried on her back. The female judges when the sac is ready to open from the time elapsed since the egg sac was made, not from signals inside the egg sac. That is, if the experimenter replaces an egg sac with an older or a younger one, the female opens it on the same date, though in the older egg sac the young will have died and in the younger one the eggs fall out. The female constructs a silken retreat before opening the egg sac and afterward attaches the egg sac to her spinnerets, preventing young from getting lost. A juvenile female of *Trochosa* stands still when young climb on her back; the climbing up inhibits movement. With young on the back, the female is also inhibited from feeding; she will readily kill flies but not feed on them. Young

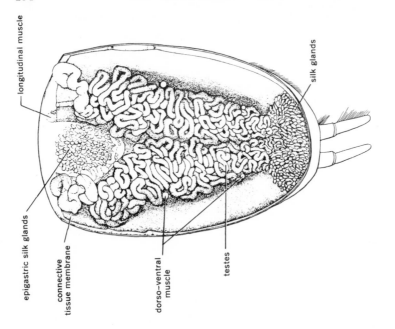

(b)

longitudinal muscle

silk glands

epigastric silk glands

connective tissue membrane

dorso-ventral muscle

testes

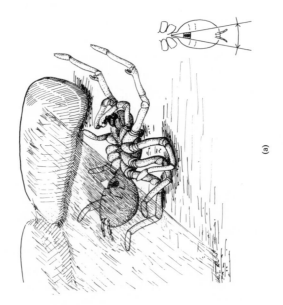

(a)

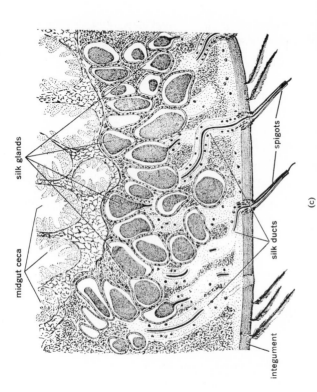

(c)

Fig. 11–16. (a) A male mygalomorph underneath sperm web making silk substrate for the sperm drop; below showing direction of movement of spinnerets; (b) dorsal view of a mygalomorph with heart, gut, midgut cecae and connective tissue removed; total length of spider, 6 cm; (c) median section through the epigastric silk glands of *Pamphobeteus* (from Melchers).

climbing anteriorly over the eyes are brushed back. Experimentally young climbed on a dead female or one smeared with butyric acid or cadaverine, and when the female was removed, they climbed on a dead bumblebee. If the mother's abdomen is covered with a nylon or velvet skirt, the young will congregate on the head or uncovered portion. Apparently contact with sclerotized setae is necessary. The female removes the empty egg sac from her spinnerets on the stimulus of the young crawling up. After a week to 10 days the young will leave the mother.

Theotima (Ochyroceratidae) is parthenogenetic and *Steatoda triangulosa* (Theridiidae) may be; otherwise parthenogenesis is unknown in spiders.

Development

The germ disc at first consists of the cephalic lobe, some segments, the posterior budding area, and the pygidium (Fig. 11–19a). Teloblastic divisions produce more segments between those already present and the pygidium, thus moving the pygidium farther from the head. While in most spiders the germ disc remains on the surface, in Mesothelae and some other primitive families the posterior part may be raised from the egg as in scorpion embryos (Figs. 4–11, 11–19b to f). Mesothelae and primitive Dysderidae have 18 segments as do members of the order Uropygi. In other spiders such as Pisauridae, Agelenidae and Araneidae, there are usually fewer. Mesothelae have appendage primordia on segments I to XII; in other families usually only segments I to VI and VIII to XI. The first six become prosomal appendages, VIII and IX give rise to the respiratory system, while the appendages themselves remain vestigial, X and XI become the spinnerets, while VII and XII are lost (Fig. 8–11). The young spiderling has to molt 5 to 12 times before maturing, males often undergoing fewer molts. Females of *Nephila madagascarensis* molt 11 times, the males 4–6 times. In the American bolas spider, *Mastophora* (Araneidae), the males hatch mature at 1.5–2 mm, and the females grow to be 9.5–12 mm. Orthognatha females (and perhaps females of some haplogyne families) molt after maturity, but this is not true of most spider families.

The number of molts and instars is the same regardless of amount of food in *Linyphia triangulosa* (Linyphiidae) and *Agelenopsis potteri* (Agelenidae). But more prey resulted in faster growth. The number of molts is variable in *Latrodectus* (Theridiidae), *Nephila* (Araneidae), and *Cupiennius* (Ctenidae). Poorly fed *Cupiennius* undergo fewer molts. For molting the spider may hang itself up by the appendages (Fig. 11–20). Large theraphosids molt while lying on one side or on the back. Most spiders do not feed immediately before or after a molt.

Fluctuations of secretion from neurosecretory cells of the subesophageal ganglion coincide with molting processes, indicating that the molting is controlled by hormones. Direct evidence is provided by experiments on first instar *Coelotes terrestris* with the abdomen ligatured off. If ligatured within 15 hours after climbing out of the egg sac they did not develop further; if ligatured after 28–35 hours, 80% continued their development and setae of new integument could be seen under the old. (First instar spiderlings were used, as spiderlings well supplied with yolk do not have to feed.) Destruction of protocerebral neurosecretory cells by a beam of ultraviolet light within 15 hours after hatching reduced the number developing normally to only 22%. If the destruction of the cells occurred 40–45 hours after hatching, all developed normally through the molt. Heteroplastic transplantation of integument from *Tegenaria* into the cephalothorax of *Coelotes* was "molted" by the host, indicating that whatever hormones exist are not species specific. It is interesting that destruction of large areas of the brain did not affect gametogenesis in the first instars. Apparently arachnid molt, like that of Crustacea and insects, is controlled by hormones.

It has been demonstrated in *Tegenaria* that as molting commences the normal blood pressure of the prosoma doubles, to 260 mm Hg. As the chelicerae are bent, the integument breaks around the carapace, continuing on the abdomen. The blood pressure is increased by increased number and volume of heart beats. Previous to molting the endocuticle is partly digested by the enzymes of the molting fluid, reducing the tear resistance of the exoskeleton to one-third its normal level. Molting is a complicated process involving, among other changes, rapid cell multiplication and differential changes in numbers of blood corpuscles.

RELATIONSHIPS. The numerous structural similarities between spiders and amblypygids are discussed under the latter order. Amblypygids, of course, lack silk glands and use a spermatophore for mating.

HABITS. Spiders are found in all terrestrial niches, in the Arctic as well as in tropics (none have yet been found in the Antarctic), and on marine and freshwater shores. *Argyroneta aquatica*, the Eurasian water spider, though air breathing, is entirely aquatic. It has few morphological adaptations other than dense body hair and abundant tracheae, the significance of which is uncertain. Other species (e.g., *Dolomedes*) hunt over the surface of pools and streams frequently diving beneath the surface to catch aquatic organisms or to escape predators. Numerous species of different families live on ocean shores below the high tide line. The European *Halorates reprobus* (Linyphiidae) presumably hides in air pockets under rocks at high tide. Some Lycosidae and the large *Desis* (Agelenidae) of the southern hemisphere run on wet beaches. *Amaurobioides maritima* of subantarctic islands, South Africa, Tasmania and New Zealand lives beween tide zones and is believed distributed over the oceans.

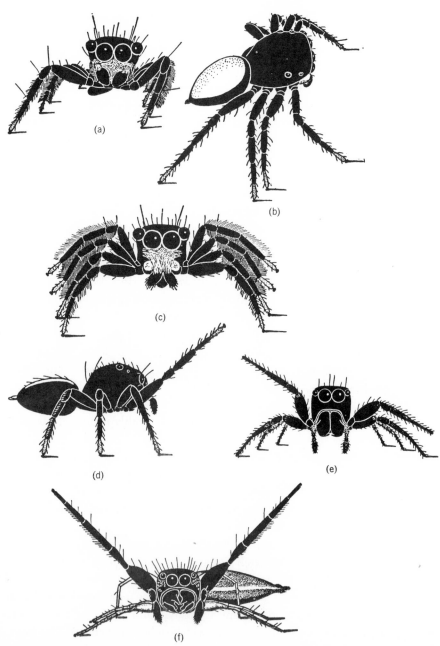

Fig. 11–17. Examples of display motions of male salticid spiders; *Gertschia noxiosa*, 2.5 mm long; others all 4 to 5 mm. (a–d) *Corythalia xanthopa*; (a, b) rocking, preface to threat and courtship; (c) threat; (d) courtship; (g) *C. chalcea* threat; dotted lines

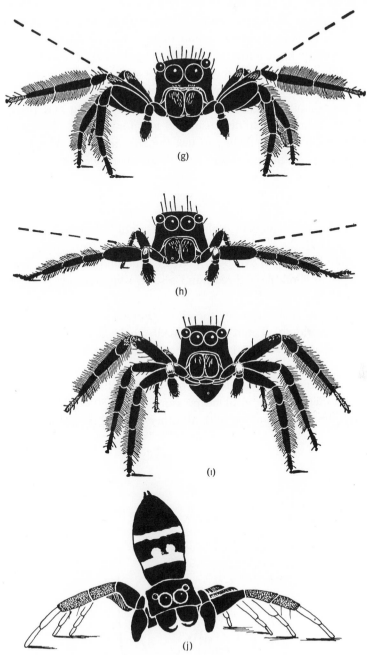

(g)

(h)

(i)

(j)

are peak positions during courtship; (h,i) *C. tropica* (=*C. fulgipedia*); (h) threat; (i) courtship; (e) *Mago dentichelis*, threat; (f) *Ashtabula furcillata*, courtship; (j) *Gertschia noxiosa*, courtship; (a to i, from Crane; j, after Emerton).

Most spiders use silk to make a retreat, which may completely enclose the spider and is opened by digestion of the silk (jumping spiders, Salticidae; sac spiders, Clubionidae). Trapdoor spiders, large wolf spiders and many mygalomorph spiders, and some Dysderidae and others make a silk-lined tube in the ground or between rocks or under loose bark (Fig. 11–23). The trapdoor spiders may close the tube with a door and camouflage it with dirt and moss. Many web spiders connect a retreat with the web that snares prey. The retreat probably also protects its inhabitant against desiccation, water logging and predators.

LOCOMOTION. Almost all spiders use all 8 legs for running. In slow walking, the first legs may be used as feelers to test the surroundings. The proximity of legs and mouthparts on the prosoma and the spread of legs on each side result in the alternate use of each pair. For instance, if we use Arabic numbers for those moving forward and Roman numbers for those on the ground, they are moved in the following sequence: right 1, left 2, right 3, left 4.

$$\begin{matrix} 1 & & I \\ II & & 2 \\ 3 & & III \\ IV & & 4 \end{matrix}$$ The

legs on the ground pull (I, II) or push (III, IV) the body forward. This rhythm is generally kept in climbing a thread and also in swimming of *Argyroneta*, the water spider.

Many spiders can move rapidly for short periods of time. A fleeing wolf spider, *Pardosa amentata*, 8 mm long, ran 90 cm in 3 seconds. A European house spider, *Tegeneria atrica*, 1.1 cm long, ran 150 cm in 5 seconds.

Salticidae, Oxyopidae, many Clubionidae and some other hunting spiders can jump. A study of the jumping mechanism of Salticidae has shown that the power comes from a sudden increase in blood pressure (up to 50 cm Hg) which causes the legs to straighten. In common with all other spiders, the salticids lack direct

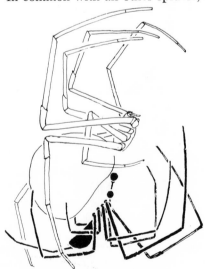

Fig. 11–18. Red widow, *Latrodectus bishopi*, mating, hanging in web; female white, male black; female 8.5 mm. (After Levi.)

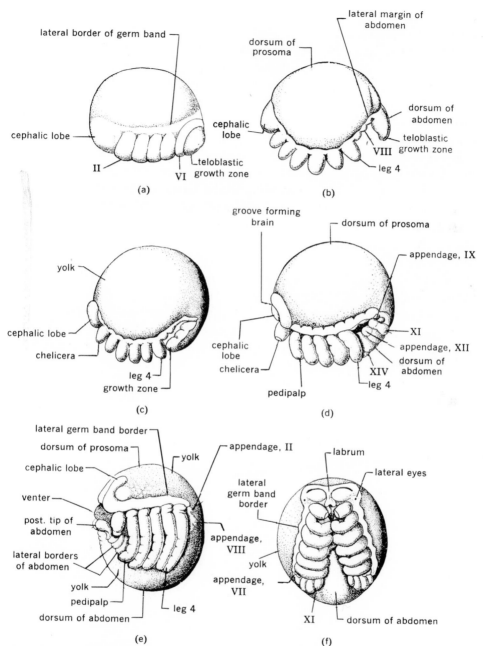

Fig. 11–19. Development of segmented spider *Heptathela kimurae*, about 1.1 mm long; Roman numerals refer to segments. (After Yoshikura.) (a) Cephalic lobes and cheliceral segments still fused, other prosomal segments separated; (b) budding zone lifting, having produced metameres VII to IX; the prosoma has appendage primordia; (c) the abdomen has lengthened with additional segments; (d) the abdomen pushes between the prosomal appendages; abdomen shows appendage primordia; (e) yolk has shifted from prosoma to abdomen, enlarging it; cephalic lobe has folded dorsally on the anterior of the embryo; (f) the same as d in ventral view.

extensor muscles. A dragline is always attached before jumping, preventing a fall if the target is missed.

Many spiders, including large mygalomorphs, can walk on smooth leaves or glass. At the tip of the tarsus there is a scopula, a cluster of spatula-shaped hairs with 800–1000 minute extensions on the distal surface. In the "banana-spider," *Heteropoda,* there are 1300 scopula hairs on each leg, providing numerous (10^6) points of attachment on each tarsus. That adhesion depends on the surface tension of the water film covering most surfaces can be tested by using a quartz surface; as quartz has little surface water, it is slippery to many spiders. The scopulae slip off glass if the water film is temporarily removed by silicone grease. Normally adhesion is so strong that a hanging 3 g *Heteropoda* might support a 70 g weight. The number of scopula hairs varies with the size of the spider. Three-clawed web spiders (including three-clawed mygalomorphs) lack these hairs but can walk on a vertical glass surface by slowly backing up, using silk spots attached to the glass surface by the spinnerets.

Numerous wolf spiders, nursery web spiders (Pisauridae), and others can run on the surface of water. The ventral side of the tarsus has numerous dense hairs which do not become wet. Therefore the tip of the tarsus rests on the surface and makes a concave dent on the water surface film. In wolf spiders locomotion depends upon the second and third legs; the fourth legs are barely moved but just support the body, while the first are used as feelers.

Many spiders balloon, especially the young in summer, fall, or spring. They are carried aloft on air currents by their silk threads. Small adult Linyphiidae

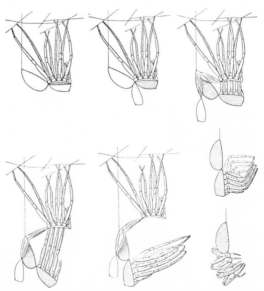

Fig. 11–20. Nursery web spider, *Dolomedes,* molting; about 12 mm long. (From Bristowe after Bonnet, courtesy Collins, Ltd.)

become aeronautic during late autumn in England. Only the mygalomorphs and some of the haplogynes are believed unable to use air currents for dispersion. To balloon, the spider ascends an elevated object and, as it raises its abdomen, somehow threads are produced that are caught by the wind. The wind then draws silk from the spider and when the pull is sufficient the spider lets go and floats off, often hooking its hind legs into the ballooning mass of threads. The masses of threads seen in spring and fall are called gossamer. Hanging onto the threads, the spiders may be carried many miles and have been collected from altitudes of several thousand feet (few thousand meters) in aerial plankton traps. Spiders have landed on ships more than 100 km from the coast. This method of transportation is of great importance in distribution of spider species and may be a regular part of the life cycle. It is of interest that the primitive groups of spiders that do not balloon have only a limited distribution and have only few (often widespread) species compared to the enormous number of ballooning spider species.

SENSES. Touch is the most important sense, and there are numerous tactile setae. Males of the cross spider, or garden spider, *Araneus diadematus,* can distinguish females of their own species from those of another by touching the web. The males can tell from the threads whether the female is mature or juvenile, even if a juvenile has been placed in the web of a mature individual or vice versa. Males of Lycosidae, Pisauridae, and Thomisidae become sexually excited if placed in a glass dish that previously contained a mature female of the same species. Probably draglines produced by the running female provide the stimulation. Also, the males tested become sexually stimulated upon touching the leg of a female, the tip of her abdomen, or only her autotomized leg. Washing the leg in ether removed the cause of stimulation, indicating that its nature is chemical rather than mechanical, but the stimulating substance reappears (in *Dolomedes*) in the glass dish after the ether in which the leg was washed has evaporated.

But other chemical stimulations can be picked up by the tarsi and appendages. Thus salticids notice crushed flies underneath moist filter paper. Other spiders can differentiatae pure water from salt, sugar and quinine solutions with the tips of their tarsi but the receptors are not completely known. They may be certain cupola-shaped, innervated invaginations, the so-called tarsal organs.

A sense of taste in the mouth region has been demonstrated in the orb weaver, *Araneus diadematus,* by flavoring flies with quinine; the spider also rejects elder pith but not elder pith saturated with broth or internal organs of flies. It is believed that the sensory cells are pores on the periphery of gland openings on the anterior of the endites of the pedipalpi.

A sense of gravity has been demonstrated in the cross spider, *Araneus diadematus.* The method used was to train the spider by throwing flies into the upper parts of the orb web for several days. The spider had to climb to retrieve the fly and descend with it. Then, if the web frame were turned 180° when the spider reached the fly, the spider would descend with the prey rather than return to the middle of the web.

The funnel weaver, *Agelena,* can sense the tension of the web. The spider made a horizontal web (Fig. 11–22) in a frame (30 × 30 × 10 cm) with hinged corners. When a fly was thrown into the web, the spider would leave its tube, capture the fly and return with it. This was also done by those spiders blinded with black lacquer. After several weeks the frame was deformed slightly while the spider killed the fly, and instead of returning to its retreat, the spider followed that diagonal of the frame having the greatest tension.

Receptors specific to tension or gravity have not been located. It is possible that the lyriform organs account for sensitivity to both. *Agelena* can orient kinesthetically on its web in optically uniform surroundings (dark room, illumination vertically from above), the web surrounded by a high cardboard cylinder. If first attracted to a fly tied down, permitted to feed for a short while, then chased into its funnnel by blowing, the spider makes searching movements and returns by the shortest route to her prey (which had since been removed). Even if first attracted to the fly via a detour, using a tuning fork, the spider after being chased away into its funnel will return by the shortest way. After being lifted and placed in the opposite corner of the web or into a strange web, the spider still makes searching movements into the learned direction (excluding the possibility that the spider orients knowing the tensions of his web). Such evidence suggests that the spider probably finds its way by memory of its own movements.

A sense of vibration that attracts spiders to prey caught in webs has been located in sensory slits at the ends of the metatarsi of walking legs (*Araneus, Zygiella, Tegenaria,* and *Amaurobius*) and it has been examined electrophysiologically in autotomized legs. Web spiders can sense irregular vibrations and vibrations at different frequencies, thus the struggling of a potential prey or the web plucking of a male.

Araneus diadematus can be trained to discriminate between the vibrations of C and C′ tuning forks by association with acceptable and distasteful (quinine-soaked) flies. Learning was complete after 15 trials and learned behavior could be elicited after an interval of several weeks.

Low notes of sound up to 9000 Hz (cps) are probably sensed by vibrations of the web. *Tegenaria atrica* responds to irregular waves at 10 Hz and higher frequencies to 100 Hz.

Particular lyriform organs on the distal ends of tibiae of the house cobweb spider, *Achaearanea tepidariorum,* have been found sensitive to high frequencies, and could be tuned by flexing the leg. The method used was to insert tungsten electrodes into the nerve of a separated leg preparation. Sensitivity to airborne sounds must be considered separately from sensitivity to sounds transmitted through the web.

Vision is important in jumping spiders, wolf spiders, crab spiders and for the funnel weaver, *Agelena*. In most other spiders the importance of the eyes is unknown; often, probably, they are relatively unimportant. The morphology of eyes is illustrated in Fig. 11–6. *Agelena* orients by seeing large light and dark areas in her surroundings. If one places a black screen on the right side of her horizontal web and a white screen on the left side, then feeds the spider for a week, exchanging the two screens will cause the spider to become disoriented in returning to her retreat.

Some spiders are able to orient themselves astronomically. That is, they recognize a particular direction on the basis of the position of the sun or of polarized light of the sky. The percentage of polarized light from the blue sky increases to 60–70% at an angle of 90° (or: as the angle from the sun approaches 90°) from the sun then is reduced again at greater angles. If we could perceive the direction of vibration and the intensity (percentage) of polarization we would see in the sky a complicated pattern that moves in unison with the sun.

Orientation by sun position and by polarized light has been particularly studied in Italy in the wolf spider, *Arctosa variana*, which lives on a stream bank. The spiders can run on the water surface and, if chased away from the bank, will return by the shortest route. They retain this direction even if transplanted, so if taken from their bank to the opposite bank and put on the water they do not go to the closest bank but out across the stream. However, the flight direction is not innate; on the new bank within 8–10 days they will learn the new direction. If the spider's view toward the sun is shielded and the sunlight is reflected with a mirror from different azimuths, the flight direction of the spider can be changed at will. If the spider is placed in the shade so that it cannot see the sun, its direction of flight is retained; if a polaroid sheet held above the spider is turned, the flight direction changes.

This mechanism of orientation is based on a circadian clock (or diurnal physiological rhythm). The spiders compensate the apparent movement of the sun, varying the angle of orientation accordingly. The course of this endogenous rhythm is controlled by the daily alternation of light and darkness, but it persists in the dark within certain time limits. By subjecting the animals to a day artificially shifted with respect to the normal day, predictable deviations in the direction of flight are obtained.

If Italian *Arctosa cinerea* are brought into the polar regions of Finland where the sun is continuously visible for the whole month of July, they are confused at night, in contrast to native individuals of *Arctosa cinerea* and *Pardosa fluviatilis* which are capable of orientation throughout the 24 hours.

If *Arctosa* is placed for several hours in the refrigerator at 4–5°C it will orient when released in the way that would have been correct several hours earlier; thus the internal clock was slowed.

If *Agelena,* as it arrives at the prey, is covered by a polaroid filter that turns the plane of polarized light, in 27% of the experiments the spider becomes confused in returning to the retreat. In another experiment, a spider is accustomed to controlled light conditions; that is, a polaroid filter under a 40 W lamp. If the filter is turned 90° after the prey has been bitten, the spider fails to return by the shortest route in 70% of the experiments. Other means of orientation seem to be secondary.

By gluing small tubes over the eyes of the spider, it can be shown that the orientation stimuli come from sky light and not from light reflected from the webs. The perception of the polarized light, then, is intraocular. Selective shielding of the eyes shows that the anterior median eyes are of paramount importance in orientation by polarized light. In *Arctosa* the electroretinogram of the anterior and posterior median eyes stimulated by polarized light changes in amplitude if the plane of polarized light is turned.

The eyes are of importance in the predatory activity of the diurnal hunting spiders. As a crab spider in ambush on a flowerhead follows passing insects with its anterior median eyes, an observer can easily see the back portion of the eye shift, the dark eye pigment being visible through the light integument. The spider slowly lifts the anterior legs when a butterfly is within 20 cm or when a bumblebee passes within 5 cm. Of course, as in most other arthropods, this is probably not recognition of the shape of the insect but awareness of movement.

The eyes of most spiders (with the exception of the Salticidae and Dinopidae) are so small that the image on the retina is minute. The small number of retinal cells divide the picture into a screen of dots, at best 1°, usually 3° to 7° apart with the result that resolution is poor. (The cones of the human fovea centralis are 25″ to 40″ apart; retinal cells number about 80 million). In the eye of *Pardosa* there are about 5000 retinal cells, in the eye of *Tegenaria,* only about 400.

Jumping spider (Salticidae) eyes differ. Besides the lateral eyes with short focal points there is one pair of very large and long anterior median eyes (Fig. 11–6). Because of their size and long focal length, they produce a large picture and an image of high resolution. The small field of vision of such a system is compensated by muscles that move the retina. Also the spider can turn the prosoma toward moving objects that appear in the other eyes, which have a large combined field of vision. The main eyes might be said to correspond to the fovea centralis of the human eye, the lateral eyes to the periphery of the human retina.

Thus in strange surroundings a jumping spider behaves more like a visual bird than like a typical arthropod. In a new container it does not run over the surface, testing the walls and floors, but stays in one place lifting and moving the prosoma around, scanning the surroundings with the main eyes.

Of a 5 mm long jumping spider the diameter of the lens is 0.29 mm, the focal distance 0.77 mm, the visual angle of the rhabdoms in the middle, 12′. The corresponding figures for the anterior lateral eyes are 0.11 mm, 0.33 mm and 35′, and for a posterior lateral eye, 0.11 mm, 0.24 mm, and 2°

The picture of a fly sitting 8 cm away covers as many visual cells in the main eyes of a jumping spider as the picture of a fly 100 cm away from the human fovea centralis. There is no accommodation. As a result of the small aperture the picture is almost always in focus; thus the infinity focus will also give clear pictures of objects close to the eye. Also the angle of the rhabdoms is too coarse to show details of the picture.

A jumping spider becomes aware of a moving object 20 cm away through the side eyes, brings the moving insect into the visual field of the main eyes, approaches slowly, and jumps on the prey from a distance of 1.5 to 5 cm. A fly that is not moving may be stalked. That the senses are mainly visual can be demonstrated by using picture of silhouettes. Presented with a moving silhouette of a female of the same species, 96% of *Evarcha* males respond with display, while only 9% react to a black disc with a diagonal line.

The functional relationship of anterior median and other eyes of jumping spiders was examined in alleylike surroundings. When one wall had vertical stripes of equal width at regular intervals and the opposing wall was plain white or colored, the salticid turned to the striped wall and jumped up. If the striped wall was then moved along the alley, movement of the main eyes could be seen. This happened even if the main eyes were covered, the stimulation resulting from information received from the lateral eyes via the protocerebrum. If all walls of the alley have stripes but one wall is moving, the spider will jump on a resting wall. The spider can separate images of the external shifts of the surroundings from the sensory input signals from the animal's own movements. The neural messages from the own movements are presumably integrated with the image shifts of the lateral eyes caused by messages from the environment.

Knowing the spider will jump onto the patterned wall, one can test color vision by a similar setup. An even colored wall was opposed by one with orange stripes on a gray background. The orange color was alternated with 26 different shades of gray in 1300 experiments. In 82–100% of the trials, *Evarcha* climbed the striped wall. Therefore the stripes must have been recognized as different colors and not just as differences in brightness. Similar experiments using vertical blue stripes gave similar results.

HUNTING. All spiders are predators, most feeding on insects; some, as the Mimetidae and Archaeidae, are specialized for feeding on other spiders. Nursery web spiders have been observed to catch small fish and tadpoles in addition to insects; large mygalomorph spiders (Orthognatha) feed on large insects and occasionally on nestling birds or other vertebrates. Many spiders may occasionally catch small vertebrates, although none feeds mainly on vertebrates. Dwarf spiders, *Erigone* sp. (Micryphantinae), of European ocean coasts appear to feed mainly on oligochaete worms. The prey species of *Linyphia triangularis* show a constant change over the season, new and unfamiliar species being at first rejected, but later accepted as they become more frequently captured.

Prey is found by nocturnal hunting spiders (most large mygalomorphs, Clubionidae and Gnaphosidae) by direct touch of tarsi and is rapidly caught with chelicerae and probably sometimes also the legs. Crab spiders ambush insects, first noticed visually and then caught with the large first legs and chelicerae, while jumping spiders stalk flies and jump on them. Wolf spiders running on the ground plunge at prey or may jump on it.

The crab spider, *Misumena vatia*, 8 mm long with chelicerae 1.4 mm and fangs 0.6 mm long, frequently takes honeybees at the thorax and holds the fighting prey for 2 minutes until the poison slows the bee down.

VENOM. With the exception of the Uloboridae, all spiders have poison glands. The venom of many spiders is lethal to insect prey, and that of a few may also affect vertebrates and man. Different protein fractions of black widow (*Latrodectus mactans*) poison, separated by electrophoresis, are lethal to insects and neurotoxic to mammals. The abundance of mimics of *Latrodectus* found in the Mediterranean area would suggest that the poison is of selective advantage in defense against visual vertebrate predators, probably lizards.

The best known poisonous spiders are the widows or malmignatte (*Latrodectus*); species are found in most parts of the world except for central Europe and northern Eurasia. The neurotoxin is extremely painful, rarely lethal to man. The bite often goes unnoticed and its symptoms can be confused with those of appendicitis. The Mediterranean *Steatoda paykulliana* is slightly poisonous to laboratory mammals. Another genus with poisonous members widespread in the Americas is the brown spider *Loxosceles*, the bite of which produces a necrotic lesion; bites of the large South American *L. laeta* may be very serious. The ctenid *Phoneutria fera* is feared in southeastern Brazil. The bite of the Australian diplurid funnel weaver *Atrax* is dangerous. Species of *Chiracanthium* (Clubionidae) found in all parts of the world may be poisonous. Most large Orthognatha, called "tarantula" in North America, are not poisonous; some species in other parts of the world may be. The hairs of many, however, are urticating.

Members of the family Scytodidae squirt the secretion of their poison glands at prospective prey. *Scytodes* closes in to a distance of about 1 cm from a fly, lifts the prosoma slightly, vibrates the chelicerae and the fly suddenly appears to be stuck. It has been glued to the substrate by zigzag threads squirted over it (Fig. 11–21). Unlike other spiders, *Scytodes* has the opening of the poison gland in the middle on the convex side of the short fang. The glands are large,

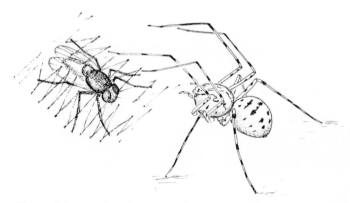

Fig. 11–21.   The spitting spider, *Scytodes thoracica*, body 4.5 mm. (After Bristowe.)

filling the characteristically domed prosoma. The spraying takes less than ⅙ of a second.

WEBS. Silk from glands associated with the spinnerets is commonly used to capture prey. The Gnaphosidae simply run rapidly around their prey, pulling a wide web of silk strands over the prey's legs. Tropical Hersiliidae wait in ambush, head down, appressed against the bark of trees or walls of houses, their long legs spread out. They jump over prospective prey, pinning it down with the silk from their long spinnerets, then circle around the prey, facing away, while the spinnerets cover it with silk. Oecobiids have been observed to make similar attacks. In these examples the silk is used only in the process of catching prey, but most web spiders construct a trap for prospective prey.

The simplest traps are those of spiders that live in tubes with threads radiating from the opening (Mesothelae, trapdoor spiders, *Ariadna, Segestria, Filistata*) (Fig. 11–23). Passing insects stumble over the radiating threads and the vibration alerts the spider in the silken tube and helps it orient toward prey. The more complicated sheet web, a funnel web widened at the mouth of the tube (Fig. 11–22), is made by the grass funnel weavers, *Agelenopsis* and *Agelena*. In *Agelena* some lines just above the sheet trip insects and prevent them from walking over the web. Such webs evolved convergently in both the funnel weavers, Agelenidae, and the funnel web mygalomorphs, Dipluridae.

The production of sticky threads that cling to the prey is more refined. An ant running against a viscous thread of the theridiid spider *Achaearanea saxatile* may stick to it, in struggling break it, and by its elasticity be pulled up into the center of the web. Sometimes sticky silk is used to subdue prey as in the theridiids that, from some distance, cover insects caught in the web with a

Fig. 11–22.   Funnel web of *Agelenopsis*, 40 cm wide.

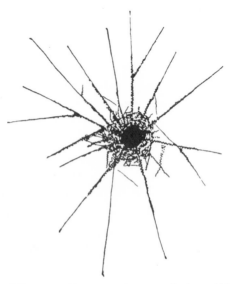

Fig. 11–23.   *Filistata insidiatrix* web, natural size. (After Wiehle.)

sheet of sticky silk threads pulled out of the spinnerets with their last legs. A 6 mm *Theridion* can easily wrap a large struggling bluebottle fly.

While hunting spiders often have only two claws, web spiders have three (Fig. 11–25a) at the tip of each leg. The median one is usually smooth. All three claws can pivot backward and forward on a terminal sclerite, the pretarsus (Fig. 11–25a). On the distal end of the last tarsal segment in the Araneoidea are a set of strong, flexible, toothed setae (the accessory claws). Together the median claw and these toothed setae manipulate silk. When the pretarsus is moved forward, the median claw hooks over the silk and firmly holds it against the tooth setae (Fig. 11–25b). The grip is relaxed by raising the median claw, which has to be moved back to free the silk.

Usually the sticky threads are used as part of the web. There are two kinds, true viscid threads of the Araneidae, Linyphiidae and Theridiidae (Fig. 11–28), and cribellate threads. The viscid threads consist of two threads covered with glue that balls into rows of minute droplets. Cribellate or hackled threads, produced by Cribellatae (Fig. 11–24), consist of several threads covered by a broad band of minute curled threads, 10–20 μm thick, the true nature of which was revealed by the electron microscope. The fine threads entangle the setae of insects when only lightly touched and each movement entangles further. This thread is produced by numerous spigots of the cribellum (Fig. 11–11). The spider, moving slowly, puts down a two-strand baseline while holding the metatarsus of one last leg across the cribellum, supporting its tarsus on the other last leg. Moving the metatarsus forward, several times each second, the spider lifts the cribellate threads with a row of curved metatarsal setae (the calamistrum) and brushes them onto the double base line (Fig. 11–25c). Many of the cribellate Dictynidae pull long threads from their retreats to plants and connect these with radii or bridges covered with cribellate threads (Fig. 11–26). Thus a trap is built near the spider's retreat, possibly an intermediate stage in the evolution toward an orb web. It is of interest that these complicated orb webs are made by members of two unrelated families, the Araneidae and the cribellate Uloboridae. The orb weavers, Araneidae, cover their spiral threads with glue condensed into minute droplets, while the cribellate Uloboridae cover their spiral threads with fine cribellate threads. The webs catch flying insects that cannot see the trap.

In building its orb web *Araneus* first establishes a bridge between twigs or stems. The bridge may start with an aimless thread carried by wind until it catches; it is tightened and second or third threads are added. From the middle of the bridge the spider drops on a thread and tightens it, forming a "Y." Frame threads are constructed, and to make the radii (spokes) the spider starts from the center, walks up a spoke, lets herself down a frame thread, tightens and fastens the thread she carries. The radii are laid in approximately alternate directions. The spider, sitting in the middle, probably can sense the angle be-

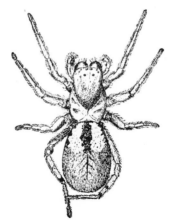

Fig. 11-24. *Amaurobius fenestralis* laying down a cribellate thread; spider 0.7 cm long. (After Nielsen.)

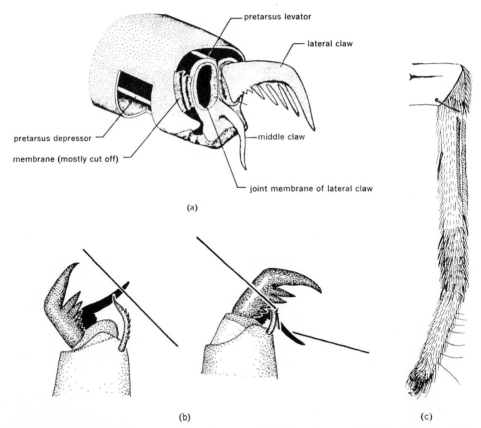

Fig. 11-25. (a) Leg claws of *Zygiella*, one lateral claw removed; 0.3 mm long (from Frank); (b) leg claws of *Araneus*, left open, right holding silk (one claw and one accessory claw removed) (after Wilson); (c) calamistrum of *Amaurobius ferox*; the tarsus, about 5 mm long, has 7 trichobothria. (After Wiehle.)

tween two adjacent radii by gripping each with the first legs. Gaps in the web are probably sensed by probing with the first legs. Other characteristics of the strands (elasticity, tension) may or may not be sensed. The temporary spiral (Fig. 11–27) is laid as the spider moves from the center outward in ever larger circles, connecting the spokes in a temporary spiral scaffolding. The spiral of viscid thread is then laid down from the outside inward. The viscid threads are much more closely spaced than the scaffolding, which is removed as the viscid spiral is laid. Because the sticky droplets on the viscid silk dry in one or two days the spiral thread must be renewed at frequent intervals. Most of the frame threads are used again, and the old thread is eaten by the spider or is hung up. Most species immediately repair spokes torn during the day.

Under favorable conditions a web may be rebuilt every day. The silk from the old web is eaten. By using labeled (radioactive) materials, it could be determined that proteins from the silk that was eaten were in the lumen of the silk glands within a day.

The building of an orb web is not learned behavior. Araneid spiderlings spin complete orbs immediately upon hatching. In some species the webs change as the spiders mature.

Lacquering the eyes does not influence web building. The webs are normally built late at night or early morning before dawn. By varying light and temperature, one controlling factor was found: *Zygiella x-notata* prefers to build at the minimum temperature. Rise in temperature and heavy feeding inhibit web building. Hungry spiders build more frequently and build larger webs with more widely spaced spirals. A starving spider whose web was removed daily

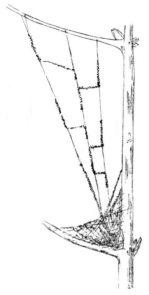

Fig. 11–26. Web of *Dictyna arundinacea*, radii 5–6 cm. (After Wiehle.)

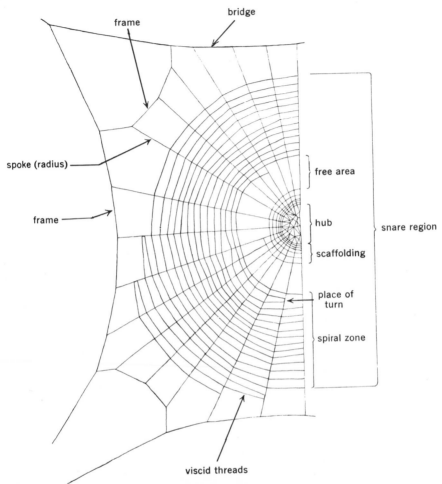

Fig. 11–27.   Orb web, diagrammatic, diameter 30 cm. (After Wiehle.)

built a web of about the same size for 6 days; after 10 days, smaller webs were built while the spider's body weight decreased. After feeding, the webs stayed small for 10 days while the spider gained weight.

Both depressant drugs and stimulants fed to the spider will change the structure of the web in characteristic ways.

In an orb web the angles of the radii in the upper part of the web are larger than those in the lower part, the spiral turns are more widely spaced above than below. If the web is turned 90° as it is being built (radii being added) in a frame in the laboratory, the spider will make additional spirals at the new bottom part. The spider in an orb web can sense insects on the web more than 30 cm away. The female spider responds to the male's plucking signal on his approach. She will also react to airborne sounds. (Most of these experiments were made with the spiders *Araneus diadematus* and *Zygiella x-notata*, both Araneidae.)

Moths and butterflies are beautifully adapted to avoid capture. Their wing scales stick to the viscid threads while the insect escapes. In a study of prey of *Argiope argentata* about 50% of Lepidoptera escaped. Those that did not were handled very differently from other insects: they were given a long bite before being wrapped in silk; other insects are swathed in silk first. Judging by various experiments the spider seems to recognize moths and butterflies by texture. (M. Robinson, personal communication.)

Cobweb spiders (Theridiidae) such as *Steatoda* make a loose horizontal web with vertical threads above and below (Fig. 11–28). The vertical threads are strung under high tension and thus break and contract when an insect runs against them. These sticky threads which are around the web have sticky droplets on them which adhere to the struggling insect. Further struggling just breaks more entangling threads before the spider comes and wraps the prey in silk. The house spider *Achaearanea tepidariorum* selects web sites at random; if the sites do not produce prey they are abandoned and a new site is chosen. The spider will remain at a site where prey is sufficiently abundant.

The sheet web weavers, Linyphiidae, make a horizontal or cupola-shaped sheet (Fig. 11–29) with dense vertical threads above and fewer below; some

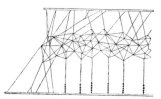

Fig. 11–28. Web of *Steatoda castanea* (=*Teutana castanea*) from the side, 3 cm high. (After Wiehle.)

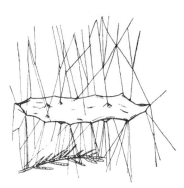

Fig. 11–29. Sheet web of *Linyphia*, 20 cm long. (After Kaestner.)

threads below are covered by sticky droplets. Insects flying against the threads above fall on the horizontal part and the few threads there permit the spider to run on the underside of the sheet and bite through it if an insect gets entangled.

Some spiders can rapidly tighten and loosen their webs. The triangle spider *Hyptiotes* (Uloboridae) makes a triangular web with only 3 sectors. A long signal thread held by the spider's claws of the first leg (Fig. 11–30) is attached to the point of meeting of the 4 radii. The spider attaches its spinnerets to a branch by a thread which is held by the 4th leg. The spider always bridges a gap. When an insect flies into the web, the spider immediately lets out silk from its spinnerets, reducing the tension on the "signal line" and therefore on the whole web. This increases the chances of the prey becoming entangled. *Theridiosoma* uses a spring trap of similar design.

The tropical *Miagrammopes* stretches a single horizontal thread 1 m, or sometimes 2–3 m long, the center of which is covered with cribellate silk. When loosened in the same way as *Hyptiotes* it can entangle a bluebottle fly. The small *Phoroncidia* (=*Ulesanis*) uses a similar thread but on a reduced scale.

Ogre-faced spiders, Dinopidae, prey in a different way. They spin a small rectangle covered with cribellate threads (Fig. 11–31). The 4 anterior legs hold

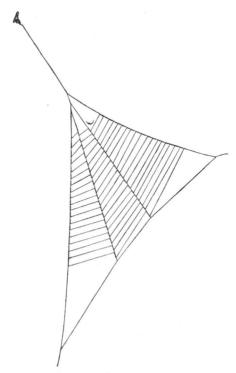

Fig. 11–30.   Web of *Hyptiotes paradoxus*, spider at left at end of thread; length 30 cm. (After Wiehle.)

the corners. If an insect approaches, the spider spreads the web 5–6 times its width and moves toward the insect, entangling it.

The dinopid web is made below a bridge (Fig. 11–31a, heavy lines) between the branches of a shrub. The first frame thread goes from A to C, the second from B to D. Threads 3 and 4 are attached about 2 cm below the previous threads. Last, threads 7 and 8 are made. While facing upward, the spider tightens the web with cross strands. Then the array of cribellate threads is laid (Fig. 11–31b, c). This all takes about 7 minutes. The spider now breaks vertical threads, 1 below A, thus freeing the elastic threads from all vertical lines (d). Now the spider backs up, holding threads 3, 4, 5 and 6 with the first and second legs, stretching the snare to several times its original size. While hanging at an angle of 45°, the spider holds the snare loosely, the third legs resting on threads 1 and 2. At the close approach of a flying insect, signalled by vibration or air-current, the spider stretches the web several times. Small drosophila-sized insects are taken from the web directly with palpi; large captives are wrapped with swathing silk and what remains of the snare. At daybreak the spider abandons the web or eats it, and returns to its resting place along a branch, appressed parallel to the branch. (After Theuer, unpubl.)

A very reduced web, consisting of a single thread, is constructed by certain orb weavers, the bolas spiders, including *Mastophora* in America, *Dicrostichus* in Australia, and *Cladomelea* in Africa. The spiders hang at night on a horizontal thread to which is attached a pendulant thread with a droplet of glue at the free end. African and Australian bolas spiders swing the bolas intermittently in a circle before taking off the insects stuck to it. *Mastophora* waits, motionless, until a moth passes, then swings the bolas in the direction of the moth.

Theridiid spiders of the genus *Argyrodes* live as symbionts in the webs of orb weavers, other theridiids, linyphiids, or pholcids. *Argyrodes* connects its own minute web to that of the host, and takes small insects caught in the periphery of the host's web or may join the host and feed at the other end of the captured prey. *Argyrodes argyrodes* cannot be raised without the web of a host. Some individuals have been observed from hatching until egg sac construction in the web of the host, *Cyrtophora*.

FEEDING AND DIGESTION. While hunting spiders feed immediately after capturing prey, orb weavers and some others may wrap their prey first in silk. Digestive juice from the midgut (and also probably poison glands) penetrate into the wounds, rapidly digesting proteins which are then pumped in before new digestive juices emerge. The endites prevent the juice from running over the sternum, its setae and spines and those of the labrum prevent large particles from entering the gut. A second filter is in the pharynx, the anterior wall of which has a series of transverse ribs that screen out particles.

All species lacking teeth on the chelicerae suck up liquid nutrient only and the empty exoskeleton of the prey is dropped or hung up in perfect condition.

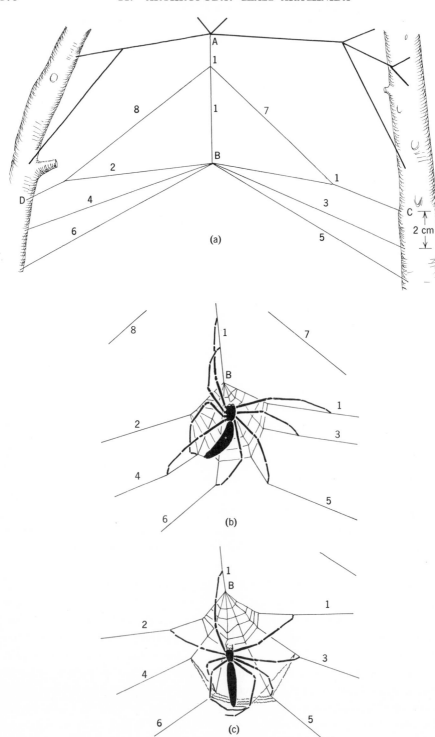

(a)

(b)

(c)

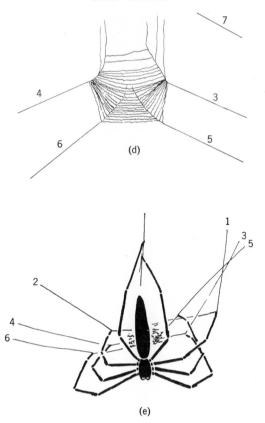

Fig. 11–31. Construction of a *Dinopis spinosus* web: (a) guy lines; distance between branches, 25 cm; (b) tightening of guy lines; (c) beginning of cribellate strands; (d) finished web; (e) spider holding snare; spider 2 cm long. (After Theuer, unpubl. thesis, courtesy of Prof. H. K. Wallace.)

Many (*Pholcus, Latrodectus, Filistata, Eresus*) simply bite into the leg of the prey and through it pump digestive juice into the body; the digested soft parts are then sucked out again. *Latrodectus* may suck out June beetles (Scarabidae) several times its size. Spiders with cheliceral teeth opposite the fang (Fig. 11–1b) chew up the prey until the exoskeleton is completely mangled. Most Theraphosidae, orb weavers, agelenid funnel weavers, and wolf spiders chew their prey. Sometimes the chewed up ball is dipped into water before being discarded, and captive spiders often discard it in the water container.

The flattened pharynx and pumping stomach pump rhythmically at certain intervals. In *Tegenaria domestica* each pumping period lasts 1–2 minutes; the consumption of a whole fly takes almost 3 hours. In transparent spiders it can be seen that the ceca of the abdomen contract rhythmically, producing additional suction. The epithelium of the ceca serves both for further digestion and for absorption. Glandular cells secrete into the lumen of the cecum while nutrient cells take up food mash and digest it intracellularly.

In extracts of prosomal and abdominal ceca of Theraphosidae there are proteinases, amylases and lipases. The food material is transported into the cellular connective tissue which surrounds all ceca and is stored there. Fecal material accumulates at the tips of nutrient cells which constrict, break off and, with the excretory material, fall into the lumen and pass via the midgut to the cloaca to be sorted with excretory material from the Malpighian tubules until finally deposited.

Many spiders regularly drink water.

RESPIRATION. The spiracles in most spiders are narrow slits that can be closed, a protection against transpiration. They are opened if touched by a stream of CO_2 or a drop of water. The CO_2 concentration within the atrium controls the spiracle opening. Plugging the book lung spiracles of *Tegenaria domestica* with vaseline immobilized the spider in 6 minutes; the heart stopped beating after 100 minutes. Presence of hemocyanin has been demonstrated in the hemolymph of several spiders.

CIRCULATION AND MOVEMENT. In spiders and probably other chelicerates the circulatory system serves the additional function of extending the legs. While flexor muscles are present, extensors are absent in most joints. The remarkably high blood pressure of 130 mm Hg (and increases are common) has been measured by cutting a leg of the funnel weaver *Tegenaria agrestis*, catching the blood on filter paper, and weighing it to calculate the blood loss per minute. Then another leg was removed and known pressures applied to obtain similar flow. The pressure necessary to break the exoskeleton of a spider about to molt was calculated to be 260 mm Hg by this method, by applying pressure to an anesthetized spider, and by finding the tearing strength. Similar pressure readings were obtained for the funnel weaver *Tegenaria atrica* by sealing the leg into a sleeve and applying known pressures until the joint membrane collapsed. The pressures measured 50 to 110 mm Hg, but reached 240–450 mm Hg for short periods when the spider was stimulated. Evidence that extensor muscles really are lacking and have not been overlooked is that thirsty spiders, spiders that have had the carapace punctured, and dying spiders hold the legs in flexed position. This is not true in arthropods that have extensor muscles; a wasp with the abdomen removed may still be able to walk about.

Classification

Spiders are grouped on the basis of differences in the cheliceral attachment and the presence or absence of an epigynum and of a cribellum (Fig. 11–11) and calamistrum. Some arachnologists consider the cribellate families more closely related to the ecribellates than to each other: the Uloboridae build orb webs similar to those of the noncribellate Araneidae, the cribellate Acanthoc-

tenidae closely resemble the noncribellate Ctenidae, and the cribellate Amaurobiidae are similar to the noncribellate Agelenidae. Others, however, observing
that only a few families of cribellate spiders fit easily into either the Orthognatha
or Labidognatha, consider the Cribellatae to represent a separate branch. Further evidence of their separate, parallel evolution is seen in certain peculiarities
reported for the abdominal musculature: cribellates all are thought to have 4
pairs of dorsoventral muscles in segments 8 to 11 and median dorsal row of
unpaired longitudinal muscles in the juvenile. A very recent study of the musculature of spinnerets and the venter of the abdomen (Peters, 1967) of *Amaurobius,*
Psechrus, and various ecribellates gives added support.

Spider nomenclature starts with C. Clerck, 1757, Aranei Suecici, rather than with
Linnaeus' 10th edition of *Regnum Animale Systema Naturae,* 1758.°

The spellings for generic names here follow accustomed usage as in Bonnet's *Bibliographia Araneorum*† (rather than the seldom used spellings of Roewer's *Katalog der
Araneae*), in keeping with the spirit "to promote stability and universality of scientific
names of animals," expressed in the Preamble of the *International Code on Zoological
Nomenclature.*

In case two or more names for a family are in use, the name adopted here is the one
correct according to the International Code on Zoological Nomenclature (1961).

SUBORDER MESOTHELAE

Although the prosoma is covered by a carapace, the abdomen is clearly segmented
dorsally from VII (pedicel) to XVIII. The spinnerets are in the middle of the venter
(Fig. 11–1). The chelicerae are orthognath (paraxial) and the pedipalpal coxae lack
endites. The fused prosomal ganglia number 18, but are more distinct than in higher
spiders. The heart has 5 pairs of ostia, located in metameres VIII to XII. There are 2
pairs of book lungs. The nine Recent species, from 1–3.5 cm long, occur in southeastern
Asia to southern Japan, and live in trapdoor tubes.

Liphistiidae‡ is the only family. *Liphistius,*‡ to 3.5 cm long, inhabits a tube as deep as
60 cm, widened at the end to form a chamber. From the opening of the tube there
are 6–8 radial threads that may serve to trip potential prey. The spider sits underneath

° This exception is in accord with a provision to the International Code on Zoological
Nomenclature, Article 26, passed by the International Commission on Zoological Nomenclature,
1948, and the International Zoological Congress, and published in the *Bull. Zool. Nomencl.*
4(10–12):315–319. After the International Congress of Zoology in London in 1958 adopted
a new code, Clerck's work was placed on the Official List of Works by Direction 104 of the
International Commission on Zoological Nomenclature (1959, *Bll. Zool. Nomencl.* 17(3–5):
89–91).

† An exception is the generic name, *Theridion,* the current spelling of which was placed on
the Official List of Generic Names in Zoology by Opinion 517 of the International Commission
in 1958.

‡ Application has been made to the International Commission on Zoological Nomenclature
to place the name Liphistiidae on the Official List of Family Names in Zoology and the name
Liphistius on the Official List of Generic Names. Existing usage is to be maintained while the
case is under consideration (Art. 80, *Internat. Code Zool. Nomencl.*)

the trapdoor, holding it shut with its chelicerae. The egg sac, 3.2 cm in diameter, is made of silk encrusted with earth. *Heptathela* (Fig. 11–1) has horizontal silk-lined tubes, penetrating 10–15 cm into embankments.

SUBORDER ORTHOGNATHA, MYGALOMORPH SPIDERS

The chelicerae are paraxial or orthognath; that is, they are attached anterior to the carapace and move parallel to the long axis of body (except in Gradungulidae). The coxae of the pedipalpi are similar to those of the legs, except in Atypidae. There are 2 pairs of book lungs, usually 4, rarely 3 pairs of heart ostia. The bulb of the male pedipalp is simple and pear-shaped (Fig. 11-14). There is no epigynum. Neither cribellum nor calamistrum is present. Segments XIII to XVIII have lost their sternites. The spinnerets are at or near the posterior end of the body. Ganglia XIII to XVIII have disappeared the others are closely concentrated. The abdomen always has fewer than 4 pairs of dorsoventral muscles and has a pair of dorsal longitudinal muscles, at least in young spiders. Most species are large, long-lived, and most occur in warm countries; about one-third of the species are found in the Americas, from Alaska as far south as Tierra del Fuego.

Ctenizidae, Trapdoor Spiders. The trapdoor spiders have 3 tarsal claws. Their chelicerae have a rastellum or rake (Fig. 11-32), a row of spines used for digging. The labium and sternum are separated. The eyes are closely grouped. The abdomen lacks sclerites and is not hairy. Most species are 3 cm long or larger. The spider constructs a silk-lined tube in the ground, its entrance covered with a hinged silk lid, camouflaged outside and held shut by the spider, which preys on passing insects or woodlice. The tube is enlarged as the spider grows. *Nemesia* is found in southern Europe; its tube has blind lateral branches, sometimes separated from the main tube by a door. *Cyclocosmia,* found in the southeastern United States and China, has a truncate, heavily sclerotized and sculptured abdomen, which plugs the bottom of the tube and protects the soft prosoma should the tube be invaded. *Ummidia* and *Myrmeciophila* are common in the southeastern states, *Bothriocyrtum* in California. In an Australian *Aganippe* burrow, the remains of 13 frogs more than half the size of the spider were once found, the spider apparently having had an accidental vertebrate food source. *Aporoptychus* is found in Santa Cruz, southern Argentina.

Antrodiaetidae. There are 3 tarsal claws. The chelicerae have a rastellum, the abdomen has tergites and is not very hairy, and the anal tubercle is separated from the 4-6 spinnerets by a considerable distance. The door of the burrow is usually a low collar or turret that is collapsed inward when closed. *Antrodiaetus,* the adult female of which measures 15 to 25 mm, occurs from eastern New York to the Pacific Coast and north to Alaska, and south to the Gulf States.

Actinopodidae, Trapdoor Spiders. The leg tarsi bear 3 claws. The chelicerae have a rastellum, and the labium is fused to the sternum. Unlike Ctenizidae, Actinopodidae have the eye region extending across the width of the carapace anteriorly. *Actinopus* occurs in Argentina, other genera in Africa and Australia.

Dipluridae, Funnelweb Mygalomorphs. The leg tarsi bear 3 claws. The chelicerae lack a rastellum. The carapace is flat; there are 4 or 6 spinnerets, the posterior (lateral) spinnerets being very long with 3 segments of equal length. The body is hairy. The funnelweb is similar to that of the Agelenidae. *Diplura, Hexathele, Evagrus* and the much-feared Australian *Atrax* belong to this family. *Trechona* of South America is poisonous but rarely comes into contact with man. *Accola* is another genus. The North American *Microhexura* is only 3 mm long.

Mecicobothriidae, Funnelweb Mygalomorphs. The legs have 3 tarsal claws. The chelicerae lack a rastellum. The carapace is flat, the abdomen always has sclerites indicating the border of segments. There are 6 spinnerets, 2 pairs short and 1 long; the anal tubercle is separated from the very long posterior spinnerets. They live among leaves or under logs, where they construct a funnel web. *Hexura,* 12 mm long, occurs along the North American Pacific coast to Washington.

Migidae, Funnelweb Mygalomorphs. There are 3 tarsal claws. Chelicerae lack a rastellum; the labium is fused to the sternum (as in atypids). There are only 4 spinnerets. All occur in the southern hemisphere. *Calathotarsus* is known from Chile.

Atypidae, Purseweb Spiders. There are 3 tarsal leg claws. The coxae have endites, unlike those of other Orthognatha; there are six spinnerets. The few species all are less than 3 cm long. *Atypus* is found in eastern United States, northern Europe, Burma, Java and Japan. It constructs an open silk tube that extends into a hole and up the outside of a tree trunk in American species or along the ground in European species. When an insect settles on the above-ground portion of the tube the spider bites through the silk, tears the tube and pulls the prey inside.

Theraphosidae (Aviculariidae). There are only 2 tarsal claws. Usually called "tarantulas" in the United States, these are very large, hairy, non-social nocturnal spiders with claw tufts, 4 spinnerets, and 8 eyes closely grouped. Most are found in the tropics and feed on large insects or occasionally on amphibians, reptiles or nestling birds. They rear up defensively when disturbed, raising the chelicerae, pedipalpi and first legs. Some produce noise at the same time by stridulation. Few if any species in the Americas are dangerously poisonous to man. The hairs of many species are urticating;

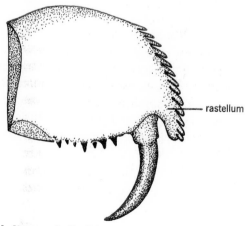

Fig. 11–32. **Left chelicera of *Bothriocyrtum* (Ctenidae), inside view, about 2 mm diameter.**

gradually lost from the dorsum of the abdomen, they are replaced at the next molt. Some, when disturbed, will actively rub the hairs off with the last legs; the irritating light hairs floating in the air, probably discouraging potential vertebrate predators. The large species mature in about 3–10 years; the males may live less than a year after becoming mature. Females live from 15 to 20 years (in captivity). North American species live in deep burrows. The members of the subfamily Aviculariinae lack spines on the legs and have long tarsi; they live in trees in the Amazon region. *Theraphosa* in the Amazon may attain a body length of 9 cm, leg span of 28 cm. *Grammostola* is almost as large. Numerous species of colorful *Aphonopelma* occur in the southwestern United States and Mexico. *Dugesiella hentzi* is common in south central United States. *Pamphobeteus* is included here.

Pycnothelidae. There are only 2 tarsal claws, but no claw hair tufts. The tarsi have scopulae; the labium is fused to the sternum but has a seam. The eyes are on a tubercle; there are 4 spinnerets. This family is found only from Brazil to Patagonia.

Paratropidae, Funnelweb Mygalomorphs. These have only 2 tarsal claws, but have claw hair tufts; there is neither rastellum (rake) nor palpal endites. The labium is fused to the sternum, which is wider than long. There are 2–4 spinnerets. The members of this family make a funnel web and are found in the Amazon region only.

Barychelidae. There are only 2 tarsal claws, but the chelicerae have a rastellum (rake) like that of the trapdoor spiders. They dig in soil or live on trees under bark, where they construct tubes. Representatives are found in South America, Australia, Africa and India.

Gradungulidae. Found only in Australia and New Zealand, members of this family have 3 claws, 2 pairs of book lungs, 4 pairs of heart ostia, 6 spinnerets, and a colulus. The chelicerae are intermediate between orthognath and labidognath placement and project forward. The palpal endites are well developed. The genital bulb of the male palpus is ventral and the females lack an epigynum. The nocturnal *Gradungula* hunt in moist forests and superficially resemble wolf spiders, but may possibly be related to the cribellate Hypochilidae. The tarsi of legs one and two have the anterior claw much longer than the posterior. The spiders make little use of silk.

SUBORDER LABIDOGNATHA, ARANEOMORPH SPIDERS

The chelicerae are labidognath (diaxial) and work like pliers against each other (Fig. 11-5). They are attached below the carapace. The pedipalpal coxae are modified as endites. There usually is only 1 pair of book lungs, sometimes replaced by tracheae, and in the 9th segment, 1 pair of lateral tracheae and usually also a pair of median tracheae derived from hollow apodemes. Both pairs open through a single median spiracle. The heart has 3, sometimes only 2, pairs of ostia. Neither cribellum nor calamistrum is present. Segments XIII to XVIII have lost their sternites and the spinnerets are usually at the posterior end of the abdomen. Ganglia XIII to XVIII are lacking, the others closely bunched. The abdomen always has fewer than 4 pairs of dorsoventral muscles, and has a pair of dorsal longitudinal muscles, at least in young spiders. The smallest species are only 0.7 mm long.

Group Haplogynae

The male palpus is comparatively simple and rigid (Fig. 11–14a). The entrance to the seminal receptacles is from the atrium inside the gonopore, and there is no epigynum. Many species are long-lived. Probably none balloon.

DYSDEROIDEA

Except in Caponiidae, there is no lamella along the cheliceral margin facing the fang. Except in Telemidae and Leptonetidae, the four spiracles are in two pairs close to each other.

Dysderidae. The 9th sternite is so short that the spiracles of the tracheae lie behind those of the book lungs. The 10th sternite is elongated. The tracheae are well developed sieve tracheae. The book lungs have few leaves (Fig. 8–13). There are only 6 eyes. *Dysdera,*° 1.4 cm long, makes a retreat between stones or at grass roots; nocturnal hunters, they feed on woodlice. *Segestria* lives under bark or in hollow trees. The wide end of the tube in which the spider lives continues as about 12 radially diverging threads over which potential prey stumbles. The other end of the funnel is open, providing an emergency exit. At night *Segestria* waits near the entrance. *Ariadna* has similar habits. Both rest holding 3 pairs of legs forward, the last pair back.

Oonopidae. These minute, mostly 6-eyed spiders, less than 3 mm long, have relatively short legs. They often lack lungs and have tracheal tubes extending into the prosoma. Many have sclera on the abdomen. They live in leaf litter. *Oonops* and *Orchestina* are included here.

Caponiidae. Book lungs are lacking, replaced by tracheae. There are only 2, rarely 8 eyes, closely spaced. The chelicera has a lamella opposing the fang. They are mainly found in warm climates.

Leptonetidae and Telemidae. These are cave spiders, leptonetids with 3 spiracles, telemids with 4.

SCYTODOIDEA

The chelicera has a lamella on the margin facing the fang.

Scytodidae, Spitting Spiders. The 6 eyes are arranged in 3 groups. The high domed carapace slopes forward; it accommodates the large poison and salivary glands. *Scytodes thoracica,* 5 mm long, is found in buildings of northern latitudes; other species are tropical. All spit at their prey or at potential enemies (Fig. 11–12). The secretion consists of a thread combined with a viscous substance, and may overpower or slow down larger animals. Pantropical *Scytodes fusca* occupies a web; other species hunt at night, moving slowly.

Loxoscelidae, Brown Spiders. These spiders have 6 eyes in 3 groups, as in Scytodidae, but have a low carapace and do not spit. They overpower their prey with poison after it becomes entangled in the irregular sheet web. The bite of all species of *Loxosceles* appears to be poisonous to mammals, causing an ulcerous growth in serious cases. Almost all bites reported are from the Americas. The brown recluse, *L. reclusa,* the North American species causing most accidents, is found from Georgia to central Indiana and west to eastern Texas. *L. laeta* is feared in some parts of South America. An individual of *Loxosceles laeta* lived more than 5 years in a terrarium (R. Wheeler, private communication); it was presumably adult when collected.

° The name *Dysdera* is on the Official List of Generic Names in Zoology.

Sicariidae. Six-eyed crab spiders are limited to the southern hemisphere except in America, where they are found as far north as Costa Rica. They have 6 eyes in 3 groups and hold the legs in a crablike position, laterigrade. They inhabit sandy or dusty sites. South African and perhaps American species make sounds. American species of *Sicarius* bury themselves under the surface of the sand.

Diguetidae. The 6 eyes are arranged in 3 groups. The long carapace and abdomen are covered with short hairs, giving them a colorful appearance. The spider lives in or underneath a vertical silk tube suspended in the center of a sheet of threads in shrubs. A loose mesh sheet extends nearly horizontally from the lower end of the tube. *Diguetia* are known only from the American southwest and Argentina.

Plectreuridae. The 8 eyes are arranged in 2 rows and the legs are heavy. They are found in the dry American southwest and eastern Mexico, hanging upside down in a loose web under stones.

Ochyroceratidae. Small spiders with 6 eyes closely grouped and 3 spiracles, they often inhabit caves. *Theotima* is parthenogenetic.

PHOLCOIDEA

These have 3 claws but do not have a complete epigynum. Despite lack of epigynum, this group is frequently placed with the entelegyne spiders because of the complicated male palpi. Probably the cellar spiders belong to a separate line of evolution. Further evidence for their not belonging to the haplogynes is seen in the different sexual behavior of the spiders, especially induction of sperm into the palpus.

Pholcidae, Daddy Longlegs Spiders. The tarsi of the long legs have many false articulations. All species lack tracheae. A swelling is present in the genital region of the female, but the entrance to the receptacles is in the vagina. They may make a loose cobweb. *Pholcus,* the cellar spider, to 1 cm long, shakes its web rapidly when disturbed, blurring the spider. A fly in the web is wound up in silk by the long fourth legs before it is bitten. *Spermophora* is the short bodied cellar spider.

Group Entelegynae

The male palpus is more complicated, with additional sclerites and inflatable haematodocha (Fig. 11–14b, c). The copulatory pores are separate from the gonopores, usually in a sclerotized plate, the epigynum, into which the papal parts are inserted in mating. Fertilization ducts connect the seminal receptacles with the vagina. Only a few groups lack the epigynum (Tetragnathidae). Most are short-lived, living only a season, or at most 2 years. Many are believed to be able to balloon at one stage in their life history.

ZODARIOIDEA

Representatives tend to have a reduced number of spinnerets; most have 3 tarsal claws on each leg.

Zodariidae. Members of this very heterogeneous family have 2, 4, or 6 spinnerets; some have only 2 claws. Most hunt on the ground. *Zodarion* and *Cryptothele* belong here.

Palpimanidae. Most have very strong front legs, which are held up in walking; there are usually only 2 spinnerets. They occur in warm climates.

HERSILIOIDEA

They have 3 leg claws. The posterior spinnerets have a long distal segment and the endites of the pedipalpi converge.

Hersiliidae. The posterior (lateral) spinnerets and legs are very long. These tropical spiders sit appressed to bark or walls, head down. *Hersilia* becomes 1–1.8 cm long.

Urocteidae. Members of this small Old World family have a large anal tubercle, short legs, and the eyes are close together, far back on the carapace. The abdomen often has bright markings. They construct silk tubes under stones. *Uroctea* is Mediterranean.

ARANEOIDEA

These have 3 leg claws. They are web spiders with anterior and posterior spinnerets short and conical, covering the smaller middle pair and forming a circle with the anal tubercle. In this superfamily our commonest spiders are included. The males of many species have very complex palpi (Fig. 11–14b).

Theridiidae, Cobweb Weavers or Comb-footed Spiders. The ventral comb of serrated bristles, usually found on the tarsi of the fourth legs, is used to throw threads over prey caught in the web. There are more than 1300 species, 0.1–1.5 cm long. *Theridion* has many species, a few with a dome- or thimble-shaped retreat. *Achaearanea tepidariorum* is the house spider of America. *Tidarren* has minute males that remove one of their huge palpi by twisting it off after the penultimate molt. *Argyrodes* (=*Conopistha*) lives as a symbiont in webs of other species. *Steatoda* (=*Teutana, Lithyphantes*) lives under bark or stones, sometimes in houses. *Phoroncidia* (=*Ulesanis*), 2 mm long, like *Hyptiotes* holds a horizontal sticky line that may have 1–3 vertical threads. *Latrodectus mactans* is the black widow or malmignatte, poisonous to mammals.

Linyphiidae, Sheetweb Weavers. Unlike most theridiids, linyphiids have many teeth on the chelicerae and chew their prey. The legs have many strong setae. *Linyphia* is a widespread genus. Micryphantinae, the dwarf spiders, include many species of the northern hemisphere and Arctic, most of them about 1–2.5 mm long. They are among the most common and abundant spiders in the northern hemisphere. *Erigone* and *Halorates* are included.

Symphytognathidae. Most of these are very small, many lack book lungs and many are heavily sclerotized. Females lack palpi or have palpi without claws. Some make an orb web, suggesting that the group is polyphyletic. They are more common in the southern hemisphere.

Hadrotarsidae. These are minute spiders with lungs reduced. Females have claws on palps. These is no colulus. The anterior median eyes are most developed, the posterior median eyes are bean-shaped. There are no teeth on the chelicerae.

Nesticidae. These possess a comb of serrated bristles on leg 4. Most species are light in color. They have teeth on the chelicerae. A large colulus is present, as in only a few

---

* The name Theridiidae is on the Official List of Family Group Names in Zoology. The names *Enoplognatha, Theridion, Latrodectus* are on the Official List of Generic Names in Zoology. The name *Theridium* has been suppressed. Placing the names *Argyrodes, Robertus,* and *Theonoe* on the List is under consideration by the Internat. Comm. Zool. Nomenclature.

Theridiidae and all Linyphiidae. They make a cobweb and carry their egg sacs attached to the spinnerets. Some live in caves or cellars. *Nesticus* is widespread.

Araneidae (Argiopidae),° *Orb Weavers.* The legs have many strong setae ("spines"), the chelicerae have many teeth. Most species make an orb web. More than 2500 species are known. *Araneus (=Aranea, Epeira)* is the largest spider genus. Some members sit in the center of the web at night and in the retreat, a rolled-up leaf, during the day. *Araneus diadematus,* the garden or cross spider (Fig. 11-33), originally European, has been introduced into North America; females reach 1.7 cm in length. The spider rests in the center of the web, and the vibrations of the prey in the web are transmitted through the spokes to the spider's legs. The spider turns to face the prey, and plucks at the threads. Experiments show that the spider can tell whether the prey has been caught and its approximate weight. It approaches large prey more slowly than small, and touches the prey with the palpi. The prey is then wrapped in silk by turning it rapidly on its longitudinal axis with the third leg while the fourth pulls out silk for wrapping. The prey is bitten, cut out of the web, and carried to the retreat. If the prey is active it is immediately bitten before wrapping. Small prey is carried in the chelicerae; large prey by spinnerets or fourth legs. Chemical stimuli are of importance in determining response to prey. Courtship consists of plucking web strands by the male and stroking the female. Copulation lasts only 10–20 seconds. The eggs are deposited in fall, enclosed in several fluffy, spherical, silk cocoons. After making the last cocoon the spider is exhausted and dies. The eggs overwinter.

° It is now under consideration by the International Commission of Zoological Nomenclature to place the name Araneidae on the Official List of Family Group Names in Zoology and place the genus *Argiope* on the Official List of Generic Names in Zoology and suppress the name *Argyope.*

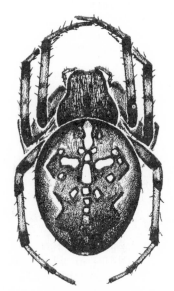

Fig. 11–33.   *Araneus diadematus,* 1.6 cm long.

Some important genera are *Zygiella, Meta, Argiope.** *Argiope trifasciata,* the common American banded argiope, is cosmopolitan but absent from Europe; *A. aurantia* is the American black and yellow argiope; both always hang head down in the center of the web. *Gasteracantha* (Fig. 11-34) and *Micrathena* are heavily sclerotized and have abdominal spines; they hang in the middle of the web. The frames of their webs are decorated with tufts of silk. Many orb weaver species have dwarf males, different in appearance from the females. *Nephila* females may reach 6 cm in length, while the males are minute. The young of *Nephila* make complete orb webs; the adults make only the lower half, filling the center with loose mesh. The males are found in the webs of the females. *Cyrtophora* and *Mecynogea* (=*Allepeira*) make horizontal dome-shaped orbs lacking a viscid spiral, but sticky threads are used in a mass of threads above the web. The bolas spiders, *Cladomelea, Dicrostichus* and *Mastophora,* make no orb webs, but use a viscous drop of silk at the end of a line to catch insects.

Theridiosomatidae. This family is characterized by the dark anterior median eyes. The area below the eyes is large, the chelicerae lack the boss characteristic of Araneidae, and the legs lack strong setae. *Theridiosoma gemmosum,* 2.8 mm, makes a vertical orb from the center of which a horizontal thread goes to a grass blade. The spider sits on the horizontal thread, holding it taut with the front legs, deforming the orb into a funnel with loops of loose thread beneath the spider's prosoma. Approaching prey is ensnared as the spider releases the tension, the funnel-shaped orb flattens, and the sticky threads draw close. The egg sac has a long stalk.

Tetragnathidae. The males have very long chelicerae, with which they hold the female during mating. The epigynum is secondarily absent. Orb webs are constructed. *Tetragnatha,* to 1.5 cm long, has a narrow, elongated abdomen. Some species build a horizontal orb, often over water. The spider may be very inconspicuous, appressed to a twig and holding the anterior legs forward, the posterior legs straight back. *Pachygnatha* adults do not make an orb.

* See footnote p. 188.

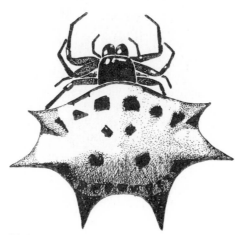

Fig. 11-34. *Gasteracantha reimondi,* 1.3 cm wide.

Archaeidae. In this small group the front of the carapace appears to be pushed up by the very long chelicerae. The chelicerae move independently and can lift prey forward, carried impaled on a fang. These are small spiders, mainly of the southern hemisphere, that prey on other spiders, which they immobilize by poison.

Mimetidae. Predators on other spiders, mimetids do not construct a web. They have a characteristic row of large setae on the first pair of legs. *Ero,* 0.4 cm long, hangs under leaves with legs flexed and catches passing spiders by suddenly extending the long legs. Others enter the webs of spiders and overpower the inhabitant. Females of *Ero furcata* have been observed to imitate the courting behavior of the male of *Meta segmentata* of Europe before attacking the female.

LYCOSOIDEA

All have 3 tarsal claws; in Ctenidae the adults lose the median claw. They have one or two rows of trichobothria on the dorsal side of each tarsus. The spinnerets are not arranged in a circle and are not short and cone-shaped. They are web builders and hunting spiders.

Agelenidae, Funnel Weavers. Most species make a funnel-shaped retreat at the edge of a flat web (Fig. 11-22). The anterior (lateral) spinnerets often are long. The grass spider of Europe is *Agelena,* of North America, *Agelenopsis. Tegenaria* the European house spider, includes some species that live under logs. *Coelotes*° feeds its young. *Desis* of Australia, 1.6 cm long, feeds at low tide on small Crustacea; at high tide it retreats into a mollusk shell or rock crevice and seals the opening with a water-impermeable silk cover. *Hahnia* has 6 spinnerets in a row and makes a web in a small depression in the soil. *Argyroneta aquatica,* the Eurasian waterspider, 2 cm long, has a large pair of sieve tracheae. Underwater a thin silvery envelope of air adheres to the feather-like hairs of the spider. At some points longer hairs, like pillars, hold the air envelope surface at some distance from the body. From time to time the spider surfaces and thrusts the abdomen and spinnerets through the surface film to renew the air. In water with vegetation the spider has to renew the bubble only every 3–4 days, there being a constant gas exchange between the spider and its surroundings. Usually the spider surfaces once or several times a day, or more often when it is building an underwater airbell that is to be filled with air. First a loose horizontal web is made, then the spinnerets, surrounded by air, strengthen it, at the same time incorporating bubbles. The spider strokes its abdomen with the last legs and so deposits a bubble, making the web dome-shaped. Within ½ to 1½ hours, as more air is collected, a 2 cm long bell, open below, is built. *Argyroneta* runs under water on plants and silk threads and swims ventral side up. The legs are hairy but have no adaptations for paddling. The spider feeds mostly on isopods, which are eaten under the bell. Courtship and mating occur within the bell and special bells are constructed for sperm web and eggs. The egg bell has two levels, the lower for the female; above there are as many as four egg sacs, each with 30–90 eggs. The mother does not feed but, by lifting the side of the bell and bending her abdomen under, she supplies fresh air. The young stay in the nest until after the fourth molt, when they are well covered with setae.

° Placing the name *Coelotes* on the Official List of Generic Names in Zoology is under consideration by the Internat. Comm. Zool. Nomenclature.

Pisauridae, Nursery-web Spiders. The eyes are usually in 3 rows (unlike previous families of entelegyne spiders). The female carries the egg sac in her chelicerae. *Pisaura* of Europe and *Pisaurina* are common in grass. The giant fishing spiders, *Dolomedes,* 2–3 cm long, are among the largest of northern spiders; they usually live near ponds and may catch small fish.

Lycosidae, Wolf Spiders. These hunting spiders carry their egg cocoons attached to the spinnerets, their young on the abdomen. Numerous species of *Pardosa* live in northern latitudes, particularly in mountains and in the Arctic. Some species of *Lycosa* (and members of some other genera) dig into soil and build tubes (Fig. 11-35). Such burrowers include *L. tarentula,* the large tarantula of southern Europe (not to be confused with the hairy mygalomorphs commonly called tarantula in North America). *Pirata* are small wolf spiders, found mostly near shores of ponds. *Trochosa* may make short tubes into the ground; *Geolycosa* may dig as deep as one meter into sand. *Sosippus* makes funnel webs. *Arctosa* is another genus.

Toxopidae. There are 8 eyes in two rows, the posterior eyes are very large, the eyes of the anterior row small. Toxopids are hunting spiders found in forests and shrubs of Australia and New Zealand, possibly north to Java. The egg sacs are fastened under stones and logs. Genera are *Toxops* and *Toxopsiella.*

Oxyopidae, Lynx Spiders. The eyes are arranged in a hexagonal pattern. They live among vegetation and jump on their prey. The egg sac, attached to vegetation, is guarded by the female. *Oxyopes, Hamataliwa* and *Peucetia* are included.

Senoculidae. Members of this small family of South American spiders have anterior median eyes far anterior of others. They hunt by moving rapidly over vegetation.

Ctenidae, Wandering Spiders. The tibiae and metatarsi of the first legs have ventral pairs of strong setae, "spines." The adults have only 2 or sometimes 3 tarsal claws, juveniles have 3. The histology of the eye structure places the family close to the

Fig. 11–35. Wolf spider, *Arctosa perita,* **at entrance of its tube; width of head, 2 mm.** (After Bristowe.)

Lycosidae, but in many characters they strongly resemble the Clubionidae. The distribution is mainly tropical. *Ctenus* is sometimes imported with bananas. The aggressive *Phoneutria*, to 4 cm, is one of the most poisonous spiders of South America. *Cupiennius* is found in the West Indies; *Zora* is European and North American.

CLUBIONOIDEA

Only 2 tarsal claws are present. The chelicerae usually have teeth and there is no colulus. The eyes are usually in two rows.

Gnaphosidae (*Drassodidae*). The anterior (lateral) spinnerets are cylindrical and separated. Nocturnal hunters, they rest at daytime under stones, moss or bark; some may enclose themselves in a dense web. *Gnaphosa*, *Drassodes* and *Zelotes* are representatives. *Micaria* are ant mimics.

Clubionidae, Sac Spiders. Similar to gnaphosids except that the anterior spinnerets are conical and close to each other. *Clubiona*, *Anyphaena* and *Agroeca* are included. *Chiracanthium* bites may be poisonous. Many *Castianeira* are ant mimics; unlike many clubionds they are dark colored.

Prodidomidae. A small family apparently close to gnaphosids, these also have anterior spinnerets separated, but have a strikingly different eye arrangement and divergent toothless chelicerae.

Platoridae. The platorid crab spiders include fewer than a dozen Asian and tropical American species. The front spinnerets are separated and the middle spinnerets are long. The body is flat, the sternum wider than long.

Homalonychidae. This includes a few species, found under stones in the southwestern United States, that do not fit well into other families. They keep the length of their legs in contact with stones or substrate when resting.

Heteropodidae (*Sparassidae, Eusparassidae*). These lack the strong setae of ctenids. The legs are held sideways like those of crabs; the large, often flattened spiders run rapidly, often sideways, and catch insects encountered. Most are nocturnal and live in tropics. *Heteropoda venatoria* (*H. regia*), the huntsman spider, pantropical in houses, is often imported on bananas. *Micrommata virescens*, to 1.3 cm long, is found in Europe on vegetation.

Selenopidae. Selenopid crab spiders are very flat, have 6 of their 8 eyes in a single row. They are found under bark or rocks in tropics and when disturbed dash sideways into crevices.

Amaurobioididae. There are only 2 tarsal claws with claw tufts; the tarsi and metatarsi have scopulae. The heart has 3 pairs of ostia. A colulus is present between anterior spinnerets. The eyes are in two rows, the anterior row strongly procurved; both eye groups occupy about half width of head. The only species, *Amaurobioides maritima*, 8 mm, occurs in South Africa, Tasmania, New Zealand and sub-antarctic islands between the tidal zones. The spider constructs a nest, 3–4 cm long, in a rock crevice sprayed by salt water; it feeds on marine crustaceans. It is believed to be distributed over the ocean.

THOMISOIDEA

All have only 2 claws. Crab spiders extend the anterior legs to the side, laterigrade (Fig. 11-36). The chelicerae are usually without teeth opposing the fang. A colulus is present between anterior (lateral) spinnerets.

Thomisidae, Crab Spiders. Philodromus is found on bark. *Misumena vatia* (Fig. 11-36), colored white or yellow, is found on flowers and can change its color to match the background. If more than half the 8 eyes are covered by black lacquer, white spiders on yellow flowers cannot change. The yellow pigment is a liquid in the hypodermis cells. On white flowers the pigment is transferred to the inside and the white guanin pigment shows. Females prefer yellow and white flowers in experiments, usually selecting the color matching them. *Xysticus* has numerous species in the northern hemisphere. *Tibellus* is included. *Aphantochilus* is an ant mimic. *Philodromus*, common in northern hemisphere, are often placed in their own family because of certain differences in embryology and eye structure.

SALTICOIDEA, JUMPING SPIDERS

The anterior median eyes are very much larger than the others. All have only 2 claws.

Salticidae, Jumping Spiders. These have the best eyes among the spiders. By far the largest family, it includes close to 3000 species, most of them tropical, but with numerous representatives in the northern temperate and arctic regions.

The visual courtship and threat display of jumping spiders has been studied experimentally for a number of Venezuelan species by J. Crane (Fig. 11-17). Distance chemoreception was found to be an important factor, second only to vision. Pheromones are given off by young adult females, and males recognize recent resting places of females. Display in response to visual stimuli does not occur if the anterior median eyes are covered. Experiments with *Corythalia xanthopa* showed that the model size has to be appropriate, less than double the size and more than half the size of the female; the shape has to be broader than high, with horizontal stripes and coloration of the female. Young adult females painted as males are courted. The white anterior band of the abdomen appears to be a directional signal for copulation. Threat display may change to courtship and vice versa. The courtship display serves several functions: mutual recognition, self protection, and not least important, an isolating mechanism between species. Threat display discourages fighting, and cannibalism is rare. The ornamentation that develops in the final instar is most pronounced in males. It is of adaptive value in making the bearer conspicuous in display, as are the long chelicerae of males.

Evarcha is included here. The zebra spider, *Salticus scenicus* (Fig. 8-1), found on walls and windows, was probably originally a cliff dweller. Numerous jumping spiders

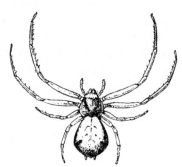

Fig. 11–36.   Crab spider, *Misumena vatia*, 6 mm long. (After Planet.)

are ant mimics. *Lyssomanes,* placed in its own subfamily, has eyes in 4 rows, while others have them in 3.

AMMOXENOIDEA

Ammoxenidae. Only 2 claws are present. The arrangement of the spinnerets is similar to that of Urocteidae, with the anterior pair far apart; there is no colulus. The chelicerae are fused near the base and lack teeth. The legs are thin, tarsi longer than metatarsi, and the palpus is very simple. These are red spiders that run rapidly on the ground. The few species are all found in Africa.

SUBORDER CRIBELLATAE

Sternites XIII to XVIII are almost obliterated; the spinnerets are at the posterior abdominal tip. The median anterior spinnerets have fused into a transverse plate, the cribellum (Fig. 11-11), which forms the end of a small truncate tubercle only in the Hypochilidae, a flat plate in others. The cribellum, with its dense small spigots, acts as a sieve for silk. In conjunction with it there is the calamistrum (Fig. 11-25c), a row of setae on the fourth metatarsus. There are 4 pairs of dorsoventral muscles in the abdomen, only a single median longitudinal muscle, and at most 12 segmental ganglia in the prosoma. The heart has not more than 4 pairs of ostia. All species use cribellate silk to catch prey. The webs are diverse but may be similar in design to those of ecribellate families. Probably all species balloon.

Hypochilidae.° Members of this diverse group have 4 lungs or 2 lungs and 2 separate tracheal slits. The pedipalpal coxae form large endites. The dorsum of the abdomen of a *Hypochilus* 0.8 cm long has 5 tergites (metameres VIII to XII). Posteriorly 4 areas are separated by folds, which also correspond to segments of longitudinal muscle. Dorsum of abdomen, including anal tubercle, therefore has tergites VIII to XV, while the undivided part has tergites XVI to XVIII. The cribellum in all is a blunt cone. The female has no epigynum. *Hypochilus* has two pairs of book lungs. The chelicerae are almost orthognath. The labium is fused to the sternum. The legs are very long. There are 4 species in North America. In all the bulb of the male tarsus is ventral. The spider constructs a lampshade-like web under overhanging cliffs and hangs in the center surrounded by web. Flies circling up are entangled in the cribellate threads of the web. The chelicerae of the Chinese *Ectatosticta davidi* are intermediate in position, diaxial but anterior of the carapace. The labium is free and the sternum has 6 plates. *Hickmania troglodytes* of Tasmania has paraxial chelicerae attached ventrally. The labium is fused to the sternum. The legs are long and thin; unlike *Ectatosticta* and *Hypochilus,* its calamistrum consists of only one row of setae. The Chilean and Argentinian *Thaida peculiaris* (=*Austrochilus manni*) has labidognath chelicerae; the labium is fused to the sternum. The posterior pair of respiratory organs are tracheae. The calamistrum is a single row of setae. Found in logs and hollow trees it makes a funnel web. The living spider resembles *Meta* superficially.

° Lehtinen (1967, *Ann. Zool. Fennici* 4:199–468) attempted to regroup the cribellate spiders and those belonging to the Agelenidae and Clubionidae. He also placed various genera of the family Hypochilidae each in their own family: Ectatostictidae, Hickmaniidae and Thaididae.

Filistatidae. The eyes are closely grouped and the legs have 3 tarsal claws. Females lack an epigynum; the male palpus is simple and at the tip of the tarsus. Chelicerae are fused at the base. The very large poison glands are branched. The cribellum may be rudimentary or perhaps absent. *Filistata,* 1.5–2 cm, builds a silken tube in a crevice with radiating trip threads at the opening. It is found in warmer parts of North America and Europe.

Acanthoctenidae. The females have an epigynum and members of the family resemble Ctenidae in eye arrangement and presence of strong setae. The tarsi have only two claws. The distribution is tropical. Cribellate threads are used near the retreat. *Acanthoctenus* probably has good vision; it reacts to a fly at a distance of 20 cm.

Zoropsidae. Unlike the Acanthoctenidae, these have the eyes in 2 rows. There is an epigynum. The adults have tarsi with 2 or 3 claws and claw tufts, the young have 3 claws. Several species of *Zoropsis* occur in Mediterranean countries.

Oecobiidae. The tarsi have 3 claws. The eyes are closely grouped and there is a large hairy anal tubercle. The group superficially resembles the much larger Urocteidae, possibly a case of convergent evolution. These minute spiders, mostly less than 2.5 mm, are found under stones and sometimes in houses.

Eresidae. The tarsi have 3 claws. These spiders have a massive, hairy head; found in the Old World only; they make a funnel-like web. The hairy body superficially resembles that of theraphosids. *Stegodyphus* is colonial; it occurs in Africa and the Orient. *Eresus niger* of Europe has males with a bright red abdomen; females are black. The eyes are relatively small and probably vision is neither acute nor important in recognition of the sexual partner.

Tengellidae. The tarsi have 3 claws, and 2 or 3 rows of trichobothria. There are scopulae, brushes of hairs on the first tarsi and metatarsi. This small family is found in Madagascar and Africa.

Dictynidae. Small spiders resembling Theridiidae, they have tarsi with 3 claws and 2 or 3 rows of trichobothria. *Dictyna* is 0.4 cm long at most. Some species live in forks of twigs in low vegetation (Fig. 11-26), others build a web underneath leaves, a cobweb of cribellate threads. *Mallos,* somewhat larger, may make a tube in crevices of cliffs.

Psechridae. Found in India, Ceylon and New Zealand, these large spiders have a brush of setae between 3 tarsal claws. They live in humid situations and make an agelenid-like funnel web. There are trichobothria.

Amaurobiidae. These (particularly *Titanoeca*) resemble Agelenidae, but the spinnerets differ. *Amaurobius** (Fig. 11-24) makes an irregular funnel between logs and stones with irregular cribellate threads near its entrance. There are 3 claws and 2 or 3 rows of trichobothria.

Uloboridae. These lack poison glands. *Uloborus,* the feather-legged spider, 0.6 cm long, makes nearly horizontal orb webs resembling those of Araneidae except that the spiral threads are cribellate. Social species of *Uloborus* make webs in dense colonies. *Sybota* makes a vertical orb web having cribellate radii and plain temporary spiral threads. The center does not float free but is attached by a thread to a branch above. Like *Uloborus,* the spider sits in the center of the web. *Miagrammopes,* to 1.2 cm long,

---

* Placement of the name *Amaurobius* on the Official List of Generic Names in Zoology and suppression of the name *Ciniflo* is under consideration by the Internat. Comm. Zool. Nomencl.

has only a single thread as snare. *Hyptiotes,* the triangle spider, to 0.6 cm long, makes a triangular web and holds taut a single thread attached to the hub (Fig. 11-30).

Dinopidae, Ogre-faced Spiders. These have eyes in 3 rows. *Dinopis,* to 2 cm long, has its huge anterior eyes directed forward; their adaptational significance is not known. It occurs in tropics around the world and sits in shrubs holding its web (Fig. 11-31). *Menneus* has smaller eyes, but constructs a similar web.

*References**

Abalos, J. W. and Baez, E. C. 1963. Spermatic transmission in spiders. *Psyche* 70:197–207.

Anderson, J. F. 1966. The excreta of spiders. *Comp. Biochem. Physiol.* 17:973–982.

Autrum, H. and Barth, F. G. 1966. Einzelzellableitung von einem Spaltsinnesorgan. *Naturwissenschaften* 53:412–413.

Baccetti, G. and Bedini, C. 1964. Microscopic and ultramicroscopic structure of the eyes of a lycosid spider. *Arch. Italiennes Biol.* 102:97–122.

Barth, F. G. 1967. Spaltsinnesorgan auf dem Spinnentarsus. *Z. Vergl. Physiol.* 55:407–449.

Barth, R. 1962. Estudos histologicos sôbre las glandulas peconhentas da *Latrodectus. Mem. Inst. Oswaldo Cruz* 60:275–292.

Bays, S. M. 1962. Training possibilities of *Araneus diadematus. Experientia* 18:423.

Bhatnagar, R. D. S. and Rempel, J. G. 1962. Postembryonic development of the copulatory organs. *Canadian J. Zool.* 40:465–510.

Billaudelle, H. 1957. Biologie der Mauerspinne *Dictyna civica. Z. Angew. Entomol.* 41:474–512.

Bonnet, P. 1945–1959. *Bibliographia Araneorum,* Toulouse. 7 vols.

————— 1966. Le nombre des espèces d'Araignées. *Senckenbergiana Biol.* 47:3–4.

Borght, O. van der. 1966. Peritrophic membranes in arachnida. *Nature* 210:751–752.

Boyd, W. C. 1937. Cross-reactivity of various hemocyanins. *Biol. Bull.* 73:181–183.

Braunitzer, G. and Wolff, D. 1955. Chemische Untersuchungen über die Fibroine von *Bombyx* und *Nephila. Z. Naturforsch.* 106:404–408.

Breed, A. L. et al. 1964. Fate of the intact orb web of Araneus. *Behaviour* 23:43–60.

Bristowe, W. S. 1939–1941. *The Comity of Spiders.* Ray Soc. London.

————— 1958. *The World of Spiders.* Collins, London.

Browning, H. C. 1942. Integument and moult cycle of *Tegenaria. Proc. Roy. Soc. London* (B) 131:65–86.

Bücherl, W. 1962. *Südamerikanische Vogelspinnen.* Neue Brehm Bücherei 302, A. Ziemsen Verlag, Wittenberg Lutherstadt.

Butler, W. H. and Main, B. Y. 1961. Predation on vertebrates by mygalomorph spiders. *West. Australian Natural.* 7:52.

Cloudsley-Thompson, J. L. 1958. *Spiders, Scorpions, Centipedes and Mites.* Pergamon, London.

Clyne, D. 1967. Construction of net and sperm-web of *Dinopis subrufus. Australian Zool.* 14:189–197.

Cooke, J. A. L. 1965. Spider genus *Dysdera. Nature* 205:1027–1028.

————— 1965. Biology of British *Dysdera. Oikos* 16:20–25.

* See also References in Chapters 6 and 8.

——— 1966. Genitalia in *Dysdera crocata*. *Senckenbergiana Biol.* 47:35–43.

Crane, J. 1948–1950. Comparative biology of salticid spiders. *Zoologica,* New York, 33:1–38, 139–145; 34:159–214; 35:253–261.

Crome, W. 1951. *Die Wasserspinne*. Die Neue Brehm Bücherei 44, Akad. Verlagsges., Leipzig.

——— 1953. Respirations und Circulationsorgane der *Argyroneta*. *Wiss. Z. Humboldt Univ. Berlin* 2:53–83.

——— 1955. Beziehungen zwischen dem dorsalen Zeichenmuster und der Metamerie des Spinnen Abdomens. *Zool. Jahrb. Abt. Anat.* 74:189–338; *Zool. Jahrb. Abt. Syst.* 85:541–638.

——— 1956. Kokonbau und Eiablage einiger *Araneus*. *Deutsche Entomol. Z.* (N.F.) 3:28–55.

——— 1963. Embryonalentwicklung ohne Umrollung bei Vogelspinnen. *Ibid.* 10:83–95.

——— and Crome, I. 1961. Wachstum ohne Häutung. *Ibid.* 8:443–464.

——— 1961. Paarung und Eiablage bei *Argyope*. *Mitt. Zool. Mus. Berlin* 37:189–252.

Czajka, M. 1963. Unknown facts of the biology of the spider *Ero furcata*. *Polskie Pismo Entomol.* (*Bull. Entomol. Pologne*) 33(2):229–231.

Dabelow, S. 1958. Biologie der Leimschleuderspinne *Scytodes*. *Zool. Jahrb. Abt. Syst.* 86:85–126.

Davies, M. E. and Edney, E. B. 1952. Evaporation of water from spiders. *J. Exp. Biol.* 29:571–582.

Deevey, G. B. 1941. Blood cells of the Haitian tarantula and their relation to the moulting cycle. *J. Morphol.* 68:457–487.

——— 1949. The developmental history of *Latrodectus* at different rates of feeding. *Amer. Midland Natur.* 42:189–219.

Dillon, L. S. 1952. Myology of the araneid leg. *J. Morphol.* 90:467–480.

Dondale, C. D. 1967. Sexual behavior and classification of the *Philodromus rufus* complex. *Canadian J. Zool.* 45:453–459.

Duffey, E. 1956. Aerial dispersal in a known spider population. *J. Anim. Ecol.* 25:85–111.

Dumitresco, M. A. 1941, 1942. Anatomie et cytologie de l'appareil sericigène des araignées. *An. Acad. Romana, Bucuresti* (3) 16:773–839; 17:263–349.

Dzimirsski, I. 1959. Bewegungssehen und Optomotorik bei Springspinnen. *Z. Tierpsychol.* 16:385–402.

Eason, R. R. 1964. Maternal care by wolf spiders. *Proc. Arkansas Acad. Sci.* 18:13–19.

——— and Whitcomb, W. H. 1965. Life history of *Lycosa punctulata*. *Ibid.* 19:11–20.

Eberhard, W. 1967. Attack behavior of diguetid spiders and the origin of prey wrapping. *Psyche* 74:173–181.

Eckert, M. 1965. Häutungsphysiologie der Spinnen. *Naturwissenschaften* 52:665.

——— 1967. Häutungsphysiologie bei Spinnen. *Zool. Jahrb. Abt. Physiol.* 73:49–101.

Ehlers, M. 1939. Formen aktiver Lokomotion bei Spinnen. *Zool. Jahrb. Abt. Syst.* 72:373–499.

Ehn, A. 1964. Determination in the spider embryo. *Acta Univ. Upsaliensis* 31:1–20.

Eisner, T. et al. 1964. Adhesiveness of spider silk. *Science* 146:1058–1061.

Engelhardt, W. 1964. Mitteleuropäische *Trochosa*. *Z. Morphol. Ökol.* 54:219–392.

Exline, H. and Whitcomb, W. H. 1965. Mating procedure of *Peucetia viridans*. *Florida Entomol.* 48:169–171.

Firstman, B. 1954. Central nervous system, musculature and segmentation of the cephalothorax of a tarantula *Eurypelma*. *Microentomology* 19:14–40.

Fischer, F. G. and Brander, J. 1960. Analyse der Gespinste der Kreuzspinne. *Z. Physiol. Chem.* 320:92–102.

Forster, R. R. 1955. New family of spiders, Gradungulidae. *Pacific Sci.* 9:277–285.

——— 1959. The spiders of the family Symphytognathidae. *Trans. Roy. Soc. New Zealand* 86:269–329.

_____ 1967. The spiders of New Zealand 1. *Bull. Otago Mus.* 1:1–124.

Frank, H. 1957. Funktionelle Anatomie der lokomotorischen Extremitäten von *Zygiella*. *Zool. Jahrb. Abt. Anat.* 76:423–460.

Frings, H. and Frings, M. 1966. Reactions of orb-weaving spiders (Argiopidae) to airborne sounds. *Ecology* 47(4):578–588.

Freisling, J. 1961. Netz und Netzbauinstinkte bei *Theridium*. *Z. Wiss Zool.* 165:396–421.

Frontali, N. and Grasso, A. 1964. Three toxicologically different components from the venom of *Latrodectus. Arch. Biochem. Biophys.* 106:213–218.

Gardner, B. T. 1964. Hunger and sequential responses in the hunting behavior of salticid spiders. *J. Comp. Physiol. Psychol.* 58:167–173.

_____ 1965. Observations on three species of jumping spiders. *Psyche* 72:133–147.

_____ 1966. Characteristics of the prey in the hunting behavior of salticid spiders. *J. Comp. Physiol. Psychol.* 62:475–478.

Gerhardt, U. and Kaestner, A. 1937. Araneae *in* Kükenthal, *Handbuch der Zoologie,* De Gruyter, Berlin 3(2):394–656.

Gering, R. L. 1953. Structure and function of genitalia in some agelenid spiders. *Smithsonian Misc. Coll.* 121(4):1–84.

Gersch, M. and Althaus, B. 1959. Herzanregende Faktoren aus dem Nervensystem von Spinnen. *Monatsber. Deutschen Akad. Wiss. Berlin* 1:1–3.

Gertsch, W. J. 1947. Spiders that lasso their prey. *Natur. Hist.* 56(4):152–158, 189.

_____ 1949. *American Spiders.* Van Nostrand, New York.

_____ 1955. North American bolas spiders. *Bull. Amer. Mus. Natur. Hist.* 106:221–254.

_____ 1958. Spider family Hypochilidae. *Amer. Mus. Novitates* 1912:1–28.

_____ 1964. Genus *Hypochilus. Ibid.* 2203:1–14.

Giulio, L. 1962. Optische Lokalisation der Beute bei der Kreuzspinne *Araneus. Z. Vergl. Physiol.* 45:376–389.

_____ 1962. Stimoli ottici e localizzazione della preda in *Araneus. Boll. Soc. Italiana Biol. Sperim.* 38:301–302.

_____ 1962. L'elettroretinogramma ocellare in *Tegenaria. Ibid.* 38:910–915.

Glatz, L. 1967. Biologie und Morphologie von *Oecobius annulipes. Z. Morphol. Tiere* 61:185–214.

Görner P. 1958. Optische und kinästhetische Orientierung der Trichterspinne *Agelena. Z. Vergl. Physiol.* 41:111–153.

_____ 1962. Orientierung der Trichterspinne nach polarisiertem Licht. *Ibid.* 45:307–314.

_____ 1965. Mehrfach innervierte Machanorezeptoren bei Spinnen. *Naturwissenschaften* 52:437.

_____ 1966. Koppelung der optischen und kinästhetischen Orientierung bei *Agelena. Z. Vergl. Physiol.* 53:253–276.

Gossel, P. 1935. Hautsinnesorgane und Hautdrüsen der Cheliceraten. *Z. Morphol. Ökol.* 30:177–205.

Hackmann, W. 1948. Chromosomenstudien an Araneen. *Acta Zool. Fennica* 54:1–101.

Helsdingen, P. J. van. 1965. Sexual behavior of *Lepthyphantes leprosus* with notes on the function of the genital organs. *Zool. Med.* 41:15–42.

Holm, A. 1952. Entwicklung und Entwicklungsphysiologie des Spinnenembryos. *Zool. Bidr. Uppsala* 29:293–424.

_____ 1954. Development of an orthognath spider *Ischnothele. Ibid.* 30:199–221.

Homann, H. 1947. Der Lichtsinn von *Aranea. Biol. Zentralbl.* 66:251–261.

_____ 1949. Wachstum und die mechanischen Vorgänge bei der Häutung von *Tegenaria. Z. Vergl. Physiol.* 31:413–440.

———— 1949. Blutdruck und Häutung bei Spinnen. *Naturwissenschaften* 36:21–24.

———— 1950, 1952. Nebenaugen der Araneen. *Zool. Jahrb. Abt. Anat.* 71:56–144; 72:345–364.

———— 1953, 1956. Entwicklung der Nebenaugen der Spinnen. *Biol. Zentralbl.* 72:373–385; 75:416–421.

———— 1957. Haften Spinnen an einer Wasserhaut. *Naturwissenschaften* 44:318–319.

———— 1961. Entwicklung der Nebenaugen bei den Araneen. *Zool. Jahrb. Abt. Anat.* 79:347–370.

Kaestner, A. 1929. Bau und Funktion der Fächertracheen einiger Spinnen. *Z. Morphol. Ökol.* 13:463–558.

———— 1950. Reaktion der Salticidae auf unbewegte, farblose und farbige Gesichtsreize. *Zool. Beitr. Berlin* (N.F.) 1:12–50.

———— 1950. Farbsinn der Spinnen. *Naturwiss. Rundschau* (8), 357–360.

———— 1952–1953. Mundwerkzeuge der Spinnen. *Zool. Jahrb. Abt. Anat.* 72:101–146; 73:3–54. *Mitt. Zool. Mus. Berlin* 29:1–74.

Kaston, B. J. 1938. Family names in Araneae. *Amer. Midland Natur.* 19:638–646.

———— 1948. Spiders of Connecticut. *Bull. State Geol. Natur. Hist. Surv.* Hartford 70:1–874.

———— 1964. Evolution of spider webs. *Amer. Zool.* 4:191–207.

———— 1965. Aspects of spider behavior. *Amer. Midland Natur.* 73:336–356.

———— and Kaston, E. 1953. *How to Know the Spiders.* W. C. Brown Co., Dubuque, Iowa.

Klingel, H. 1967. Beobachtungen an *Liphistius batuensis*. *Verh. Deutschen Zool. Ges.* 30:246–253.

Kraus, O. 1965. *Hypochilus*. *Natur Mus.* 95:150–162.

Kühne, H. 1959. Neurosekretorische Zellen und der retrocerebrale neuro-endokrine Komplex von Spinnen. *Zool. Jahrb. Abt. Anat.* 77:527–600.

Kullmann, E. 1958. Netzbau und Biologie von *Cyrtophora*. *Zool. Jahrb. Abt. Syst.* 86:181–216.

———— 1959. Verhalten der theridiide *Conopistha*. *Mitt. Zool. Mus. Berlin* 35:275–292.

———— 1961. Eierkokonbau von *Cyrtophora*. *Zool. Jahrb. Abt. Syst.* 89:369–406.

———— 1964. Netzbau und Sexualverhalten einiger Spinnenarten. *Z. Zool. Syst. Evolutionsforsch.* 2:41–122.

Lagerspetz, K. and Jäynäs, E. 1959. Behavioural regulation of water content of *Linyphia*. *Ann. Entomol. Fennici* 25:210–223.

Legendre, R. 1953. Les glandes prosomatiques des araignées. *Ann. Univ. Saraviensis* 2:305–333.

———— 1959. Système nerveux des aranéides. *Ann. Sci. Natur. Zool.* 12:339–473.

———— 1959. La periode larvaire (*Archaea*). *Mém. Inst. Scien. Madagascar* (A)13:67–79.

———— 1961. *Archaea*, la capture des proies et la prise de nourriture. *Bull. Soc. Zool. France* 86:316–319.

———— 1963. L'audition et l'emission de sons chez les Aranéides. *Ann. Biol.* 2:371–390.

———— 1965. Morphologie et développement des Aranéides. *Fortschr. Zool.* 17:238–271.

———— 1965. Anatomie musculaire du prosoma (*Archaea*). *Ann. Sci. Nat. Zool. Biol. Anim.* (12) 7:397–412.

Le Guelte, L. 1966. Apprentissage chez *Zygiella x-notata*. *Compt. Rend. Acad. Sci. Paris* 262:689–691.

———— 1966. La toile de *Zygiella x-notata* et facteurs qui régissent le comportement de d'Araignée pendant la construction de la toile. *Public. Univ. Nancy Fac. Sci. Thèses.*

Lehmensick, R. and Kullman, E. 1957. Feinbau der Fäden einiger Spinnen. *Verh. Deutschen Zool. Ges.* 20:123–129.

Levi, H. W. 1961. Palpal sclerites in the Theridiidae. *J. Morphol.* 108:1–9.

_____ 1965. An unusual case of mimicry. *Evolution* 19:261–262.

_____ 1967. Adaptations of respiratory systems in spiders. *Ibid.* 21:571–583.

_____ 1968. The spider genera *Argiope* and *Gea* (Araneidae) in North America. *Bull. Mus. Comp. Zool.* 136:319–352.

_____ 1968. The spider family Hadrotarsidae. *Trans. Amer. Microscop. Soc.* 87:141–145.

_____ 1968. Behavior of the spider *Sicarius*. *Psyche.* 74:320–330.

_____ and Levi, L. R. 1968. *Spiders and Their Kin.* Golden Press, New York.

Liesenfeld, F. J. 1956. Netz und Erschütterungssinn von *Zygiella*. *Z. Vergl. Physiol.* 38:563–592.

_____ 1961. Leistung und Sitz des Erschütterungssinnes von Netzspinnen. *Biol. Zentralbl.* 80:465–475.

Locket, G. H. and Millidge, A. F. 1951–1953. *British Spiders.* Ray Soc., London.

Lucas, F. 1964. Spiders and their silks. *Discovery* 1–7.

_____ et al. 1960. Comparative studies of fibroins. *J. Molecul. Biol.* 2:339–349.

Magni, F. et al. 1962. Electroretinographic responses to polarized light in the wolf spider. *Experientia* 18:511.

_____ 1964. The role of different pairs of eyes in astronomical orientation of a lycosid spider. *Arch. Italiennes Biol.* 102:123–136.

_____ 1965. Electroretinographic responses to polarized light. *Ibid.* 103:146–158.

Manton, S. M. 1958. Hydrostatic pressure and leg extension in arthropods. *Ann. Mag. Natur. Hist.* (13) 1:161–182.

Marples, B. J. 1962. Spiders of the family Uloboridae. *Ann. Zool.,* Agra 4:1–11.

_____ 1967. The spinnerets and epiandrous glands of spiders. *J. Linnean Soc. London* 46:209–222.

Maretić, Z. 1966. Latrodectism. *Jugoslavenska Akad. Znan. Umjet. Bull. Internat.* 17:63–87.

_____ and Jelašić, F. 1953. Einfluss des Toxins der Spinne *Latrodectus* auf das Nervensystem. *Acta Trop.* 10:209–224.

_____ et al. 1964. Theridiid spider *Steatoda paykulliana*, poisonous to mammals. *Toxicon* 2:149–154.

Mayer, G. 1953. Herstellung und Struktur des Radnetzes von *Aranea* und *Zilla*. *Z. Tierpsychol.* 9:337–362.

McAlister, W. H. 1961. Spitting habit of *Scytodes intricata*. *Texas J. Sci.* 12–13:17–20.

McCrone, J. D. and Netzloff, M. L. 1965. An immunological and electrophoretical comparison of *Latrodectus* venoms. *Toxicon* 3:107–110.

Melchers, M. 1963. Biologie und Verhalten von *Cupiennus salei,* einer amerikanischen Ctenide. *Zool. Jahrb. Abt. System.* 91:1–90.

_____1964. Zur Biologie der Vogelspinnen. *Z. Morphol. Ökol.* 53:517–536.

_____ 1967. Der Beutefang von *Cupiennus salei*. *Ibid.* 58:321–346.

Millot, J. 1949. Aranéides *in* Grassé, *Traité de Zoologie,* Masson et Cie, Paris, 6:589–743.

Nemenz, H. 1954. Der Wasserhaushalt einiger Spinnen. *Österreichische Zool. Z.* 5:123–158.

Neri, L., Bettini, S. and Frank, M. 1965. The effect of *Latrodectus* venom on *Periplaneta* nerve cord. *Toxicon* 3:95–99.

Nørgaard, E. 1951. The ecology of two lycosid spiders from a sphagnum bog. *Oikos* 3:1–21.

_____ 1956. Behavior of *Theridion saxatile*. *Ibid.* 7:159–192.

Papi, F. 1955. Astronomische Orientierung bei der Wolfspinne *Arctosa*. *Z. Vergl. Physiol.* 37:230–233.

———— 1959. Sull'orientamento astronomico in specie del gen. *Arctosa. Ibid.* 41:481–489.

———— 1959. Sull'orientamento astronomico di *Arctosa. Pubbl. Staz. Zool. Napoli* 27:76–103.

Papi, F. and Serretti, L. 1955. Sull'orientamento e il senso nel tempo in *Arctosa. Mem. Soc. Toscana Sci. Natur. Pisa* 67(B):98–104.

———— and Syrjämäki, J. 1963. Sun-orientation rhythm of wolf spiders at different latitudes. *Arch. Italiano Biol.* 101:59–77.

———— and Tongiorgi, P. 1963. Innate and learned components in the astronomical orientation of wolf spiders. *Ergebn. Biol.* 26:259–280.

Parry, D. A. 1957. Spider leg muscles and autotomy mechanism. *Quart. J. Microscop. Sci.* 98:331–340.

———— 1960. Spider hydraulics. *Endeavour* 19:156–162.

———— 1965. The signal generated by an insect in a spider's web. *J. Exp. Biol.* 43:185–192.

———— and Brown, R. H. J. 1959. Hydraulic mechanism of the spider leg. *Ibid.* 36:423–433.

Peakall, D. B. 1964. Origin of silk fibroins. *J. Exp. Zool.* 156:345–351.

———— 1964. Effects of cholinergic and anticholinergic drugs on the synthesis of silk fibroins. *Comp. Biochem. Physiol.* 12:465–470.

————1964. Composition and function of silk fibroin of the spider *Araneus diadematus. J. Exp. Zool.* 156:345–352.

———— 1965. Differences in regulation in the silk glands of the spider. *Nature* 207:102–103.

———— 1965. Regulation of the synthesis of silk fibroins at the glandular level. *Comp. Biochem. Physiol.* 15:509–515.

———— 1966. Regulation of protein production in the silk glands of spiders. *Ibid.* 19:253–258.

Peters, H. M. 1953. Ethologie und Ökologie tropischer Webespinnen. *Z. Morphol. Ökol.* 42:278–306.

———— 1955. Spinnapparat von Nephila. *Z. Naturforsch.* 10b:395–404.

Peters, R. 1967. Bau und Funktion der Spinnwarzen und Spinnwarzenmuskulatur. *Zool. Beitr.* N.F. 13:1–119.

Petrusewiczowa, E. 1938. Bau des Netzes der Kreuzspinne. *Prace Towarz Przy. Nauk Wilna* 13:1–24.

Pickford, G. E. 1942. Digestive enzymes of spiders. *Trans. Connecticut Acad. Sci.* 35:33–37.

Pikelin, B. S. G. and Schiapelli, R. D. 1963. Llave para la determinación de familias de arañas argentinas. *Physis* 24:43–72.

Pross, A. 1966. Die Entwicklung von *Pardosa hortensis. Z. Morphol. Ökol.* 58:38–108.

Rabaey, M. and Verriest, G. 1958. L'hémolymphe de 33 espèces d'Araignées. *Ann. Soc. Roy. Zool. Belgique* 88:373–383.

Rasmont, R. 1952. Myologie abdominale d'une theraphoside et d'une dipluride. *Ibid.* 83:225–242.

Rathmayer, W. 1967. Elektrophysiologische Untersuchungen an Proprioreceptoren im Bein einer Vogelspinne. *Z. Vergl. Physiol.* 54:438–454.

Reiskind, J. 1965. Self-burying behavior in *Sicarius. Psyche* 72:218–224.

Rempel, J. G. 1957. Embryology of the black-widow. *Canadian J. Zool.* 35:35–74.

Richter, G. 1956. Struktur und Funktion der Klebefäden in den Fanggeweben Ecribellater Radnetzspinnen. *Naturwissenschaften* 43:23.

Roberts, N. L. 1955. The Australian netting spider *Deinopis. Proc. Roy. Zool. Soc. New South Wales* 1953–54:24–33.

Roewer, C. F. 1942–1955. *Katalog der Araneae.* Bremen and Brussels. 2 vols.

Rovner, J. S. 1966. Courtship without sperm induction. *Science* 152(3721):543–544.

_____ 1967. Copulation and sperm induction by normal and palpless male linyphiid spiders. *Ibid.* 157:835.

_____ 1967. Acoustic communication in *Lycosa rabida. Anim. Behaviour* 15:273–281.

Savory, T. H. 1952. *The Spider's Web.* Warne, London.

Shear, W. A. 1967. Palpi of male spiders. *Breviora, Mus. Comp. Zool.* 259:1–27.

Smith, D. S. and Russell, F. E. 1967. Structure of the venom gland of the black widow spider *Latrodectus mactans in* Russell, F. E. and Saunders, P. R. *Animal Toxins.* Pergamon Press, Oxford.

Steinbach, G. 1953. Chelicerenmuskulatur einiger Araneen. *Wiss. Z. Humboldt Univ.* Berlin 2:25–33.

Stradal-Schuster, H. 1944. Aussenverdauung bei Spinnen. *Verh. Zool. Bot. Ges. Wien* 90–91:83–128.

Streble, H. 1966. Das hormonale System der Spinnentiere. *Zool. Jahrb. Abt. Physiol.* 72:157–234.

Szlep, R. 1965. Web-spinning process and web structure of *Latrodectus. Proc. Zool. Soc. London* 145:75–88.

Tambs-Lyche, H. 1964. Semi-marine spider *Halorates. Sarsia* 17:17–19.

Theuer, B. 1954. Life-history of *Deinopis spinosis.* Master of Science thesis, Univ. of Florida, Gainesville (unpubl.)

Tilquin, A. 1942. *La Toile géometrique des Araignées.* Presses Univ. France, Paris.

Tongiorgi, P. 1959. Reversal of the rhythm of nycthemeral illumination on astronomical orientation and diurnal activity in *Arctosa. Arch. Italiennes Biol.* 97:251–265.

Tretzel, E. 1954. Reife und Fortpflanzungszeit bei Spinnen. *Z. Morphol. Ökol.* 42:634–691.

_____ 1955. Intragenerische Isolation und interspezifische Konkurrenz bei Spinnen. *Ibid.* 44:43–162.

_____ 1961. Biologie, Ökologie und Brutpflege von *Coelotes terrestris. Ibid.* 49:658–745; 50:375–542.

Turnbull, A. L. 1960. Prey of *Linyphia triangularis. Canadian J. Zool.* 38:859–873.

_____ 1964. Search of prey by a web-building *Achaearanea tepidariorum. Canadian Entomol.* 96:568–579.

_____ 1965. Prey abundance and development of *Agelenopsis potteri. Ibid.* 97:141–147.

_____ 1966. Population of spiders and their potential prey. *Canadian J. Zool.* 44:557–583.

Tuzet, O. and Manier, J. F. 1959. La spermiogenèse des araignées. *Ann. Sci. Natur. Zool. Paris* (12) 1:91–103.

Vachon, M. 1957–1958. Développement post-embryonnaire des araignées. *Bull. Soc. Zool. France* 82:337–354; 83:429–461.

Vicari, G. et al. 1965. Action of *Latrodectus* venom and fractions of cells cultivated in vitro. *Toxicon* 3:101–106.

Walcott, C. and Kloot, W. G. van der. 1959. Physiology of the spider vibration receptor. *J. Exp. Zool.* 141:191–244.

Weigel, G. 1941. Farbwechsel der Krabbenspinne *Misumena. Z. Vergl. Physiol.* 29:195–248.

Whitcomb, W. H. and Eason, R. 1965. Rearing wolf and lynx spiders. *Proc. Arkansas Acad. Sci.* 19:21–27.

_____ 1965. Mating behavior of *Peucetia viridans. Florida Entomol.* 48:163–167.

_____ et al. 1966. Life history of *Peucetia viridans. J. Kansas Entomol. Soc.* 39:259–267.

Whitehead, W. F. and Rempel, J. G. 1959. Musculature of the black-widow. *Canadian J. Zool.* 37:831–870.

Wiehle, H. 1931–1954. Spinnen, *in* Dahl, *Die Tierwelt Deutschlands,* G. Fischer, Verlag, 23, 33, 42, 44, 47, 49.

———— 1949. *Vom Fanggewebe einheimischer Spinnen.* Die Neue Brehm Bücherei 12, Akad. Verlagsges., Leipzig.

———— 1954. *Aus dem Spinnenleben wärmerer Länder.* Die Neue Brehm Bücherei 138, Akad. Verlagsges., Leipzig.

Wilson, R. S. 1962. Dragline control valves in the garden spider. *Quart. J. Microscop. Sci.* 103:549–571.

———— 1965. The pedicel of *Heteropoda venatoria. J. Zool.* 147:38–45.

———— 1967. Heartbeat of *Heteropoda. J. Insect Physiol.* 13:1309–1326.

Winkler, D. 1955. Das Tracheensystem der Dysderiden. *Mitt. Zool. Mus. Berlin* 31:25–43.

Witt, P. 1956. *Die Wirkung von Substanzen auf den Netzbau der Spinne als biologischer Test.* Springer, Berlin.

———— 1963. Environment in relation to behavior of spiders. *Arch Environm. Health* 7:4–12.

———— et al. 1964. Laser lesions and spider web construction. *Nature* 201:150–152.

———— and Reed, C. F. 1965. Spider web-building. *Science* 149:1190–1197.

Yoshikura, M. 1954–1955. Embryological studies on the liphistiid spider *Heptathela. Kumamota J. Sci.* 1B:37–40; 2B:1–86.

———— 1958. Development of a purse-web spider *Atypus. Ibid.* 2B; 3(2):73–86.

Zapfe, H. 1955. Filogenia y función en *Austrochilus. Trab. Lab. Zool., Univ. Chile* 2:1–54.

12.

Orders Ricinulei, Ricinuleids; Pseudoscorpiones, Pseudoscorpions; and Solifugae, Windscorpions

ORDER RICINULEI, RICINULEIDS

The Ricinulei include about 25 described species; the largest is *Ricinoides afzelii*, 1 cm long.

Ricinuleids are heavily sclerotized arachnids characterized by a flap (cucullus), on the anterior edge of the carapace, that hangs down over the mouthparts. The abdomen appears broadly joined to the uniform prosoma, and the posterior segments of the abdomen are so reduced as to be barely visible. The pedipalpi are small and leglike; their coxal endites fuse to form a trough.

Anatomy

Only rarely found, ricinuleids are readily recognized by the cucullus and the heavy exoskeleton. The abdomen consists of 10 segments, the first 2 being very short and tucked under the carapace and last leg coxae. Because the gonopore is on the posterior border of the small, most anterior sternite, it is assumed that this is sternite VIII and that sternite VII has been lost. The large tergites and sternites therefore must be X to XIII (Fig. 12–1). They are followed by four narrow, movable, telescoping rings (segments XIV to XVII), resembling the little tail of the Schizomida. The leg coxae completely cover the venter of the prosoma. The chelicerae are small, two-segmented and chelate (Fig. 12–2); they are inserted into the frontal area of the prosoma with a long collarlike articulating membrane that probably permits them to extend forward. The pedipalpi are leglike and ventral. The internal skeleton consists of small ectodermal apodemes; there is no endosternite.

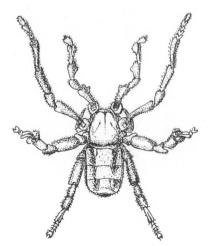

Fig. 12–1. *Cryptocellus simonis*, male, 5 mm long. (After Hansen and Sörensen, from Dahl.)

NERVOUS SYSTEM. The only sensory organs in evidence are hairs; trichobothria and eyes are lacking. All ganglia have shifted to the prosoma, where they form a compact brain.

DIGESTIVE SYSTEM. Behind the cucullus (Fig. 12–3) is the preoral cavity, its floor and walls formed by the lateral walls of the fused pedipalpal coxae (as in Fig. 8–9), its roof by the chelicerae and prosoma. There is a precerebral pumping stomach. Only a few tube-shaped ceca extend from the prosomal midgut, along the long axis of the body, and fill the posterior part of the prosoma as well as the abdomen with loops; details of their number and structure are unknown.

EXCRETORY SYSTEM. There is a pair of Malpighian tubules. Coxal glands open on the posterior border of the third coxa.

RESPIRATORY AND CIRCULATORY SYSTEMS. The respiratory organs are paired sieve tracheae; their atria lie in the prosoma with hundreds of tracheae going directly to the organs. The spiracles, protected by thorn-like and branched projections, lie laterally on the posterior wall of the prosoma in a deep groove above the last pair of coxae. The circulatory system consists of the heart, lying partly in the prosoma, partly in the abdomen, and surrounded by the pericardial sinus. Only one pair of ostia and anterior and posterior aortae are present.

REPRODUCTIVE SYSTEM. The gonads are paired. The atrium of the female has a posterior gland and a large median gland.

Reproduction

Tarsal and metatarsal articles of the third legs of the male are modified for sperm transfer (Fig. 12d). The male, on encountering a female, strokes and

taps her with his long second pair of legs. After 2 to 5 minutes the male mounts
the female, facing in the same direction with the edges of his cucullus wedged in
a groove between dorsal prosoma and abdomen of the female. Stroking and
tapping is continued for about 5 minutes. The male then lifts his abdomen
and with one of his third legs reaches underneath and picks up a white sphere
of sperm, its surface slightly hardened. He reaches down and applies the sperm
mass to the female genital opening, moving his leg in and out for 15 minutes.
"Amplexus" lasts for another hour.

Females of an African species have been observed with eggs. The female,
1 cm long, carries a single egg, 2 mm in diameter, with her cucullus and pedipalps. If disturbed, the female may eat the egg.

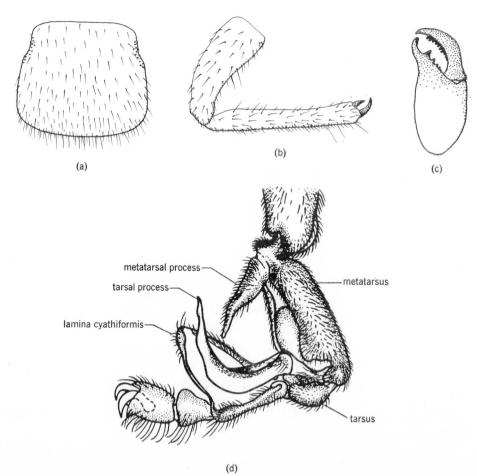

Fig. 12–2. *Cryptocellus lampeli* (courtesy J. A. L. Cooke and Zool. Soc. London): (a)
cucullus of female, 1 mm wide; (b) right male pedipalp, distal segment 1.5 mm long;
(c) right male chelicera, anterior view after cucullus is lifted, 0.8 mm long; (d) modified
right third leg of male, metatarsus 0.8 mm long.

Development

Nothing is known of the embryonic development. The youngest instar, a 6-legged larva, molts to become an 8-legged nymph. The last pair of legs is feeble; probably it is the last pair that the larva lacks. Molting occurs in burrows, in which young spend most of their time, and has not yet been observed. Ricinuleids have been kept captive for 3½ years, and are probably long-lived.

Habits

The animals are very secretive, and freeze on sensing the slightest air movements or light. Therefore they can be observed only at low light intensities.

Ricinuleids have been found in forest litter, under logs, and in caves. *Ricinoides afzelii* is a dull orange color when alive, others are grayish or brownish. They seem very sensitive to desiccation and probably move into the soil during dry periods. Some captives that died were believed unable to excrete surplus water. Two species of *Ricinoides* have been found together under one log in Africa. In South America some have also been found in the lower axils of leaf bases of coconut palms growing in a swamp. They probably are more common than is suspected and could be collected more frequently by using Tullgren funnels or sifting litter.

FEEDING. *Cryptocellus osorioi,* found in Mexican caves, has been observed to feed on the larvae of dipterous parasites of bats. *Ricinoides* readily feeds on termites. *Cryptocellus* from Guyana fed on small termites, spider embryos and young mygalomorph spiders of the genus *Accola.* In the laboratory they fed on *Drosophila* larvae. Termites are captured by the head, cucullus and palpi and are turned so that the soft abdomen can be reached by the chelicerae.

DISTRIBUTION. The animals occur in the equatorial region of West Africa and in tropical America as far north as Texas. Fossil Ricinulei are known from the northern hemisphere.

Classification

Ricinoididae. There is only one family. *Ricinoides (=Cryptostemma)* is found in West Africa, *Cryptocellus* in America.

ORDER PSEUDOSCORPIONES, PSEUDOSCORPIONS

Pseudoscorpiones, also called Chelonethi, include 2,000 species, the largest being *Garypus titaneus,* 12 mm long.

Pseudoscorpions are usually flattened and have the oval opisthosoma clearly segmented and broadly attached to the prosoma. The chelicerae are usually large, sometimes small, the pedipalpi large and chelate, like those of scorpions. The pedipalpal endites form part of the preoral cavity. Two pairs of respiratory tracheae are present.

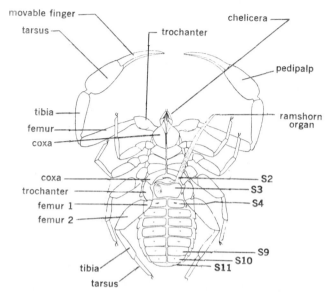

Fig. 12–3.   *Chelifer cancroides,* ventral view of male, 3 mm long; S — numbers refer to abdominal sternites. (After Beier.)

Anatomy

The little pseudoscorpions, usually only 2–4 mm long, are readily distinguished from true scorpions by the uniform abdomen, lack of a stinger, and by the different structure of the preoral cavity. Most species are black or brown, some olive-colored.

In the Monosphyronida only the dorsum of the prosoma has one or two transverse grooves (Fig. 12–5); their relationship to the segmentation is not known. The abdomen has distinct tergites VII to XVII and a posterior anal plate, possibly belonging to metamere XVIII (Fig. 8–2). On the anterior of the venter there is a plate with the gonopores at its posterior edge; the plate, then, must be sternite VIII. Pregenital sternite VII is suppressed (Fig. 12–3).

APPENDAGES. The chelicerae, two-articled and chelate, project forward (Fig. 12–4). Their fingers, toothed distally, bear serrulae, soft membranes with toothed border used for grooming. Silk glands open near the tip of the movable finger on a hump (Diplosphyronida) or on a branched galea. At the distal ends of the pedipalpi are the long, toothed fingers of the chelae. The pincer contains a poison gland that opens through the distal tooth; rarely there is a poison gland and openings in both fingers (Cheliferidae). The gland fills either finger or sometimes both and may reach to the proximal end of the chela. The anterior edges of the pedipalpal coxae are enlarged mesally and, with the chelicerae, form the preoral cavity (Fig. 12–5). The walking leg tarsus bears two claws and an attachment organ, the arolium, on a short pretarsus. The short endo-sternite lies behind the subesophageal ganglion.

NERVOUS SYSTEM. All ganglia are concentrated in the prosoma as a brain (Fig. 12–5). As in many other small forms, the brain is relatively large. There is a central body and a protocerebral bridge, probably the vestige of the paired globulus (association organ). No optic centers are differentiated.

There are simple sensory hairs, trichobothria on the palpal fingers, slit sense organs, and usually one or two pairs of lateral eyes. There are about 20 retina cells, the rhabdoms of which face a tapetum.

DIGESTIVE SYSTEM. The mouth is at the base of a projection, of which the dorsal part forms the labrum, while the grooved venter encloses the labium (Fig. 12–5). Both labrum and labium lie within a narrow space laterally en-closed by the pedipalpal coxae. The whole projection extends into a preoral cavity formed by the long parallel pedipalpal endites (Fig. 12–3). The sclero-tized pharynx has an X-shaped lumen and serves as a pump. The long esoph-agus passes through the brain and widens into a midgut having nine unbranched ceca on each side. The first pair lies in the prosoma and opens directly into the gut while the others lie between the dorsoventral muscles of the abdomen (Fig. 12–5). As in scorpions, the posterior four to five have a common duct opening into the gut lumen. Also there is an unpaired ventral cecum in the anterior of the abdomen. In the region of segment XI the midgut narrows and loops, but widens posteriorly in an endodermal rectal pocket which opens through a short ectodermal hindgut.

EXCRETORY SYSTEM. The excretory organs are prosomal nephrocytes and coxal glands; these open on the posterior wall of the third coxa. Malpighian tubules are absent, but the epithelium of the gut ceca, and possibly the silk glands, are excretory in function. The silk glands lie in a compact mass of tubes anterior in the prosoma, sometimes extending into the abdomen; they are some-

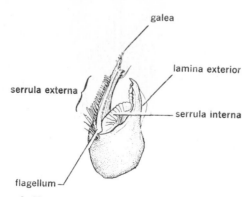

Fig. 12–4. Chelicera of *Chernes*, ventral view, 0.3 mm long. (After Kroneberg, from Kaestner.)

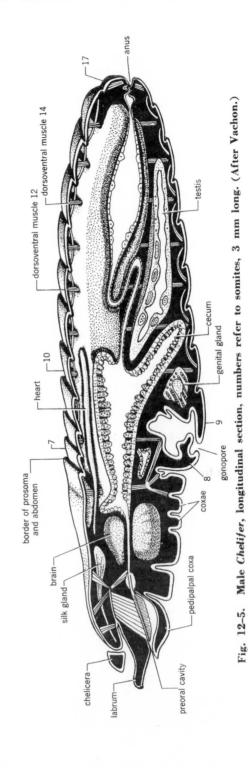

Fig. 12–5.   Male *Chelifer*, longitudinal section, numbers refer to somites, 3 mm long. (After Vachon.)

times reduced in **adult males**. Their ducts open in the tip of the movable finger of the chelicera (Figs. 12–4, 12–5).

RESPIRATORY SYSTEM. There are two pairs of tracheae with spiracles on the posterior borders or membranes of sternites IX and X. Many species have sieve tracheae, the atria of which project into the region of the third leg coxae. In the Dithidae the anterior tracheae branch along their entire length into tracheal capillaries.

CIRCULATORY SYSTEM. The tracheae deliver oxygen directly to the tissues. Correspondingly the arterial system is absent, and the heart, located in the abdomen (under tergites VII to XI), has only an anterior artery and a pair of posterior ostia (Fig. 12–5).

REPRODUCTIVE SYSTEM. The sexes differ little in structure. The testis is an unpaired ventral sac with paired diverticula that fuse laterally in some species. The paired vas deferens opens into a mesodermal atrium, and that in turn into a glandular ectodermal portion that produces the complicated spermatophore and stalk. The ovary also is unpaired, sometimes branched; anteriorly the ectodermal atrium has a pair of seminal receptacles. In chernetids there is a median seminal receptacle.

Reproduction

As in scorpions, the female picks up the sperm from the stalked spermatophores previously deposited by a male. In the more primitive families belonging to the orders Heterosphyronida and Diplosphyronida and in Cheiridiidae, the female is assumed to find the spermatophore chemotactically. However, members of the Chernetidae and Cheliferidae court and the male leads the female to the spermatophore.

The spermatophores consist of a stalk and a sperm mass that, in most species, is enclosed in a sperm package. The stalk stands straight up in the forms that do not court, but is inclined in most chernetids and cheliferids. The sperm package is emptied by swelling until it bursts. The spermatophores of the chernetids and cheliferids bear, under the sperm package, a drop of fluid that helps to trigger the swelling mechanism in sperm transfer.

The males of *Chthonius, Neobisium* and some cheiridiids deposit spermatophores even in the absence of females. The females, possibly led by chemical senses, search for the spermatophores. As the female, her body held high, walks over a spermatophore, a drop of fluid from her gonopore triggers the swelling mechanism, and the sperm is sprayed into the gonopore. *Chthonius* and *Cheiridium* regularly destroy their old unused spermatophores and replace them.

The male *Serianus* (Olpiidae) deposits spermatophores only in the presence of females, minutes after he has encountered one. Then he marks a way to the spematophore with a row of silken threads on both sides, attached in a zig-zag line between the ground and something above. This path leads the female to

the spermatophore. The silk used for this purpose is produced not in the prosomal silk glands but in the rectal pocket, differentiated in the male of this
species into a silk gland. As in chthoniids and cheiridiids, old spermatophores
and their paths are replaced.

Courting chernetids grasp one or both pedipalpal hands of the female and,
holding on throughout mating, pull her back and forth (Fig. 12–6). The male
may display with the free hand or, in some species, with his first pair of legs.
Finally, heads almost touching, the male deposits the spermatophore. Then as he
pulls the female over it she picks up the sperm package with her opened gonopore. The pair may remain together for 2–3 hours, the male depositing a
spermatophore every 8–10 minutes. In the chernetid, *Lamprochernes,* the female tends to initiate mating. Males of *Lasiochernes* and *Lamprochernes* will
take the pedipalp of any male or female of the same species and try to force
the partner to walk back and forth.

Some cheliferids, at the posterior wall of the ectodermal genital atrium, have a
pair of soft cylindrical tubes, the "ram's horn organs," which can be everted by
blood pressure so far that they may touch the anterior of the prosoma (Fig. 12–
3). The male of *Dactylochelifer latreillei* initiates courtship by grasping both
female pedipalpi and walking back and forth. But he releases his grasp and
continues to dance. As the female approaches him, the male signals with his
palps for her to walk backward and he steps forward. Then he steps backward
again, dances and waits until she approaches closely. This stepping forward

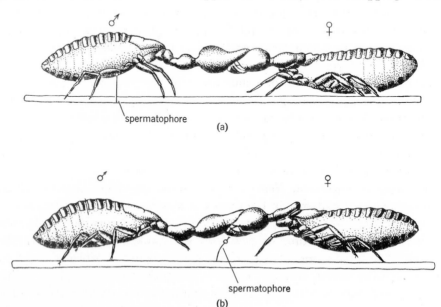

Fig. 12–6. Mating of *Dendrochernes cyrneus,* male left, lateral view; each animal 4
mm long (after Kew): (a) male deposits spermatophore; (b) male pulls female over
spermatophore.

and backward is repeated several times, without contact between mates. The ram's horn organs are pulled in and out. Finally the male deposits a spermatophore and steps back over it. Then as the female moves forward and touches it, the male quickly moves forward, pushes his prosoma under the female's coxae, hooks the large tarsal claws of his first legs into her genital opening, and pulls her over the spermatophore. The male of *Chelifer cancroides* "dances" about 1 cm from the female, making lateral pedipalpal movements and vibrating the raised abdomen with the ram's horn organs evaginated, before depositing the spermatophore. Then the male moves back and while the female moves forward he grasps her palpal femora with both chelae, pushes his prosoma underneath her and, with both first legs touching the female genitalia, shakes the female 8–10 times in 3–4 minutes. It is assumed that the female follows the movements of her partner chemotactically or perhaps visually (only those with eyes break physical contact) or with trichobothria. Males of *Chelifer cancroides* may dance toward other males of the same species, but deposit a spermatophore only in the presence of a receptive female. *Chelifer* males display only in a territory, presumably marked with scent secreted by the coxal sacs; the male has been observed to rub the ground with its venter.

Development

Several weeks after mating, in many species, the female retires to a silken nest where she remains during the egg-laying and early development of her young. Before egg-laying, a brood pouch is secreted. Two projections of the ectodermal genital atrium are evaginated by blood pressure and are covered by a secretion of the large glands. The secretion hardens to produce a ventral pouch. Into this sac the eggs are deposited one after another, 7–40 in *Chelifer cancroides*, 2–5 or 6 in *Cheiridium museorum*. The eggs stay at the periphery of the sac, stretching its walls (Fig. 12–7). After producing eggs, the ovary wall becomes glandular and the female secretes into the pouch a nutrient "milk" on which the embryos feed.

The embryos take up the fluid by means of two embryonic organs. At first, during cleavage and gastrulation, a syncytial layer forms under the egg shell. This layer absorbs and stores the nutritive fluid secreted into the brood pouch by the female. Later the embryo develops a complicated pumping organ, consisting of a large muscular upper lip, a platelike lower lip, and a small preoral chamber formed by pedipalpal coxae; with this pumping organ the syncytial layer with the stored nutrient is consumed. Now the embryo molts and ruptures the egg shell. In this second stage the embryos lie free but closely packed in the brood sac and feed on the much larger quantity of nutritive fluid now being secreted into the brood pouch. After that they complete organogenesis and finally, by means of a hatching tooth, rupture their cuticula and the brood sac membrane to emerge as protonymphs.

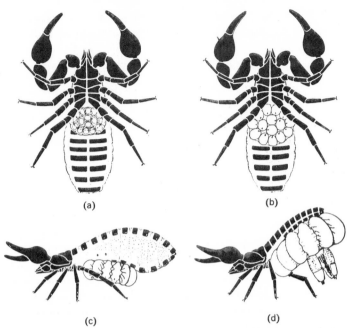

(a)   (b)

(c)   (d)

Fig. 12-7. Female *Pselaphochernes scorpioides* with brood sac (from Weygoldt):
(a) sac with eggs; (b) sac with embryos after first feeding; (c) after molting and
breaking of egg membrane; (d) young emerging from brood sac.

The various families and genera display considerable difference in development. The primitive *Chthonius* does not have a complete brood sac. First the
eggs are carried in a drop of fluid attached to the gonopore. Later, material is
secreted that glues the eggs together and imbeds the embryos. The pumping
organ of *Chthonius* persists and functions nearly until the end of the embryonic
development; after that it is transformed directly into the mouthparts of the
protonymph. The "milk" is not completely used up by the embryos, and the
protonymphs remain attached by their chelicerae to the secretions around the
female gonopore and continue for some days to pump fluid. Young *C. tetra-
chelatus* stay with their mother until reaching the deutonymph stage. Unlike
other species, the female *Chthonius* feeds on the remains of the secretions and
membranes.

In *Neobisium* too the pumping organ works over a long period, but not
through the entire embryonic development. During metamorphosis of the
pumping organ into the mouthparts, most of its muscles degenerate, only a few
remaining ones being incorporated into the upper lip. The development takes
about 4–5 weeks.

In *Cheiridium*, *Chernes*, and *Chelifer* feeding in the second embryonic stage
is much shorter, a few hours or, in some cheliferids, only seconds. This takes
place in an early stage of development, before the rapid organogenesis begins,

and results in a sudden increase in volume, three to four times, of the embryos. After that the pumping organ degenerates, only a small part remaining to contribute later to formation of the mouthparts. *Chelifer,* while molting to begin the second embryonic stage, also ruptures the brood sac membrane, the embryo's back protruding out of the brood sac.

Females of most of these forms, too, carry the brood sac until emergence of the protonymphs, but the presence of the mother is no longer necessary after the embryos have absorbed all the nutritive fluid. The females of *Cheiridium* and *Apocheiridium,* however, drop the brood sac at this time, the embryos completing their development in the nest abandoned by the mother. *Serianus* females also drop the brood sac, but remain in the nest with it until after the protonymphs hatch (Weygoldt, personal communication).

The protonymph, in most cases, leaves the mother some days after hatching, molts to become a deutonymph, then a tritonymph, and finally an adult, which does not molt again. The nymphs are smaller than adults and have fewer palpal trichobothria. In laboratory cultures of *Chelifer cancroides,* the embryo stage takes 5–18 days, the second embryonic stage 16–25 days (the time in the brood sac 16–41 days). The nymph stage takes 10 to 24 months. The adult females live 3½ to 5 years, maturing in 1–2 years.

Molting takes place in a silken chamber. The nymph rests for several days, unable to move. In a few days, strong contraction of the abdomen presses fluids into the prosoma and inflates it, tearing the anterior edge of the dorsal cover. The chelicerae move out of the tear, free from the old cuticle. Strong movements tear the dorsal prosomal cover loose to the base of the abdomen on each side. Within 8 hours the old skin slowly moves posteriorly, freeing the animal within. As they are freed, the new appendages slowly flex. The whole process of molting, including the previous quiescent period, takes 1–2 weeks.

Relationships

In form, pseudoscorpions resemble scorpions. In structure of the abdomen and preoral cavity, they resemble more the Amblypygi, while in the gut structure they resemble the Uropygi; in brood sac and genital atrium they resemble both.

Habits

Pseudoscorpions live in crevices; most species prefer somewhat humid conditions under bark and in plant litter. The cosmopolitan *Chelifer cancroides* lives in houses, where it hunts booklice, small insects and bedbug nymphs; only rarely is it found outside, under bark. The cosmopolitan *Cheiridium museorum* lives in barns and buildings.

Chthoniidae and Neobisiidae live in moist habitats: in leaf litter, moss, under stones and a few under bark. The Olpiinae prefer dry areas, even deserts. Some species, especially Neobisiidae, are found in caves, adapted to their habitat by the long appendages, long sensory setae, and lack of coloration commonly seen among other cave arthropods. The large *Garypus* lives on ocean shores; the European *Neobisium maritimum* inhabits the intertidal area, covered by water twice daily. In Florida *Dinocheirus tumidus* and in North Carolina another *Dinocheirus* live in the driftline, covered by water twice a day. The nests of small mammals and some birds support a fauna of a pseudoscorpions, mostly Monosphyronida, that prey on the larvae of beetles, flies, fleas, and mites. Ant and bee nests are inhabited by chernetids and cheliferids.

Phoresy is often observed; mature females, rarely males but never juveniles, attach themselves to legs or flies or sometimes other insects, and are transported— an important means of dispersal for some species, originating presumably from attacking prey too large to handle.

NEST BUILDING. Pseudoscorpions are protected by their silken nests, made before each molt, for overwintering, and for oviposition. The nests, 2 to 10 mm, are usually about twice the length of the inhabitant. The inside is a papery silk wall, while the outside generally is covered by particles of wood, pebbles, sand grains and food remains. First, *Dendrochernes* and *Chelifer* build a circle of these particles, picked up with the pedipalpi and arranged with the chelicerae. Then the animal, moving to and fro, spins the material together. With each forward movement the galeae touch a particle with silk and connect it to a neighboring one. Presently the pseudoscorpion turns to weave the next section. When the nest is almost complete, the pseudoscorpion may move outside to collect more particles, and possibly to build a cupola. The whole task takes 10–12 hours. Then the inner wall and floor are finished. The 6 threads coming from each galea do not stick to each other, so about 10–12 threads are made with each movement. The finished nest protects its inhabitant from predators, excess moisture, and desiccation. After molting, the pseudoscorpion may tear the wall with pedipalpi and chelicerae, and abandon the nest.

LOCOMOTION. Pseudoscorpions walk rapidly with all 8 legs, sometimes faster backward than forward, permitting them to retreat into a crevice while brandishing the pedipalpi. Some species (*Chthonius*) may make small jumps, probably propelled by their strong fourth femora.

SENSES. Touch and vibration are no doubt the most important senses. Chemical senses are also important in feeding and sperm transfer behavior. All species project their pedipalpi when running and presumably receive distant stimuli through their trichobothria. *Chelifer cancroides* notices prey 1–4 cm distant, but *Chelifer* will also respond to a tuning fork by pedipalpal movement. The structure of the eyes precludes pictorial vision. They probably recognize movement of objects close by. If a piece of paper is moved toward *Chelifer*, it will retract the pedipalpi when the paper is about 5 mm distant, before extending them toward the paper. In experimental dishes, *Chelifer cancroides* does not avoid light or darkness when moving about but prefers to rest in the dark and on rough surfaces.

FEEDING. Chthoniidae and Neobisiidae tear food with their large chelicerae. *Chthonius*, with its large chelicerae, may use them for attack rather than the pedipalpi. The chelicerae may open up the prey and chew it. A 4 mm *Drosophila* larva will be chewed into a little ball, 1 mm in diameter, in 1–2 hours. Garypids, olpiids, and all Monosphyronida take prey with the pedipalpi and move it to the small chelicerae, which bite the hole in the prey. Once the chelicerae have a good hold, after some handling, the pedipalpi let go; the immovable cheliceral finger is in the prey, the movable one holds on. Digestive juice is pumped into the prey, and predigested fluid is sucked in. The pedipalpi may take the prey back to facilitate insertion of chelicerae at another point. It takes 15–20 minutes to feed on a small caterpillar. The injection of digestive juice can be recognized by the swelling of the caterpillar; later it collapses as it is sucked out.

Food preferences, expressed by dropping certain prey already in the chelicerae, have been observed in only a few species. *Neobisium muscorum*, living in litter, prefers Collembola and *Blothrus* feeds on beetles. *Chelifer cancroides* prefers booklice, also preys on bedbugs, rejects mites, and takes Collembola only exceptionally. In captivity they will take plant lice, larvae and adults of small Lepidoptera, *Drosophila* and fleas.

SOCIAL HABITS. *Chthonius* and *Neobisium* may spend a lot of time grooming. *Chthonius* washes with a drop of liquid from the oral cavity. Many pseudoscorpions are gregarious; some species sit almost on top of each other. When two individuals of *Chelifer* meet, one waves the palpus slowly. Similar movements on meeting an individual of the same species have been described for several species.

Classification

Pseudoscorpions are divided into 3 suborders, which differ by the size of their chelicerae, their leg tarsi and also in their mating behavior.*

SUBORDER HETEROSPHYRONIDA

Each first and second leg has 5 articles excluding the coxa, and each third and fourth leg has 6 articles excluding the coxa. (Legs 1 and 2 have one tarsal article; legs 3 and 4 have two.) Chelicerae are large and strong. The two families included are Tridenchthoniidae and Chthoniidae, with the genus *Chthonius*.

---

* The names used are those proposed by J. C. Chamberlin, 1929, who first grouped the pseudoscorpions. The names later proposed by Beier, 1932, which are used in Europe, are Chthoniinea, Neobisiinea, and Cheliferinea.

SUBORDER DISPLOSPHYRONIDA

The tarsus of each leg is divided into metatarsus and telotarsus, so each leg has 6 articles excluding the coxa. Usually there are 4 eyes. Seven families are included. Neobisiidae includes the genera *Blothrus*, *Microcreagris* and *Neobisium*. *Neobisium* inhabits leaf litter. The European *N. muscorum* reproduces only at cool temperatures, 10–15°C. Other families are Syarinidae with *Syarinus* and *Chitrella*, Hyidae, Ideoroncidae, Menthidae, Olpiidae with *Olpium* and *Serianus*, and Garypidae with *Garypus*. *Garypus* is found under stones on ocean shores.

SUBORDER MONOSPHYRONIDA

The tarsi are not divided, so each leg has 5 articles excluding coxa. Anteriorly the prosomal dorsum is tapered or rounded. Usually there are two eyes or fewer. Families are: Faellidae with *Faella*; Pseudogarypidae with *Pseudogarypus*; Cheiridiidae with *Cheiridium* and *Apocheiridium*; Sternophoridae with *Garyops*; Atemnidae; Chernetidae with *Chernes*, *Chelanops*, *Lamprochernes*, *Hesperochernes*, *Dendrochernes*, *Pselaphochernes* and *Dinocheirus*. *Lasiochernes*, from mammal nests gives off a strong odor; it readily attaches itself to bristles of a brush. Cheliferidae includes *Chelifer cancroides* found in buildings. The tropical *Ellingsenius* lives only in tropical bee colonies and is transported by bees. Other cheliferid genera are *Dactylochelifer* and *Withius*.

ORDER SOLIFUGAE, WINDSCORPIONS

The order Solifugae (also called Solpugida) includes 800 species, the largest being *Galeodes caspius*, 7 cm.

Solifugids are arachnids that have the prosoma divided into a proterosoma and two free segments. The abdomen is narrowed at the anterior end. The chelicerae are huge, the pedipalpi leglike. There is a well developed tracheal system with two large longitudinal trunks and many branches.

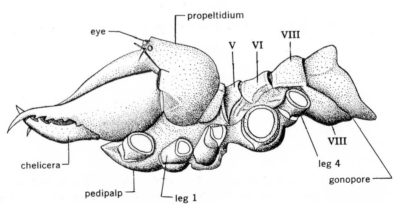

Fig. 12–8.   Anterior body of *Galeodes graecus*, lateral view; 2 cm long. (After Kaestner.)

Anatomy

Windscorpions can direct their huge chelicerae toward an adversary by bending the domed proterosoma up (Fig. 12–9). The proterosoma is probably connected by a thin membrane to flexible tergites V and VI (Fig. 12–9) and there is also a ventral joint, between the fused coxae, in the shape of a transverse membrane behind the coxae of the second walking legs (Fig. 8–3). This segmentation, present in the embryo, is probably not secondarily acquired. The barrel-shaped opisthosoma has distinct tergites and sternites VIII to XVII, while the plates of metamere VII are reduced to a soft pedicel (Figs. 8–3, 12–8). In contrast to the hard proterosoma, which provides attachment sites for muscles, the abdomen has a flexible exoskeleton, which may expand greatly after feeding or in females carrying eggs.

APPENDAGES. The huge, projecting chelate chelicerae are two-articled armed with teeth but not with poison glands. Pedipalpi are leglike, their coxae widened but otherwise similar to leg coxae (Fig. 8–3). The terminal article has an eversible attachment disc instead of claws. The first walking legs are thin and weak compared with the others (Fig. 12–9).

Fig. 12–9. *Galeodes arabs* female in defensive position; 5 cm long. (After Millot.)

There is no mesodermal endosternite. Instead the strong muscles are attached to an ectodermal internal skeleton. Flat apodemes extend toward the inside from the immovably fused coxae. A large median apodeme arises between the coxae of the first and second walking legs. Its two parallel ridges extend diagonally into the posterior of the prosoma, where they unite into a flat plate.

Separating the prosoma and abdomen is a diaphragm of muscular fibers that connect the anterior borders of the first abdominal tergite and sternite. The vestiges of segment VII are thus included in the prosoma. The internal pressure of the prosoma is independent from that of the abdomen, but the diaphragm is penetrated by gut, heart, nerves and main tracheae through openings having circular muscles.

NERVOUS SYSTEM. The nervous system comprises the brain, a subesophageal ganglion containing ganglia II to XI, and a small ganglion in VIII containing the five posterior ganglia. The protocerebrum has a central body, a pair of globuli, and simple optic centers. The most anterior optic ganglia have moved behind the eyes as in the compound eyes of Crustacea and Insecta.

Long sensory hairs cover the windscorpions (Fig. 12–9). The pedipalpal tarsus and the tarsus of the first leg contain sensilla ampullacea, special short sensory hairs within small pits. Ventrally, proximal articles of the last walking legs bear stalked mallet-shaped structures, the racquet organs or malleoli, containing sensory nerve endings. There is a pair of large median eyes in which the rhabdoms face the lens, and at the propeltidium border there may be vestiges of lateral eyes.

DIGESTIVE SYSTEM. The mouthparts are simple. The mouth is at the tip of the projecting rostrum. Above the convex dorsal side of the rostrum is the labrum, and below it is the labium. Although wide and drawn out, the pedipalpal coxae do not border the preoral cavity (Fig. 8–3). The pharynx is a pump, which in turn continues into a sclerotized esophagus. The midgut has four pairs of projecting prosomal forked ceca; the last two reach the coxae of the third and fourth leg. In the eighth segment originate a pair of much branched ceca which resemble those of spiders, and fill the abdomen. The short ectodermal posterior gut is sclerotized and laterally compressed.

EXCRETORY SYSTEM. A pair of Malpighian tubules opens into the gut; there are nephrocytes in the pericardium, ameboid cells in the blood, and a pair of coxal glands. The coxal glands are unique in that they have a blind secreting tube at the beginning of the labyrinth and they empty anterior to the pedipalpal coxae.

RESPIRATORY SYSTEM. The much-branched tracheae open on the abdomen, at the posterior border of sternites IX, X and XI (Fig. 8–3). The anterior two open as paired spiracles, the posterior opens medially. There are additional prosomal spiracles posteriorly on the second walking leg (segment IV), unusual for arachnids. Two main tracheae extend the length of the animal, giving off branches, some of which have expanded airsacs resembling those of insects. Indeed, the entire tracheal system resembles that of insects more than that of arachnids. In other arachnids tracheal systems tend to be associated with vestiges of abdominal appendages. Undoubtedly, it is of secondary origin, not a primitive character, as is evidenced by the prosomal spiracles.

CIRCULATORY SYSTEM. Corresponding with the complex tracheal system, the circulatory system is reduced to a short heart having 8 pairs of ostia and extending from somites V to XII. Two pairs of ostia are prosomal, a condition otherwise found only in the Holopeltidia (Uropygi). There are unbranched anterior and posterior aortae, continuations of the heart, but no lateral arteries.

REPRODUCTIVE SYSTEM. Male windscorpions are usually smaller and longer legged than females. On the fixed cheliceral finger, some males have a spoon-shaped appendage, the flagellum, derived from one or several modified bristles. Its function is unknown and removal does not prevent mating. There is no flagellum in eremobatids. The ovaries are a pair of long tubes. The testes are 2 pairs of coiled canals that continue as four vasa deferentia and fuse into two ducts that enter the median atrium. The spermatozoa are enclosed in a spermatophore cover within the vasa deferentia.

Reproduction

Mating has been observed in Galeodidae and Eremobatidae. In *Galeodes caspius* the male stops when approaching a female, then jumps on her and grasps her abdomen with his chelicerae. At the same time, the female prosoma is embraced by the pedipalpi and legs. While the female becomes completely passive, the smaller male may carry her 2 m, turn her on her back and pinch her genital region; the female genital pore opens wide. Now the male raises his abdomen and produces the spermatophore. It is placed on the substrate and picked up by the chelicerae. Alternately the right and left chelicerae push it into the female genital pore, which is then closed by the male. Suddenly the male jumps off and runs away; the female immediately turns upright. Mating lasts only minutes. Mating of *Galeodes arabs* and *Othoes saharae* is very similar. *Galeodes caspius* deposits eggs in a previously dug pit, as deep as 20 cm in the hot, hard ground. Lying on her side, the female deposits about 100 spherical eggs, within which embryos are already well-developed. The eggs hatch in 1 or 2 days. The larvae remain immobile 2 to 3 weeks, and only after molting acquire the appearance of the adult and the ability to move.

Although mating of captive individuals of a number of American species has been attempted, only several *Eremobates* (Eremobatidae) species have mated in captivity. All have similar behavior. Both male and female assume attack position with palpi and first legs elevated (Fig. 12–10a), chelicerae open, and a rocking motion of the body. From this position both may leave or the male may jump forward. If the female submits, she closes her chelicerae, relaxes her legs

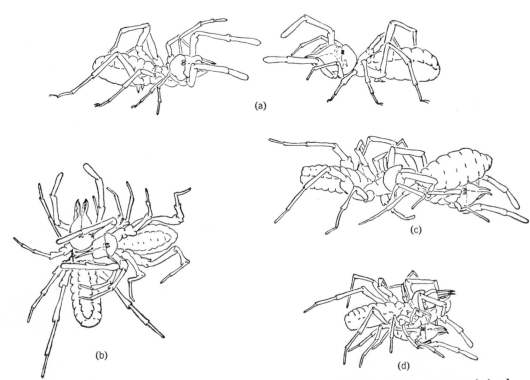

Fig. 12–10. *Eremobates* sp. mating; each 2.5 cm long (from Muma, courtesy Animal Behavior Society.): (a) male approaching female; (b) male right, grasping female, left; (c) turning female; male left, female right; (d) sperm transfer, male left; female with abdomen folded upright.

and bends her prosoma back. Once a male was seen to chase a female. The male takes a female, turns her over, and pushes the fixed cheliceral fingers deep into her gonopore. Then she is placed back in walking position with her abdomen bent up (Fig. 12–10c). The male chews the opercular area, occasionally lifting the female. Then the male bends the abdomen of the female back over her prosoma (Fig. 12–10d) and a droplet of seminal fluid is transferred directly from male to female gonopores. This takes only a second or two. The male turns and again thrusts the chelicerae into the gonopore for a variable length of time, possibly forcing the sperm into the receptacles or breaking the mass up while the female becomes active. Separation varies as did the preliminary encounter. Finally the male cleans his chelicerae. *Eremobates durangonus* differs in that the male grasps the free posterior prosomal segments (Fig. 12–10b) of the female. The mating takes 4–17 minutes. A female that was wounded was consumed, and once in a while a male is eaten.

In *Eremobates durangonus* the males become adult in late July and disappear in September. The females are in evidence from early August to October. Egg masses have been found in September. Egg laying occurs 9–14 days after mating. If not mated, the females did not produce eggs, or the eggs were sterile. In captivity, females have laid 1–5 egg masses with 20–164 eggs each, each 1.9 mm in diameter. Egg deposition requires 40–60 minutes, the female lying on her back or side. The first masses of eggs were all fertile or entirely sterile, later ones had a high percentage of sterile eggs. At 26°C, 70% relative humidity, eggs hatched in about 28 days; 15°C seemed near the critical low temperature. The egg masses were deposited in burrows 5–8 cm deep in the laboratory, probably deeper under natural conditions. The newly hatched young cannot open their chelicerae, but the upper finger has an egg tooth. The legs lack tarsi and claws, but the larvae can wiggle away. About 7–12 days later at 26°C, probably closer to two weeks in nature, they molt to become nymphs that resemble adults. Nymphs of the first instar do not feed and molt again in less than 2 weeks. The second instar nymphs appear on the surface and tend to keep together. They feed together on their first prey, as many as five on a termite, and may feed on each other. There are at least 8, possibly 10, nymphal instars. Nymphs of early instars have a reduced number of malleoli. From 5–15 days prior to molting the animal digs a burrow and becomes quiescent. The second to fifth instars overwinter, remaining active and feeding at temperatures as low as 5°C. The galeodid *Othoes* has a variable number of instars before becoming adult. While *Eremobates* has a lifespan of less than a year, *Othoes* is believed to live two spring reproductive seasons.

Development

The embryology is not well known. There are 16 segments, a head and a tail lobe. Metameres VIII to XVI have button-shaped appendages that disappear later. Before hatching, the prosoma shows segmentation into an anterior portion and metameres IV to VI.

Relationships

Windscorpions are characterized by a mixture of primitive and specialized characters. The equal segmentation of body and heart, the leglike pedipalpi and the simple preoral cavity appear primitive, while the respiratory system with connected tracheae and the heart reduction are secondary. Solifugids are known from the Carboniferous.

Habits

Most windscorpions are desert dwellers. There are six species in Europe, some in Indian forests, others in Florida and throughout the West Indies, and many in western United States, more than 120 species north of Mexico. In the Andes they have been collected at altitudes over 3000 m. They have not been found in the Amazon and Congo basins, Australia, and the South Sea Islands.

Windscorpions are usually crepuscular or nocturnal, often frightening campers when they come into tents or to campfires. A few are diurnal. If an adversary appears, the prosoma is raised and the chelicerae opened. African and Eurasian species make stridulating sounds by rubbing the median sides of the chelicerae.

LOCOMOTION. The rapid movement of these animals has given them the name "windscorpion." Like some spiders, they run with great speed, making sudden stops. Only the last 3 pairs of legs are used in running, the first and pedipalpi being held above the substrate. Species with an eversible vesicle on the palpus tip readily climb smooth stone or vertical glass surfaces. The windscorpions observed run in a straight line but circle objects encountered: rocks, logs, and cow dung. Pitfall traps at the end of halfburied logs will capture specimens.

American species, on being sprinkled with rain or water, run and rapidly start burrowing. Although most Solifugae have no specialized morphological structures for burrowing, most of them dig and may make as many as 40 burrows during their lifetime. The burrows are used for rest, digestion, molting or hibernation. The burrows in the laboratory reach 1–23 cm below the surface, probably going deeper in nature. The burrowing is done by biting, raking and plowing. Obstructions are bitten free and carried out of the way with the chelicerae. In raking with the dorsolateral macrosetae on the tibiae of legs 2 and 3, sand and clay particles are hurled back several centimeters. When there is an accumulation, the excavator turns around and pushes it back by lowering the body and pushing like a snow plow. The pile is first pushed out of the entrance, but later, when the burrow is several body lengths deep, the dirt is plowed only to the entrance, which is thus closed. The completed chamber is oval to spherical. In most observations the animal was digging between two panes of glass. Digging by *Galeodes arabs* is similar to that of American species.

The animals survive submersion in water, possibly an adaptation to the flash floods common in arid regions. They stop moving completely as soon as covered by water.

SENSES. The many sensory setae are the main receptors for touch, air currents, and vibration. A chemical sense can be demonstrated; they will stop 2.5 cm from eucalyptus pieces, and males sense females before actually touching them. There is no response if the pedipalpi with their sensory setae are amputated. Experiments with *Galeodes* demonstrate that if the eyes are covered by black lacquer they are slower in catching prey. *Galeodes arabs* has been observed to jump at a hand passing on the other side of its glass container, and a high percentage of dark 5 cm cardboard squares on the other side of the glass were attacked. The function of the mallet-shaped organs is not known, but possibly they are vibration receptors.

FEEDING. Touch and vibration are used to find food. The diurnal *Hemerotrecha californica* can probably see prey. They may capture prey by chase or ambush, and may congregate in places of high prey density, such as termite nests where they only have to pick up termites with their palps and place them in the chelicerae. The prey is manipulated, lacerated, rotated by the chelicerae. Exoskeletal and setal fragments are found in stomach contents and feces. Females and juveniles engorge so that the abdomen expands to several times its normal size. Males do not feed so much. Satiated *Ammotrechula* has been observed to kill termites and bury them. However, juveniles can survive for 2 months without food. Large species do not necessarily feed on large prey. *Eremorhax magnus* takes beetles and earthworms; *E. striatus* takes almost any insect except termites, the preferred food of most American species. Small species are limited to small food. *Eremobates durangonus* accepted a wide variety of food, but preferred termites, 20–40 at a feeding. *Ammotrechella stimpsoni* feeds primarily on termites. They will take droplets of water. Feces are ejected several centimeters beyond the abdomen.

Old world solifuges also have a ravenous appetite. A *Galeodes* took successively four large acridids and fed on flies soon after. The prey is held by the chelicerae. The chelicerae open and close, cutting the food, and also extend and pull back. Large beetles are decapitated and eviscerated. Grasshoppers are held transverse to the main axis of the body, crushed, and chewed until the remains form a ball. An 18 cm long lizard was eaten up, except for a wad of remains, within 30 minutes. Large species will bite if carelessly handled, but no poison is present.

Classification

The dentition of the chelicerae is used to separate species. Of the 10 families, only two are found in the Americas: Ammotrechidae and Eremobatidae. All others are African or Eurasian.

Ammotrechidae. Found from the United States to southern Argentina, these have the anterior edge of the propeltidium rounded, and they lack claws on the first pair of legs. Males have a cheliceral flagellum. *Ammotrecha* is found in the southern United States, *Ammotrechella stimpsoni* from Florida, under bark of stumps inhabited by termites. *Ammotrechula* is another genus.

Eremobatidae. North American, these have the anterior edge of the propeltidium truncate, one or two claws at the tip of the first leg, and on legs 2 and 3, a spine on the tarsus. Males lack a cheliceral flagellum but do have flagellar bristles. *Eremobates* is common in the southwestern United States; *Hemerotrecha* and *Eremorhax* are also included.

Rhagodidae. The anus is ventral (in all others it is dorsal). These occur in Africa and from the Near East to Tibet.

Hexisopodidae. There are no free tergites behind the propeltidium on the prosoma. Spatulate leg articles are used for digging; the fourth legs lack claws. The distribution is South and Southwest Africa.

Galeodidae. The tarsal claws are hairy. *Galeodes* occurs in Africa and from Greece to India and China, *Othoes* in northwest African deserts.

Karschiidae. There are two tarsal claws on leg 1; tarsi 2 to 4 each have one article. The distribution is Greece, Africa, and from the Near East to Mongolia.

Ceromidae. There are two tarsal claws on leg 1; the claws are not hairy. Tarsi of legs 2 to 4 have two articles. They occur in South and East Africa.

Solpugidae. Tarsal claws are lacking on leg 1. Tarsi of legs 2 and 3 have four articles; tarsus of leg 4 has at least six articles. This large family inhabits Africa and Arabia.

Melanoblossiidae. Tarsal claws are lacking on leg 1; tarsi of legs 2 and 3 have one or two articles; the cheliceral flagellum is a cluster of bristles. They occur in South Africa and Annam.

Daesiidae. Tarsal claws are lacking on leg 1; tarsi of legs 2 and 3 have one or two articles; the cheliceral flagellum is awl-shaped and can be turned through 180°. They are found in Africa and Europe to India.

References

RICINULEI

Beck, L. 1968. Aus den Regenwäldern des Amazonas. *Nat. Museum* 98:71–80.

Bolivar Pieltain, C. 1941. Ricinulideo de la Caverna de Cacahuamilpa, México. *Rev. Soc. Mexicana Hist. Natur.* 2:197–209.

Cooke, J. A. L. 1967. The biology of Ricinulei. *J. Zool.* 151:31–42.

Gertsch, W. J. and Mulaik, S. 1939. A ricinuleid from Texas. *Amer. Mus. Novitates* 1037:1–5.

Kaestner, A. 1932. Ricinulei *in* Kükenthal, *Handbuch der Zoologie,* De Gruyter, Berlin 3(2):99–116.

Millot, J. 1945. Sur l'anatomie interne des Ricinulei. *Ann. Sci. Nat. Zool. Biol.* (11)7:1–29.

——— 1949. Ricinuléides *in* Grassé, *Traité de Zoologie,* Masson et Cie, Paris, 6:744–760.

Pollock, J. 1966. Life of the ricinulid. *Animals* 8(15):402–405.

PSEUDOSCORPIONES

Beier, M. 1932. Pseudoscorpionidea *in* Kükenthal, *Handbuch der Zoologie,* De Gruyter, Berlin 3(2):117–192.

——— 1948. Phoresie und Phagophilie bei Pseudoscorpionen. *Österreichische Zool. Z.* 1:441–497.

——— 1964. Pseudoscorpionidea *in* Aguilar, J. et al. ed. *Bestimmungsbücher zur Boden-fauna Europas,* Akad. Verl., Berlin 1:1–313.

Chamberlin, J. 1931. The Arachnid Order Chelonethida. *Publ. Stanford Univ.* 7:1–284.

——— 1943. The genus *Synsphyronus* and sporadic loss of stability in generally constant morphological characters. *Ann. Entomol. Soc. Amer.* 36:486–500.

Gabbutt, P. D. 1962. Nests of the marine false scorpion. *Nature* 196:87–89.

——— 1966. The silken chambers of the marine pseudoscorpion *Neobisium maritimum. J. Zool. Soc. London* 149:337–343.

——— and Vachon, M. 1965. External morphology and life history of *Neobisium muscorum. Proc. Zool. Soc. London* 145:335–358.

Gilbert, O. 1951. Observations on the feeding of some British false scorpions. *Proc. Zool. Soc. London* 121:547–555.

————— 1952. The histology of the midgut of the Chelonethi. *Quart. J. Microscop. Sci.* 93:31–45.

Heurtault-Rossi, J. and Jézéquel, J. F. 1965. Observations sur *Faella mirabilis. Bull. Mus. Nat. Hist. Natur. Paris* (2)37:450–461.

Hoff, C. C. 1949. The pseudoscorpions of Illinois. *Bull. Illinois Nat. Hist. Surv.* 24:413–498.

————— 1958. List of the pseudoscorpions of North America north of Mexico. *Amer. Mus. Novitates* 1875:1–50.

————— 1959. Ecology and distribution of the pseudoscorpions of north-central New Mexico. *Univ. New Mexico Publ. Biol.* 8:1–68.

Janetschek, H. 1948. Zur Brutbiologie von *Neobisium jugorum. Ann. Naturhist. Mus. Wien* 56:309–316.

Kaestner, A. 1927. Pseudoscorpiones *in* Schulze, *Biologie der Tiere Deutschlands,* Verl. Gebr. Borntraeger, Berlin, 18:1–68.

Levi, H. W. 1948. Notes on the life history of the pseudoscorpion *Chelifer cancroides. Trans. Amer. Microscop. Soc.* 67:290–298.

————— 1953. Observations on two species of pseudoscorpions. *Canadian Entomol.* 85:55–62.

Roewer, C. F. 1940. Chelonethi *in* Bronn's *Klassen und Ordnungen des Tierreichs,* Akad. Verlagsges., Leipzig, 5(4)6:1–354.

Schlottke, E. 1940. Zur Biologie des Bücherskorpions. *Ber. Westpreussichen Bot. Zool. Ver.* 62:1–31.

Strebel, O. 1937. Beobachtungen am einheimischen Bücherskorpion *Chelifer cancroides. Beitrag Naturkundl. Forschungsges. Südwestdeutschlands* 2:143–155.

Vachon, M. 1935. Une particularité dans le développement d'un Pseudoscorpion, *Cheiridium museorum. Bull. Soc. Zool. France* 60:330–333.

————— 1938. Recherches anatomiques et biologiques sur la reproduction et la développement des Pseudoscorpions. *Ann Sci. Natur. Zool.* (11):1–207.

————— 1940. Remarques sur la phorésie des Pseudoscorpions. *Ann. Soc. Entomol. France* 109:1–18.

————— 1947. Nouvelles remarques sur la phorésie des Pseudoscorpions. *Bull. Mus. Nat. Hist. Natur. Paris* (2)19:84–87.

————— 1947. Remarques sur l'arthrogenèse des appendices. *Bull. Biol. France, Belgique* 81:177–194.

————— 1948. Quelques remarques sur le nettoyage des pattes machoires et les glands salivaires. *Bull. Mus. Nat. Hist. Natur. Paris* (2): 20:162–164.

————— 1949. Pseudoscorpions *in* Grassé, *Traité de Zoologie,* Masson et Cie, Paris, 6:437–481.

————— 1951. Les glandes chélicères des pseudoscorpions. *Compt. Rend. Acad. Sci. Paris* 233:205–206.

————— 1951. Sur les nids et spécialement les nids de ponte chez les Pseudoscorpions. *Bull. Mus. Nat. Hist. Natur. Paris* (2)23:196–199.

Weygoldt, P. 1964. Embryologische Untersuchungen an Pseudoscorpionen. *Z. Morphol. Ökol.* 54:1–106; *Zool. Beitr.* 10:353–368.

————— 1965. Entwicklung von *Neobisium. Z. Morphol. Ökol.* 54:321–382.

————— 1965. Spermienübertragung bei einem Pseudoscorpion. *Naturwissenschaften* 52:218.

————— 1965. Fortpflanzungsverhalten der Pseudoscorpione. *Ibid.* 52:436.

————— 1966. Fortpflanzungsbiologie der Pseudoscorpione. *Z. Morphol. Ökol.* 56:39–92.

————— 1966. Die Ausbildung transitorischer Pharynxapparate bei Embryonen. *Zool. Anz.* 176:147–160.

————— 1966. Mating behavior and spermatophore morphology in the pseudoscorpion *Dinocheirus* (Chernetidae). *Biol. Bull.* 130:462–467.

———— 1966. *Moos - und Bücherskorpione*. Neue Brehm Bücherei no. 365, Ziemsen Verl., Wittenberg Lutherstadt.

———— 1966. Spermatophore web formation in a pseudoscorpion. *Science* 153:1647–1649.

SOLIFUGAE

Babu, K. S. 1965. Anatomy of the central nervous system of arachnids. *Zool. Jahrb. Abt. Anat.* 82:1–154.

Cloudsley-Thompson, J. L. 1954. Function of the palpal organ of Solifugae. *Entomol. Monthly Mag.* 90:235–237.

———— 1961. Natural History of the Camel spider, *Galeodes*. *Ibid.* 97:145–152.

———— 1961. Some aspects of physiology and behavior of *Galeodes arabs*. *Entomol. Exp. Appl.* 4:257–263.

Junqua, C. M. 1957. Aspects histologiques du système nerveux d'un solifuge. Note préliminaire. *Bull. Soc. Zool. France* 82:136–138.

———— 1962. La reproduction d'un solifuge, *Othoes*. *Compt. Rend. Acad. Sci. Paris* 255:2673–2675.

———— 1966. Recherches biologiques et histophysiologique sur un solifuge saharien. *Mém. Mus. Nat. Hist. Natur. Paris* A 43:1–124.

Kaestner, A. 1933. Solifugae *in* Kükenthal, *Handbuch der Zoologie*, De Gruyter, Berlin 3(2):193–199.

———— 1952. Zur Entwicklungsgeschichte des Prosoma der Solifugen. *Zool. Anz.* 148:156–168.

———— 1952. Über zwei Entwicklungstadien von Solifugen. *Ibid.* 149:1–20.

Lawrence, R. F. 1947. Some observations on the eggs and newly hatched embryos of *Solpuga*. *Proc. Zool. Soc. London* 117:429–434.

———— 1949. Observations on the habits of a female Solifuge. *Ann. Transvaal Mus.* 21:197–200.

Millot, J. and Vachon, M. 1949. Solifuges, *in* Grassé, *Traité de Zoologie*, Masson et Cie, Paris, 6:482–519.

Muma, M. H. 1951. The arachnid order Solpugida in the United States. *Bull. Amer. Mus. Nat. Hist.* 97:35–141.

———— 1962. The arachnid order Solpugida in the United States, Supplement 1. *Amer. Mus. Novitates* 2092:1–44.

———— 1963. Solpugida of the Nevada test site. *Brigham Young Univ. Sci. Bull. Biol. Ser.* 3(2):1–13.

———— 1966. Mating behavior in the solpugid genus *Eremobates*. *Anim. Behaviour* 14:346–350.

———— 1966. Feeding behavior of Solpugida. *Florida Entomol.* 49:199–216.

———— 1966. Egg deposition and incubation in *Eremobates*. *Ibid.* 49:23–31.

———— 1966. Life cycle of *Eremobates*. *Ibid.* 49:233–242.

———— 1967. Burrowing habits of Solpugida. *Psyche* 73:251–260.

———— 1967. Behavior of North American Solpugida. *Florida Entomol.* 50:115–123.

Rao, K. P. and Gopalakrishnareddy, T. 1962. Nitrogen excretion in arachnids. *Comp. Biochem. Physiol.* 7:175–178.

Roewer, C. F. 1934. Solifuga *in* Bronn's *Klassen und Ordnungen des Tierreich*, Akad. Verlagsges, Leipzig, 5(4)4:1–723.

Warren, E. 1939. On the genital system of certain Solifugae. *Ann. Natal. Mus.* 9:139–172.

13.

Order Opiliones, Harvestmen

The harvestmen include 3200 species, the largest being *Trogulus torosus* with a body 2.2 cm long, and *Mitobates stygnoides* with a body 6 mm long, and posterior legs 16 cm long. The order of harvestmen is sometimes called Phalangida.

Harvestmen are arachnids that have the prosoma usually divided by two transverse dorsal grooves into a proterosoma and two free segments. The abdomen (opisthosoma) is distinctly segmented and broadly attached to the prosoma. The coxae of both the pedipalpi and the first pair of legs have endites enclosing the preoral cavity. The legs are often immensely long; the tarsi may have many articles. One pair of tracheae is much-branched. Both a penis and ovipositor are present and may be very long.

Anatomy

Harvestmen are diverse in appearance: the Cyphophthalmi are small, short-legged and mitelike (Fig. 13–1); Trogulidae are flattened, their legs about as long as the body (Figs. 13–2, 13–14); Laniatores are heavily sclerotized (Fig. 13–3) and sometimes long-legged; and the Eupnoi are the soft, very long-legged "daddy longlegs" common in northern latitudes in America and Europe (Fig. 13–13). The dorsum of the prosoma often has one or two transverse grooves, present in the embryos of *Phalangium*, and probably representing the borders of tergites V and VI (Fig. 13–4), judging by the longitudinal muscles and the embryos of Eupnoi. The abdomen in primitive forms has 10 tergites, belonging to metameres VII to XVI. In the adult the last two are reduced or split (Figs. 4–7, 13–6). The anterior five tergites are often fused into a scutum (sometimes only in males) that shows vestiges of segment borders (Figs. 13–2, 13–3).

On the venter sternites IX to XVI are present, the last usually more or less reduced (Figs. 4–7, 13–6). The anterior sternites have moved between the coxae of the fourth legs (Fig. 13–7), or in the Eupnoi, between the coxae of the

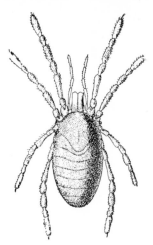

Fig. 13–1. *Siro duricorius;* the dorsal scutum shows borders of metameres VI to XIII; tergites XIV to XVI are ventral; body 2 mm long. (After Hansen and Sörensen, from Claus, Grobben, Kühn.)

last three pairs of legs (Fig. 13–6). In many common North American and European species, the part of the abdomen between the coxae has become a uniform, narrow plate, the genital operculum (Fig. 13–6).

Embryological studies in Phalangiidae show that sternite VII, present earlier, becomes reduced to two minute lateral plates while sternite VIII fuses to the prosomal sternites without leaving a seam. Later an ectodermal invagination arises between the last coxae that afterwards forms the gonopore. In the course of postembryonic development an anterior growth covers the gonopore ventrally, resulting in a secondary gonopore directly behind the labium. In the other suborders, however, the gonopore is always behind the third leg coxae. Thus in contrast to other arachnids (except mites) the gonopore is not at the posterior border of sternite VIII, although it is in the general area of the sternite.

Usually harvestmen are gray, brownish, or black, the brightly colored ones being mainly tropical species. In the Cosmetidae and in species of *Gagrella* there are waxy yellowish and greenish colors. *Lacinius dentiger* can change color during a period of a month to match green or black backgrounds.

APPENDAGES. The three-segmented chelicerae are chelate and sometimes relatively long (Fig. 13–5). The pedipalpi are leglike, but always much shorter than the legs, leglike in the Cyphophthalmi and Palpatores, strong and armed with spines in the Laniatores. The anterior three leg coxae almost completely cover the venter of the prosoma in Laniatores (Fig. 13–7) while in Palpatores there is space between the last 3 pairs for the genital operculum (Fig. 13–6). The legs in many species are three to five times the body length. The second walking leg of North American and European *Leiobunum* species may be 15 times the body length; the fourth leg of *Metamitobates genusulphureus* is 39 times the body length.

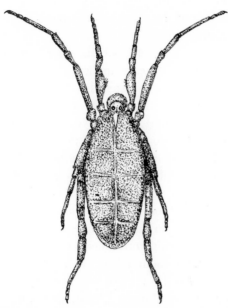

Fig. 13–2. *Trogulus*, dorsal view; body 10 mm long. (After Dahl.)

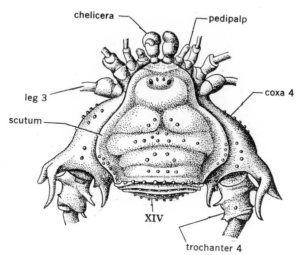

Fig. 13–3. *Discocyrtus prospicuus*, male (Gonyleptidae), dorsal view of body; the 8th abdominal tergite belongs to metamere XIV; 6.5 mm long. (After Kaestner.)

All long-legged species have the tarsi divided into numerous secondary articles, as many as 50 in the second leg of *Phalangium opilio* and *Opilio parietinus*, more than 100 in some other species.

The ectodermal apodemes are small, but there is a large mesodermal H-shaped endosternite above the subesophageal ganglion.

NERVOUS SYSTEM. The nervous system has three centers: the brain, a subesophageal ganglion made up of the ganglia of segments II to X, and in about the tenth metamere a small paired ganglion from which nerves pass posteriorly to segments XI to XIII. But these parts of the nervous system have been studied only in the Eupnoi. The protocerebrum contains the association organs: the central body and 3 pairs of globuli in Laniatores, 1 pair in Phalangiidae. The Phalangiidae have, in addition, a well-developed visual center consisting of two optic masses, one behind the other, serving the median eyes. There are slit sense organs and many sensory setae on the legs; the endites have sensory cells close to the mouth. Laniatores and Palpatores have a pair of large median eyes of complicated structure, usually mounted on each side of a tubercle. The rhabdoms face the lens (Figs. 13–3, 13–4, 13–8).

DIGESTIVE SYSTEM. The mouthparts become increasingly complex within the order. Labrum and labium are always widely separated; the space is walled on the sides by the endites of the pedipalpi and of the first legs. The endites differ from those of other arachnids in that each originates from the coxal base rather than from the distal end, a difference that can be explained by their ventral transverse position (Fig. 13–7). The coxa projects ventrally, and a soft endite is formed on the anterior edge of the projection (Fig. 13–7).

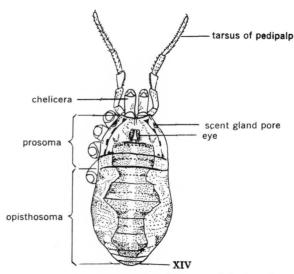

Fig. 13–4. *Phalangium opilio*, female, dorsal view of body; 6 mm long. (After DeLessert.)

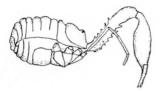

Fig. 13–5. *Ischyropsalis*, lateral view with chelicera and pedipalp; body 6 mm long. (After Dahl.)

Behind the labium there may also be smaller endites, not present in the Dyspnoi, that originate from the second leg coxae. In the primitive Laniatores the coxae are continuous with the endites; in others there are seams; in Eupnoi there is a hinge. In the Phalangiidae the pedipalpal endites consist of 3 jointed parts (Figs. 13–6, 13–8). The mouth is hidden at the base of the labrum and leads into a pumping pharynx, star-shaped in cross section. The esophagus continues between the brain and the subesophageal ganglion. The anterior midgut consists of two egg-shaped chambers, one behind the other. The anterior chamber has three pairs of ceca on its roof, one in the prosoma, two in the abdomen. These tubes are slightly branched in the Laniatores and Trogulidae, while there is increasing branching in the Nemastomatidae and Eupnoi. *Phalangium*, for instance, has 15 pairs of secondary and tertiary branches. The ectodermal hindgut is short.

These ceca arise in the embryo of *Phalangium*, as in other arachnids, by growth of mesodermal septa from the sides toward the middle of the yolk, separating five successive, paired compartments; two arise in the prosoma, three

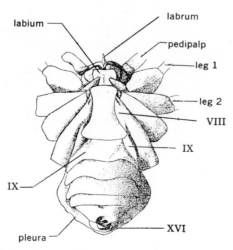

Fig. 13–6. *Phalangium opilio*, venter, 6 mm long. (After Kaestner.)

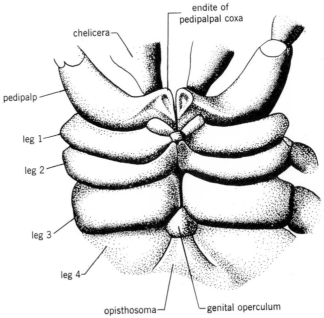

Fig. 13–7. *Acanthepedanus armatus* (Laniatores), venter of prosoma showing primitive endites; 2 mm wide. (After Kaestner.)

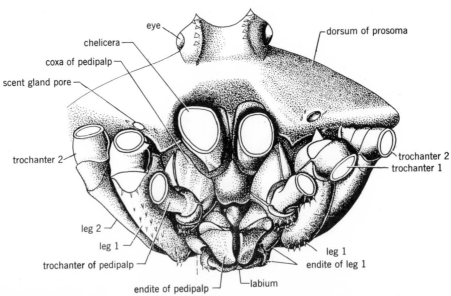

Fig. 13–8. *Platybunus bucephalus,* anterior view; appendages are cut off from trochanter; the endites of the palp and first leg articulate with their coxae. The endites consist of 3 articles, unlike those in Fig. 13–7. Between the pedipalpal coxae is the base of the labrum, below it the conical labrum; 2.6 mm wide. (After Kaestner.)

in the abdomen. In the adult the walls of the anterior three converge medially so that they open into the gut through one pore. The cecum of segment VIII divides into a median and a lateral cecum (Fig. 13–9, second gut cecum). The following one develops the same way and grows finally to the posterior (Fig. 13–9, third cecum).

EXCRETORY SYSTEM. The excretory organs are the coxal glands, nephrocytes and perineural organs. There are no Malpighian tubules. The labyrinthian duct of the coxal gland and a bladder reach deep into the abdomen; the duct empties through a pore on the posterior wall of the third coxa. The bladder empties into the nephridial canal near its pore. In the Eupnoi the nephridial canal reaches the pericardium and loops along its side (Fig. 13–9). In the Phalangiidae the coxal gland develops from the wall of the coelom pouch of the segment belonging to the first walking leg, where it opens until after hatching. A small homologous primordium of the coelom of the third walking leg segment grows into it and short-circuits it. After the disappearance of the anterior pore, the coxal gland opens at the third leg coxa. The perineural organs are knotlike accumulations of cells resembling blood cells that take up particles and fluids injected into the blood. *Phalangium* has four pairs, one on each of the three nerves and one on the large connective leading to the abdomen from the subesophageal ganglion.

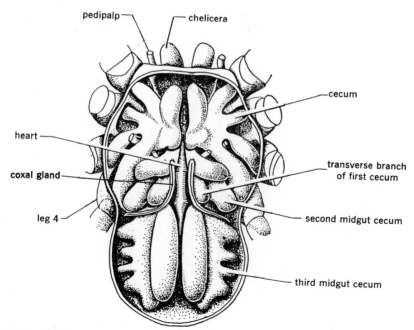

Fig. 13–9. *Opilio parietinus,* dorsal exoskeleton removed; 6 mm long. (After Kaestner.)

RESPIRATORY SYSTEM. The only respiratory organs are tracheae. A pair of spiracles lies in the deep grooves between the last coxae and abdomen or on sternite VIII. Spiracles of Cyphophthalmi, Laniatores and Dyspnoi are screened, those of Eupnoi are open. Large tracheae from the spiracles into the prosoma branch to the appendages and organs. There is no relationship between the position of tracheal branches and segmentation (Fig. 13–10). The Eupnoi have additional small round spiracles, only 0.02–0.04 mm in diameter, at the end of the tibia of each walking leg. Opilionids are sensitive to lack of oxygen and die 2–15 minutes after complete submersion in water; but, if the accessory spiracles remain above the water surface they survive for more than an hour.

CIRCULATORY SYSTEM. Corresponding with the elaborate respiratory system, the circulatory system is reduced to a short heart with 2 pairs of ostia at the posterior of the 7th and 8th tergites in the Phalangiidae (Fig. 13–9). Neither anterior nor posterior aorta is branched; the anterior opens as a funnel that surrounds the brain. The blood has 10,000–50,000 corpuscles per mm^3, lymphocytes with pseudopods and leucocytes.

REPRODUCTIVE SYSTEM. In the Gonyleptidae, Cosmetidae and Phalangiidae the males have larger chelicerae, longer appendages, smaller bodies, or are more sclerotized than the females. The two branches of the ovary are grown together posteriorly. The ducts unite in the area of the eighth segment into a long internal atrium (uterus). The eggs, before their deposition, fill the atrium as well as the long distal duct leading to the external atrium. This ectodermal atrium is a complicated ovipositor unique among the arachnids, and consists of 3 parts. The ovipositor sheath begins an invagination of the epidermis at the genital

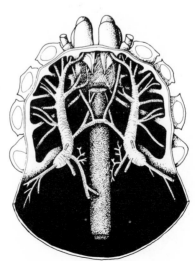

Fig. 13–10. Tracheae of *Opilio parietinus*, dorsal view; entire dorsum and venter of posterior part of abdomen removed; 5 mm long. (After Kaestner.)

pore. The tube-shaped duct is produced by an anterior bend of the base of the sheath. The vagina is a short ectodermal canal open at the tip with the external atrium at its base. Laniatores and Dyspnoi have an unsegmented ovipositor tube which, when evaginated from the sheath, becomes the apical part, while the evaginated sheath forms the base. The Cyphophthalmi and Eupnoi have the ovipositor divided into a number of short sclerotized tubes separated by membranes and telescoped together when not in use. This tube, when evaginated by internal pressure (Fig. 13–13), may be several times body length and can be bent by longitudinal muscles. The ovipositor of *Phalangium opilio* has about 30 sections separated by as many membranes.

The male organs correspond to those of the female. The testes are grown together posteriorly, their ducts opening into the internal atrium. The tube-shaped internal atrium continues into an external ectodermal atrium, as in the female. There are 3 parts to the penis: the sheath, the tube, with its ectodermal canal to the internal atrium; the tip, often jointed, bearing the pore. In the Eupnoi the penis is very long, different in different species, and useful therefore as a taxonomic character (Fig. 13–11).

Reproduction

There is no prenuptial display. In *Nuncia*, the Nemastomatidae and the Eupnoi, males and females face each other. The male then pushes his penis between the chelicerae of the female into the gonopore (Fig. 13–12). In the

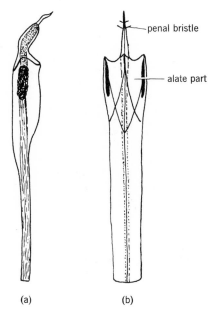

penal bristle

alate part

(a)   (b)

Fig. 13–11. Penis of *Leiobunum lineatum*; (a) lateral; (b) dorsal; 1.3 mm long. (After Edgar.)

Trogulidae the male climbs on the back of the female and then climbs laterally to her venter, holding her dorsum with his legs pressing against her. The penis is then inserted and remains 10–20 minutes.

Abdominal pressure due to muscle contraction extends the ovipositor for egg-laying. Trogulidae, which have a short stiff ovipositor, deposit their eggs in empty snail shells, carried with their chelicerae to a suitable place. One to 8 eggs are deposited as deep inside the shell as possible and are sealed in with a lid made of secretion. Six to 25 snail shells are filled. *Nemastoma quadri-punctatum* deposits annually 6–35 eggs on the undersides of stones.

Females of Phalangiidae bury their eggs or deposit them under bark of dead trees. The long ovipositor, moving like an elephant's proboscis, penetrates between the soil particles deep into the soil (Fig. 13–13). *Mitopus morio* deposits 20–80 eggs in fall in plant stems, using holes bored by insects.

Development

Development time of eggs differs. In northern latitudes some eggs deposited in fall will hatch within four weeks, others the following spring. The embryology of *Phalangium opilio* has been investigated. The body development resembles that of entelegyne spiders with the difference that appendages do not appear on the abdomen. The dorsum of the embryo shows 12 segments: the first two, belonging to the prosoma, are tergites V and VI; the others must be abdominal tergites VII to XVI. Later, segmented dorsal longitudinal muscles develop, giving further evidence of the metameres. The young opilionids almost resemble adults. The genital operculum between the coxae has not yet formed; the legs are short,

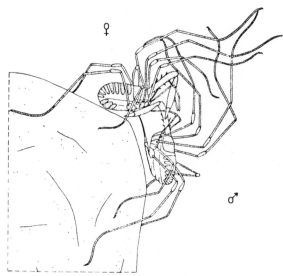

Fig. 13–12. Mating of *Ischyropsalis strandi*; body of each about 5 mm long. (From Juberthie.)

and their secondary segmentation is incomplete. The number of molts differs in different species: *Trogulus* has six, *Nemastoma quadripunctatum* seven. *Mitopus morio* molts after hatching from the egg. After the molt it passes through 5 instars before becoming adult. A laboratory culture fed on mealworms and bananas matured in 6–8 weeks at 15–20°C. The adult does not molt. While most Eupnoi die in fall or winter, *Trogulus* becomes 3, *Siro rubens* about 9 years old.

Molting brings difficulties in removing the long legs. Molting harvestmen hang themselves on branches, and pull the legs out of the old skin, first with the pedipalpi, then with the chelicerae.

Relationships

The Cyphophthalmi (Fig. 13–1) resemble the segmented mites (Notostigmata), as does the body of the Eupnoi. Other mite-like characters are the broad connection between prosoma and abdomen, the anterior gonopore, the gut ceca, and the presence of a penis. However, mouthparts differ markedly from those of mites and resemble more the mouthparts of scorpions.

Habits

The Cyphophthalmi live in caves or in shady places in leaf litter or under stones. Little is known about the life of Laniatores. Dyspnoi live on the soil surface. Trogulidae are found in debris, moss, or under stones, always in well-vegetated areas protected against heat. *Nemastoma* species live below the herb layer as do young Phalangiidae. With increasing age Phalangiidae climb on shrubs, and even tree branches. It was observed in England that in July and August *Leiobunum rotundum* descended from the trees into the herbs in search of food every night at 9 pm and returned to the trees in the morning. A direct relationship between habits and temperature and humidity preferences has been demonstrated in the laboratory: *Nemastoma lugubre* and *Oligolophus tridens* living on herbs in forests prefer temperatures of 8–11.9°C and humidities of

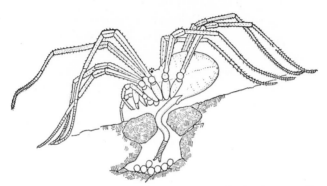

Fig. 13–13. *Oligolophus tridens*, female ovipositing; body 6 mm. (From Šilhavý.)

64–78% in the laboratory. Their preferred habitats measured 85–100% and 70 80% humidity. The tree climbing *Oligolophus hanseni* and *O. agrestis* prefer 47– 61% humidity in experiments, 50–60% in nature.

Different species belonging to the same genus, as in other terrestrial animals, are isolated from each other by temperature and humidity preferences even though occurring in the same forest. Thus, *Oligolophus tridens* is found on the ground and herbs, *O. agrestis* in shrubs and trees. In others, young hatch at different times: *Leiobunum blackwalli* in England hatch one month later than *L. rotundum*. The earlier broods thus are taking larger prey and are in higher vegetation when the later broods hatch.

Most soil dwellers prefer shade, and many are nocturnal; others are active during the day. In England, *Mitopus morio* and *Leiobunum rotundum* are active between 9 and 1 o'clock at night. *Phalangium opilio* likes sunny places.

DEFENSE. Autotomy of legs of Phalangiidae is the main protection against enemies, the captured leg breaking off between coxa and trochanter. The separated appendage many continue to move for 30 minutes while the harvestman escapes. If the proximal end of the femur of the separated leg is pressed, movement stops. Thus impulses must come from femoral nerve cells. *Opilio parietinus* can hold 20 g on a leg without autotomizing, but if narcotized, it holds only 2 g before throwing the leg off. Harvestmen do not regenerate lost legs.

The saclike scent glands, opening on the anterior edge of the prosoma (Figs. 13–4, 13–8), are also defensive. If a leg of *Siro rubens* is pinched with forceps, a droplet appears at the gland, is picked up by another leg, and is thrust at the forceps. Other opilionids let the droplet evaporate. The South African triaenonychid, *Larifugella*, can spray a jet upward, posteriorly, or to the side of the body, about 2.5 cm. The spray has an iodoform odor, and is believed defensive.

The chemical nature of the secretion of only one opilionid, a Uruguayan gonyleptid, has been studied. The substances turned out to be quinones, with strongly antibiotic properties. This might suggest that the secretion is used in grooming. It has been called gonyleptidine.

Total immobility also provides protection against enemies. Such behavior by *Nemastoma quadripunctatum* is released by vibrations. The animal folds its legs over its body, and *Trogulus* may remain immobile for 20 minutes (Fig. 13–14). In addition, *Trogulus* is disguised with dirt glued on by a secretion that probably comes from the little warts covering the body. Gonyleptids also "play dead" when disturbed and, despite their bright colors, are hard to find on the underside of a rock or log (Fig. 13–14d). *Leiobunum rupestre* has been observed to sway with grass blades in the wind.

LOCOMOTION. The soil-dwelling Dyspnoi are all slow in contrast to the fast-moving phalangiids. Soil dwellers generally have shorter legs than inhabitants of shrubs or trees. The long legs permit climbing between leaves, and the

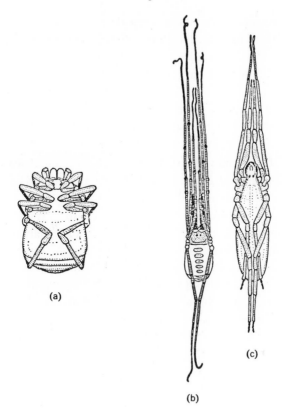

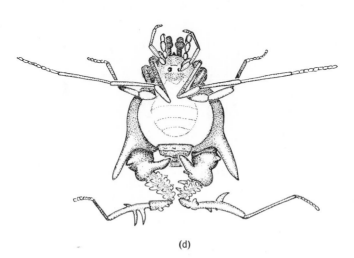

Fig. 13–14. **Resting position:** (a) *Nemastoma lugubre*, 2.3 mm long; (b) *Ischyropsalis dacica*, body 6 mm long; (c) *Trogulus nepaeformis*, body 14 mm long; (d) *Acrographinotus* sp., body 13 mm long. (a to c from Šilhavý.)

flexible many-segmented tarsi allow a good hold (Fig. 13–15a). The hold is facilitated by the structure of the tarsal article, which is far superior to claws or tufts or hairs.

If a *Leiobunum* is chased into grass, it will not crawl between the blades but gropes aimlessly against an obstacle, gets hold of it, climbs rapidly up to the top and in short "jumps" climbs down again on the other side—a maneuver made possible by the structure of the tarsi, which spiral like the prehensile tail of a monkey.

Each article of these tarsi, and there are more than 50 articles on the second leg, is trapezoidal in shape, the dorsal side longer than the venter (Fig. 13–15b). As the dorsal joint membrane is short, the ventral long, they can flex only in a ventral direction. There are no muscles between the articles but all are traversed by the long tendon of the claw-flexing muscles that lie in the tibia. If the muscle contracts, the claw and all tarsal articles flex, first into an arc, finally into a spiral. Thus a harvestman, with one muscle movement, can rapidly grasp a grass blade or petiole. Standing or walking, the weight rests on the tarsi, the dorsal edges of the articles supporting each other.

SENSES. As in other arachnids, touch is an important sense. The long second legs especially are used as antennae to feel the area surrounding the animal. Opilionids are also vibration-sensitive, and will immediately become aware of prey settling nearby. *Mitopus morio* becomes aware of food if a fly settles 1 cm in front of it. *Nemastoma* will move toward prey as soon as it moves. A chemical sense could be demonstrated in *Nemastoma;* pure agar cubes were not eaten but cubes containing glucose were. The threshhold was 0.05%; the optimum, 2%. Removal of appendages indicates that the sense of taste is in the mouth,

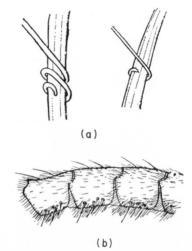

(a)

(b)

Fig. 13–15.   (a) *Leiobunum rotundum,* tarsus wound around grass blade, diagrammatic; (b) middle articles of tarsus, right is proximal; diameter 0.13 mm. (After Kaestner.)

chelicerae and endites. Xylol is noticed by *Trogulus* at 10 cm, and a *Nemastoma* would not cross a streak of xylol or benzol on paper.

Experiments show that *Nemastoma* has sensory structures for temperature and humidity but the sense organs have not been identified. The eyes distinguish only dark and light and the light direction. All those tested by covering their eyes with black lacquer behaved normally, suggesting that space orientation depends upon other senses. As most animals are nocturnal this is not surprising. They are active during dark periods, or in leaf litter and caves. Not even the eyes of Phalangiidae form an image. The eye of *Lacinius*, for instance, has only 588 rhabdoms.

FEEDING. *Siro* in captivity fed on podurid springtails. Nothing is known about the food of Laniatores. The slow Trogulidae feed on snails their own size, catching them with surprising dexterity, pulling pieces out with their chelicerae. *Ischyropsalis*, with very large chelicerae, feeds on small snails, holding the shell vertically in order to reach in with the chelicerae and pull out pieces of meat. The chelicerae can break the shell to reach a snail that has withdrawn. The related *Taracus* probably has similar food habits.

The Nemastomatidae feed mainly on mites and Collembola. Phalangiidae feed on various live insects but will also take dead ones, fallen apples, and, in captivity, soft bread and fruit. *Platybunus* and *Leiobunum* have been observed to catch flies, *Lacinius* a mite. In feeding, the two chelicerae alternate holding the prey and tearing pieces off, and bringing pieces to the mouth. The endites separate and a drop of digestive fluid appears in the preoral cavity, into which the food is stuffed. Closing the endites pushes food into the mouth. The labium prevents droplets from spilling. There is strong mechanical action, mainly tearing, and some digestion in the preoral cavity. Unlike most other arachnids, harvestmen swallow some particles, judging by the presence of sclerotized pieces in the excrement. Nutrient material enters the wide ceca. In captivity, Phalangiidae drink water.

DIGESTION. Half an hour after feeding, digested material mixed with pieces of exoskeleton are found in the midgut and ceca. The cecal epithelium resembles that of spiders. Its glandular cells have secreted enzymes and the nutrient cells begin intracellular digestion. As soon as 1½ hours later, solid particles are found in the mid- and hindgut. Twelve hours later the tips of many nutrient cells are filled with the excretory material and some proteins separate and fall into the lumen. The proteins are taken up by the midgut epithelium. The parts containing excretory material with midgut cells, and all insoluble parts, reach the hindgut, the cells of which secrete a cover and form a ball of fecal material. The digestive system may contain gregarines.

Classification

The opilionids are grouped into 3 suborders.

SUBORDER CYPHOPHTHALMI

About 25 species are included, all mite-like in appearance. Legs are 1½ times body length (Fig. 13-1), the leg tarsi one-segmented. The prosoma and first 8 abdominal tergites are fused dorsally into a hard scutum. The pedipalpi are leglike. The gonopore lacks an operculum. Uncommon, they are found in north Pacific coastal states, north-western Florida, Appalachians, and isolated locations in Europe.

Sironidae. Siro. Four North American species are known, each of which has at one time or another been placed in a different genus. *Rakaia* with many species occurs in New Zealand.

SUBORDER LANIATORES

About 1500 species are included. The second leg is twice the body length. The raptorial pedipalpi have a strong claw and strong spines. The leg tarsi usually have several articles, and tarsi 3 and 4 have 2 claws or 1 trident claw. The gonopore is covered by an operculum, which separates the fourth coxae. The species, mostly tropical, are found in southern and western United States and as far north as Austria in Europe.

Phalangodidae. These have two claws on the last legs. Many species inhabit caves. *Phalangodes* is North American, *Acanthepedanus* is found in Sumatra.

Triaenonychidae. There is a single trident claw on fourth leg. Representatives are found in Madagascar, Australia and America. The red *Sclerobunus* of Colorado mountains is found in logs. *Nuncia* is found in New Zealand and Australia.

Cosmetidae. There is a small median third claw on the fourth legs and the palpi are flattened. Members are all American, mostly tropical. *Vonones ornata* is common in the southeastern states, other species in California.

Gonyleptidae. There is a median third claw on the fourth leg; the palpi are large, not flattened. Common in the American tropics, the family includes over 600 species, some of which are characteristically heavy-bodied (Figs. 13-3, 13-14). *Mitobates, Metamitobates,* and *Acrographinotus* are included.

SUBORDER PALPATORES

More than 1000 species are included. They have the second leg more than one and one-half times as long as the body (except in Trogulidae). Pedipalpi are palpus-like (Fig. 13-4). Tarsi of legs 3 and 4 have only one claw. Gonopore is covered by an operculum which usually separates all the leg coxae (Fig. 13-6).

Infraorder Dyspnoi

Spiracles are covered by sclerotized screen, and there are no spiracles on legs. Second leg coxae are without endites. Pedipalpal tarsus is shorter than tibia. There are about 150 species.

Trogulidae. The eye tubercle projects anteriorly over mouthparts (Figs. 13-2, 13-14), and a scutum covers the prosoma and the first five abdominal tergites. The legs are relatively short, the tarsi one to three articled. Soil grains encrust the dorsum. *Trogulus* of Europe feeds on snails. The head projection appears only after the first molt.

Oncopodidae. The pedipalpi are leglike, each with a long claw. The first eight tergites are fused to form a dorsal scutum. The leg tarsi have one or only a few articles. All are 1–6 mm in length and are found in southeastern Asia and Indonesia.

Synthetonychidae. Members of this family lack an eye tubercle and the two eyes are not near the anterior margin. The anterior margin lacks spines. The pedipalpi are long and slender. Legs 1 and 2 have a long tarsal claw; claws on legs 3 and 4 have a median plate and lateral branches. They are found in New Zealand in moss and forest floor debris.

Assamiidae. A dorsal scutum covers the carapace and first five abdominal segments. The anterior margin has five teeth above the chelicerae, two on each side. The pedipalpal femur is S-shaped with tibia and tarsus flattened, and the tarsus has a large claw. The legs are long and thin; legs 1 and 2 have simple claws, 3 and 4 have two simple or comblike claws. The family is represented in Africa and Southeast Asia to Australia.

Nemastomatidae. These lack an anterior projection on the prosoma and usually have the dorsal plate of prosoma and first five abdominal tergites fused to form a scutum. The leg tarsi have several articles. *Nemastoma* (Fig. 13-14) includes many species that inhabit caves. Collembola stick to viscid droplets on the setae of the pedipalpi and are eaten. After molting the droplet is missing but reappears soon. *N. dasycnemum* is found in eastern United States.

Ischyropsalidae. These lack the anterior prosomal projection, and the plate of the prosomal dorsum is never fused to the abdominal tergites. The chelicerae are very strong. Leg tarsi have many segments. *Taracus* is found in well decayed logs of Colorado mountain forests. *Sabacon* is widespread. *Ischyropsalis* of European forest floor feeds on snails (Figs. 13-5, 13-14).

Infraorder Eupnoi

The spiracles are open and lie between the last leg coxae and abdomen. There are accessory spiracles on the leg tibiae. The second coxa has an endite (Fig. 13-6) and the pedipalpal tarsus is always longer than the tibia. The legs are very long (Fig. 13-13). There are about 1000 species.

Phalangiidae, Daddy Longlegs. Mitopus morio, 4.8 mm, has holarctic distribution. *Phalangium opilio,* 3.5–9 mm long, holarctic in distribution, is found in gardens, meadows, fields, on herbs to tops of pines; it prefers sunny mesic areas. The male has a dorsal projection on the second cheliceral article. *Opilio parietinus,* 7.5 mm long, holarctic, is usually found near human dwellings. *Caddo,* 1.5 mm, in eastern North America, has large eyes and is sometimes placed in its own family. *Homolophus biceps,* 6 mm, is common in Rocky Mountains. *Leiobunum* includes numerous species in North America and Europe. *Gagrella, Oligolophus* (Fig. 13-13), *Platybunus,* and *Lacinius* are other genera.

References

Bishop, S. C. 1949. The Phalangida (Opiliones) of New York. *Proc. Rochester Acad. Sci.* 9:159–235.

Berland, L. 1949. Opilions *in* Grassé, *Traité de Zoologie,* Masson et Cie, Paris, 6:761–793.

Edgar, A. L. 1963. Proprioception in the legs of phalangids. *Biol. Bull.* 124:262–267.

_____ 1966. Phalangida of the Great Lakes Region. *Amer. Midland Natur.* 75:347–366.

Estable, C. *et al.* 1955. Gonyleptidine. *J. Amer. Chem. Soc.* 77:4942.

Fieser, L. F. and Ardao, M. I. 1956. The chemical nature of Gonyleptidine. *Ibid.* 78:774–781.

Gabe, M. 1954. Situation et connexions des cellules neurosécrétrices chez *Phalangium opilio.* *Compt. Rend. Acad. Sci. Paris* 238:2450–2452.

Hoffmann, E. 1953. Die Verwendbarkeit der Penes für die Taxonomie der Phalangiidae. *Mitt. Zool. Mus. Berlin* 29:55–74.

Holm, Å. 1947. Development of *Opilio parietinus. Zool. Bidr. Uppsala* 25:409–422.

Immel, V. 1954. Biologie und Physiologie von *Nemastoma. Zool. Jahrb. Abt. Syst.* 83:1–184.

————— 1955. Einige Bemerkungen zur Biologie von *Platybunus bucephalus. Ibid.* 83:475–484.

Janczyck, F. 1956. Anatomie von *Siro. Sitz. Ber. Österreichischen Akad. Wiss. Math-Naturwiss.* (1)165:475–522.

Juberthie, C. 1957. Développement de deux Phalangiidae. *Compt. Rend. Acad. Sci. Paris* 244:2747–2750.

————— 1960. La biologie d'un Opilion endagé *Siro rubens. Ibid.* 251:1674–1676.

————— 1961. Structure des glandes odorantes et modalités d'utilisation chez cyphophthalmes. *Bull. Soc. Zool. France* 86:106–116.

————— 1962. Structure et function des glandes odorantes chez Opilions. *Verh. Deutschen Zool. Ges.* 25:533–537.

————— 1964. La biologie des Opilions. *Ann. Spéléol.* 19:1–237.

Kaestner, A. 1935. Opiliones *in* Kükenthal, *Handbuch der Zoologie,* De Gruyter, Berlin 3(2):300–393.

————— 1935. Die Funktion der sympathischen Ganglien und die Exkretion bei Phalangiiden. *Zool. Anz.* 109:273–287.

Lawrence, R. F. 1938. Odoriferous glands of South African harvest spiders. *Trans. Roy. Soc. South Africa* 25:333–342.

Levi, H. W. and Levi, L. R. 1968. *Spiders and their Kin.* Golden Press, New York.

McAlister, W. H. 1962. Local movements of *Leiobunum townsendi. Texas J. Sci.* 14:167–173.

Moritz, M. 1957. Embryonalentwicklung der Phalangiiden (Palpatores) Opiliones. *Zool. Jahrb. Abt. Anat.* 76:331–370.

————— 1959. Embryonalentwicklung der Phalangiiden (Opiliones, Palpatores) II. *Ibid.* 77:229–240.

Naisse, J. 1959. Neurosécrétion et glandes endocrines chez les Opilions. *Arch. Biol.* 70:217–264.

Pabst, W. 1953. Biologie der Mitteleuropäischen Troguliden. *Zool. Jahrb. Abt. Syst.* 82:1–45.

Phillipson, J. 1960. Contribution to feeding biology of *Mitopus. J. Anim. Ecol.* 29:35–43.

————— 1960. Food consumption of different instars of *Mitopus* under natural conditions. *Ibid.* 29:299–307.

————— 1961. Histological changes in the gut of *Mitopus* during protein digestion. *Quart. J. Microscop. Sci.* 102:217–226.

————— 1962. Histological changes in the gut of *Mitopus* during digestion of lipid and carbohydrate. *Ibid.* 103:85–91.

————— 1962. Respirometry and the study of energy turnover in natural systems with particular reference to harvestspiders (Phalangiida). *Oikos* 13(2):311-322.

Rafalski, J. 1958. Morphology and systematics of the Cyphophthalmi. *Acta Zool. Cracoviensia* 2:521–556.

Roewer, C. F. 1923. *Die Weberknechte der Erde.* G. Fischer, Jena.

Sáez, F. A. and Drets, M. E. 1956. Chromosome alterations induced by gonyleptidine. *Biol. Trab. Inst. Biol. "Juan Noe" Fac. Med. Univ. Chile* 22:36.

Šilhavý, V. 1956. Opiliones. *Fauna ČSR 7,* Československá Akad. Věd, Prague.

Spoek, G. L. 1963. The Opilionida (Arachnida) of the Netherlands. *Zool. Verhandel., Rijksmus. Natuur. Hist. Leiden* 63:1–70.

Tischler, W. 1967. Biologie und Ökologie des Opilioniden *Mitopus morio*. *Biol. Zentralbl.* 86:473–484.

Todd, V. 1949. The habits and ecology of British harvestmen. *J. Anim. Ecol.* 18:209–229.

Winkler, D. 1957. Entwicklung der äusseren Körpergestalt bei den Phalangiidae (Opiliones). *Mitt. Zool. Mus. Berlin* 33:355–389.

14.

Order Acari, Mites

About 20,000 species of mites have been described, probably representing only a small fraction of the total mite fauna. The largest species is the tick, *Amblyomma clypeolatum*, females of which may reach a length of 3 cm after feeding; the males are only 0.6 cm long. The order is also called Acarina.

Acari are small or very small arachnids; almost all have the abdomen unsegmented and shortened. The opisthosoma, together with the segments of the last two walking legs, forms one tagma, the hysterosoma, which is broadly attached to the proterosoma. The pedipalpal coxae are fused with one another, with the vestiges of the sternum, and with a dorsal body extension to form a gnathosoma. The heart is usually absent. The respiratory organs in most species are tracheae, the spiracles of which open (certainly secondarily) in various body regions. The first juvenile instar, the larva, has only three pairs of legs. The fourth legs become reduced before hatching from the egg and reappear after later molts.

Mites are dwarf forms, the usual body length being 0.5–2 mm, some only 0.1 mm. Unlike all other arachnids, some feed on plants, detritus, or stored products, and many are plant or animal parasites; therefore, many are of economic importance. Though mainly terrestrial, about 2800 species of Acari are aquatic, some of them marine.

Anatomy

Prosoma and abdomen are fused without constriction; the abdomen is shortened. The development of only a few mites has been studied. Behind the fourth leg there arise six segments at most, indicated by transverse rows of setae in some mites (Fig. 14–24). The shortening of the body obliterates internally the border between prosoma and abdomen, and the organs have lost all traces of segmentation. The position of the internal organs appears to be dictated by lack of space rather than by ontogeny, but externally also there are shifts. Only in the Notostigmata and Parasitiformes do the leg coxae have the usual position.

In other suborders they are no longer equally spaced, one behind another, but are grouped into two sets of pairs, often separated (Fig. 14–3).

Segmentation is found only in a few species of Notostigmata, in which the dorsum has grooves separating the twelve segments; the anterior two correspond to the third and fourth walking legs, and therefore must be derived from segments V and VI (Fig. 14–2). In other groups, the grooves cannot, with certainty, be assigned to particular metameres (except those of some Tarsonemini and Ixodidae). Even the division between prosoma and abdomen is visible in only a few Acarina, but the prosoma is often divided by a dorsal and sometimes a ventral groove in the region behind the second leg pair (Fig. 14–1). Thus the body has a proterosoma (acron plus segments I to IV) and a hysterosoma (segment V to the posterior end). While the proterosoma is an ancestral character, found in Schizopeltidia, Palpigradi and Solifugae, the uniform hysterosoma is otherwise unknown in arachnids, although in some scutum-covered Opiliones, combination of the last two leg-bearing segments with those of the abdomen is suggested (only dorsally). Another unique character of the Acarina is that the mouthparts (acron with segments I and II) form a distinct anterior section of the body, the gnathosoma (Fig. 14–1).

On the venter an anterior shift of sternite VIII with gonopores can be seen, a shift also observed among scorpions and harvestmen. This varies in different genera, so that the gonopores may be between the first legs, or between the second, third or fourth coxae (Fig. 14–3).

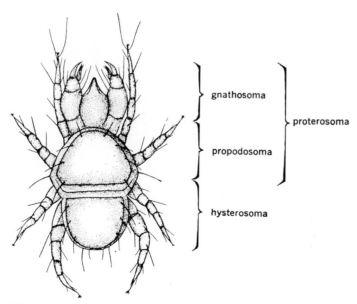

gnathosoma

proterosoma

propodosoma

hysterosoma

Fig. 14–1. *Cheyletus eruditus,* dorsum showing strong pedipalpi of a predator; 0.3 mm long. (After Vitzthum and Homann.)

Fig. 14–2. *Paracarus hexophthalmus*, dorsum of segmented notostigmatic mite; the first two segments are metamere 5 and 6; 1.6 mm long. (After Redikorzev.)

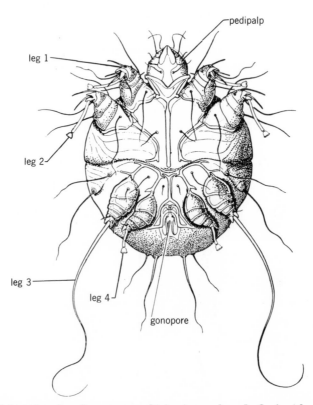

Fig. 14–3. Male itch mite, *Sarcoptes scabiei*, venter; legs 1, 2, 4 with suckers, details of mouthparts omitted. Anus not visible as it is dorsal; 0.2 mm long. (After Hirst.)

The hair follicle mites, Demodicidae, and the gall mites, Tetrapodili, have become worm-shaped by elongation of the hysterosoma, probably an adaptation to their habit of living in narrow burrows (Fig. 14–4).

The exoskeleton of the gall mites, most Acaridei, and some mites of other groups, is very thin and flexible (Fig. 14–3). In most other mites at least the area of the first two walking legs is sclerotized, forming a propodosomal scutum that is stiff even in soft-skinned species (Figs. 14–1, 14–20, 14–21). Often this scutum covers a larger area. There may also be ventral sclerotized plates. The adult oribatid mites (moss-mites), have a complete, heavily sclerotized exoskeleton (Fig. 14–28), often with wing-like extensions that in some species can be folded over the legs, protecting the legs and venter.

Coloration of mites may be due to pigment in the exoskeleton, and depending on its thickness may vary from yellowish to brown. Color patterns are usually due to internal organs visible through the integument, but may be obscured by integumentary pigments. In ticks, especially tropical species, coloration may be structural; the midgut gland may produce numerous bright iridescent or glossy colors, the biological significance of which is unknown. More commonly, pigments are present in the hypodermis, such as the bright red of the Prostigmata, the red, blue, green and yellow of the colorful water mites, and the yellow with violet spots of the Notostigmata. Many Acaridei are colorless or whitish. In many transparent mites the coloration of internal organs may show through the integument. In some plant feeders, such as the Tetranychidae, the coloration may depend on the food taken in.

Fig. 14–4. Hair follicle mite, *Demodex ovis* of sheep, venter; 0.23 mm long. (After Hirst.)

The chelicerae usually have two or three articles and are chelate, but in many genera they have transformed into fine, needlelike stylets. This transformation has evolved numerous times, in various ways. In the Stigmatidae and Entonyssidae, the two-articled chelicera has two sharp fingers and can be used to pierce. In some Dermanyssidae the basal article also is narrowed (Fig. 8–4). In others the immovable finger is rudimentary, so that the two-articled chelicera has only one tip. This evolution may be observed in different stages in the Trombidiformes. In most Eleutherengona, the Trombidiidae, and the majority of water mites, the terminal finger is usually a curved finger (Figs. 14–11, 14–12). In the Tarsonemini, the Cheyletidae, Tetranychidae, Hydrachnidae and others, the movable finger is needle-shaped (Fig. 14–7). A similar transformation is found in gall mites. In some Acaridei, in two genera of Oribatei (*Gustavia*), and in females of the bird mite, *Dermanyssus*, the distal article, which is the movable finger, disappears, and the basal article becomes needle-shaped (Fig. 8–4).

The distal article of the pedipalp, except in some predacious mites in which it is raptorial, is smaller than that of the walking legs. In the Acaridei and Tetrapodili it is shortened to two very thin segments (Fig. 14–3) but the coxae are large and are part of the gnathosoma.

Almost all adult mites have four pairs of walking legs; larvae lack the last pair, even though primordia are present in the embryos of Gamasina and Ixodides. Parasitic species from narrow habitats have the legs shortened (e.g., Demodicidae, *Sarcoptes* and gall mites, Figs. 14–2, 14–3). Gall mites lack third and fourth pairs of legs in all stages. An extreme case of leg reduction is seen in the females of some Podapolipodidae; these become a sac filled with embryos, and have only one pair of legs. The coxae in Trombidiformes, the Acaridei, and most Oribatei, are fused with the body and are not separate articles. The lateral walls extend into the body, forming apodemes. The tarsi bear claws or attachment discs (Fig. 14–3).

NERVOUS SYSTEM. Many mites have a mesodermal endosternum above the subesophageal ganglion. The nervous system is concentrated in the prosoma. The brain, as in most dwarf forms, has relatively large dimensions, covering most of the subesophageal ganglion below.

In *Trombidium*, one of the few forms studied, the simple protocerebrum lacks globuli but has a central body. In species with eyes, the optic nerve enters the protocerebral region, and its optical center is connected within the protocerebrum with its opposite by a long commissure. The subesophageal ganglion in *Ixodides* has nine fused ganglia, numbers two through ten.

SENSE ORGANS. Sense organs include sensory setae, trichobothria, slit sense organs, the Haller's organ and eyes. The numerous, diverse, sensory setae on the body and on appendages may be simple, forked, three-pronged, feather-like, club-like or tube-shaped. The trichobothria, called pseudostigmatic organs by taxonomists, are also of various shapes.

The Haller's organ is found on the dorsum of the first walking leg tarsus in the Ixodides. In its simplest form it is a broad groove in the exoskeleton, open its entire length. The walls bear setae on conical bases attached to nerve cells. Their neurons connect with the large glomeruli of the third ganglion in the subesophageal gangliar mass.

With few exceptions, there are one or two pairs of lateral eyes in the Noto-stigmata, some Ixodides, Eleutherengona and Parasitengona. Their diameter is small, and the few retina cells have their rhabdoms facing the lens.

DIGESTIVE SYSTEM. The complicated preoral cavity, located in the gnatho-soma, is structurally similar to that of the Uropygi as is shown by the ontogeny of *Ixodes* and *Pediculopsis*. The walls of the gnathosoma consist of two compo-nents, fused along a longitudinal axis. One is the tectum, an extension of the anterior margin of the proterosoma, fused laterally with the wall of a pedipalpal coxa (Fig. 14–5). The other is the pedipalpal coxae, lying parallel to the longi-tudinal axis of the body; their anterior and ventral walls and endites fuse with each other, sometimes enclosing vestiges of the sternum (Figs. 14–5, 14–6, 14–19).

The gnathosoma thus forms a preoral cavity, open anteriorly and enclosing in its dorsal half the chelicerae, which lie parallel to the body axis. The **lower half** of the preoral cavity has a trough-shaped floor, formed by the fused pedipalpal

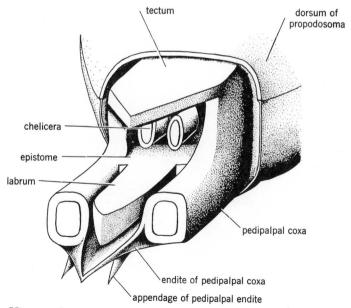

Fig. 14–5. **Mite gnathosoma as seen from diagonal anterior–dorsally; chelicerae cut off near base.**

coxae and their anterior endites (Figs. 8–9, 14–5, 14–6). As in all other arachnids, there is a bridge-shaped base (epistome) of the labrum between the bases
of the pedipalpal coxae. The epistome becomes free anteriorly and covers the
trough from above (Fig. 14–5). Above the epistome on the anterior wall of the
body and below the tectum, the chelicerae insert. Their joint membrane may
be long and may form a collar-like fold surrounding the base of the chelicera
(Fig. 14–6). This arrangement permits extension and withdrawal of the chelicera. Also the tectum and the pedipalpal coxae in many species may be connected to the prosoma by a folded joint membrane. Thus the whole gnathosoma
with its preoral cavity may be withdrawn toward the prosoma—sometimes deep
into the prosoma.

In most mites these structures are more or less specialized; particularly the
endites may be modified into separate splinter-shaped, lamellate, cone-shaped or
toothed structures, completely transforming the shape of the coxae. Even the
piercing mouthparts of certain mites are structurally essentially similar. In
spider mites there is, under the small tectum, a large, oval, club-shaped retract-
able structure, the fused basal article of the chelicerae (Fig. 14–7). From two
cavities of its venter rise the stylet-shaped distal articles. Both lie in a deep
dorsal groove of the epistome and labrum (Fig. 14–8). The groove guides the
stylets.

The mouth, as in all arachnids, is at the base of the labrum at the tip of the
epistome. The mouth leads into a pumping pharynx, X-shaped in cross section
(Fig. 8–10) (Nostostigmata, Parasitiformes), or sometimes crescent-shaped (Fig.

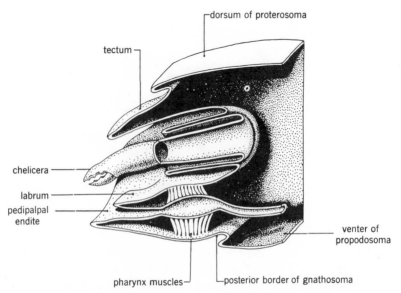

Fig. 14–6. Mite gnathosoma, longitudinal section.

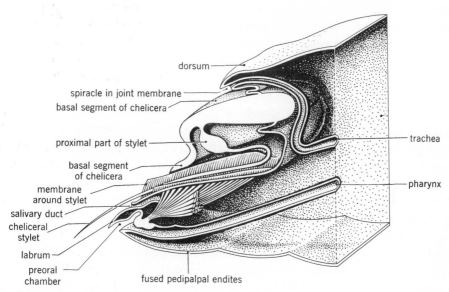

dorsum

spiracle in joint membrane

basal segment of chelicera

proximal part of stylet

basal segment of chelicera

membrane around stylet

salivary duct

cheliceral stylet

labrum

preoral chamber

fused pedipalpal endites

trachea

pharynx

Fig. 14–7. Longitudinal section of piercing mouthparts of a tetranychid. (After a section of Blauvelt.)

14–9). An exception is that in *Tetranychus* the pharynx is a spherical sucking apparatus with a sclerotized stopper, muscular withdrawal of which creates suction (Fig. 14–8).

The midgut has tube-like ceca, the number (to 7 pairs) and length of which are greatest in bloodsucking ticks, while in Sarcoptiformes the gut has only one pair of ceca, and ceca are absent in the worm-shaped Tetrapodili (Figs. 14–10 to 14–12).

In the Trombidiformes the midgut is blind behind and does not connect with the excretory pore. This adaptation probably could arise only in animals that take up liquid or preorally liquefied food and digest it intracellularly. Under these circumstances there are few food remains, only excretory substances. In the Ixodides the end of the midgut that opens into the hindgut tends to transform into a string of cells and lacks a lumen. In *Ixodes*, however, fecal material passes into the hindgut and out the anus.

EXCRETORY SYSTEM. Usually the excretory organs include the midgut cells, Malpighian tubules, an unpaired median excretory duct, and coxal glands. Nephrocytes have been demonstrated only in *Parasitus*. The Malpighian tubules open into the hindgut. There are two pairs in the Holothyrina, but only one pair in the Notostigmata and Parasitiformes, where the tubules may move actively. They are absent in other mites, but remains are found in some Acaridei. The Prostigmata, having a blind midgut, usually have an unpaired dorsomedian excretory pouch dorsal to the midgut, with a short ectodermal duct and excretory pore (Fig. 14–12). This pore may correspond to the anus of other mites. The embryology shows that the pouch develops in *Cheyletus* through invagination of a dorsomedian ectodermal groove. Coxal glands have been found in the Holothyrina and the Argasidae. They have the usual structure and empty near the first leg coxae. Reports of coxal glands in Notostigmata, Uropodina, Trombidiformes and Sarcoptiformes have to be verified by sectioning.

GLANDS. Besides accessory glands of the gonoducts, the mites have various skin glands and glands related to the mouthparts. Skin glands are found in Ixodides (except *Argas*), the Hydrachnellae, and as a pair of oil glands in most Sarcoptiformes. (Only a few sarcoptid Acaridei have regular skin glands.) *Parasitus* has a gland opening through the cheliceral tip; a similar gland opens at the base of the curved distal cheliceral segment of most Prostigmata. The glands opening into the preoral cavity under the labrum differ in different mite groups (Figs. 14–11, 14–12). Only in the Tetranychidae do we know their function. In this group, the alveolar gland reaches back to the fourth leg coxae and produces silk through openings in the preoral cavity (Fig. 14–7).

RESPIRATORY SYSTEM. While small soft gall mites and Acaridei, as well as most mite larvae, respire through the skin, other groups have more or less branched tracheae. The spiracles, in contrast to those of primitive chelicerates, only rarely lie ventrally in the abdomen; they are not metameric and are believed to be secondary structures. Their position may be at the base of chelicerae, at the pedipalpal coxae or the leg coxae. In the Tarsonemidae only the females have tracheae; the smaller males do not. The spiracles in Prostigmata and Mesostigmata are at the end of a groove, sometimes long, on the surface of

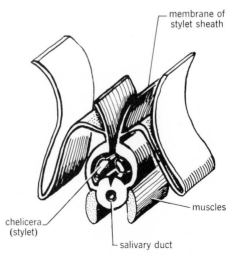

Fig. 14–8.   Diagram of the position of two stylet-shaped chelicerae of a tetranychid. (After a section of Blauvelt.)

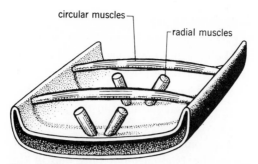

Fig. 14–9.   Pharynx section of a trombidiid.

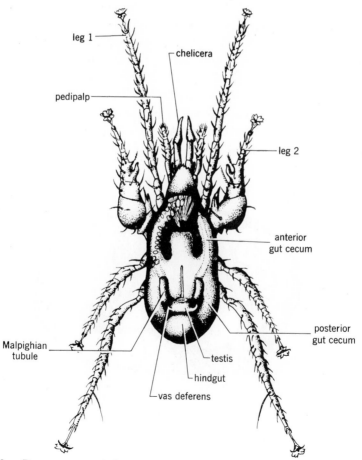

Fig. 14–10.   *Pergamasus crassipes*, dorsal integument removed. Anterior of the testis is a transverse heart with a pair of ostia, and anterior aorta; 1 mm long. (After Winkler.)

the body. The groove, or peritreme, has a circular cross section strengthened by sclerotized rings and is open its entire length. In the Mesostigmata and the Argasidae, there is a pair of spiracles lateral to the second, third, or fourth leg coxae; in the Ixodidae, behind the fourth leg coxae; in the Prostigmata, between the chelicerae. Many Oribatei have three pairs of spiracles: a pair in the first and third leg trochanter and one in the groove behind the second coxa. Notostigmata have four pairs of dorsal spiracles in the area of abdominal grooves.

CIRCULATORY SYSTEM. Blood moves through spaces between organs. In the Holothyrina, Ixodides, and some Mesostigmata, there is a dorsomedian heart that has two pairs of ostia in the Ixodidae, but only one in the Mesostigmata and the Argasidae (Fig. 14–10). The anterior and posterior aortae are short.

REPRODUCTIVE SYSTEM. Mites have sexes separate. The testes and ovaries are generally paired and open into a median ectodermal atrium (Acaridei, Ixodides and most male Mesostigmata); in many families the gonads are fused, but may be U-shaped, circular or saclike. The testes may at times have blind diverticula, large during reproductive periods. Both gonoducts may fuse to a median duct, sometimes only part of the way. Both males and females may have accessory glands. Sarcoptiformes have a penis; some Trombidiformes have a structure that produces spermatophores. The Oribatei have an ovipositor. The gonopore is anterior between the leg coxae (Fig. 14–3). Acaridei, in addition to the gonopore, have a copulatory slit behind and above the anus, leading through a coiled duct into a median seminal receptacle. The seminal receptacle connects by a duct to each of the two ovaries. If this apparatus is present in the last nymphal state, it permits mating by the nymph.

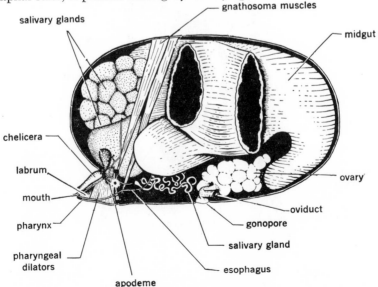

Fig. 14–11. Water mite *Najadicola ingens*; sagittal section; midgut with one ventral and two lateral ceca, 3 mm. (After Mitchell.)

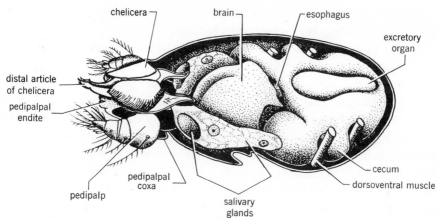

Fig. 14–12. Harvest mite larva, *Neotrombicula autumnalis*, dorsolateral view without integument and legs, 0.25 mm. (After Jones.)

Reproduction

Sperm is transferred in any one of the three ways found among arachnid orders: with a penis (Acaridei), with gonopods, or as a stalked spermatophore. In gamasid mites, transfer is effected by a tubelike appendage in the movable finger of the chelicerae. The *Parasitus* male pushes his abdomen underneath that of the female, venters touching, his specialized second legs holding the female's last pair (Fig. 14–10). His chelicerae then lift a spermatophore from the gonopore, and holding it like a half-empty sac, introduce it into the female gonopore. Many water mites have the third legs modified as gonopods. Or the sperm may be transferred by means of a stalked spermatophore that is picked up by the female gonopore. The male of the water mite, *Arrenurus globator*, attaches the female with glandular secretions to his abdomen so that the long axis of the female is at right angles to that of the male (Fig. 14–13). For about 10 minutes the male walks about with the female, twitching its body once every one to two seconds. The male deposits a spermatophore on the ground and walks forward until the female gonopore is in position to pick up the spermatophore. After about four spermatophores have been picked up, there is a period of three to four hours in which the male shakes his abdomen. Finally he pushes the distal articles of his last legs against the abdomen of the female above the place of attachment, making it possible for the female to separate and move away.

Males of *Collohmannia gigantea* place their first legs on the sides of the females and walk about for an hour behind her, keeping in contact. Copulation has not been seen. In many oribatids the male deposits a spermatophore with a penis but has no contact with a female. A passing female later tears off the head of the spermatophore with her gonopore after carefully touching it with her first legs. *Allothrombium fuliginosum* deposits a spermatophore only after stroking and encircling the female with his legs.

In mating, many males hold the female in an embrace at times secured with suction cups or by cement. Males may hold on with one or more legs, which may be modified for the purpose. In many species of Acaridei that live on birds (e.g., *Analges*) the legs of different males of the same species are of variable length on the same host. Nevertheless all can copulate with the females. The small leg may work as well as the large one. In other species the chelicerae of the males may be modified to various degrees. That this is not due to differences in food habits, or reproductive habits could be demonstrated in the individual species. Also the appearance of individuals with greater modifications on one side than on the other would exclude environment as the cause for the modification. Probably this phenomenon, also known from insects with strong sexual dimorphism, is genetically determined. The differential development of the legs seems to be a balanced polymorphism. Such modifications make it possible, for example, in the genera *Analges, Analgopsis* to separate sibling species, while it may be difficult to separate species in which the males lack modified appendages.

In the Acaridei (e.g., *Acarus, Tyroglyphus, Rhizoglyphus, Caloglyphus*) the male usually attaches to the female with a pair of ventral suction cups at the posterior end, so that male and female face away from each other.

Parthenogenesis has been demonstrated for only a few species. Unfertilized eggs of the snakemite, *Ophionyssus natricis,* produce males, fertilized eggs, females.

The eggs are deposited singly (many Acaridei) or in small clusters, glued together by secretions. Feather and hair mites glue their eggs to the host.

Development

The small size of the eggs makes the study of mite embryology difficult and there are only a few publications on the subject. In three species that have

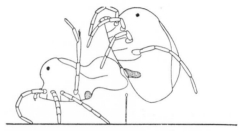

Fig. 14–13. Spermatophore transfer in the water mite, *Arrenurus globator:* left, male; right, female; gonopores stippled; male 0.8 mm long. (After Böttger.)

been studied, the abdomen is already reduced in the embryo. In *Ixodes* the embryonic abdomen has five distinct anterior segments and an indistinct posterior section, and contains four pairs of ganglia. Grooves in the abdomen of *Pediculopsis* also indicate six segments. Remains of coelomic pouches have been found only in *Cheyletus*, which for a short period has five pairs in the prosoma, four pairs in the abdomen. There are generally four postembryonal stages of development, separated by molts. The nymphs are not much different from the adult, but by convention are called larva, proto-, deuto-, and tritonymphs. The larva has only six legs (Fig. 14–24), although primordia of eight are present in the embryos of many genera. With some exceptions the nymphs are similar to the adults. Only the Holothyrina, the Oribatei and a few Acaridei have all four states. The Mesostigmata omit the tritonymph; the Trombidiidae and Hydrachnellae omit the proto- and tritonymph; *Pyemotes* omits all juvenile instars.

The chigger mite, *Eutrombicula batatas,* at molting has the legs of the next stage appressed against the body rather than inside the legs of the old skin. In the Parasitengona there appear to be suppressed stages in the form of excessive exoskeletons. In the larva ready to molt, the body contents withdraw from the exoskeleton. As a result of histolytical processes all appendages are withdrawn from those of the exoskeleton. Underneath the old integument two sclerotized layers form. The outer layer forms a wide outer skin, often only a loose sac having extensions for appendages, and underneath it, covering the appendages, there is a second skin, to which the muscles are attached. The outer skin is the remains of the protonymphal stage, the inner one is the integument of the deutonymph. If the deutonymph molts later, the same procedure is followed: underneath the deutonymphal skin develops a rudimentary tritonymphal integument, and enclosed by it is the skin of the adult.

The ecology of the larva of the Parasitengona differs from that of the adult. In other groups there may be a nymphal stage that survives unfavorable conditions or has special adaptations for dispersal.

Different species differ greatly in their life span. The adults of *Arrenurus globator* live three years, those of *Eylais infundibulifera,* four to six weeks, those of *Parasitus coleoptratorum,* only 6 to 10 days.

Relationships

The mites may be compared with the Opiliones, especially the body form, the shift of the gonopores, the gut ceca and presence of a penis. The mouthparts differ, however. Schulze (1943) found interesting points of comparison between the outer body of ticks and the fossil Anthracomarti, even with the trilobites. Despite that, it is not certain from which group the Acari are derived. During the Devonian a species lived that had all attributes of recent Acari.

Habits

Mites are found in all possible terrestrial habitats; in the soil, in litter, on and inside of plants, in nests of ants, bees, wasps, birds and mammals, in barns, storage bins and dwellings, and as ecto- and endoparasites of invertebrates, reptiles, birds and mammals. More than 2500 species of mites live in fresh water, over 100 are marine. Many are of economic importance in agriculture, and since World War II their importance has increased explosively, as the widespread use of modern insecticides has removed many of their predators or competitors.

Small size brings some biological advantages for free-living mites and symbionts: ability to enter small spaces and utilize areas not accessible to larger animals as well as potential predators; the possibility of living in areas that provide little nourishment; rapid reproduction in areas of adequate food (storage mites); protection from many large predators.

The small size, however, brings with it the problem of water loss due to the proportionally large surface. Thus most mites search for moist microclimates and others are able to take up moisture from the air (e.g., *Echinolaelaps, Acarus siro*). Weighing such mites after bringing them from an area of low humidity into an area of high humidity shows that they act as hygroscopic substances.

Protection against water loss through heavy sclerotization is found only in the Holothyrina, most Parasitiformes and especially Oribatei, while Trombidiformes and Acaridei are usually lightly sclerotized. The turtlelike Uropodina can withdraw their legs into depressions, reducing the surface exposed to possible predators; some of the Oribatei may ball up, hiding appendages in a sclerotized sphere. While the lightly sclerotized juvenile oribatids are sensitive to drying, some adults may be found on stones in the sun.

Aquatic mites have retained the bodily characteristics of free-living species, but have lost body setae. Some feather and fur mites, especially those living in the feather shaft, have the body elongated. The extremes are found in the follicle mites, Demodicidae, and the gall mites, among both of which the abdomen has become worm-shaped. As a result of their shape and annuli (Fig. 14–29) the gall mites, Tetrapodili, move wormlike, facilitating passage among feltlike galls. In contrast, the small body and mange mites (Fig. 14–3), which gnaw their tunnels, have a spherical shape that facilitates turning.

Many adaptations (not yet sufficiently investigated) are shown by appendages, their diversity of setae, spines and apophyses, the often complicated pretarsal structures, the claws and suction structures (Figs. 14–3, 14–10). Many feather mites hook the bent apophyses of their legs into the feathers (Figs. 14–14, 14–16); others press lateral projections against feather barbs (Fig. 14–15), protecting them from falling off in air currents. Species that live in fur usually have long curved claws; the Listrophoridae have in addition a pair of hair-embracing, concave attachments on the pedipalpal endites, or have two leg pairs distally widened, permitting them to hold on to smooth hairs (Fig. 14–17). Species living on shiny smooth millipedes or other smooth animals often lack claws and attach themselves to the host with suckers or by adhesion of long tarsal hairs (Figs. 14–3, 14–26). In contrast, nose and lung dwelling Mesostigmata have enlarged claws that permit wading through the thin mucous membranes. Legs are short in species that live in galls, feather shafts, skin pores, and burrows (Figs. 14–3, 14–4, 14–29). The legs of swimming mites bear rows of long hairs. Males often have specialized appendages to clasp females.

LOCOMOTION. All species move by walking. Many species use the first leg normally as a feeler but rarely for walking. Despite being small, many mites run rapidly or climb rapidly among the feathers or fur of their host. Gall mites move on only two legs, dragging the long abdomen on setae. All Halacaridae walk, as do many spring and stream inhabitants, holding onto the substrate with claws to prevent being swept away by the currents.

Of gamasid mites inhabiting meadow soils, those living in deeper layers have shorter legs than those living on the surface. Species living to 1 cm deep, about 1.2 mm long, have legs 1.8 mm; species living 1–5 cm deep and 0.4–0.5 mm long, have legs as long as the body; species 10–15 cm deep are only 0.2–0.3 mm long and their legs measure 0.14–0.2 mm.

The Hydrachnellae, which inhabit ponds and lakes, usually use the swimming hairs on the two posterior legs at least for paddling. Though they swim rapidly the travelled distances are usually small; distribution of the species depends upon passive transport of young or adults. Soft Tetrapodili may be carried by wind or blown with leaves. Many mites, however, attach themselves to insects, especially to detritus feeding beetles (Silphidae, Histeridae, Scarabaeidae) or to bees, bumble bees and wood lice. The mites stay attached to the carrier without feeding usually throughout one growth period, often the deutonymph until the next molt or copulation. Such passive transportation, common also in pseudoscorpions, is called phoresy.

The deutonymphs of *Parasitus coleoptratorum* appear excited and run about (at a speed of 1.5 cm/sec) if a scarab beetle (*Geotrupes stercorarius*) passes within a distance of 2 cm in quiet air. On contact with the beetle, the mites climb up. A brush that has touched the beetle has the same effect on the deutonymphs, suggesting that it is odor that attracts the deutonymphs to the beetle. The mites are thereby transported to a fresh food supply. *Poecilochirus* deutonymphs sit on the silphid beetle, *Necrophorus*, which oviposits on small mammals and then undermines and buries them. The mites take part in the meals of the beetle. Often the venter of the beetle is so densely populated with mites that the integument is completely covered.

The deutonymphs of Uropodina cement themselves quickly, with a secretion from the anal opening to the integument of the transporting insect. The cement draws out to a hardened thread (Fig. 14–18), and the attached nymph can move

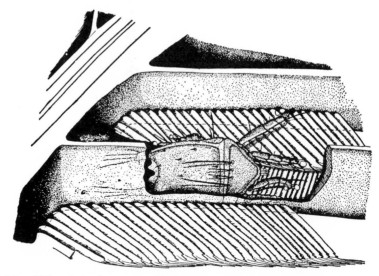

Fig. 14–14. Male of feather mite, *Michaelichus heteropus*, anchored by the long left second leg between the barbules of a primary feather; 0.65 mm long. (After Dubinin.)

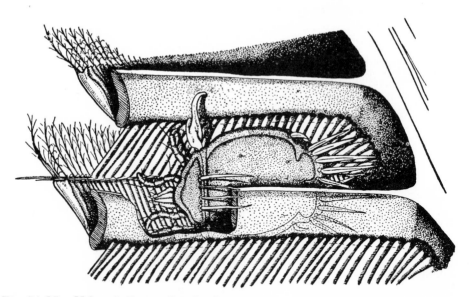

Fig. 14–15. Male of *Freyanella plataleae* using a wide propodosomal appendage, present only on the right side, between the barbs of a primary feather; 0.65 mm long. (After Dubinin.)

and can leave the beetle at any time by tearing loose the attachment. Some Acaridei develop regularly or at a certain time a deutonymph that is armed with disks or hairs that attach to tarsi of arthropods (Fig. 14–26). An important adaptation of deutonymphs to phoresy is their greater resistance to lack of food

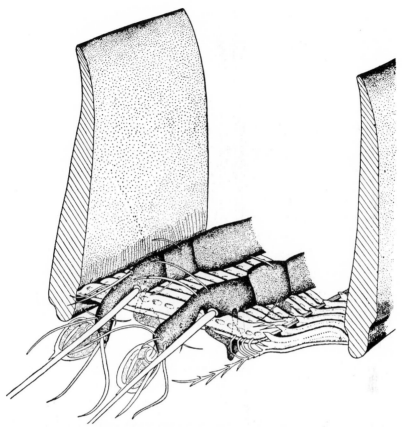

Fig. 14–16. Male of *Sulanyssus caputmedusae* presses hook-shaped appendages of its first legs against the barbules of a primary feather; to left and right are barbs. (After Dubinin.)

and desiccation, compared with other instars. Deutonymphs of *Parasitus coleoptratorum* above CaCl$_2$ at 21°C become dried out in 9–10 hours, protonymphs in half an hour. Also 60% of *Parasitus* deutonymphs withstood eight weeks starvation while other instars will die within a few days without food.

In dermanyssid and tarsonemid mites only the adult females seek insect transportation.

SENSES. Sensory hairs and touch are the dominant senses. Most species use the first legs as feelers. Water mites sense prey at a distance of 2 mm. Larvae of *Eylais,* at more than 1 cm, sense disturbance of the water surface caused by their hosts, the waterboatmen *Corixa.* Trichobothria, the pseudostigmatic organs, respond to air currents of 10 sec/cm as well as to vibrations of 0.001–0.004 mm amplitude. If the trichbothria are touched with quick-drying glue and are then torn out the oribatid ceases to react to such stimuli.

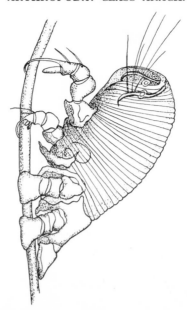

Fig. 14–17. Hair mite, *Labidocarpus megalonynx*, a listrophorid, climbing and feeding on a hair; 0.9 mm long. (After Berlese from Dahl.)

Predation of water mites depends upon mechanical senses: whatever the mite touches is embraced and considered edible if it moves.

A chemical sense is activated in ticks by touching the Haller's organ, located at the tip of the first walking leg tarsus. Parasitidae and oribatids have been shown to have a sensory organ at the same location. On the first tarsus of the snake mite, *Ophionyssus natricis,* a chemical sense in clusters of setae containing club-shaped setae was localized by removing segments distal to the clusters.

Ixodes running over filter paper will stop on touching with the first legs a place under which there was fresh cattle skin. The response is not repeated if the first walking leg tarsi are extirpated. Deutonymphs of *Parasitus coleoptratorum* ignore their transport host if the tip of the first leg tarsus has been cut off.

Many ground inhabiting Parasitidae quickly attack any prey they touch with the first legs while moving about. *Parasitus coleoptratorum* took prey only after examining it with the tips of the pedipalpi, thus was not dependent on the tarsal organ of the first leg. *Parasitus* deutonymphs, ticks, and cheese mites distinguish varying intensities within the odor area and, as they run around, turn back where the intensity diminishes. In tests to determine whether varying humidities are recognized, *Parasitus* moved to the most humid part even if the palpi and first leg tarsi were removed. Ticks no longer responded to varying humidity after removal of tarsi of the first legs. While *Ixodes* selects low humidity, cheese mites will move immediately toward a vial containing moist cotton rather than toward the dry vial used as control. Lead pipes filled with water at 80°C attract *Ixodes* from a distance of 6 cm. The temperature receptors appear to be spread over the body, but a temperature sense appears to be more localized at the tips of the posterior legs. If these are cut off covered membranes above warm blood solution will not be penetrated by *Ixodes*, provided that at the same time the Haller's organ has been removed. In choice of temperature ticks move to a certain optimum. But if the tarsi of the last legs are amputated they find the optimum only after considerable time and will spread themselves out over a wide zone of temperatures. *Ixodes* is attracted to sheeps' wool at 37°C, repelled by the heat alone, and insensitive to wool at room temperatures.

Leptotrombidium chiggers form excited clusters on approach of humans. In the laboratory, various factors were investigated and human breath was found to cause the excitement. When the components of human breath were tested, the chiggers responded to CO_2 gas. They were also found to be negatively geotactic and negatively phototactic. As a further step, free amino acids on skin of a host were found to be a more specific stimulus. CO_2 was also found to be an attractant for the rat mite, *Ornithonyssus bacoti*.

Cheese mites, Oribatei and *Ixodes*, despite their lack of eyes, are light sensitive. Ticks move toward intense light. Harvest mites react to every shadow, raising the anterior part of the body and moving the first legs toward the shadow; a shadow would frequently be cast by a potential host. The light sensitive organ has not been located in ticks despite selective painting with black lacquer. Possibly light directly effects the brain or nerves.

The light sense of the snake mite, *Ophionyssus natricis*, has been investigated. The mites responded to light of all colors except red. It was noticed that the first pair of legs waved from side to side in moving about and that there was no reaction to light if the legs were removed. Two photoreceptors were found

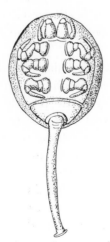

Fig. 14–18. *Uropoda* **deutonymph cemented with stalk; 0.6 mm diameter. (After Berlese from Dahl.)**

on each pulvillus of the first legs, spots measuring 1.0×3.0 μm. After the pulvilli were torn off, the reaction to light stopped after 3–4 days; presumably the torn nerve endings were light sensitive until healed over. With one pulvillus half torn off, the other completely, the half blinded mites circled in diffuse light, but moved straight in horizontal light if the leg remained in the shadow of the body.

FEEDING. In contrast to other archnids, mites display diverse feeding habits.

1. Predators and carrion scavengers feed on nematodes, mites, and small insects, including maggots. Water mites feed on ostracods, Cladocera, and copepods. To this group belong many Mesostigmata and Prostigmata.

Ground inhabiting gamasids have the chelicerae modified depending on their food specialties. Those that pull out nematodes and feed on them have cheliceral teeth that fit into each other, so that the chela close tightly. Collembola and mite feeders have long cheliceral digits with barbs suitable for catching fast moving prey.

General predators that also attack insect larvae have heavier chelae with teeth of various sizes and the curved tip of the movable tips fits the edge of the immovable one.

Trombiculids feed on insect eggs.

2. Plant feeders. Armed with stylets, Tetranychidae and Tetrapodili suck out cells of living leaves. Feeding *Caloglyphus* make channels in onions and potatoes; other acarids feed on fungi, dried fruit and other plant products, and like the flour mites appear in huge numbers in granaries, where they feed on wheat and flour. Dead and rotting vegetable matter, including wood, is eaten by oribatids.

3. Commensal mites. Five hundred species of Acaridei are found in fur and feathers where they feed on skin, scales, hairs or fatty secretions. A number of Mesostigmata live with beetles or beetle larvae, feeding on their skin secretions or their prey; others live with social insects and feed on excrement and corpses of wasps and bumble bees.

4. Parasites living on tissues and fluids of their hosts are numerous. Insect parasites destroy tissues and hemolymph close to the integument, sucking it out (e.g., Parasitengona larvae). Vertebrate parasites, especially mange mites and their relatives, also live on dermal cells and lymph. Only a few species have chelicerae long enough to reach through the vertebrate integument; these species include the ticks, Ixodides, and among the Mesostigmata, *Dermanyssus* and *Haemogamasus*. The hard ticks (Ixodidae) are stationary parasites; most stay on the host during one instar. The soft ticks, Argasidae and Mesostigmata, are temporary parasites that live in nests and feed for hours at a time. A few mites are endoparasites of vertebrates, having invaded the body cavity via the lungs.

Mites (and all other arachnids) feed on material previously liquefied by secreted enzymes, but mites with chelate chelicerae may take in small particles:

in the midgut of *Opilioacarus* sclerotized pieces have been found; in *Knemi-dokoptes,* pieces of horn; in oribatids, leaf or wood fragments; starch grains in storage mites. The predatory mites tear off pieces of prey as do scorpions and place them in the preoral cavity where (at least in *Parasitus*) they are dissolved. However, predatory prostigmatids with hook or stylet chelicerae, stab their prey and suck it without cutting or tearing. The hook-shaped chelicerae of trombibiids (Fig. 14–12) stay inserted by holding the place of penetration with their pedipalpi against the inserted chelicerae. The pedipalpi and chelicerae work against each other. In addition the anterior legs hold on. Other Prostigmata, Cheyletidae, Cunaxidae, Bdellidae, and Hydrachnellae grab and hold the prey with pedipalpi while overpowering and sucking it out.

Plant feeders suck out cells (Tetranychidae, Tetrapodili) or may remove and chew small parts with their chelicerae as do certain Oribatei that feed on algae or pollen.

Parasites can be divided into those that feed on lymph and skin tissues and those that feed on blood. Parasitengona suck out insects as stationary parasites that penetrate the integument and dissolve the tissues with secreted enzymes. They attach themselves with the chelicerae to the border of the fracture and their preoral cavity is pressed against the wound. From the parasite's mouth there extends into the host a branched tube, the walls of which consist of hemolymph coagulated around the stream of saliva from the parasite. Leucocytes that accumulate around the tubes also are digested and taken in as food by the parasite.

The actions of the chigger *Neotrombicula autumnalis,* a parasite of man, are similar. It penetrates at an angle with the chelicerae through the stratum corneum of the skin to the epidermal cells. The saliva dissolves the upper cells. Fluids, small nuclei and breakdown products are sucked in. In the meanwhile the epidermal cells encapsulate the wound which is penetrated again by saliva. Thus the saliva penetrates deeper and deeper into the epidermis and the tube, a protective capsule, extends to 0.2 mm length, while the chelicerae themselves are only 0.03 mm long (Fig. 14–24).

Parasites among the Acaridae that have chelate chelicerae, especially the mange mites, feed on the stratum corneum of mammals and then with chelicerae and enzymes work on the epidermis cells and take up dissolved cells and lymph.

The mesostigmatids having long needle-shaped chelicerae (*Dermanyssus*) penetrate vertebrate skin to the capillaries and suck blood (Figs. 8–4, 14–21). The red poultry mite, *D. gallinae,* is 0.7 mm long, with chelicerae 0.5 mm long. Ticks also have long chelicerae with two movable fingers (one is the distal article) that separate laterally and bear teeth on the sides. *Ixodes ricinus,* by contraction of the dorsoventral body muscles, extends its chelicerae and drills their tips into the stratum corneum. Separating the movable fingers slits the skin open, and the tip of the pedipalpal endites (hypostome) is pushed into the

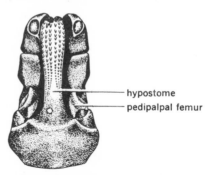

hypostome
pedipalpal femur

Fig. 14–19. Gnathosoma (capitulum) of the tick *Hyalomma cypriacum*, venter. On the medially fused pedipalpal coxae arises the short pedipalpus. The hypostome, armed by barbs, is the fused pedipalpal endites and may include part of the labium; 1 mm long. (After Schulze.)

wound and anchored by barbs (Fig. 14–19). In 12–15 minutes the hypostome is completely within the skin (hypostome 0.5 mm long, human epidermis 0.1 mm thick). The saliva flowing into the wound anesthetizes and acts as a blood anti-coagulant, increasing bleeding. In seven to eight days female *Ixodes* take up 200 times their weight in blood, which is stored in gut ceca, and undergo a corresponding increase in body size (1.5–2.5 mg to 250–400 mg). In *Boophilus*, the cattle tick, the transformation from unfed larva to fed female may involve a ten-thousandfold increase in weight.

DIGESTION. Digestion occurs in the midgut and its ceca; it is intracellular in *Ixodes* and *Parasitus*. The blood taken in by a tick has lost its ability to coagulate; it is hemolysed in the gut lumen and is concentrated by removal of water. The walls of the gut ceca increase the number of their cells which are stretching into the lumen and slowly take up the contents. As the material is digested in the cells they are filled with metabolic wastes, and fall apart. The excretory material is transported to the hindgut.

The pH of the flour mite midgut and two ceca is between 5 and 6; in the hindgut, the pH is between 7 and 8. The hindgut absorbs water from the excretory material, the food of the flour mite and its surroundings being dry so that water has to be conserved. Nutrients are taken up in the midgut and its ceca. Glycogen is stored. As in other arachnids the excretory product is mostly guanin.

Classification

The classification of mites is still not settled. About 700 new species were described annually in 1962 and 1963, placed by some authors in 240 families.*

---

* For comparison, there are almost 200 families of beetles, the largest insect order, with 10 times the number of species.

The tendency is to combine the many families. The small size and adaptations to diverse habitats have caused acarologists to devise an unusually large number of categories between suborder and superfamily. The taxa of the categories often have a number of names. Lack of space prevents naming all known families, so those of economic importance, whose habits are better known, are represented here in unusually large proportion.

The suborders have been grouped according to birefringence of the cuticle of setae: the Actinochitinosi (Actinochaeta, Actinotrichida) with birefringent setae and trichobothria present (Trombidiformes, Tetrapodili, Sarcoptiformes), and the Anactinochitinosi (Anactinochaeta, Anactinotrichida) with setae not birefringent, trichobothria lacking. The internal anatomy resembles that of other arachnid orders by the presence of Malpighian tubules and usually presence of a heart. (Parasitiformes and possibly Notostigmata). The Actinochaeta are believed to contain actinochitin. Birefringence is also used as the basis for separating other classes of arachnids into four groups and to substantiate the hypothesis of polyphyletic origin of mites. But to separate the classes on this basis would disperse Schizopeltidia, Amblypygi and Holopeltidia into three of the four groups (Zakvatkin, 1952). It is more likely that the presence of actinochitin is of no phylogenetic importance at all and has been acquired several times independently. Also it may be an artifact.

SUBORDER NOTOSTIGMATA

This primitive group has the hysterosoma dorsally divided by transverse grooves into 12 sections and a pair of anal scuta probably correspond to tergites V to XVI (Fig. 14-2). The venter has a large sternum between the free coxae of the legs. There are four pairs of spiracles laterally on the first four abdominal tergites (VII to X); a heart is present. The chelicerae are three-segmented. A gonopore lies between the coxae of the third legs.

Found in Texas, Arizona, Caribbean, South America, the Mediterranean, Africa and Asia they live under stones and in organic debris, and are predators of millipedes, opilionids and mites. *Opilioacarus*, 1.5–2.2 mm, *Paracarus* (Fig. 14-2), and *Panchaetes* are included.

SUBORDER PARASITIFORMES

All postlarval instars have lateral or lateroventral spiracles, rarely laterodorsal; a heart often is present. The midgut opens into a short ectodermal hindgut (except in some Ixodides), and the ceca have a greater combined volume than has the midgut (Fig. 14-10). One pair of long excretory ducts opens into the hindgut. Palp has a pretarsus (except Ixodides).

Infraorder Holothyrina

The body is unsegmented, with dorsal and ventral unsegmented plates. The leg coxae are free. There are two pairs of pores, perhaps gland openings or spiracles; one is above the third coxa, in the joint membrane between dorsal and ventral plates, and leads into an atrium from which 16 tracheae branch into the body and appendages. The posterior pair of spiracles lies behind and above the last coxae, on the border of the dorsal plate, and opens into a short atrium into which open numerous membraneous sacs that lead posteriorly toward the hindgut. A heart is present; the gonopore opens between the last coxae and in the female is flanked by four shields.

Members of the Holothyrina have been collected in New Zealand, Australia, New Guinea, Ceylon, on Indian Ocean Islands, Trinidad and Costa Rica. *Holothyrus,* 7 mm, lives on the ground. On Mauritius Island, the deaths of fowl have been attributed to swallowing the mites.

Infraorder Mesostigmata

The spiracles open dorsally to the coxae, below the dorsal sclerites; the coxae are free. A heart is usually present. The gut opens through the anus. The chelicerae are usually chelate. A well-developed tectum is present.

COHORT GAMASINA

Gamasina have a cylindrical to pear-shaped body. Spiracles usually lie above the third coxae, rarely above the fourth. A heart is present. The gnathosoma is dorsally exposed. Usually these have predatory habits.

Parasitidae. Most of these yellow-brown mites are longer than 1 mm. Second legs of the male have apophyses (Fig. 14-10). There are one or two dorsal plates (Fig. 14-20). Deutonymphs are phoretic on insects. *Parasitus fucorum* in bumble bee nests feeds on their fecal material; *P. coleoptratorum,* is a symbiont of beetles (Fig. 14-20). *Eugamasus* has been seen to feed on shore oligochaetes. Most are probably predators of small insects and mites. *Poecilochirus,* associated with silphid beetles, joins its host in feeding on maggots in carrion.

Phytoseiidae are beneficial mites found on plants where they prey on spider mites, small insects and pollen.

Dermanyssidae. This family includes free-living species, occurring in a variety of habitats, as well as forms displaying various degrees of symbiosis with arthropods and vertebrates. *Laelaps,* 0.5–1 mm, found in nests of small mammals, is viviparous. Larvae

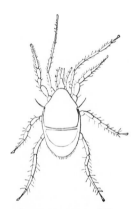

Fig. 14–20. *Parasitus coleoptratorum,* 1.2 mm. (After Hertwig.)

are free-living, nymphs feed on lymph, females on blood. *Myrmonyssus phalaenodectes* lives in the tympanic organs, "ears," of the noctuid moth *Pseudaletia unipuncta*, destroying the ear; the mites occupy only one ear, rarely both, the ears being of survival value to the moth (and, consequently, to the mite) by enabling the moth to evade bats. The female mite lays up to 90 eggs after puncturing the inner chamber. It defecates at only two places, minimizing fouling. Young hatch after two days. As new arrivals enter the same ear, the animals become crowded, making their movement difficult. Some deutonymphs transform into males, which mate immediately with the emerging females. Young impregnated females climb anterior on the moth, descend on a flower and infect another feeding moth. The mite climbs on the moth along the midline between the ears, and crosses a number of times before entering; a second mite will invade the same ear as the first. Colonies may be on either the right or left, and a mite from the left may choose the right if transferred to another moth. *Halarachne,* with a worm-shaped abdomen, are parasites in the respiratory system of seals. The female bores into mucous membranes with her anterior body. The immovable digit of the chelicera is reduced, the chisel-shaped movable digit has teeth. The torn tissues and lymph are used as food. Nymphs are unknown, males rare. Unlike the females, larvae can move about outside the nasal cavities and can infect other animals. *Pneumonyssus,* lung mite of monkeys, is 0.6–1.5 mm long. The female bores into mucous membranes and feeds on cells and lymph, not blood. They are viviparous. Larvae wander about and are infective. *Pneumonyssoides* is found in nasal passages of dogs.

The chicken mite, *Dermanyssus** gallinae,* is the red mite of birds (Fig. 14-21); only 0.75 mm, it becomes much larger after feeding. The chelicerae of the female are stylet-shaped (Fig. 8-4). During the day, this pest of chickens and other domestic fowl and cage birds resides in crevices. If starved, it will attack mammals, and may transmit encephalitis virus to man. Other species are known to transmit filaria and rickettsia bodies. *Ornithonyssus,* parasites of birds and rodents, transmit rickettsial and virus

* Dermanyssus is on the Official List of Generic Names in Zoology and (*Acarus*) *gallinae* on the Official List of Specific Names.

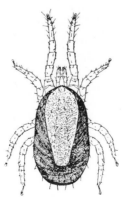

Fig. 14–21.   Female red bird mite, *Dermanyssus gallinae,* dorsum; 0.7 mm. (After Hirst.)

diseases. *Ophionyssus* is parasitic on snakes. *Entonyssus* occurs in the lungs of snakes. *Rhiononyssus* and *Ptilonyssus* live in bird nasal cavities, sucking blood from mucous membranes. The spiracles are dorsal, thus lie above the mucous membrane of the host. *Sternostoma* includes the canary lung mite.

Spinturnicidae, 0.5–1 mm long, with heavy legs and strong claws, are found under bats' wings.

COHORT ANTENNOPHORINA (FREDRIZZINA)

Antennophorina are associated with insects and large Myriapoda, rarely with snakes and lizards. *Antennophorus,* circular in outline, lives under the heads of ants and in food transfer between ants takes a share; or the mite may stroke the ant with its legs to get food droplets.

COHORT UROPODINA

In this group the body is tortoise-shaped, and the legs may often be withdrawn into recesses in the body armor. Next to the second and sometimes third coxae there are spiracles; there is no heart. Chelicerae are extensible but chelae small. Deutonymphs of nonmyrmecophile species are carried by beetles (Fig. 14-18).

Uropodidae. The dorsal plate is shiny, smooth and finely punctate. Dorsal and ventral scuta are fused, leg recesses well developed. *Uropoda*, 0.7–0.9 mm, found in leaf litter, feeds on dead insects and earthworms.

Trachytidae. The body is tortoiselike, but without leg recesses. Chelicerae are very long and extensible; chelae large or small.

Infraorder Ixodides, Ticks

The spiracles open lateral to the third or behind the fourth coxae; heart and midgut are present. The chelicerae have lateral teeth. Anterior edges of the palpal endites are fused to form a hypostome, and are laterally armed with barbs (Fig. 14-19). Haller's organ is present on the first tarsus.

Ixodidae, Hard Ticks. The gnathosoma is visible from above (Fig. 14-22). A pair of spiracles opens behind and lateral to the fourth coxae. Female has an anterior dorsal scutum (Fig. 14-22); male has entire dorsum covered by scutum. Large to very large, they often are brightly colored and iridescent. All are stationary ectoparasites, feeding on blood of reptiles, birds and mammals. A few, such as the cattle tick, *Boophilus*, stay on one host; others change host on becoming adult; most species have a new host for each stage. All attach by the hypostome and do not move until they drop off after feeding. Ticks are of economic importance as parasites and as vectors of numerous diseases of man and domestic animals.

Young of the wood tick of North America, *Dermacentor* andersoni,* parasitize small mammals while the adult parasitizes large ungulates and man. The cattle tick, *Boophilus annulatus,* attaches in the larval stage and leaves its host only to lay eggs. *Amblyomma,** worldwide in distribution, has many species; the lone star tick, *A. americanum*, attacks

---

* *Dermacentor, Amblyomma, Rhipicephalus,* and *Haemaphysalis* are on the Official List of Generic Names in Zoology, (*Ixodes*) *sanguineus* on the Official List of Specific Names.

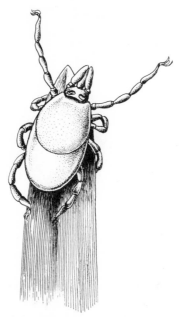

Fig. 14–22. Female castor bean tick, *Ixodes ricinus*, waiting on a grass blade; 3 mm long. (After Pomeranew.)

various mammals and man in the south central states; *A. hebraeum* of South Africa is a serious pest and transmits disease among large mammals. The cosmopolitan brown tick, *Rhipicephalus sanguineus,** feeds on dogs and rabbits and transmits numerous diseases. *Haemaphysalis** *leporispalustris* transmits spotted fever among rabbits. The castor bean tick, *Ixodes ricinus*, of Eurasia is a sheep and cattle pest. In large numbers, ticks may cause anemia of the host; attached to the back of the neck they cause temporary paralysis of the host, a reaction that is not understood. Among important disease organisms transmitted are the protozoan *Babesia* (Texas fever) of domestic animals, transmitted by *Boophilus*, relapsing fever spirochaetes, spotted fever rickettsia of man and animals, Q fever rickettsia, tularemia bacteria, *Pasteurella tularensis,* and various viruses, as well as *Salmonella* and paratyphoid in rodents. Spirochaetes invade all tissues of the tick, remain throughout its life, five to seven years, and are passed on to its offspring. Spotted fever, long known from the Rocky Mountains, and widespread throughout the United States, Mexico, and some parts of South America, is usually transmitted by *Dermacentor*.

Argasidae, Soft Ticks. The gnathosoma is hidden by the back. The spiracle is lateral on the third coxa. The integument is leathery and lacks scuta in postlarval instars. Except for one species, all are temporary parasites, attacking the host during the night.

Argas† are parasites of birds and bats; *A. reflexus,*† the pigeon tick, may attack man.

* See footnote on page 274.

† *Argas* is in the Official List of Generic Names in Zoology and (*Acarus*) *reflexus* on the Official List of Specific Names.

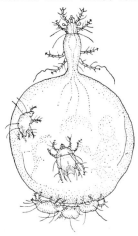

Fig. 14–23.   Female louse mite, *Pyemotes herfsi*, with several males on the abdomen; 0.8 mm diameter. (After Herfs from Hesse.)

They live in crevices of pigeon cotes or in association with other birds. The larva feeds seven days; nymphal stages and adults feed only 20–40 minutes. The female, 9 mm after feeding, alternately feeds and deposits eggs. Ticks fed on humans die after about 9 days but cause dermatitis. *Argas persicus* transmits fowl relapsing fever. *Ornithodorus*, which transmits numerous diseases including relapsing fever among mammals including man, is of importance in western North America.

SUBORDER TROMBIDIFORMES

The spiracles are on or near the gnathosoma (Fig. 14-7). The immovable coxae are joined to the body. The midgut has less volume than its ceca and is closed behind. There is a large dorsomedial ectodermal excretory organ, usually branched anteriorly and opening through a pore that might be the anus (Fig. 14-12).

Infraorder Tarsonemini (Heterostigmata, Tracheostigmata)

Larvae and males lack a tracheal system, or at most have rudimentary spiracles. Females have tracheae, sometimes already as nymphs. The chelicerae are fused at the base, stylet-shaped distally.

Pyemotidae. Pyemotes females live on Hymenoptera, Coleoptera and Lepidoptera larvae. *Pyemotes herfsi* males are 0.13–0.23 mm, young females, 0.2–0.3 mm. The female parasitizes the clothes moth larva, paralyzing it. Enzymes dissolve the internal organs and the mite sucks the fluid out, its body becoming spherical, the size of a pinhead, in 7–11 days at 25°C (Fig. 14-23). The embryonal and postembryonal development occur within the mother's body, and the young are born sexually mature only 9–12 days after the mother begins to feed. There may be between 7 and 284 young, as many as 40 born per day. The males continue to parasitize their mother, penetrating her abdomen near the genital pore. As soon as a sister appears she is grasped and pulled out of the pore and mating takes place immediately. This obstetrical help is not essential, however, as the firstborn may be female. The mated female leaves in search of a new host, which it must find in 1½ to 2 days.

Tips of grass blades and spikes are destroyed by *Siteroptes graminum (=Pediculopsis graminum)*, males 0.12 mm, females 0.22 mm. Males are short-lived, having only rudimentary mouthparts, and mate with just-hatched nymphs, either inside the dissolved hysterosoma of the mother or outside. There are only a few males, but unfertilized females give rise to males having haploid chromosome number.

Tarsonemidae. Tarsonemus species injure plants and cause gall formation.

Scutacaridae. Acarpis woodi, 0.1–0.2 mm, live in tracheal tubes of bees, causing weakness and starvation. Import restrictions on honeybees have prevented infestation of North American colonies.

Podapolipodidae. Podapolipus are insect parasites; the female may be legless or has only one pair of legs.

Infraorder Prostigmata

The spiracles open on or above the cheliceral base (Fig. 14-7). A tracheal system is usually present, lacking only in *Demodex*.

FAMILY GROUP ELEUTHERENGONA

Mites of this group are predators or parasites. The larvae of the predators are not parasitic and they resemble the adults.

Eupodidae. Linopodes, with first legs four times body length, is a pest of cultivated mushrooms.

Tetranychidae, Spider Mites. All are plant parasites, 0.2–0.8 mm in length, with a soft, pear-shaped body and yellowish, greenish, orange or red color. The chelicerae are illustrated in Fig. 14-8. Paired silk glands in the anterior part of the body open on the tip of the labrum. The silk secretion flows along the stylets, which attach it to the substrate, and the pedipalpi brush the silk off the chelicerae and draw it out as two threads that fuse. The strand passes between the mite's legs and becomes longer as the mite moves forward. Colonial species have the webs fused, sometimes between or underneath leaves. The mites stay below leaves, protected by the webs from falling and from rain and dehydration. Eggs are deposited on the leaves. The mites penetrate leaf cells and empty them, causing brown spots. If the mites are abundant the leaf epidermis disintegrates and the leaf dries up. *Tetranychus* feeds on many plants, overwinters in litter. The red spider, *Panonychus ulmi*, 0.26–0.47 mm, damages fruit trees, destroying the palisade layers of leaves; *P. citri* is a pest in California orchards. Clover mite, *Bryobia praetiosa*, is a serious pest on clover, alfalfa, peas and berries.

Syringophilidae. Syringophilus, 0.5–1 mm, live in the quills of primary and tail feathers and feed on other mites.

Cheyletidae. The chelicerae are stylet-shaped. *Cheyletus*, 0.3–0.8 mm (Fig. 14-1), is a predatory mite that catches tyroglyphid mites, bites and paralyzes its prey and sucks it out completely. It is found hunting mites in grain and seed bins; it reproduces parthenogenetically. *Cheyletiella parsitivorax* is the rabbit fur mite; its habits are unknown.

Myobiidae. Myobia lives in the fur of soil-dwelling insectivores and Muridae, climbing dexterously among hairs, holding with the first tarsi onto two hairs; the larvae and nymphs feed on tissue fluid. *Myobia musculi* is found on the house mouse, *Radfordia ensifera* on white rats.

Demodicidae, Follicle Mites. Worm-shaped, secondarily annulate, with legs only 0.09–0.4 mm long, and chelicerae stylet-shaped (Fig. 14-4), these all live in hair follicles of mammals, feeding on oil. *Demodex folliculorum*° is 0.3–0.4 mm long. One to four animals live in each hair follicle of man, especially in the face, causing no damage at all. Once very common, it is now becoming rare. It is believed to be transmitted from mother to baby during breast feedings; bottle fed babies do not harbor the mites. In mammals the demodecids reproduce within the follicle. Dogs may have 100 *D. canis* within one follicle, causing the hair to fall out; the associated red mange bacterium may cause severe injury or death of the dog.

Bdellidae. These are characterized by the very long, narrow gnathosoma and chelicerae with small chelae. Most are reddish, but many are other colors. *Bdella,* 0.6–0.9 mm, feeds on Collembola and small dipterous larvae.

Halacaridae. Mostly marine mites, a few are found in fresh water; 0.14–2 mm long, they are rhomboid in body shape, often with dorsal body plates. Chelicerae have the immovable finger reduced. They do not swim, but walk on algae or plant symbionts of crabs and mollusks. Most are predatory, feeding on small crustaceans, oligochaetes, etc. *Rhombognathus* and relatives feed on plants. *Limnohalacarus* and its relatives live in fresh water, some free-living, others in the gills of crayfish. *Enterohalacarus minutipalpis* is an intestinal parasite of the sea urchin *Plesiodiadema indicum,* found at 430 m depth. *Halacarus* and *Halacarellus,* 1 mm or less, are marine predators.

Cunaxidae. These predacious red mites, 0.35–0.5 mm, have long spines medially on the pedipalpi. Chelicerae are long with the movable finger sickle-shaped. *Cunaxa* feeds on Collembola.

FAMILY GROUP PARASITENGONA

The larvae are parasites, the adults predators. The larval opisthosoma expands in feeding to 6-12 times its length. Under its cuticle a deutonymph forms.

Trombidiidae. One of the largest mite families, this often is split into many subfamilies.

Trombidiinae, Velvet Mites. Most are terrestrial, some almost amphibious. The integument is usually soft, the propodosomal scutum reduced to a dorsomedian crista metopica. Larvae, however, have a scutum, as well as other dorsal plates. Most live on soil; both adults and nymphs are predators. The larvae parasitize insects. Adults of *Trombidium holosericeum,*† 4 mm, of Europe (Fig. 14-25) have scarlet velvety hair; they feed on insect eggs and decaying animal matter. The larvae parasitize various insects and somtimes spiders. *Eutrombidium* is a locust parasite. Others are probably important insect predators.

Trombiculinae, Harvest Mites. Larvae (redbugs, chiggers) are parasitic on amphibians, reptiles, birds and mammals. The chelicerae are shown in Fig. 14-12. Similar in structure to the Trombidiidae, but the body is constricted. The larvae usually have only a single dorsal plate. *Trombicula,* 1–2 mm, white or red adults and nymphs feed on

---

° *Demodex* is on the Official List of Generic Names in Zoology, (*Acarus*) *folliculorum* on the Official List of Specific Names.

† *Trombidium* is on the Official List of Generic Names in Zoology, (*Acarus*) *holosericeum* on the Official List of Specific Names.

insect eggs, including those of mosquitoes *(Culex, Aedes, Mansonia)*. The larvae take tissue fluid; a few species attack man. In the Far East larvae of *Leptotrombidium* transmit scrub typhus *(Rickettsia tsutsugamushi)* from rodents to man. In the United States, the larvae of *Eutrombicula alfreddugesi, E. splendens* and *E. batatas* are responsible for dermatitis. *Neotrombicula autumnalis* of Europe, 2 mm, lives in soil, coming to the surface in warm moist weather; it overwinters 40–60 cm deep in soil. In late summer the larvae, 0.25 mm (Fig. 14-24), hatch and attack passing birds and mammals including man, usually in humid gardens, and penetrate the skin in places where the clothing is tight or on joints. The larvae remain there three to five days, their saliva causing a severe itch, growing to 0.75 mm, then fall off. In the soil they molt to become nymphs. Another species is an important sheep parasite in Australia.

Erythraeidae are terrestrial. The very long, unsegmented, styletlike chelicerae can be withdrawn. The larvae are parasitic on insects and arachnids. *Erythraeus*, 2–3 mm, brown, is found under stones; its larvae parasitize insects. *Leptus* has been found on Opiliones.

Freshwater Mites (Hydrachnellae). Hydrachnellae are not related to marine mites and are probably polyphyletic, from several prostigmatid ancestors. They are included in a series of families of similar habits. The Hydryphantidae can be derived from trombidiids, *Johnstonia* especially (on the basis of trichobothria and larval setae). Limnocharidae resemble trombidiids. The Sperchonidae can be compared to the Cunaxidae (pedipalp, prosomal dorsal scutum). With exception of the marine *Pontarachnida* all live in fresh water, especially in shore vegetation, but many are stream species, and some are found deep in lakes and subterranean waters. Aquatic adaptations are few: the loss of body setae and body spines, acquisition of large skin glands, acquisition of long leg setae fused for paddling, reduction of claws and of gut ceca.

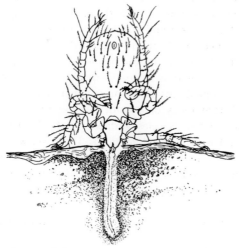

Fig. 14–24. Chigger, larva of harvestmite, *Neotrombicula autumnalis* feeding; 0.25 mm long. (After Vitzthum.)

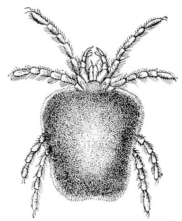

Fig. 14–25.   Female velvet mite, *Trombidium holosericeum*; 3 mm. (After Raillet from Martini.)

Some are planktonic animals; they can be observed from rowboats as slowly swimming red spots, only sometimes moving their legs, spreading them to keep afloat in the current. Most Hydrachnellae row slowly with their legs, some run on plants. Some are parasitic in clams. Those in currents live on the stream bed, often are small, flat-bodied and with strong armor and large leg claws instead of swimming hairs. Most have a soft integument and many are bright red, yellow, blue or green. Most families related to the *Trombidiidae* have curved chelicerae; only the Hydrachnidae have them stylet-shaped. There is a pair of eyes on each side. The tracheal system, except in larvae, is well developed and filled with air. The spiracles are closed to the outside by a membrane. As water mites do not surface they must be able to take oxygen dissolved in water. In many species the integument probably permits respiration, certainly in *Unionicola*, which lack tracheae. Most are predators. Various species attack planktonic animals or insect larvae. Prey caught with the pedipalpi and legs is penetrated by chelicerae, digested within its skin and sucked out. Eggs, red in red-colored mites, or pale orange to white colored in others, are deposited in layers, strings or clumps. The six-legged larvae are almost always parasitic on insects. As in other trombidiid relatives, there is only one free-living immature stage, the deutonymph. Larvae attack amphibious insects; they may attack aquatic insect larvae or pupae and when the imago hatches, will immediately attack it and stay on it until the insect returns to deposit eggs (e.g., *Arrenurus* on Odonata). Other species surface to attack amphibious insects (e.g., *Limnochares* attacks water-surface Heteroptera). Hydryphantid larvae climb aquatic plants and can jump eight to ten cm; some have been found on flies. *Diplodontus* larvae circle rapidly on the surface and attack *Chaoborus* midge imagoes. The larvae feed on the host and increase in size for 1–2 weeks, but may overwinter on aquatic beetles.

Hydrachnidae. Hydrachna, 2–8 mm, red spherical with black spots, is a slow swimmer in ponds.

Limnocharidae. Red, to 5 mm long, they walk on the roots of aquatic plants; most lack swimming setae.

Eylaidae. Each of the two lateral eye pairs lies in a sclerotized capsule, often connected by a transverse ridge to form "spectacles." Large, red, usually oval-shaped swimmers, they use the bare last leg as a rudder. *Eylais* is 2–7 mm.

Thyasidae. Usually red or yellow mites that lack swimming setae and have sclerotized scuta. They live in springs and waterfalls and temporal pond and streams where they walk on the bottom and on plants.

Hydryphantidae. Hydryphantes, to 2.4 mm long, is red.

Sperchonidae. Sperchon, to 1.5 mm long, yellow to brown, lacks swimming setae; it inhabits strams.

Pontarachnidae. Marine mites lacking tracheae, the family includes *Pontarachna.*

Unionicolidae. These have swimming hairs on the legs. *Unionicola,* clam mites, live in open ponds as pelagic predators. Twenty-five to thirty eggs are deposited in the incurrent siphon of clams *(Unio, Anodonta)* underneath the mantle epidermis. The larvae hatch in spring and leave the mollusk. Later the larvae return to clams and enter the gills where, below the epidermis, they transform into deutonymphs. After molting, the deutonymphs leave the host and become planktonic predators, but again enter mollusk gills to molt into adults. The host does not seem to be damaged. Some species stay in mollusks, except for the free-living larvae. *Unionicola crassipes* of Europe lives in fresh water sponges.

Arrenuridae. Strongly sclerotized integument; the males usually have the posterior of the abdomen elongated. They live in ponds with rich vegetation. *Arrenurus,* to 1.7 mm, may be various colors.

SUBORDER SARCOPTIFORMES

Spiracles absent, or numerous but difficult to see in those adults which are heavily sclerotized (Oribatei). Chelicerae usually chelate. The lumen of the midgut is more voluminous than that of the single pair of ceca, and empties through an anus (Fig. 14-27). Excretory organs usually are absent, but in many Acaridae and *Pteronyssus* they may appear in form of paired short evaginations of the hindgut. Circulatory system absent.

Infraorder Acaridei (Astigmata)

The gnathosoma is usually visible from above (Fig. 14-27). The soft integument has few dorsal plates if any. Trichobothria are absent on anterior of dorsum. The coxae are fused to ventral integument, with an apodeme inside (Fig. 14-3); then venter is only rarely sclerotized. Sexual dimorphism is distinct and usually there are three free-living juvenile forms; larva, protonymph, and tritonymph, but under special conditions some genera have a deutonymph of different shape, called hypopus. The hypopi, either male or female, have the back sclerotized; the mouthparts degenerate, the mouth closed and the esophagus solid (Fig. 14-26). There are two kinds, but most species have only one or the other. The wandernymph, having a plate with rows of suckers on the venter behind the coxae (Fig. 14-26), is sensitive to touch and will attach to any passing object, usually insects or other arthropods. They have been found in gill chambers of mollusks and millipede gonads. They are sensitive to dryness and temperature extremes. They change to a tritonymph in suitably moist environment. Resting deutonymphs, having the legs reduced or lacking *(Glycyphagus),* do not move. Some stay within the

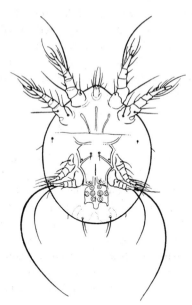

Fig. 14–26. Wandernymph of the flour mite, *Acarus siro*; venter with sucker plate behind the last legs and reduced mouthparts; 0.25 mm. (After Schulze.)

cuticle of the protonymph. The mouthparts are degenerate. In contrast to wandernymphs, they are insensitive to climatic extremes, may remain for months in dry flour and withstand a temperature of 34°C for 14 days (*Acarus*), or −7°C for 24 hours.

Acaridae, Storage Mites. The body is short, white to yellowish; the chelicerae are chelate. Some storage mites, *Acarus* (=*Tyroglyphus*), *Glycyphagus* and some related mites may attack man, causing dermatitis called grocer's itch, conjunctivitis and asthma. Even dust from infested materials can cause allergic reactions in some people. In moist dwellings, some acarids and other storage mites may migrate from flour, dried plums, or mattress fillings and, as dense crawling dust, cover dishes, cupboards, laundry and stored foods. Modern packaging methods have reduced the abundance of these mites.

The flour mite, *Acarus siro** (=*Tyroglyphus farinae*), 0.4–0.6 mm, male with thick legs (Fig. 14-27), is found in all parts of the world, arctic to tropics, and may actually be a group of species. At temperatures of 17–20°C there is a new generation every 17 days, at 10–15°C, every 28 days. The mites inhabit grain and flour mills and storage places and may become unbelievably abundant, feeding on seeds, oatmeal, or flour. If the products attacked dry to less than 13% moisture, the mites may die, but the resting nymphs survive 2 years and molt when moisture increases. They are spread by contaminated shovels and flour sacks. There may also be a few wandernymphs.

Two similar species can be separated only by the tarsal setae. However, they act differently: *A. farris*, if the food is used up, produces a wandernymph; *A. siro* does not. Adults of *Acarus siro* require a relative humidity of 70–95% and lose water at low

---

* *Acarus* is on the Official List of Generic Names in Zoology and (*Acarus*) *siro* on the Official List of Specific Names.

relative humidities. They take up moisture from the air if the air becomes more humid. Individuals needing water in choice experiments move toward high humidity. Animals kept 16 hours at 92% relative humidity chose the lower humidity when offered containers with 80 and 85% humidity. In the range of 75–85% relative humidity, they can distinguish differences as small as 0.25%.

The fungus inhabitant, *Caloglyphus berlesei*, 0.4–1.2 mm, lives on fungi and garbage if at least 25% humidity is present, but prefers 75 to 80%. The mite may also attack living insects and may flourish in cultures of mealworms, dissolving their exoskeletons with saliva. Wandernymphs are formed under normal conditions, possibly through food shortage.

A dead-insect scavenger, *Threophagus entomophagus* (=*Monieziella*), 0.3–6 mm, lives in old bee hives and insect collections. *Rhizoglyphus echinopus*, 0.45–1 mm, lives on stored onions, bulbs and potatoes, starting to feed at rotting spots. It does little damage in the field. The species has two kinds of males, one with an enlarged third leg.

European cheese mites, *Tyrolichus*, 0.45–0.7 mm, live together with *Tyrophagus*, mainly on cheese; there may be 100–2000 mites per cm².

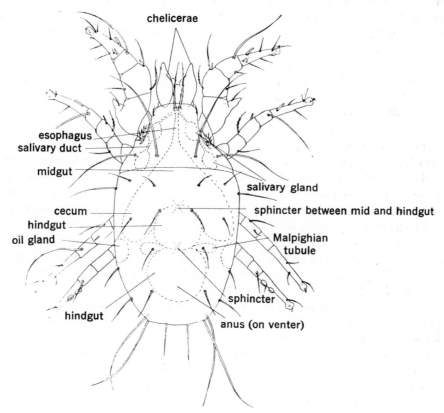

Fig. 14–27. Male flour mite, *Acarus siro*, dorsum with internal organs indicated; a transverse groove separates proterosoma from hysterosoma; 0.4 mm long. (After Hughes.)

Carpoglyphidae. Carpoglyphus lactis, 0.4 mm, the dried fruit mite, lives on sugar-containing foods, plums, apples, figs, raisins. It takes up the sugar solution from the surface and tears up pieces of fruit with the chelicerae. Their feeding suppresses molds. The females produce about 72 eggs and, like males, have an average life span of 40–50 days. Out of a thousand protonymphs, one may develop into a long-legged wander-nymph which runs rapidly.

Glycyphagidae. Glycyphagus domesticus, the upholstery mite, 0.3–0.7 mm, has feathered dorsal setae and lives in dried plant material, hay in barns and haylofts, upholstery and mattresses. *Glycyphagus destructor* (=*G. cadaverum*), 0.4–0.6 mm, lives in hay, plant material, and fruits. Both species prefer mildew, both cause grocer's itch, and in humid dwellings both can become very abundant. Males and females live 50–70 days, produce 25–35 eggs. Sometimes 40% of *G. domesticus* become resting nymphs, thereby surviving temporary drying of the hay or dwelling; further development follows in 3 months to over a year. *Glycyphagus domesticus* is the intermediate host of a rodent cestode, *Catenotaenia pusilla.*

Sarcoptidae. Almost spherical, these are the more short-legged of the two families. Skin parasites of birds and mammals, with chelate chelicerae, they do not feed on blood. *Sarcoptes scabiei,*[*] male 0.18–0.25 mm, female 0.3–0.4 mm, itch mite (Fig. 14-3), causes scabies in man in places where the skin is thin, between fingers, joints, sides of feet. Usually there are only a few, rarely more than 50 female mites in an infection (but also larvae and nymphs), causing severe itching. The mites burrow vertically into the skin's stratum corneum. The pedipalpal endites lift up little pieces of skin scales, which are then cut by the chelicerae. Underneath the mite feeds on epidermis cells and lymph. The saliva liquefies on the epidermis, and damages the stratum germinativum. The epidermis produces new scales and the mite bites through them to reach nutrient. Secondary infection may set in. Simultaneously, the mite burrows parallel to the layers in the epidermis, moving 0.5–3 mm a day, depositing feces and eggs. The tunnel is surrounded by epidermis cells with a corneal layer; it may be 5 cm long and is visible as a fine line. The female lives 2 months, producing 20–50 eggs, one after another in the tunnel. The eggs hatch in 3–8 days. The larvae, 0.1–1.6 mm, leave the parental tunnel. Others remain behind, digging lateral shafts. Fertilized females probably cause new infections. The postembryonic development takes 4–6 days for males, 10–14 days for females. The females have two nymphs, males one. Mites living on horses, sheep, pigs, dogs, and rabbits cannot live longer than 3 weeks on man, being physiologically specialized. Mange may cover the whole body of horses; rubbing leads to loss of hair, inflammation, and scars before the animals die.

Notoedres causes head mange in various mammals, mainly rodents; *Notoedres cati,* 0.14–0.23 mm, on rabbits and cats may be transferred to horses, dogs, and man. It is less dangerous than *Sarcoptes* but may cause death of squirrels.

Knemidokoptidae. Knemidokoptes mutans, 0.4 mm, causes scaly-legs in chickens and domestic birds. The mite digs between the leg scales, causing disintegration of the epidermis and inflammation of joints. The birds become lame and listless; *K. laevis* causes loss of feathers in birds.

---

[*] *Sarcoptes* is on the Official List of Generic Names in Zoology, (*Acarus*) *scabiei* is on the Official List of Specific Names.

Psoroptidae, Mange Mites. Psoroptes equi, 0.8 mm, lives on the surface of the skin of various mammals, digging in with the chelicerae, and may even suck blood. In sheep *P. ovis* causes sheep-scab, in rabbits, *P. equi* infests the outer ear canal. The ear mite *Otodectes cynotis,* 0.5 mm, lives in the ears of dogs and cats; the itching causes the animal to shake its head. *Chorioptes bovis* causes chorioptic mange in cattle, a localized mange.

Feather Mites. Dermoglyphidae, Pterolichidae, Analgesidae and Falculiferidae, feather mites, are much less damaging to their host. About 600 species live on feathers, mainly the primaries and tail feathers. Without damaging the skin, they feed on oil, dead skin, and horny scales. The eggs are attached in rows along the quills or barbs. The genera *Falculifer* (Faliculiferidae) and *Gabucinia* (Pterolichidae) have a deutonymph that is egg-shaped with short legs; its nonfunctional mouth lies below the epidermis in the adipose tissue. Analgesidae have the third or fourth leg or both of males strongly developed, and they are used to hold on to females. Falculiferidae have males with huge first, second or fourth legs, sometimes hypertophied chelicerae. Dermoglyphidae are elongated and live within feather shafts. All species are specialized to certain hosts, but sometimes to several species closely related.

Cytoditidae. These are egg-shaped mites whose gnathosoma is a sucking tube. *Cytodites nudus,* 0.6 mm, inhabits bronchia, lungs, airsacs of gallinaceous birds, and may invade the body cavity as an internal parasite. Small numbers do not damage the host; large numbers cause suffocation, possibly peritonitis.

Listrophoridae. Living in the fur of small mammals, these all are cylindrical and have appendages modified for holding on. The mites slide down hairs and probably feed on scales and oil. *Myocoptes,* 0.4 mm, may cause mange in laboratory mice. *Campylochirus caviae* lives on guinea pigs.

Infraorder Oribatei (Cryptostigmata), Moss Mites

The oribatid mites, sometimes called beetle mites, may be armored with a heavily sclerotized integument. Anteriorly on the dorsum of the propodosoma there is a pair of trichobothria (pseudostigmatic organ). Usually there is a "tracheal" system opening in the region of the coxae. In only a few species is there sexual dimorphism. The sculptured, usually spherical, dark mites, 0.2–1 mm long, live in leaf litter, humus, moss, tree stumps and on lichens. They walk slowly. Some feed on fungal hyphae, spores, algae, pollen; others on moist leaves, pine needles, roots, and pieces of wood. They often appear in large numbers and may be of importance in breakdown of organic material and humus formation. Only the Phthiracaridae feed on wood without breakdown of lignin. *Nothrus* may feed on insect eggs, *Scheloribates* on insect pupae. Some species are vectors for tapeworms of domestic animals: cystocercoids of the sheep and cattle tapeworm, *Moniezia,* live in various oribatids. The larvae and nymphs of oribatid mites are usually soft. The placement of the Oribatei into the Sarcoptiformis is controversial. They probably are a separate suborder.

INFERIOR ORIBATIDS

Mites have usually genital and anal plates elongated and extending the length of the venter; the ventral plate is divided by a transverse, horizontal or parabolic suture into

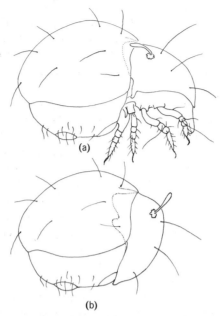

Fig. 14–28. *Mesoplophora* sp., an oribatid mite: (a) walking; (b) with propodosoma and appendages folded in, covered; less than 1 mm long. (After Schaller.)

two parts. The propodosoma may or may not be bent ventrally against the hysterosoma. In molting the exuvium does not split in a circle. Included are about 29 families. The lower oribatids comprise about 29 families. Common genera are *Liochthonius*, *Hypochthonius*, *Epilohmannia*, *Nothrus* and *Nanhermannia*. *Mesoplophora* (Fig. 14-28), *Phthiracarus* and *Rhysotritia* may have the form of small spheres.

SUPERIOR ORIBATIDS

Mites that have the genital and anal plates usually polygonal to rounded and not extended. The ventral plate is usually not divided into two parts. In molting the exuvium splits in a circle.

Common genera of the higher oribatids are *Belba*, *Damaeus*, *Cepheus*, *Gustavia*, *Scheloribates*, *Achipteria*, *Eupelops*, *Oribatula*, and *Carabodes*.

SUBORDER TETRAPODILI (ZEMIOSTIGMATA), GALL MITES

Tetrapodili are minute plant parasites probably derived from the Tenuipalpidae, false spider mites (Trombidiformes), and often considered a group of Trombidiformes. They are the smallest arthropods, 0.08–0.27 mm. The body is worm-shaped, secondarily annulate; the annuli facilitate movement in narrow tunnels (Fig. 14-29). Third and fourth leg pairs are lacking. Chelicerae are stylet-shaped. Midgut is without ceca but with anus. The rectal area, used for attachment to the host plant, may be everted. Gall mites may move inchworm-like on smooth surfaces. Heart, excretory, and respiratory organs are absent, a deficiency related to small size. All tap plant cells with their chelicerae and feed on their contents, liquefied by enzymes. Most live on perennial phanerogams and are specialized as to species or genus. The mites may cause strong growth reactions in plant tissues, forming galls, solid or filled with hair-like growth. Often there are changes in growth direction or in leaf or bud growth, adventitious shoots or cabbage-like growths. The type of growth depends on the species of mite and plant, and on the age and part of the plant attacked.

In summer only 10–15 days elapse from egg to adult, so that a gall containing one female soon will be filled with descendents. Larvae and the two nymphal stages resemble the adult in the Eriophyinae, but in the Phyllocoptinae, the larvae have annuli as in Eriophyinae but unlike its own adults. Two types of females may be produced: one stays, the other moves out. Soon the galls are overpopulated and some animals emigrate, carried by wind (mites have been found in the stomach contents of swifts, birds that feed exclusively on aerial plankton). They may overwinter in buds. A gall population may have only two to three per cent males.

Eriophyidae. This is the only family; the subfamily Phyllocoptinae has fewer annuli in the adult and many do not form galls. About 430 species have been described (Fig. 14-29). Only about 50 are of economic importance in North America. The most important are the citrus bud mite, *Aceria sheldoni,* and the vector of wheat streak mosaic virus, *Aceria tulipae.* The silver bud mite, *Aculus cornutus,* infects peach trees. *Eriophyes insidiosus* transmits peach mosaic virus among fruit trees; others are suspected of transmitting plant virus diseases.

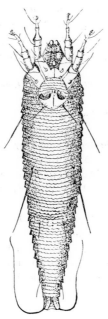

Fig. 14-29. Gall mite, *Eriophyes* sp., venter; 0.2 mm long. (After Nalepa from Dahl.)

References

Aeschlimann, A. 1958. Développement embryonnaire d'*Ornithodorus*. *Acta Trop.* 15:15–64.

André, M. 1949. Acariens *in* Grassé, *Traité de Zoologie*, Masson et Cie, Paris, 6:794–892.

———— 1953. Observations sur la fécondation chez *Allothrombium fuliginosum*. *Bull. Mus. Nat. Hist. Natur. Paris* 25:383–386.

Arthur, D. R. 1951, 1953. The capitulum and feeding mechanism in *Ixodes hexagonus*. *Parasitology* 41:82–90; 42:187–191.

———— 1957. The capitulum and feeding mechanism of *Dermacentor*. *Ibid.* 47:169–184.

———— 1960. *Ticks*. Cambridge Univ. Press, Cambridge.

———— 1962. *Ticks and Disease*. Pergamon Press, London.

Babu, K. S. Anatomy of the central nervous system of arachnids. *Zool. Jahrb. Abt. Anat.* 82:1–154.

Bader, C. 1954. Das Darmsystem der Hydracarinen. *Rev. Suisse Zool.* 61:505–549.

Baker, E. W. 1958. *Guide to the Families of Mites*. Univ. Maryland Press, College Park.

————, Evans, T. M., Gould, T. M., Hull, D. J. and Keegan, H. L. 1956. *A Manual of Parasitic Mites of Medical and Economic Importance*. Natl. Pest Control Assoc., New York.

———— and Wharton, G. W. 1952. *An Introduction to Acarology*. Macmillan, New York.

Böttger, K. 1962. Biologie and Ethologie der Wassermilben *Arrenurus* (*Megaluracarus*) *globator*, *Piona nodata* und *Eylais infundibulifera*. *Zool. Jahrb. Abt. Syst.* 89:501–584.

Brown, J. R. C. 1952. The feeding organs of the adult of the common "chigger." *J. Morphol.* 91:15–51.

Browning, T. O. 1954. Water balance in the tick *Ornithodoros* with particular reference to the influence of carbon dioxide. *J. Exp. Biol.* 31:331–340.

Camin, J. H. 1953. Life history and sensory behavior of the snake mite, *Ophionyssus natricis*. *Spec. Publ. Chicago Acad. Sci.* 10:1–76.

———— 1963. Host-finding behavior and life histories in ectoparasitic Acarina. *in* Naegele, J. edit. *Advances in Acarology* 1. Cornell Univ. Press, Ithaca, pp. 411–424.

———— and Gorirossi, F. E. 1955. A revision of the suborder Mesostigmata. *Spec. Publ. Chicago Acad. Sci.* 11:1–70.

Chandler, A. C. and Read, C. P. 1961. *Introduction to Parasitology*. 10th edit. Wiley, New York.

Costa, M. 1966. The biology and development of *Hypoaspis* (*Pneumolaelaps*). *J. Zool.*, 148:191–200.

Cross, H. F. 1964. Formation of the feeding tube by *Trombicula*. *Compt. Rend. 1ᵉʳ Congr. Internat., Acarologia* 4 (hors sér.): 255–261.

Dubinin, V. B. 1951. [Feather mites (Analgesoidea)]. *Fauna USSR* 6(5):1–139.

Edwards, E. E. and Arthur, D. R. 1947. Seasonal activity of the tick *Ixodes ricinus*. *Parasitology* 38:72–85.

Evans, G. O., Sheals, J. G. and MacFarlane, D. 1961. *The Terrestrial Acari of the British Isles*, Vol. 1. British Museum, London.

Fritzsche, R. 1960. Morphologische, biologische und physiologische Variabilität und ihre Bedeutung für die Epidemiologie von *Tetranychus urticae*. *Biol. Zentralbl.* 79:521–576.

George, J. 1963. Responses of *Haemophysalis* to light. *in* Naegele, J. edit. *Advances in Acarology* 1, Cornell Univ. Press, Ithaca: 425–430.

Gregson, J. D. 1960. Morphology and functioning of the mouthparts of *Dermacentor andersoni*. *Acta Trop.* 17:48–79.

Hafiz, H. A. 1935. Embryological development of *Cheyletus*. *Proc. Roy. Soc. London* 117B:174–201.

Hammen, L. van der. 1961. Description of *Holothyrus grandjeani* and notes on the classification of mites. *Nova Guinea (Zool.)* 9:173–194.

Hirschmann, W. 1966. *Milben, Acari.* Kosmos Verl. Stuttgart.

Hughes, T. E. 1949. Functional morphology of the mouthparts of *Liponyssus. Ann. Trop. Med.* 43:349–360.

_____ 1950. Physiology of the alimentary canal of *Tyroglyphus farinae. Quart. J. Micros. Sci.* 91:45–61.

_____ 1950. Embryonic development of the mite *Tyroglyphus farinae. Proc. Roy. Soc. London* 119:873–886.

_____ 1953. Mouthparts of the *Anoetus. Proc. Nederlandse Akad. Wetensch. Amsterdam* 56C:278–287.

_____ 1954. Internal anatomy of the mite *Listrophorus. Proc. Zool. Soc. London* 124B:239–256.

_____ 1959. *Mites or the Acari.* Athlone Press, Univ. London.

_____ 1964. Neurosecretion, ecdysis and hypopus formation. *Compt. Rend. 1er Congr. Internat., Acarologia* 4 (hors sér.):338–342.

Jakeman, L. A. R. 1961. Internal anatomy of the spiny rat mite, *Echinolaelaps echidninus. J. Parasitol.* 47:329–349.

Jayewickreme, S. H. and Antonipulle, P. 1953. Feeding habits of an adult trombidiid mite. *Ceylon J. Sci.* 25:157–160.

Johnson, C. G. and Mellanby, K. 1942. Parasitology of human scabies. *Parasitology* 34:285–290.

Jones, B. M. 1950. The sensory physiology of the harvest mite *Trombicula autumnalis. J. Exper. Biol.* 27:461–494.

_____ 1950. Penetration of the host tissue by the harvest mite *Trombicula autumnalis. Parasitology* 40:247–260.

Karg, W. 1961. Ökologische Untersuchungen von edaphischen Gamasiden. *Pedobiologia* 1:53–74; 77–98.

_____ 1962. *Räuberische Milben im Boden.* Neue Brehm-Bücherei 296. Ziemsen Verl., Wittenberg Lutherstadt.

Keifer, H. H. 1952. Eriophyid mites of California. *Bull. California Insect Surv.* 2:1–123.

Kitaoka, S. 1961. Physiological and ecological studies on some ticks. *Quart. Nat. Inst. Anim. Health, Tokyo* 1:85–112; 142–149.

Klumpp, W. 1954. Embryologie und Histologie der Bienenmilbe *Acarapis. Z. Parasitenk.* 16:407–442.

Knülle, W. 1957. Oribatei im Boden. *Z. Morphol. Ökol.* 46:397–432.

_____ 1961. Die Luftfeuchte-Unterschiedsempfindlichkeit der Mehlmilbe *Acarus siro. Z. Vergl. Physiol.* 44:463–477.

_____ 1962. Die Abhängigkeit der Luftfeuchte-Reaktionen der Mehlmilbe *Acarus siro* vom Wassergehalt des Körpers. *Ibid.* 45:233–246.

_____ 1963. Dauerformenbildung bei der Mehlmilbe. *Naturwissenschaften* 50:160–161.

Knülle, W. and Wharton, G. 1964. Equilibrium humidities in arthropods. *Compt. Rend. 1er Congr. Internat., Acarologia* 4 (hors sér.):299–306.

Korth, U. 1960. Die Domatienmilben *Typhlodromus* und ihr Verhältnis zur Linde. *Zool. Jahrb. Abt. Syst.* 88:135–164.

Langenscheidt, M. 1958. Embryologische, morphologische und histologische Untersuchungen an *Knemidocoptes. Z. Parasitenk.* 18:349–385.

Lees, A. D. 1947. Transpiration and the structure of the epicuticle in ticks. *J. Exp. Biol.* 23:379–410.

Lipovsky, L. J. 1954. Food habits of postlarval stages of chiggers. *Bull. Univ. Kansas* 36:943–958.

Michener, C. D. 1946. Observations on the habits and life history of a chigger mite, *Eutrombicula batatas. Ann. Entomol. Soc. America* 39:101–118.

Mitchell, R. D. 1955. Anatomy, life history, and evolution of the mites parasitizing freshwater mussels. *Misc. Publ. Mus. Zool. Univ. Michigan* 89:1–28.

————— 1961. Behavior of the larvae of *Arrenurus fissicornis*, a water mite parasitic on dragonflies. *Anim. Behav.* 9:220–224.

————— 1962. Musculature of a trombiculid mite, *Blankaartia. Ann. Entomol. Soc. Amer.* 55:106–119.

————— 1964. Anatomy of an adult chigger mite, *Blankaartia. J. Morphol.* 114:373–381.

Müller, E. W. 1960. *Milben an Kulturpflanzen.* Die Neue Brehm Bücherei 270, Ziemsen Verl., Wittenberg Lutherstadt.

Neumann, K. W. 1941. Anatomie und Histologie von *Parasitus kempersi. Z. Morphol. Ökol.* 37:613–682.

————— 1943. Lebensgeschichte der Käfermilbe *Poecilochirus. Zool. Anz.* 142:1–21.

Oboussier, H. 1939. Biologie und Anatomie der Wohnungsmilben. *Z. Angew. Entomol.* 26:253–296.

Oliver, J. H. 1964. Karyotypes and sex determination in the Acari. *Compt. Rend. 1ᵉʳ Congr. Internat., Acarologia* 4 (hors sér.):288–293.

Orosi-Pal, Z. 1934. Bau, Entwicklung und Lebensweise des Bienen Parasiten *Acarapis woodi. Z. Parasitenk.* 7:233–267.

Pauly, F. 1952. Die "Copula" der Oribatiden. *Naturwissenschaften* 39: 572–573.

————— 1956. Zur Biologie einiger Belbiden (Oribatei, Mossmilben). *Zool. Jahrb. Abt. Syst.* 84:275–328.

Perron, R. 1954. Bau, Entwicklung und Physiologie der Milben *Histiostoma laboratorium. Acta Zool.* 35:71–176.

Pflugfelder, O. 1952. Reaktion des Hühnerlaufs bei *Cnemidocoptes* Befall. *Z. Parasitenk.* 15:290–307.

————— 1954. Über eigenartige Abwehrreaktionen bei Milbenbefall. *Mikrokosmos* 42:169–171.

Pomerantzev, B. I. and Anastos, G. 1951. *Fauna of USSR 4. Ixodid Ticks.* Amer. Inst. Biol. Sci., Washington.

Popp, E. 1961. Bau und Funktion des Ambulacrums der Larve von *Orthohalarachne. Zool. Anz.* 167:29–33.

————— 1962. Semiaquatile Lebensräume in Hoch- und Niedermooren. *Internat. Rev. Gesam. Hydrobiol.* 47:533–579.

Radford, C. D. 1950. Mites (Acarina) parasitic on mammals, birds and reptiles. *Parasitology* 40:366–394.

————— 1953. Mites (Analgesidae) living on or in the feathers of birds. *Ibid.* 42:199–230.

Rapp, A. 1959. Biologie und Ethologie der Käfermilbe *Parasitus coleoptratorum. Zool. Jahrb. Abt. Syst.* 86:303–366.

Richards, W. S. 1950. Distribution and biology of the harvest mite in Great Britain. *Parasitology* 40:118–126.

Riha, G. 1951. Ökologie der Oribatiden in Kalksteinböden. *Zool. Jahrb. Abt. Syst.* 80:407–450.

Sasa, M. 1965. Sensory physiology of parasitic mites. *Acarologia* (hors série) 6:233–234.

Schulze, P. 1942 Über die Hautsinnesorgane der Zecken. *Z. Morphol. Ökol.* 38:379–419.

————— 1943. Rückensinnesfelder der Zecken. *Ibid.* 39:1–20.

Schuster, R. 1956. Der Anteil der Oribatiden an den Zersetzungsvorgängen im Boden. *Ibid.* 45:1–33.

————— 1962. Das marine Litoral als Lebensraum terrestrischer Kleinarthropoden. *Internat. Rev. Gesam. Hydrobiol.* 47:359–412.

———— 1962. Nachweis eines Paarungszeremoniells bei den Hornmilben (Oribatei). *Naturwissenschaften* 49:502.

Skaling, P. and Hayes, W. J. 1949. Biology of *Liponyssus bacoti*. *Amer. J. Trop. Med.* 29:759–772.

Sømme, L. 1965. Changes in sorbitol content in overwintering eggs of the European red mite *Panonychus ulmi*. *Canadian J. Zool.* 43:881–884.

Sonenshine, D. E. 1963. Humidity behavior of ticks, *in* Naegale, J. A. *Advances in Acarology* 1: Cornell Univ. Press, Ithaca, pp. 431–434.

Sparing, I. 1959. Die Larven der Hydrachnellae, ihre parasitische Entwicklung und ihre Systematik. *Parasitol. Schriftenreihe* 10:1–165, Fischer, Jena.

Spickett, S. G. 1961. *Demodex folliculorum* life history. *Parasitology* 51:181–192.

Strandtman, R. W. and Wharton, G. W. 1958. *Manual of Mesostigmatic Mites*. Univ. Maryland Press, College Park.

Sweatman, G. K. 1958. Population reduction of chorioptic mange mites on cattle in summer. *Canadian J. Zool.* 36:391–397.

———— 1958. *Otodectes cynotic*, the ear canker mite of carnivores. *Ibid.* 36:849–862.

———— 1958. The life history and validity of the species in *Psoroptes*, mange mites. *Ibid.* 36:905–929.

Teschner, D. 1963. Die Biologie, Verbreitung und Ökologie der Grundwassermilbe *Lobohalacarus weberi*. *Arch. Hydrobiol.* 59:71–102.

Treat, A. E. 1954. A case of peculiar parasitism. *Natur. Hist.* 67:366–373.

Tsvileneva, V. A. 1964. Nervous structure of the ixodid ganglion. *Zool. Jahrb. Abt. Anat.* 81:579–602.

Viets, K. 1936. Wassermilben (Hydracarinen) *in* Dahl, *Die Tierwelt Deutschlands*, G. Fischer, Jena, 7:1–574.

———— 1955–56. *Die Milben des Süsswassers und des Meeres*. G. Fischer, Jena.

Vitzthum, H. G. 1929. Milben, Acari *in* Brohmer, *Tierwelt Mitteleuropas*, Quelle & Meyer, Leipzig, 3(7):1–112.

———— 1931. Acari *in* Kükenthal, *Handbuch der Zoologie*, De Gruyter, Berlin, 3(2):1–160.

———— 1940–1943. Acarina *in* Bronn's *Klassen und Ordnungen des Tierreichs*, Akad. Verlagsges., Leipzig, 5(4)5:1–1001.

Wallace, D. R. J. 1960. Observations on hypopus development. *J. Insect Physiol.* 5:216–229.

Wharton, G. W. 1954. Feeding of prostigmatid larvae (Acarina: Trombidiformes) on arthropods. *J. Washington Acad. Sci.* 44:244–245.

———— 1964. First Internat. Congress Address [no. of mite species]. *Compt. Rend 1ᵉʳ Congr. Internat. Acarologia* 4 (hors sér.): 37–43.

———— and Kanungo, K. 1962. Temperature and relative humidity on water balance in females of the spiny rate mite, *Echinolaelaps echidninus*. *Ann. Entomol. Soc. Amer.* 55:483–492.

Willman, C. 1931. Oribatei *in* Dahl, *Die Tierwelt Deutschlands*, G. Fischer, Jena, 5:79–200.

Winston, P. and Nelson, E. 1965. Regulation of transpiration in the clover mite *Bryobia*. *J. Exp. Biol.* 43:257–269.

Wisseman, C. L. and Sulkin, S. E. 1947. Laboratory care, life cycle and hosts of the chicken mite *Dermanyssus gallinae*. *Amer. J. Trop. Med.* 27:463–469.

Yalvaç, S. 1939. Der weibliche Geschlechtsapparat von *Ixodes*. *Z. Morphol. Ökol.* 36:310–314.

Woolley, T. A. 1961. The phylogeny of mites. *Ann. Rev. Entomol.* 6:263–284.

Zakhvatkin, A. A. 1952. [The division of Acarina into orders and their position in the system.] *Mag. Parasitol. Moscow* 14:5–46.

Zumpt, F. 1961. The arthropod parasites of vertebrates in Africa south of the Sahara. *Publ. South Afric. Inst. Med. Res.* 1(9):1–147.

15.

Class Pycnogonida, Sea Spiders

The sea spiders include 600 species, the largest being *Dodecolopoda mawsoni*, with a body 6 cm long, legs 24 cm long.

Pycnogonida are marine chelicerates, sometimes called Pantopoda in some European references. The very narrow body is usually rod-shaped, rarely disc-shaped, and usually only 0.2–1.5 cm long. The volume of the trunk is less than that of the appendages (Fig. 15–1), and the internal organs have diverticula into the appendages, which number between 4 and 9 pairs. The body consists mainly of the prosoma, the extremely small abdomen being just a stump. Or, in some the abdomen may be a very long tubular process, ornately spined and longer than the trunk segments combined. During development it contains only two pairs of ganglia, indicating that the abdomen consists of only a few segments. There are no respiratory organs and no segmental excretory organs.

Anatomy

The cephalic part and first trunk segment bears the first three appendages and the first pairs of legs. A posterior trunk, which may have transverse grooves, bears the remaining walking legs on short projections (Figs. 15–1, 15–2). The head region has a dorsal hump bearing eyes and an anterior proboscis. The proboscis is usually long and thick, sometimes slender or short, and may be straight or bent down. Its anterior shows three radial sections that result from the grouping of three paired rows of longitudinal pharyngeal muscles. Secondary longitudinal supports arise in connection with the three radial divisions of the pharynx. At the tip of the pharynx is the mouth. The muscles may be as illustrated by Fig. 15–3, or the dorsal muscles may pass inside the circumesophageal commissure.

The integument is of variable thickness. Many deep sea species are bright red, some have sclerotized chelicerae and proboscis tips black. Others are bright green, some with purple and red leg bands. The hypodermis stores nutrients and excretory materials.

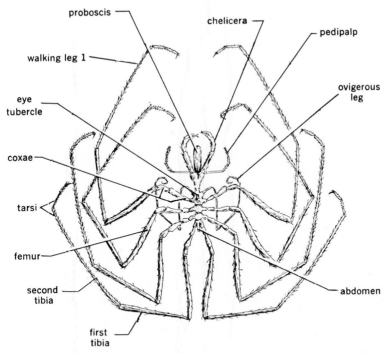

proboscis

chelicera

pedipalp

walking leg 1

ovigerous leg

eye tubercle

coxae

tarsi

femur

second tibia

abdomen

first tibia

Fig. 15–1. *Nymphon*, **male, dorsum; trunk 4 mm long. (After Möbius.)**

APPENDAGES. The appendages are of two kinds; the last are similar to each other and function as walking legs. The slender anterior legs, of which there are at least three pairs in the young, include the chelicerae, the palpi and the ovigerous legs (Fig. 15–1), and are not used for walking. In the female these three may all become vestigial during postembryonal development; in the male only the first two may become vestigial. The number of appendages thus may vary. In some genera, additional leg pairs, a fifth and rarely a sixth, may appear. This suggests that, unlike *Limulus*, in which metameres I to VII bear tube-shaped legs, the pycnogonids have appendages also on VIII and IX, a unique situation among chelicerates. It might be concluded that the sea spiders were derived from ancestral chelicerates similar to the trilobites before differentiation of prosomal and abdominal appendages occurred. Or perhaps the additional legs can be explained by a further division of a metamere. Ventral ganglia appear for each additional pair of legs. Such division is not known among arachnids but does occur among Crustacea (in *Triops*) in which there are several leg pairs on a single posterior metamere. The increased leg number appears in three different families. There are several species pairs, the members of which differ mainly by leg number (*Nymphon* and *Pentanymphon*; *Pycnogonum* and *Pentapycnon*). Thus it is likely that the ten-legged species can be derived from the eight-legged ones, the additional leg resulting from division of a primordium.

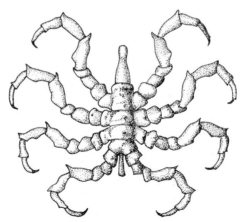

Fig. 15–2. *Pycnogonum littorale,* female, dorsum; the anterior three appendages are vestigial; 15 mm. (After Hedgpeth from Hesse.)

They may be a polymorphic species. Related pairs of eight-legged and ten-legged species have been found in the Antarctic on the one hand and in the Atlantic American tropics on the other. Ten-legged species live in the same region as eight-legged species but also extend into neighboring colder or warmer areas. Unfortunately, nothing is known about the possibility of polyploidy. The twelve-legged animals seem to be related to the ten- and eight-legged ones. Additional leg pairs have apparently appeared in numerous genera.

The chelate chelicerae are usually three-articled. In many genera with a long proboscis the young have chelicerae, which become reduced and may completely disappear. In *Colossendeis* the chelicerae are apparently deciduous, falling off in preadult stage, but in the related 10- and 12-legged forms the chelicerae are retained and apparently functional although the proboscis is very large. In some other species there are functional chelicerae (*Ascorhynchus*) that cannot possibly be of use in holding anything against the tip of the proboscis. Behind the chelicerae are slender pedipalpi which may have up to ten articles. The ovigerous legs, with ten thin articles at most, are always present in the male and carry the eggs (Fig. 15–5). In the female they are less developed or vestigial.

One species of *Pycnogonum* was described not long ago with no ovigers on the male at all. The ovigers carry the eggs in a ball around the long articles, or in a mass held by the long articles against the ventral surface, and usually the terminal articles are free of the egg mass. In several genera (*Colossendeis, Nymphon, Ascorhynchus*) the ovigers are indistinguishable in size and structure in the two sexes. The terminal articles are carried as a crook, often armed with a row or field of elaborate spines (useful taxonomically). Some motion pictures taken in the Antarctic show clearly the grooming action of the ovigers. The animal reaches out and hooks its leg with the crook and then pulls the leg through the crook to the tip. One often finds large Antarctic species encrusted with bryozoa, *Scalpellum,* etc. on the dorsal surface, but not often on the legs where they can be reached by ovigers.

The four to six leg pairs are similar and very long. They bear one claw, at times one or two additional claws.

SENSE ORGANS AND NERVOUS SYSTEM. The numerous innervated hairs and setae covering the body and appendages are sense organs. At the anterior of the prosoma there are four simple eyes; they may be fused into two or may be absent. The rhabdoms of the few retinal cells face the pigmented back. The nervous system consists of a supraesophageal brain made up of the protocerebrum and the cheliceral ganglion (which is postoral in the embryo). A subesophageal ganglion contains the neuromeres of pedipalpi and ovigerous legs. The few abdominal ganglia are fused to the last pair of the chain of paired leg ganglia. The concentration of the nervous system and the length of the connectives depend on the number of legs and the compactness of the entire animal.

DIGESTIVE SYSTEM. The mouth is at the tip of the proboscis, opening into an ectodermal pharynx of triangular cross section, muscular and functioning as a suction pump. The adjacent short esophagus passes between the brain and subesophageal ganglia and opens into the midgut, a tube that continues as the hindgut to a posterior anus. Paired ceca, which usually extend into all walking legs and in some species also into the three anterior appendages and the proboscis, increase the surface used for digestion. There are no excretory or respiratory organs, probably an adaptation to the large surface to volume ratio of the animals.

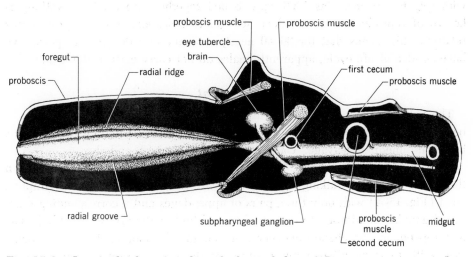

Fig. 15–3. Longitudinal section through the cephalon of *Pycnogonum stearnsi.* Joint membranes are shown by lines, muscles are shown only on left side; part shown about 1.5 mm long. (After Fry.)

CIRCULATORY SYSTEM. The heart extends the length of the prosoma. It is formed by a V-shaped muscular membrane, the two borders of which are attached to the dorsal wall, the ventral edge to the midgut. Near the base of the second and third walking legs, *Pallene* and *Nymphon* have a pair of ostia.

Peristaltic waves of the heart carry blood through the aorta anteriorly to the eyes. First reaching the proboscis and the chelicerae, blood flows back ventrally, reaching the appendages. The body and appendages are divided into an upper and a lower compartment by a thin, partly muscular membrane. The blood flowing in the ventral level in the legs reaches the dorsal level in their last article before returning to the cardiac ostia.

REPRODUCTIVE SYSTEM. The sea spiders have the sexes separate. The paired gonads lie on each side of the heart adjacent to the gut and have extensions into the appendages. The gonopores are usually ventral on the second coxae of all walking legs (up to twelve); unlike other chelicerates, pycnogonids have multiple gonopores. One hermaphroditic species is known.

Reproduction

Mating has been observed once in each of three different genera though the sperm and fertilization of the ova have not definitely been seen. The male of *Anoplodactylus* with his ovigerous legs takes the eggs pouring out of the female gonopores and glues them together with a cement gathered from the integument glands located dorsally on the femora of all walking legs. The hypodermis has numerous many-celled skin glands that empty to the outside. In males of many species groups of glands empty into a common duct or receptacle with a spigot on the femur. Each femur has several groups of glands and several openings with spigots. As many as 1000 eggs, balled together, are carried. Nothing is known of reproduction in the deep sea genus *Colossendeis* or its polymerous relatives—this means that for 30–40 nearly cosmopolitan deepwater species we have no idea of life cycle; apparently males do not carry eggs in this genus.

Development

The yolk content of the egg varies in different species; the egg diameter is between 20 and 675 μm. Eggs with little yolk have total equal cleavage; others have total unequal cleavage. Gastrulation occurs through epiboly.

Only a few sea spiders (e.g., *Pallene* sp., *Nymphon brevicaudatum*) hatch with three or four pairs of walking legs. Most species leave the egg as a protonymphon larva (Fig. 15–4) with only three pairs of appendages and a corresponding number of ganglia, in addition to the ganglion and bud of the first walking leg. The first appendage, the chelate chelicera, lies behind the mouth. Later the chelicerae, with their ganglion, move anterior of the mouth as in arachnids. After many molts, more body segments develop posteriorly with their legs and gan-

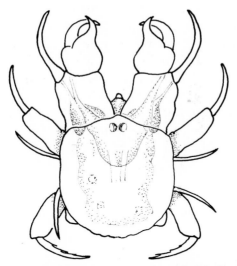

Fig. 15–4. Protonymphon larva, 0.1 mm. (Modified after Dohrn.)

glia; the details differ among the different genera. The last walking leg is the last to develop.

The development of the second and third appendages is very complicated; though present in the protonymphon, in many genera they disappear only to reappear in the older animal. Some biologists have assumed that the final second and third appendages do not arise from the larval primordia of the earlier appendages. Since the new appendages have the same position and connect with the same ganglia as the previous ones, they probably are homologous (as is the fourth leg in mites, which is absent in the larva but present in the embryo).

The larvae of some common European species and littoral species all over the world are removed by the male and live as parasitic symbionts on hydroids or other coelenterates, causing a gall, or in the gastrocoel on the body wall, holding on with chelicerae. Some species infest bivalves and nudibranchs. In species with eggs rich in yolk, the larvae stay with the male until the completion of their metamorphosis (Fig. 15–5). In several Arctic species the young are carried about by the male until one-third adult size, but this has not been observed in the Antarctic members of the same genus.

Relationships

There are two current views relating the Pycnogonida to the arthropods.

1. Some consider the Pycnogonida to be chelicerates. Reasons for this view are several. The first appendage is not an antenna but a chelicera, and its ganglion resembles the cheliceral ganglion of the Chelicerata. As in the Uropygi and Amblypygi, the second and third appendage pairs are specialized. The legs

Fig. 15–5. *Nymphon robustum*, male with young; trunk length 22 mm. (After Thompson from Hesse.)

are arachnid-like. In its anatomy and its tissue physiology the midgut resembles that of the chelicerates. Most have seven tubular appendages, as does *Limulus*.

2. Other zoologists consider the group to be a separate subphylum of the arthropods. They emphasize that, unlike the chelicerates, the Pycnogonida are born with only three pairs of appendages; the remaining appendage-bearing segments develop teloblastically only after postembryonic molts. The multiple gonopores are unique and also the unusual structure of the ovigers makes it difficult to homologize with any other appendages. Others believe that the few ten- and twelve-legged species are ancestral, and that the eight-legged ones evolved through reduction of the appendage-bearing segments.

At present the relationship remains enigmatic, but an older view relating the group to the Crustacea has been abandoned, since the nauplius and proto-nymphon larve have no similarity.

Habits

Pycnogonids occur from intertidal regions to depths as great as 6800 m. They are occasionally abundant, but are more often found only in small numbers at given localities, especially tropical species. Species and individuals are more abundant in colder waters; pycnogonids as a group predominantly inhabit cold water. One bathypelagic species is known. Its lack of specialization would suggest that it rides as a symbiont with a larger organism. The sporadic neritic records from plankton tows perhaps result from stirring up, or represent individuals ascending to breed, although this is not certain.

LOCOMOTION. Sea spiders are often difficult to discern among the hydrozoan colony as a result of their protective coloration and shape, and their slow gait. Some can swim by treading water slowly.

SENSES. Touch appears to be the most important sense. As soon as the distal end of a leg is touched on the inside, the claw flexes, grasping the object, so that touching with any object causes the animal to hang on. The chemical sense seems to be of importance in many specialized feeders. The more active species are phototactic as long as they walk or swim, but as soon as they touch a hydrozoan colony they crawl into the dark between the animals.

FEEDING AND DIGESTION. Sea spiders feed on soft animals, especially hydroid polyps, and on medusae, Anthozoa, Bryozoa, mollusks, and, rarely, sea cucumbers. Some are specialized feeders. A *Nymphon* climbing on *Campanularia* with its pedipalpi touches the hydrozoan tentacles and grasps the hydrocaulus with the chelicerae putting the hydranth to its mouth and sucking it during the following 10 minutes. On small animals they are predators, on large ones, parasites. *Pycnogonum littorale* of Europe pushes its proboscis underneath the pedal disc of an actinian, into the inside, rarely from the side, possibly avoiding nematocysts. *Pycnogonum stearnsi* of the Pacific coast is most often around the outside base of a large sea anemone. It is pink and shows up clearly against the green surface of the anemone. The suction of the pharynx is strong. The sucked-up tissue is torn apart through movements back and forth over the setae of the posterior of the pharynx, and reaches the esophagus as a soft paste. Peristaltic contractions every few seconds move the material back and forth and into all ceca. The gut epithelium, which resembles that of many arachnids, secretes enzymes into the lumen while other cells take up the partly digested material and complete the digestion intracellularly. Many nutrient cells with their excretory products fall into the lumen and are removed with the feces. Cells loaded with food may loosen and move through the gut to places where their contents are taken up by other cells. Thus the branched gut also serves to transport nutrients.

Classification

The pycnogonids are a compact group; the families are almost arbitrary divisions.

Nymphonidae. The proboscis is wide and short. The chelicerae are usually chelate and two-jointed, the palpi five-jointed, ovigerous legs ten-jointed. Usually they have four pairs of walking legs; one genus has five, another six. *Nymphon*, 4–5 mm, has numerous species in the North Atlantic (Figs. 15-1, 15-3). There is also a 12-legged *Nymphon*. With 125–150 species, *Nymphon* is the largest genus.

Callipallenidae. The chelicerae have small chela; the pedipalps are rudimentary or absent. Ovigerous legs are present in both sexes, 10-jointed. There are 4 pairs of walking legs. *Callipallene brevirostris* is without pedipalpi, 2 mm long, on both sides of North Atlantic; others in the Pacific. *Pellenopsis* occurs in the North Atlantic. *Pallenopsis* is a sublittoral to relatively deep water worldwide genus.

Phoxichilidiidae. The chelicerae are chelate; pedipalpi rudimentary or absent, oviger-ous legs in male only. There are 4 pairs of walking legs. *Anoplodactylus petiolatus,* 1.5 mm, occurs on both sides of the Atlantic, other species throughout tropics in shallow water. *Phoxichilidium femoratum,* 3 mm, is very common in the North Atlantic and Pacific.

Endeidae. The chelicerae and palpi are absent; ovigerous legs are found in the male only. *Endeis spinosa* occurs on both sides of the Atlantic, one Antarctic and several tropical species.

Ammotheidae. All 3 anterior appendages are present, chelicerae often reduced or without chela. There are 4 pairs of walking legs. *Ammothea* is a group of large Arctic species. *Achelia* is littoral to sublittoral on cold and temperate coasts. *Tanystyle* includes several species on the West Coast, one in the western Atlantic. *Ascorhynchus* has several large deep water species.

Colossendeidae. Chelicerae are retained in the adult in *Decolopoda* and *Dodecolo-poda,* but not in the ten-legged *Pentacolossendeis* from the Caribbean. Palpi and ovig-erous legs are present in both sexes. These are deep water forms with four to six pairs of very long walking legs. *Collossendeis,* 50 mm, has four pairs of walking legs, occurs in eastern North Atlantic. *Pantopipetta* has a body barely thicker that the femora. *Decolopoda,* to 35 mm, has five pairs of legs. *Dodecolopoda,* to 60 mm, has six pairs of walking legs. Reproduction and life histories are unknown.

Pycnogonidae. The female lacks anterior three appendages; male has ovigerous legs 6 to 9 jointed. There are eight (two species with ten) short stubby walking legs. *Pycnogonum littorale* (Fig. 15-2), with four pairs of walking legs, occurs on both sides of the north Atlantic, other species on other coasts. *Pentapycnon,* with five pairs of walking legs, occurs in the Antarctic Caribbean. Of the 25 species in the family, all known are associated with solitary sea anemones or sometimes hydroid colonies. The male of one species lacks ovigers.

References

Fage, L. 1949. Pycnogonides *in* Grassé, *Traité de Zoologie,* Masson et Cie, Paris 6:906–941.

Fry, W. 1965. Feeding mechanism and preferred foods of three species of Pycnogonida. *Bull. Brit. Mus. Natur. Hist.* 12:197–223.

Hedgpeth, J. W. 1941. A key to the Pycnogonida of the Pacific coast of North America. *Trans. San Diego Soc. Natur. Hist.* 9(26):253–264.

————— 1947. Evolutionary significance of the Pycnogonida. *Smithsonian Misc. Coll.* 106(18):1–53.

————— 1948. The Pycnogonida of the western North Atlantic and the Caribbean. *Proc. U.S. Nat. Mus.* 97:157–342.

————— 1954. Phylogeny of the Pycnogonida. *Acta. Zool. Stockholm* 35:193–213.

————— 1955. Pycnogonida *in* Moore, R. C. edit. *Treatise on Invertebrate Zoology.* Univ. Kansas Press, Lawrence. P:163–170.

————— 1962. A bathypelagic pycnogonid. *Deep-Sea Res.* 9:487–491.

————— 1963. Pycnogonida of the North American Arctic. *J. Fish. Res. Board Canada* 20:1315–1348.

————— and Fry, W. C. 1964. Dodecopodous pycnogonid. *Ann. Mag. Natur. Hist.* (13)7:161–169.

Helfer, H. 1932. Pantopoda *in* Kükenthal, *Handbuch der Zoologie,* De Gruyter, Berlin 3(2):1–64.

Helfer, H. and Schlottke, E. 1935. Pantopoda *in* Bronn's *Klassen und Ordnungen des Tierreichs,* Akad. Verlagsges., Leipzig 5(4)2:1–314.

Henry, L. M. 1953. The nervous system of the Pycnogonida. *Microentomology* 18:16–36.

Sanchez, S. 1953. Développement des Psycnogonides. *Arch. Zool. Exp. Gén.* 90:1–7.

_____ 1954. Les glandes neurosécrétrices des Pycnogonides. *Compt. Rend. Acad. Sci. Paris* 239:1078–1080.

_____ 1959. Dévéloppement des Pycnogonids et leurs affinitiés avec les Arachnides. *Arch. Zool. Exp Gén.* 98:1–101.

16.

Subphylum Mandibulata

There are over 780,000 species of mandibulates, the largest being the spiny lobster, *Jasus huegeli,* up to 60 cm long.

Mandibulates are arthropods that have one or two pairs of antennae on the head and one pair of mandibles. Posterior to the mandibles there is at least one pair, usually two pairs of maxillae. The proximal part of the maxilla is well developed, while the telopodite, segments distal to the coxa, remains small. In Crustacea the endites of each pair of maxillae work against each other; in insects and Symphyla only those of the first pair do. The second maxillae (or the first in those having only one) in myriapods and insects function as a lower lip or labium; the proximal segments of each side fuse to a uniform plate that covers the preoral chamber posteriorly. The Crustacea are here treated as mandibulates, although this placement is considered controversial by some authors.

The Head Appendages

MANDIBLES. In the adult the mandibles only rarely retain their ancestral leg shape. For instance, leg-shaped mandibles are found in some copepods and ostracods (Fig. 16–1), but otherwise only in the nauplius and metanauplius larvae of Crustacea. Usually only the proximal segment with a median endite is well developed. The telopodite articles of the appendage either remain as a small palp consisting of few segments (as in many Crustacea) or are completely lost (in some Crustacea and in all myriapods and insects) (Figs. 16–9, 16–10). The endite is firmly attached to the proximal article, except in the Branchiura, the Diplopoda, and Symphyla. In these three groups the endite is inserted with an articulation and special muscles move it.

In the simplest arrangements, as in the Branchiopoda and the thysanuran insect family Machilidae, the attachment of the mandibules resembles that of the walking legs (Fig. 16–2). The longitudinal axis of the basal article lies more or less parallel to the lateral wall of the body, the length of its lumen opening into the

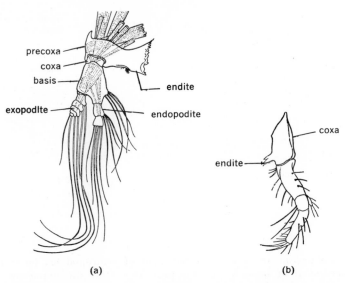

Fig. 16–1. Leglike mandibles: (a) mandible of 5th copepodite stage of *Calanus cristatus*; (b) mandible of the ostracod *Philomedes globosa*. (After Snodgrass.)

body cavity (Fig. 16–2). The endite or its teeth, however, is bent at a right angle, so that its distal surface lies next to the mouth (Figs. 16–2, 16–3). The point of close union with the head is more or less well developed at the dorsal end. Study of the fairy shrimps (Anostraca) indicates the main movement corresponds with that of a leg protopodite. It consists of foreward and backward swing in a vertical axis. Swinging (or rolling) forward moves the endites posteriorly and apart; swinging back (the muscles for this movement are very strong) causes the endites to move anteriorly and together (Fig. 16–5). Thus the food, fine filtered particles, is ground between them and pushed anteriorly toward the mouth. In addition there are only transverse muscles (Figs. 16–3, 16–4) that function as adductors, closing the endites against each other. Their antagonist (Fig. 16–3) is a weaker abductor.

The forceps-like movement of the mandibles of most Crustacea and insects comes about by forward rotation of the basal article in the axis of its dorsal articulation to take a diagonal or horizontal position (Figs. 16–6, 16–8). The former dorsal joint is now a posterior articulation. Usually, in insects almost always, there is also an anterior articulation, formerly the ventral tip of the basal article. The movement of the mandible is thus limited to a single axis: biting or lateral parting of the biting surfaces.

The most specialized crustacean biting mandibles are found in the amphipods and isopods, and by convergent specialization, in pterygote insects with biting mouthparts. In these groups a horizontal axis of rotation of the biting move-

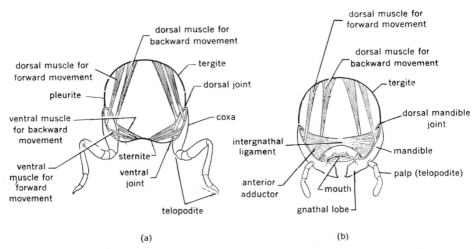

(a)   (b)

Fig. 16–2. Comparison of primitive attachment of arthropod leg on trunk (a) and primitive attachment of mandible on the head (b). Only the important muscles are indicated. Anterior dorsal muscles insert on anterior margin, posterior on posterior margin of coxa. (After Snodgrass.)

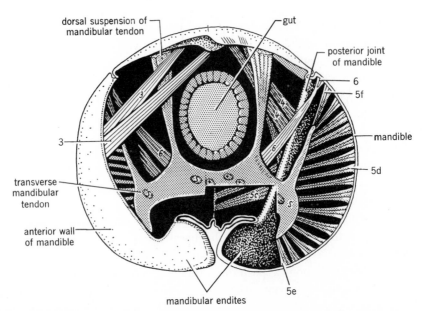

Fig. 16–3. Cross section of head showing joints and muscles of the anostracan mandible (*Chirocephalus diaphanus*). Anterior wall of mandible on the right has been cut off. On the right the tendon has been partly cut off to show muscle 5c. Muscles for the forward swing, 3, 5b; muscles for the backward swing, 4, 4a, 5a, 5c; weak adductor muscles, 5d, 5e; weak abductor muscles, 5f, 6; mandibular tendon, S. 1.3 mm wide. (After Manton.)

ments is made possible by an adductor and an abductor muscle (which in the Anostraca were muscles causing the backward (4) and forward (3) swing). Only a weak adductor (5a) remains of the numerous transverse muscles of the Anostraca (Fig. 16–7).

The mandibles of the crayfish *Astacus,* being in a diagonal position and having two condyles, have evolved in a different direction and have retained a larger number of anostracan muscles: adductor 5a and for backward movement 4 as adductors, and for forward movement 3 and abductor 6 as abductors. In addition there are adductors 1 and 3, which insert at the anterior of the basal segment and are also known from primitive Malacostraca. The basal articles converge diagonally anterior and below; in biting motion their cutting endites open laterally and close medially like trap doors. (Fig. 16–9).

Intermediate between the anterior-posterior swinging of the anostracan mandible and the biting movement of the crayfish, *Astacus,* is the orientation of the mandibles of *Anaspides* and *Hemimysis.* Here the joint axis is diagonal (Fig. 16–8); the articulation is not stiff as there is only the dorsal condyle. The endites have a grinding surface and also a cutting edge. The muscles resemble those of Anostraca, and transverse muscles are present. An additional adductor (2, producing back-swinging) unlike adductor 4, inserts at the anterior of the basal segment; it is divided into two groups (1 and 2) in decapod crabs.

MAXILLAE. The one or two pairs of maxillae are posterior and close to the mandibles. Thus they are flattened, almost plate-like (Fig. 16–6). Unlike the mandibles, which have limited movement, the maxillae have several basal articles and can make various movements (Fig. 16–11). With the proximal articles extended, the endite-bearing distal article moves forward and may take up a bit

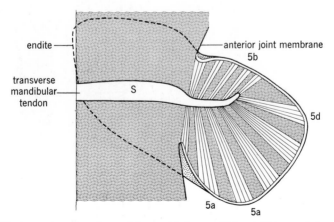

Fig. 16–4. Horizontal section through base of left mandible of *Chirocephalus* after swinging back. The endite lying in back of the figure is indicated in outline. The abbreviations are those of Fig. 16–3. (After Manton.)

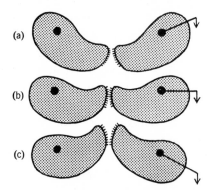

Fig. 16–5. Diagram to show backward swing around vertical axis (black spot) of pair of outlines resembling anostracan mandible in horizontal view: (a) forward swing of basal segment; (b,c) backward swing of basal segment. (After Manton.)

of food; then as the basal articles flex, they move to the mouth and deliver to the mandibles. Usually each maxilla has several endites, each of which can insert on a basal article or, as also in insects, both insert on a basal segment. Figures 16–12 and 16–13 show examples of the diverse specializations that have evolved in the maxillae of mandibulates. The number and diversity of maxillary endites can only be understood by studying their often complicated function in Crustacea. The posterior pair fuses medially in insects forming a wide plate, the labium, behind the anterior mouthparts. The labium is therefore serially ho-

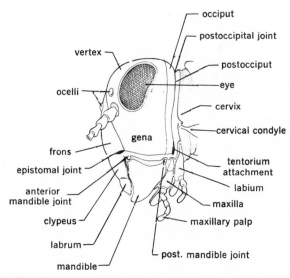

Fig. 16–6. Insect head showing insertion of mandible with a double joint; postoccipital joint probably metamere border separating first and second maxillae. (After Snodgrass from Weber.)

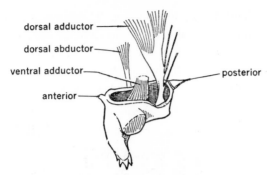

Fig. 16–7. **Right mandible of the amphipod** *Talorchestia longicornis,* **mesal view showing chewing surface (with lines); the joint moves around the anterior-posterior axis. The adductor muscles used in biting are stronger than the abductor. (After Snodgrass.)**

mologous to legs in insects, while in Crustacea and Chelicerata the labium is derived from sternites (Fig. 16–9). The telopodite of the maxillae is also reduced, but usually vestiges remain as a palp.

ANTENNAE. Most articles of the antennae are similar, short rings. The hairs they bear are sensory perceptors, partly olfactory, partly mechanical. Crustacea have two pairs of antennae, while myriapods and insects have only one pair. The second antenna in these last groups disappears although its metamere with its ganglion, the tritocerebrum, is always present (Figs. 4–8, 16–6, 16–10).

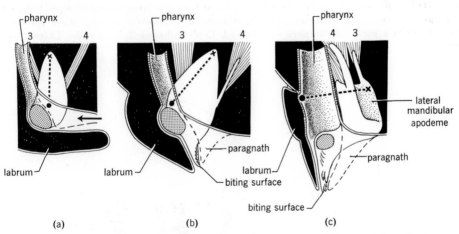

Fig. 16–8. **Sagittal section through the mouth parts of: (a)** *Chirocephalus diaphanus;* **(b)** *Paranaspides lacustris;* **(c)** *Ligia oceanica.* **Internal organs have been removed to expose mandibles (white) attached to lateral walls of head; molar area (stippled) lies below mouth. The dotted line gives axis of movement of basal segment of mandible; the cross indicates the dorsal (posterior), the black spot the ventral (anterior), connection to the head exoskeleton. (3) muscle for forward swing or abductor; (4) muscle for backward swing or adductor. Arrows indicate direction of food intake. (Adapted from Manton.)**

Antennae are, without doubt, appendages. Their primordia develop behind or next to the stomodeum in the embryo, as do those of appendages. Furthermore their ganglia resemble those of appendages. It is of interest that in the fruit fly, *Drosophila,* a mutation is known that causes a developmental anomaly, aristopedia, in which the antenna is replaced by a leg with tarsal segments and claws.

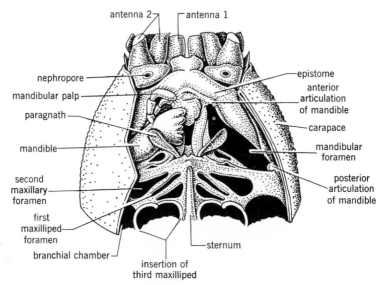

Fig. 16–9.   Mouthparts of the crayfish *Cambarus longulus* from venter of cephalothorax; all appendages except antennae and right mandible removed, leaving their foramina. On the right a piece of carapace is removed. Cephalothorax 2.5 cm wide. (After Snodgrass.)

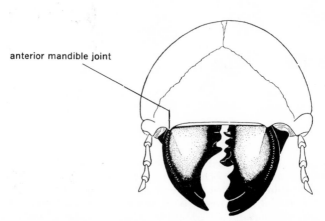

Fig. 16–10.   Insect mandibles as in grub of the rhinoceros beetle *Oryctes nasicornis,* head in anterior view, clypeus and labrum removed. Head with mandibles 12 mm high. (After Crome.)

The Segmentation of the Head

The antennae and at most three pairs of mouthparts arise on a uniform anterior tagma; the head. But in only a small minority of Crustacea is the head sharply defined. Usually in the Crustacea some of the following metameres, together with their appendages, combine with the head to form a longer tagma, the cephalothorax. Internally a pair of ganglia corresponds to each pair of appendages (Fig. 4–8). Anterior of these five pairs of head ganglia is the protocerebrum (brain), containing the optic center and two different association organs, the median central body and the paired globuli. This anterior part of the head is not associated with any appendage and develops in the embryo from ectodermal proliferation of the acron. In all mandibulates the protocerebrum is fused to the ganglia of the first antenna, the deutocerebrum, and in most the ganglia of the second antenna, the tritocerebrum, is appressed to the anterior mass so that there is an anterior dorsal suprapharyngeal ganglion above the stomodeum, whose last (tritocerebral) part has a postoral commissure (Figs. 4–8, 4–10). In only a few Crustacea (Branchiopoda) does the tritocerebrum not lie against the deutocerebrum (Fig. 4–9).

From the 5 pairs of appendages with 6 pairs of ganglia it can be concluded that the head consists of a fusion of the acron with 2 antennal and 3 mouthpart metameres. There is no other anatomical evidence concerning the composition of the head, as the head, unlike posterior tagmata, does not show segmental borders on the exoskeleton. It is helpful to look for indications of metamerism in the embryo.

The head of the embryo differs from that of the adult in having structures that can be explained only as vestiges of a lost preantennal metamere between the acron and the first antennal somite.

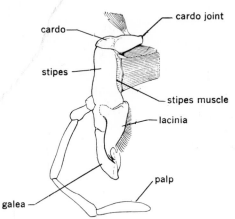

Fig. 16–11. First maxilla of the cockroach *Periplaneta*; endites (lacinia, galea) and palp insert on the stipes. Stretching is effected by movement of the cardo joint and the cardo-stipes joint. (After Snodgrass from Weber.)

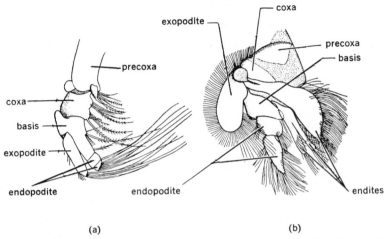

(a)   (b)

Fig. 16–12. First maxilla of Crustacea (after Hansen from Vandel): (a) leglike maxilla lacking endites of the ostracod *Polycope*; (b) the first maxilla of the mysid *Gnathophausia* having two endites.

Thus the embryos of Chilopoda, Symphyla, Pauropoda, some Crustacea and a number of Insecta have a preantennal coelom pouch. This pouch cannot be merely a diverticulum of the coelom of the antennal somite, as in some Crustacea (*Palaemonetes, Nebalia, Hemimysis, Gammarus*) it quite clearly is derived from an isolated mesodermal proliferation (Fig. 16–14). From this proliferation arise the muscles of the foregut, the labrum and parts of the cephalic aorta and its branches. Also in two crustaceans (*Gammarus*, Fig. 16–15, *Heterotanais*) and less distinctly in the centipede *Scolopendra* and symphyean *Hanseniella* (Fig. 16–16) there are primordia of paired ganglia which have to be ascribed to this preantennal metamere because they lie between the most anterior optical centers and the antennal ganglia. In these Crustacea the ganglion primordia, called prosocerebrum, fuse with the anterior (optic) ganglia forming the medial part of the protocerebrum and give rise to the central body and the commissure. The same association organs develop in the embryo of the walking stick, *Carausius*, from a pair of median lobes of the ganglionic swelling of the cephalic lobes. Their position and fate would indicate their homology with the prosocerebrum of *Gammarus*. More uncertain are the serial homologies of a preantennal appendage, the third indication of a metamere. Traces of such an appendage may be present as a pair of humps, anterior to the antenna primordia, visible in the germ band of the centipede *Scolopendra,* a walking stick insect and June beetles (each recorded once by a single author).

While the existence of a single metamere is made certain by the preantennal coelom pouches, the presence of additional somites between acron and antennal metamere has not been successfully demonstrated. The two pairs of preantennal

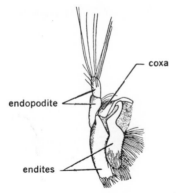

coxa

endopodite

endites

Fig. 16–13.   Second maxilla of *Gnathophausia*. (After Hansen from Vandel.)

pouches seen in the walking stick *Carausius* probably arise from a splitting of the perantennal somite.

The mouth develops in the embryo at the posterior border of the acron (Fig. 16–15a). The posterior growth of the labrum leaves the mouth in the mandibular segment. A deep depression in the sternites forms the preoral chamber (Fig. 16–15b). The first antennae, at first posterior to the mouth, now are with the second antennae anterior to the mouth (Figs. 16–6, 16–9).

The Eyes *

The eyes of almost all mandibulates are built along the same plan. Both the crustaceans and insects may have simple median eyes and additional compound eyes similar to those of the marine chelicerates. Myriapods have no median eyes.

OCELLI. The median ocelli are of diverse structure. In crustaceans they develop as cup-shaped nauplius eyes, in insects as typical ocelli. They are always

---

* This section has been only slightly changed in translating from the German. Most of the references are from German literature which is more oriented toward habits than is the American counterpart.

Summaries on the physiology of mandibulate eyes with literature references are:

Bullock, R. H. and Horridge, G. A. 1965. *Structure and Function in the Nervous Systems of Invertebrates*, vol. 2, W. H. Freeman, San Francisco, Calif.

Burtt, E. T. and Catton, W. T. 1966. Image formation and sensory transmission in the compound eye *in* Beament, J. W. L. et al. *Advances in Insect Physiology*, vol. 3. Academic Press, London.

Dethier, V. G. 1963. *The Physiology of Insect Senses*. Methuen, London.

Goldsmith, T. H. 1964. The visual system of insects *in* Rockstein, M. edit. *The Physiology of Insecta*, vol. 1. Academic Press, New York.

Prosser, C. L. and Brown, Jr., F. A. 1961. *Comparative Animal Physiology*, Saunders, Philadelphia, Pa.

Waterman, T. H. 1961. Light sensitivity and vision *in* Waterman, T. H. edit. *The Physiology of Crustacea*, vol. 2, Academic Press, New York.

small and contain only a small number of optic cells in groups of two or four, each with a connected rhabdom. Only rarely does the retina form two layers. The lens is absent if neither the cuticle nor the hypodermis is swollen above the retina. But usually there is a refractive body and also, behind the optic cells, a tapetum.

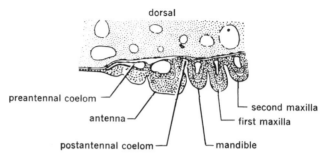

Fig. 16–14. Longitudinal section through anterior germ band of the centipede *Scolopendra*, showing limb primordia and coelomic pouches; 0.6 mm long. (After Heymons from Snodgrass.)

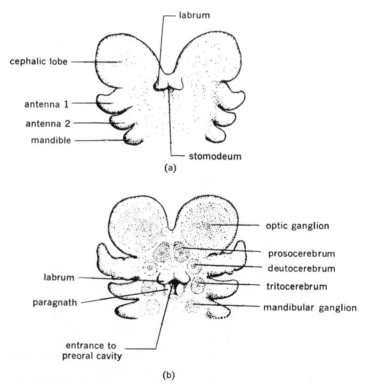

Fig. 16–15. Anterior end of germ band of *Gammarus pulex*: (a) early stage with 11–12 pairs of appendages, showing primordia; (b) late stage. (After Weygoldt.)

STEMMATA. Simple eyes also appear on the sides of the head in myriapods and insect larvae that undergo metamorphosis. These lateral eyes are called stemmata; while the median simple eyes are usually referred to as ocelli. The stemmata may be structurally similar to the ocelli or they may differ by having crystalline cone cells (Fig. 16–17) and an increased number (up to 100) of optic cells (tiger beetle larvae, Cicindelidae, have up to 6300). They may even resemble compound eyes in image formation, color vision and sensitivity to polarized light.

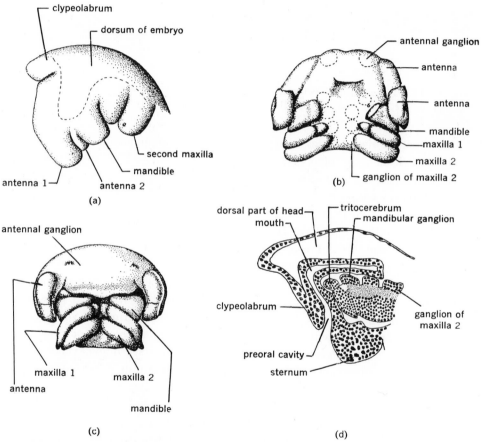

Fig. 16–16. Head development of the symphylan *Hanseniella agilis*; parts illustrated are about 0.25 mm long (after Tiegs): (a) lateral view of an early stage whose acron has folded dorsally; primordium of 2nd antenna can be seen; (b) venter of head at later stage; most of acron is now invisible in ventral view, having folded back; thus segment of first antenna is on anterior; mouth is already behind it, but still anterior of mandibles; the 2nd antenna primordium disappears; on right nephropore can be seen behind ventral organ of 2nd antenna; (c) venter of head at an advanced stage; sterna of segments of 2nd antennae and of mouth parts have sunk in forming the preoral cavity; (d) cross section through same stage as (c), showing preoral cavity; supraesophageal ganglion (not indicated) derived from the acron will be in dorsal area of head.

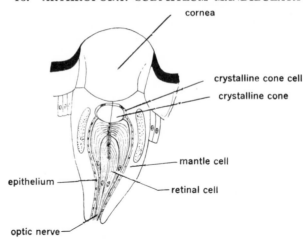

Fig. 16–17. Longitudinal section through stemma of the caterpillar *Arctica caja*; without cornea 0.15 mm long. (From Hesse after Weber.)

Larvae of the tiger beetles *Cicindela*, with 3 pairs of stemmata, can see motion and judge distance by binocular vision. They respond to humans at a distance of 1 m, to small prey at distances of 3 to 6 cm. The predatory reflexes start when the prey moves within the field of vision of two stemmata and at the same time is within reach of the mandibles.

Some caterpillars that have fewer visual components in the stemmata than *Cincindela* larvae, for instances those of the tussock moth *Lymantria monacha*, are also able to differentiate images and color. When various complexly divided surfaces of equal area but different shapes were presented to the moths, they climbed on the ones that narrowed above, only rarely on rectagular ones or on shapes that narrowed below. In corresponding choice experiments, vertical color bands were presented with different shades of gray on colored or gray background. The caterpillars could separate three colors: orange-yellow-green, blue-green and blue-violet. Stemmata can also distinguish polarized from unpolarized light.

COMPOUND EYES. Compound eyes are characteristic of arthropods. They first appear in trilobites of the lower Cambrian, and similar structures are found even in some polychaetes (*Branchiomma, Sabella*). Their origin can be explained as an accumulation of neighboring stemmata. Such clustering can be seen in sections through the loosely built compound eyes of silverfish (*Lepisma*) which consists of only 12 facets, compared with a section through the stemma of a caterpillar (Figs. 16–17, 16–18). In other arthropods, as in the arachnids, the lateral simple eyes are perhaps vestiges of compound eyes such as those found in the surviving horseshoe crabs (*Limulus*).

If a larger number of eyes is included, the circular surface of the lenses, the facets, become usually hexagonal (Fig. 16–6). Large mandibulates with well developed eyes may have 12,000 individual eyes (ommatidia) within a compound eye (e.g. dragon fly *Aeschna* and death's head moth *Acherontia atropus*). Each ommatidium consists of a dioptric and a sensory part. The cell number of the ommatidium is usually constant within the order. In insects all cells within an ommatidium may be derived from a single hypodermal cell. The divisions of the cell can be studied in sections through the primordium of the compound eye of ants, *Lasius flavus*. Within any one section along the border of the primordium toward the center, ommatidia appear in regular succession, each one of a different age (Fig. 16–19).

The dioptric part is derived from distal cells and consists of a lens (cornea) and the crystalline cone directly below it. In insects four cells take part in its formation, in Crustacea two to five and in the centipedes (Scutigeridae) an even larger number of cells. The cone may consist entirely of these fairly large cells (acone type) in some insects and in the centipede *Scutigera*, or it may have an intracellular soft or hard body (eucone type) in crustaceans and some other insects. In still other insects a pseudocone type is found; the crystalline cone is formed extracellularly by the four crystalline cone cells and may at times fuse to the back of the cornea.

The sensory part, the retinula consists in Crustacea of 5, 7 or 8 cells, in Insecta usually 8, of which one or two may be much shorter than the others or may even disappear. Proximally each retinula cell sends a fiber to the optic nerve. Toward the center of the retinula each cell forms a rhabdom (Fig. 16–20). The rhabdoms of the individual retinula cells are called rhabdomeres because in some insects (e.g., bees, *Apis mellifica*) they lie in the axis of the ommatidium so closely appressed that in the light microscope they appear to have fused to a central uniform rhabdom. Their borders can be seen with the electron microscope. In other insects (e.g., bluebottle flies, *Calliphora*) the rhabdomeres do not lie close against each other.

Electron micrographs show that each rhabdomere consists of numerous parallel closely packed tubelike elements, microvilli, each 40–120 nm in diameter, with its longitudinal axis diagonal or at right angles to that of the rhabdom (Fig. 16–28).

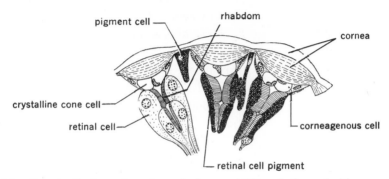

Fig. 16–18. **Longitudinal section through 3 ommatidia of the primitive compound eye of the silver fish *Lepisma saccharina*; the one on the left is without pigment; each ommatidium 0.07 mm long. (After Hesse from Weber.)**

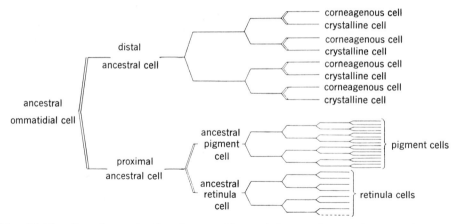

Fig. 16–19.   Genealogy of cells of ommatidium of the ant *Lasius*; differential division indicated by double lines. (From Kühn.)

Each ommatidium is surrounded by pigment that optically insulates it from the neighboring ommatidia (Fig. 16–20). In insects from the lens to the retina there are distal accessory pigment cells in the area of the cornea, primary pigment cells in the area of the crystalline cones, and basal pigment cells in the area of the retinula. The distal pigment cells are also referred to as iris pigment cells (Fig. 16–20). The optic cells themselves contain a granular pigment. The pigments are ommochromes or pteridines.

The angle between the axis of neighboring ommatidia, the axial divergence of ommatidia, is equal to the angle of the ommatidia, the angle of opposing borders in a median section through the ommatidium.

The angle of ommatidia in compound eyes of some mandibulates is:

Hoplocarida	*Squilla mantis*	12′
Decapoda	*Leander serratus*	2.2°
	Lysmata seticaudata	3.2°
Isopoda	*Porcellio scaber*	20–40°
	Oniscus asellus	13.7°
Dermaptera	*Forficula auricularia*	8°
Odonata	*Aeschna* sp.	1°
Coleoptera	*Chrysomela fastuosa*	5.4°
	Coccinella semptempunctuata	2.9°
	Phyllobius urticae	7°
Hymenoptera	*Apis mellifica*	1.4°
Lepidoptera	*Pieris brassicae*	1.8°
Diptera	*Eristalis tenax*	1.3°
	Calliphora sp.	2°

Two kinds of compound eyes may be separated; those forming apposition images in which the rhabdoms touch the proximal wall of the crystalline cone (Fig. 16–21A) and those forming superposition images in which the rhabdom is some distance from the crystalline cone (Figs. 16–20, 16–21B, C). The area between cone and rhabdom is filled by cone-shaped elongations of the crystalline cone (Fig. 16–20) or from intracellular material of the optic cells which in these instances form the rhabdom proximally (Fig. 16–23). In superposition eyes

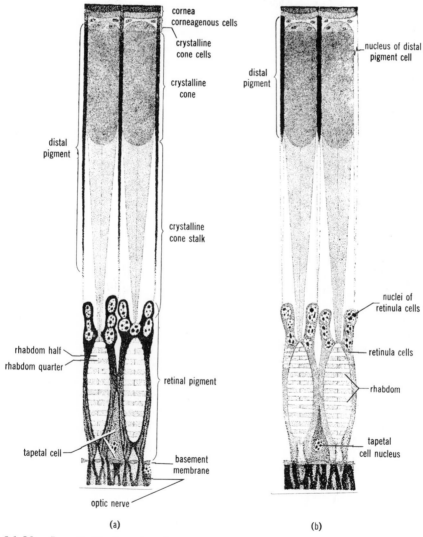

(a) (b)

Fig. 16–20. Longitudinal section through two ommatidia of the crayfish *Astacus:* (a) position of pigment in light; eye is an apposition eye; (b) position of pigment in dark; eye is a superposition eye; 0.7 mm long. (After Bernhards.)

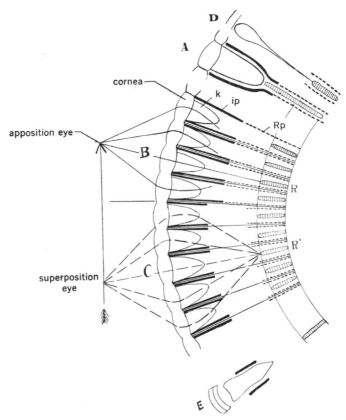

Fig. 16–21. Diagrams of apposition and superposition eyes in longitudinal section. ip, distal pigment cell; k, crystalline cone; R, R', rhabdom; Rp, retinula pigment cell. (After Plate.) A, ommatidium of an amphipod which always remains an apposition eye; B, C, ommatidium of a decapod which functions as apposition eye or superposition eye depending upon light intensity; D, ommatidium of the amphipod *Phronima* which has only retinal pigment; E, ommatidium of a deepsea crustacean having only main pigment cells.

diagonal rays leaving the crystalline cone may enter neighboring ommatidia (Fig. 16–21C), unless fenced out by a pigment barrier (Figs. 16–20a, 16–21B).

Since the compound eye plays an important role in the sensory physiology and behavior of many mandibulates, familiarity with its performance is essential.

IMAGE FORMATION. The apposition image formed by the compound eye of bumble bees, *Bombus*, can be studied by slicing the eye off with a razor blade. The proximal surface of the cut is then examined in a hanging drop preparation under the microscope. If the eye was cut barely distal to the rhabdoms, one can recognize a uniform picture of an object if the microscope tube is focused on the image in the microscope mirror. The picture is a mosaic of numerous small parts seen in the ommatidia. A crude comparison can be made between the eye with the apposition image and a bundle of narrow cardboard tubes, into each of which light may enter from a very restricted angle (as in an ommatidium).

To study the image of an individual ommatidium, the section must be made through the optic cells. If the eye is illuminated by a light disc while it is examined under a microscope, those rhabdoms in which the disc shows will light up. If the size of the disc is reduced so that its diameter as seen from the preparation corresponds to only a fraction of the divergence angle of the ommatidium, it still shows in several neighboring ommatidia (not in only one, as might be expected). In these ommatidia, the angle at the borders of the visual field is larger than the angle of the ommatidia. This phenomenon, not yet studied, is due to the effect of lens and crystalline cone, and results in overlapping of the fields of vision of neighboring ommatidia.

The optic cells react less to diagonal light than to light parallel to the axis of the ommatidium, as can be seen in electrophysiological studies of individual optic cells of *Calliphora* (divergence angle of the ommatidia, 2°). If the angle of the light differs by only 2° from that of the ommatidium, the stimulation falls to 1/10, at 5° to 1/100. A light point some distance from the eye thus stimulates one ommatidium 10 times as much as its neighbor because the light rays enter the one parallel to the optic axis, but enter the neighboring one at an angle of 2°.

In the eye of the horseshoe crab (*Limulus*) overlapping of the visual fields and resultant blurring is partly compensated by nervous suppression. During stimulation the retinula cells inhibit their neighbors. Brightly illuminated ommatidia surrounded by poorly illuminated ones are less inhibited and therefore are more stimulated than similar brightly illuminated ommatidia surrounded by brightly illuminated ones. The reverse is true for brightly illuminated ommatidia neighboring a weakly illuminated one. Contrasts are emphasized in this way and it is assumed that similar phenomena occur in the optic ganglia of mandibulates.

If conical cardboard tubes are substituted for the compound eye, the picture seen on the bottom of the tubes is dark. Many light rays entering the opening are absorbed by the converging walls and do not reach the retina. In the compound eye the ratio of the light rays reaching the rhabdom to those shielded by the pigment walls is much improved by the dioptric apparatus, in which the

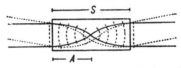

Fig. 16–22. Path of light rays in a cylindrical lens: A, length of the lens cylinder in an apposition eye; S, length of the lens cylinder in a superposition eye. Lines, rays falling straight from left into the cylinder; dots, rays falling from an angle at left into the cylinder. (After Homann.)

crystalline cone is of the greatest importance. Though it has been studied in only few insects and crustaceans, we know that the crystalline cone directs light rays from the periphery of the ommatidium and also diagonal rays into or near the axis of the ommatidia (Fig. 16–21B).

The surface of the crystalline cone is flat. The full width of the beam of light passes through the same distance within the cone, which would not be the case in a convex lens (Fig. 16–22). But in the crystalline cone the refractive index is high in the middle and decreases toward the sides; therefore the light is slowed down in the center more than at the periphery, resulting in the rays converging to a point (Fig. 16–22). In eyes with apposition images the crystalline cone ends at this level, where it borders the rhabdom, and delivers to the rhabdom the concentrated light. The large refractive difference between the rhabdom and the surrounding cells prevents the light from escaping. Nevertheless, the light is weak because of the small aperture of the ommatidium. There are three other

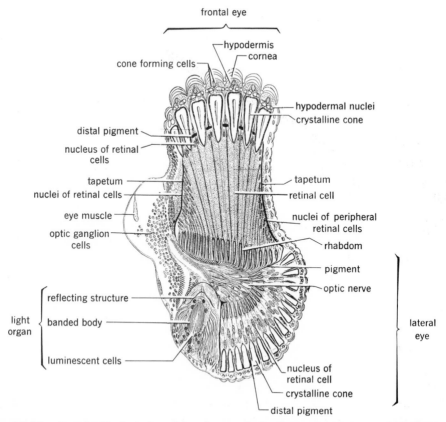

Fig. 16–23. Longitudinal section through eye of the deep-sea crustacean *Stylocheiron longicorne*. On the left side, below, there is a luminescent organ. Field of vision 50°. 1 mm long. (After Chun.)

possible ways in which the intensity of light can be increased: (*1*) The diameter of the outer surface of the cornea could be larger, and the ommatidium longer, without changing the divergence angle of the ommatidium. (*2*) The light rays entering at an angle (diagonal light) could be used to form superposition images. This device, especially useful in animals active in semidarkness, is seen in many moths, fire fly beetles, other insects and in many decapod crustaceans. The rhabdoms are some distance from the proximal surface of the crystalline cone (Figs. 16–21B, C, 16–23), and in these ommatidia each crystalline cone is elongated by its focal distance. The light entering the cone at an angle emerges at the same angle and reaches neighboring ommatida (Fig. 16–21C), so that each rhabdom receives not only the light from its own crystalline cone but also light from neighboring ommatidia (Fig. 16–21C). The light intensity is thus increased, but there is overlapping of visual fields. (Fig. 16–21 is only diagrammatic.) The picture received, though poor, is sufficient for the coarse screen of the optic cells, as has been demonstrated in the crustaceans *Leander* and *Lysmata*. In a light environment these crustaceans isolate the ommatidia by a proximal migration of the iris pigment (Figs. 16–20A, 16–21B). Optomotoric experiments have demonstrated that sharpness of image is the same in light or dark in these crustaceans.

Perhaps in arthropods (as in some vertebrates) the optic (retinal) cells have a different sensitivity to the different directions of the light being more sensitive to light in the axial direction than to light coming in at an angle. In this way, and also through suppression of light from neighboring ommatidia (see above), the sharpness of the image might be compensated.

In very long superposition eyes so many ommatidia, each with its dioptric apparatus, take part in stimulating an individual rhabdom, that all the crystalline cones work together as a lens in relation to the retinulae. An exception is found in the long eyes of some deep sea Galatheidae in which the proximal end of the crystalline cone is enclosed in the widened tip of a filament that continues between the retinula cells to the rhabdom. The light is thus gathered and brought directly to the rhabdom. It cannot leave the filament at the sides, because the filaments' refractive index is higher than that of the surrounding retinula cells (1.55 in contrast to 1.33 to 1.44). A similar structure is found in the eyes of many Euphausiacea (Fig. 16–23), but the refractive index of the filament, which has a diameter of only 1 μm, could not be measured. These long eyes probably also function as apposition eyes as they do in the younger larvae, in which the rhabdoms still lie directly proximal to the crystalline cone.

(*3*) A further intensification of the light meeting a single rhabdom is brought about by a reflective tapetum in the back of the eye. A tapetum is found in many crustaceans and in a large number of insects. The light passing the rhabdom is reflected, increasing the stimulation of the optic (retinal) cells.

In crustaceans the tapetum consists of cells containing guanin platelets, while the insect tapetum is composed of tracheal capillaries (Fig. 16–20). In semidarkness the reflection from the tapetum can be seen by directing a flashlight toward a moth (Sphingidae, Noctuidae, Bombycidae) or the scarabid beetle, *Oryctes*. The eyes glow, red or golden, from the light reflected by the tapetum. At daytime the tapetum is covered by pigment.

PHOTORECEPTION AND SPECTRAL SENSITIVITY. Light can stimulate only if absorbed within the cell. But because the cell contents are as transparent as glass to light of the visual spectrum, most optic cells must have visual pigments. The more light is absorbed by the visual pigment the greater the sensitivity of the cell. By studying the sensitivity of the eyes to various wave lengths, one can measure the spectral absorption of the visual pigment.

The mandibulate eye usually has maximum sensitivity in the ultraviolet spectrum at a wave length of approximately 350 nm and a second peak in blue-green at approximately 500 nm. The compound eyes of most mandibulates do not respond to light stimulations above 600 to 650 nm.

The sensitivity curve to light at various wave lengths is similar to that of visual pigment of vertebrates and cephalopods. These pigments, e.g., the visual purple or rhodopsin of vertebrate eyes are chromoproteins consisting of a carotene, retinene and the protein opsin. In extracts of bee heads with dark adapted eyes, retinene and some vitamin A could be identified, while extracts from light adapted eyes contained mainly the vitamin A formed from retinene during illumination. Vitamin A is otherwise not found in insects.

The visual pigments are part of the rhabdomeres of the retinula cells. This was recently demonstrated in living ommatidia of *Calliphora* using microspectrometric methods. The characteristic absorption of the individual rhabdomeres of dorsal ommatidia indicates that the pigment of the central rhabdomere differs from that of others. The light absorption thus takes place in the rhabdomeres.

Ommochromes and pteridines are present as screening pigments or filters, but not as intermediate substances for light transformation. Their function has been studied, using electrophysiological methods combined with measurement of carbohydrate metabolism, in normally pigmented eyes of *Calliphora* flies as well as in ommochrome- and pteridine-free compound eyes.

VISUAL ACUITY. The acuteness of vision or resolution can be defined as the smallest angle measured from the center of the eye within which two dots of light can still cause two separate stimulations. Images of light spots in two separate visual components have to be used, between which another component is not stimulated or is less stimulated (Fig. 16–24). The minimum angle may equal the anatomical angle of axial divergence of the ommatidia, but if the image in the eye is poor the angle may be larger. Optomotor methods are used to study the visual acuity in mandibulates.

Placed within a vertical, slowly revolving cylinder with vertical black and white stripes of equal width on the walls, an insect follows the stripes with head movements, movements of the antennae, or by turning with the cylinder. These reactions stop if the pattern is so small that in a vertical row of ommatidia there is always reflected one black or one white stripe. From the eye the width of the stripe corresponds with the angle between the axes of the ommatidia. If each retinula cell of an ommatidium could be stimulated individually, the direction of movement of the spot would be recognized within each ommatidium and a corresponding behavioral response might be expected. As there is no reaction, it must be assumed that all retinula cells within an ommatidium are stimulated at the same time. If so, with each turn of the striped cylinder, the appearance of the white stripe in those ommatidia that previously saw a black one (or the reverse) is completely independent of the direction the cylinder turns. In other words, if the retinula is a functional whole, it makes no difference whether the change comes from left or right, as it is perceived only as alternating stimulation of a row of ommatidia, which produces no change in behavior.

The critical point at which the stripes are so narrow as to produce no changes in behavior, may be used as a measure of resolution. Generally it agrees with the angle of divergence of the ommatidia. The same result can be obtained with behavioral studies in orientation.

Many insects and some crustaceans (*Talitrus, Tylos, Idotea*) use a source of light, in nature the sun or moon, for orientation. They walk or fly so that the image of the source of light remains within the same ommatidium. Their direction of movement thus always forms a definite angle toward the light. If in a dark room an artificial source of light is moved a certain angle, the animal will change its direction of movement to agree with the angle. The change of direction only takes place if the shift is so large that the image of the light moves from the stimulated ommatidium to a neighboring ommatidium.

The angle between the ommatidia, except in the mantis shrimp *Squilla,* and some Odonata is at least 1° (see above). Compared with vertebrates this is very large. If the angle of vision in the fovea centralis of man is about 0.9′, it means that a picture of a flower 7 m away falls on the same number of visual compo-

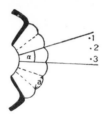

Fig. 16–24. The importance of the angle of the axis of the ommatidium for the acuteness of vision. Points 1, 2, 3 cannot be separated since all fall in the same ommatidium. (After Weber.)

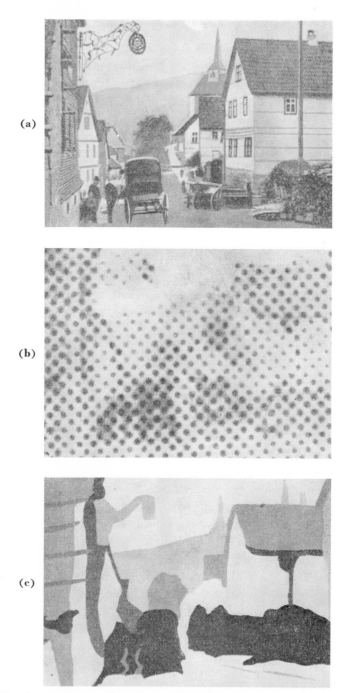

Fig. 16–25. An attempt to demonstrate the different resolutions of the human eye and that of a bee of the same picture (after Uexküll and Brock): (a) resolution of human fovea, distance of cones about 0.9′; (b) same picture viewed through visual elements having an angle of 66′; visual elements are pictured by corresponding size of the screen; (c) neighboring spots of (b) have been combined to areas to obtain an approximation of the picture that might be seen on the basis of the resolution.

nents (ommatidia) as that of a bee at 10 cm. It can be seen that compound eyes do not have any means of accommodating; their picture is so coarse that a fine adjustment would not improve it (Fig. 16–25). Furthermore, the focal distance of the crystalline cone is very short and in apposition eyes the tips of the rhabdoms lie in the focal point, not in the image plane.

The capability is probably better. Insects will react to individual dark stripes separated by wider intermediate spaces even if the angle is much smaller than that of the ommatidia. The minimum angle visible is less than 2.5′ in the wood louse, *Porcellio,* while the angle of the ommatidia is 20 to 40°; that of the blue-bottle fly, *Calliphora,* is less than 4′ while the angle of the ommatidia is 2°.

Resolution is equal in all parts only in the superposition eyes of nocturnal insects. Such eyes have the form of segments of a sphere and only here do the axes of the ommatidia all meet at the same angle in the center of the sphere of which the eye is a part. Apposition eyes, however, have many irregularities. Particularly in nonspherical eyes, some of which are more convex in the transverse than in the vertical direction (e.g., bees), there are areas of greater and lesser resolution (Fig. 16–26). The distribution of these areas may have a parallel in the fovea of vertebrates.

The total number of ommatidia and also the size of their angle of divergence depends on the size of the eye, as the volume of the cells has a definite minimum. Therefore small arthropods with smaller eyes have smaller resolution than their larger relatives, as may be observed in the proportionately sized eyes of three related beetles: The angle between the ommatidia of *Phyllopertha* is 3 times greater than in *Polyphylla.*

Polyphylla fullo	32 mm long	12,150 ommatidia
Melolontha vulgaris (May beetle)	25 mm long	5,475 ommatidia
Phyllopertha horticola	12 mm long	3,700 ommatidia

THE THEORY OF THE UNIT CONTRIBUTION OF THE OMMATIDIUM IN IMAGE PERCEPTION. Results from rotating drum experiments as well as observations on orientation lead to the assumption that the ommatidium in image formation is a functional whole, producing only one point of the image. The whole ommatidium, instead of each retinula cell, would be the visual component of the compound eye. This is true especially for those eyes in which the rhabdomeres have fused to a single rhabdom. In microscopic studies of the eyes, sliced off by a razor blade, as mentioned above, the rhabdoms light up as a whole and therefore all retinula cells of the ommatidium receive the same stimulation. (The ommatidium of Fig. 16–24 does not produce a picture of 3 dots, but of a single gray spot, its intensity a mixture of the white background and the black of the three spots). If, however, the individual rhabdomeres of an eye are separate, as in the bluebottle fly, *Calliphora,* it is possible that individual retinula cells receive different stimuli. The theory of a uniform function of the ommatidium is

Fig. 16–26.   Sagittal section through every 5th ommatidium of the worker bee showing that it does not have the radius of a hemisphere. (After Portillo.)

true only for image formation. In analysis of polarized light, and also probably in color vision, the optic cells of an ommatidium may receive independent diverse stimuli as a result of specific sensitivity. Thus it can be understood that the retinula cells always have separate axons.

ADAPTATIONS TO LIGHT INTENSITIES. Compound eyes may adapt in various ways to the predominating light conditions.

(*1*) Pigment may migrate in both apposition and superposition eyes. In daylight the pigment granules in many superposition eyes evenly distribute themselves in the pigment cells as well as in the optic cells. Only then can the eye work as an apposition eye. In darkness, the pigment of the long pigment cells (in Crustacea, in the retinula cells also) moves toward one end of the cell. In some crustaceans the whole pigment cell may contract (Fig. 16–20), the movement being controlled in Crustacea by eyestalk hormones. As the pigmental divisions between ommatidia disappear, the compound eye can function as a superposition eye and its light sensitivity will increase. In some crustaceans the tapetum cells may move from the back of the eye toward the rhabdoms. The movement of the pigment is slower in changing from light to dark than in the reverse. In the prawn, *Palaemon*, the pigment movement in light adaption takes 30 minutes, in dark adaption, 60–90 minutes; in the hawk moth, 1–3 minutes and 60 minutes.

(*2*) There may be shifts of the rhabdom. At dusk the rhabdoms of the back-swimmer, *Notonecta*, move distally, penetrating 4/5 of the length of the soft crystalline cone cells. The maximal extension of the rhabdoms is reached in about 50 minutes; withdrawal with sudden illumination takes only 10 seconds. Similar observations have been made in a mosquito (*Culex*).

(*3*) The adaptation may be an increase in sensitivity of optic cells. It has been demonstrated by using electrophysiological methods that eyes of nocturnal insects may considerably increase their sensitivity in the dark (movement of pigments may be part of the explanation). Examples are the walking stick *Carausius*, the greenhouse stone cricket *Tachycines,* water beetle *Dytiscus* and dragonfly naiads.

Within 30 seconds after dark the sensitivity is increased 670 times in *Carausius;* within 30 minutes, 22,000 times. This is of particular importance to nocturnal animals; those in water or in dense vegetation. Rapidly flying diurnal insects live under different conditions but are exposed to very quick and strong light changes between sun and shadow. Their absolute sensitivity is low and is independent of adaptation (in *Apis, Vespa, Bombus, Eristalis, Calliphora, Aeschna* but not *Vanessa*). This may partly explain why diurnal insects rest in dusk or during dark overcast days.

VISION OF FORMS. The ability to recognize forms is assumed for many mandibulates, especially for predators and for insects that visit flowers. Only in honey bees has there been a careful study. In experiments in which different equal sized figures were presented, *Apis* chose one with many contours, one strongly subdivided (Fig. 16–27). There was a direct relationship between the number of subdivisions of equal-sized figures and the number of times bees flew to the figure. In nature flower heads may correspond to these conditions. That bees can really differentiate figures can be demonstrated by training the bees in checker board experiments, as is described below (Fig. 16–27).

Because bees fly rapidly, the picture travels rapidly over the retinulae. The subdivided figures cause more stimulation, changes between light and dark, to optic cells. The subdivision of the figures incorporates not only a two-dimensional element but, as a result of the bee's movement, there is a time element in changing of the stimulation of the retina. Each ommatidium can visually examine the contours of figures one after another, changing the element of space to one of time. However the stimulation frequence in time is not alone a standard for vision of forms.

Trained bees, *Apis mellifica,* on approaching a vertical wall, can separate a painted black diagonal band painted at an angle of 45° from the horizintal from one at an angle of 135° (a band going the opposite direction). They can separate a black vertical band from one that is off by an angle of 10°. Similar observations have been made for patterns of squares. Vision with moving eyes has been described in a crab (*Carcinus maenas*) while resting. If a contrasting ob-

Fig. 16–27. Trained honey bees can separate the figures of the upper row from those of the lower row, but cannot separate the figures within the upper row or within the lower row. (After von Frisch and Hertz.)

ject was brought into the crab's visual area, the eye stalks vibrated with a frequency of 2–5 times per second and an amplitude of 3′ of an arc.

THE SPEED OF THE EXCITATION. The speed of excitation depends on the habits of crustaceans or insects. In slow-moving insects which fly rarely and have slow flight (e.g., greenhouse stone cricket *Tachycines,* walking stick *Carausius,* roach *Periplaneta,* aquatic beetle *Dytiscus* and butterfly *Vanessa*) as well as slowly walking crustaceans (e.g., wood louse *Asellus,* crayfish *Cambarus,* hermit crab *Pagurus*) the electroretinograms of the retina cells are relatively slow. The slowness ascertains the timing of the stimulation of the optic centers. Thus the excitability of the stimulated optic cell is renewed after a refractory period of 1/10 to 1/50 second, depending on light intensity and temperature. If there are 50 light flashes per second one after another, the eye responds as if the illumination were constant. The pictures continue into one another since the next flash appears before the previous one has faded.

In rapidly flying insects (e.g., bees, bumblebees, wasps, various flies, dragonflies, the running sea slater *Ligia*), the refractory period of an optic cell takes only a few milliseconds. A dragonfly *Aeschna* can thus separate 175 stimulations per second, and the blue bottle *Calliphora* and bees separate even 300 flashes per second. (If ganglia of the distal optic mass, the lamina ganglionaris, are excised in *Calliphora* or if its activity is slowed by lack of oxygen, the restoration of the optic cells after the potential takes longer).

In insects, as in man, temperature, light intensity and size of the stimulated area are of importance in determining the number of stimulations that can be separately received per minute. In *Calliphora,* if the spot of light is so small as to fill only one ommatidium, the refractory period is 1/165 second, and is a maximum of 1/300 if 7–10 ommatidia are stimulated.

The efficiency of the compound eye is realized if one considers that bees' eyes can separate 300 separate stimulations per second, while under the same conditions man can separate only 50 flashes. The recovery in bees is 6 times as fast as in man. This is of importance in rapid flight. Here the pictures will not melt into bands as readily as they do in the eye of a rapidly driving man, who looks at the road to the side parallel to the motion of his car. (The flight speed of a house fly is 5 m per second, of a bee, 5–9 m per second, and of a large dragonfly, 10–15 m per second).

COLOR VISION. Color vision has been demonstrated in a small number of crustaceans and in many insects using experimental methods of food training, measurements of optomotor responses and electrophysiological methods.

Food training can be used in flower-visiting insects and was the classical method used by K. von Frisch in 1914 to prove that an invertebrate can distinguish colors. For this experiment paper squares, 15 × 15 cm, of different shades of gray with the extremes white and black were arranged in a checkerboard pattern into which one square of blue paper was placed. A container with sugar solution was placed on the colored paper, on each gray square a similar container with water. The bees rapidly learned that the one container on blue contained sugar. After removing all containers, the squares were shuffled into a new pattern. The majority of bees flew directly to the blue even though its position had been changed and its container, like the others, lacked sugar water. By introducing other shades of gray, it was demonstrated without doubt that the bees can distinguish blue from different intensities of gray. In the same way other colors or two colors at the same time can be tested.

Optomotor experiments also can be used to demonstrate color vision. The animal is placed within a turning drum with equal sized vertical stripes of one color alternating with equal sized stripes of gray. Later this is repeated with the same color but a different shade of gray. Using the same assumptions as in jumping spider color experiments, a crustacean or insect can separate colors if he reacts to a colored stripe among various stripes of gray. In these experiments the intensity of the color cannot be determined by physical methods, since the same color has different values of intensity in different insects.

The color scale seen by crustacean and insect eyes probably consists of only a few steps, and is not as rich as that seen by human eyes, which can easily separate neighboring wave lengths of similar intensities.

The bee, which seems to have an especially well-developed color sense, can separate three complementary color pairs from various intensities of gray:

blue green (510–480 nm): ultraviolet (400–300 nm)
yellow   (650–500 nm): bee violet, a mixture of blue and violet and ultra-
                                      violet
blue   (480–410 nm): bee purple, a mixture of yellow and ultraviolet

The bee spectrum, compared to that of man, is shifted toward the short wavelength; red is not seen and may be confused with black, but ultraviolet is seen as a color and is responded to as the lightest, most saturated, and most noticeable color.

Thus the mixture of colors at the spectrum end resembling human purple is a bee purple, a mixture of yellow and ultraviolet, the specific color value of which has been found by using training experiments with color filters.

Corresponding with the shift of the spectrum, there is a bee white, a mixture of two complementary colors and ultraviolet, received as neutral or noncolored by the bee. In training experiments the bee separates bee white from ultraviolet and blue-green. Bee white, as demonstrated with color filters and papers, is clearly separated from human white, which does not contain ultraviolet. Human white, seen as color by the bee, is confused with unsaturated blue-green.

Even within the abovementioned complementary colors, bees can still separate various steps, especially between blue-green and blue (490–474 nm). Here a difference in wave length of 16 nm can be separated. The bee eye is much less sensitive in the yellow color range. Only after 3–4 hours' training can yellow, orange and green be separated.

Of course, it is very difficult to imagine how bees see color, just as difficult as for a red-green colorblind person to imagine how red looks to a normal eye. Only indirectly can we get an idea of the reaction of the insect to light. Often the abilities of the bee eyes are surprising.

Even though the bee is blind to red, red flowers are visited. On study the flowers turned out to be not pure red but slightly purplish, reflecting some blue colors that stimulated the bee eye. Red poppies also reflect ultraviolet rays and were thus noticed by bees. In training experiments, the bees did not differentiate between poppy petals underneath two ultraviolet-transmitting glass panes, one clear and one black. On the other hand, white flowers, if on white background that reflects ultraviolet, are visited by bees trained to this paper. They regard the white ultraviolet absorbing flower as colored in contrast to the bee-white background.

Color vision has been demonstrated for many other flower-visiting insects, such as bumblebees, butterflies, diurnal, and nocturnal moths, and flies. The colors differentiated vary from group to group; for instance, some butterflies see red as a color.

As in vertebrates, color vision is probably due to light absorption by various kinds of cells with different spectral sensitivity. The different receptors react to the same light stimulation differently. This difference in excitation depends on the spectral composition of the light and are evaluated by the central nervous system to make differentiation of color possible.

In blue bottles *Calliphora* and honey bees *Apis mellifica* microelectrodes whose tip diameter is less than 1 μm have been successfully used to measure action potentials of individual optic cells and determine their color sensitivity. The dorsal part of the eye of blue-bottle flies contains only a single receptor with a maximum sensitivity at 490 nm (blue-green) and a second maximum at 350 nm (ultraviolet). In the ventral part of the compound eyes of *Calliphora* there are two additional types of optic cells with differential spectral sensitivity. In honeybee workers four different types of optic cells have been described, with maximal sensitivities at 340 nm (ultraviolet), 430 nm (border between violet and blue), 460 nm (blue) and 530 nm (green). These electrophysiological findings agree well with training experiments.

The ability to distinguish between colors displayed by certain Crustacea (e.g., prawns) is related to their ability to change color to match the background; that of flower-visiting insects to finding the source of food; that of butterflies often to finding sexual partners. But for some animals we do not know the biological significance of color vision (e.g., the crabs *Carcinus*, the lamellicorn beetles *Geotrupes* and dragonfly naiads).

POLARIZED LIGHT SEN'SITIVITY. Sensitivity to polarized light and to its plane of polarization has been demonstrated for several crustaceans (e.g., the side-swimmer, *Talitrus*) and for a number of insects. First demonstrated by Karl von Frisch in orientation experiments with honeybees, this discrimination makes it possible for some mandibulates to navigate, using a cloudless sky as a compass. Phototaxis can be changed without changing polarotaxis in the aquatic beetle, *Bidessus* and in *Daphnia*, indicating an intraretinal mechanism for polarized light vision. Potentials from receptor cells also suggest that a single retinular cell can act as the analyzer element (in the land crab *Cardisoma*, in *Calliphora* and *Lucilia*). All evidence suggests that the rhabdom is not only the location of the visual pigment but also contains the polarization analyzers. The microvilli in rhabdoms of compound eyes of mandibulates are oriented at 90° to one another (Fig. 16–28) suggesting two channel polarization analyzer, for which experimental evidence has been obtained. Two channel analyzers are also present in crustacean superposition eyes but this is weaker in discrimination of polarized light.

Microspectrometric measurements of individual rhabdomeres of the eye of *Calliphora* illuminated with polarized light of about 450–570 nm indicate dichroic absorption. Further experiments showed that the analyzer of the polarized light is the rhodopsin as result of the oriented stacking in the rhabdomeres.

THE ADVANTAGES OF COMPOUND EYES. The superiority of the compound eye in recognition of motion and orientation in space is due partly to the large field of vision due to the convexity of the retina. Its resolution of resting images is inferior.

The characteristics in which the compound eye excel are of greatest importance to running or flying insects in finding prey or sexual partners. The large field of vision of each eye of the tiger beetle, *Cincindela campestris,* scans 206° in the horizontal plane, 172° in the vertical plane. Every moving object in its surroundings is seen by the beetle to migrate through a number of ommatidia, causing excitation. But the picture need not fill the entire area of the cornea. The smallest moving object visible is smaller than the minimum resolution (see above) and also only small movements cause excitation. *Locusta*, which has a divergence angle of about 1.1° in the central ommatidia, notices movements of only about 0.1° as demonstrated by electrophysiological experiments. Diurnal insects therefore have a very effective alarm built into the compound eye. In flying toward the moving object, the picture increases on approach, so despite the coarse visual angle and resolution, insects can distinguish, for instance, between potential prey and a mate. That the central nervous system is geared to the compound eye facilitates such recognition.

For instance, in the butterfly, *Eumenis semele* (=*Satyrus*), some indistinct characters alert the male to the proximity of a female. Analyzed experimentally the stimuli reduce to up and down dancing movement and turning of a dark disc, as large or preferably larger than the female, but contrasting with the sky. Therefore a male need not recognize form and pattern, nor even color, of a female passing at 40 cm.

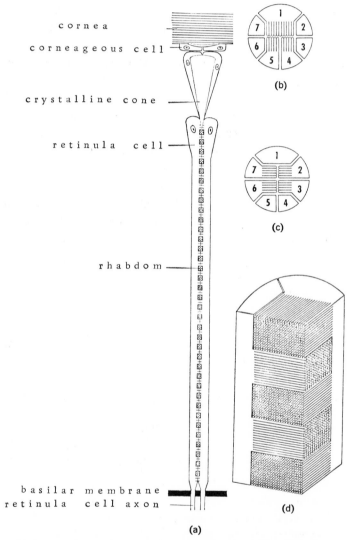

Fig. 16–28. Structure of a crab rhabdom: (a) longitudinal section through the optic axis, with a facet diameter of 20 μm; (b) cross section of the retinula showing one of alternating types of microvilli layers having three rhabdomere components contributed by retinular cells 1, 4, 5; (c) similar section through other layer in which cells 2, 3, 6 and 7 form rhabdomeres; (d) part of a rhabdom quarter showing close packing and stacking of the straight microvilli. (From Waterman and Horch, courtesy of the authors and American Association for the Advancement of Science.)

But it would be a mistake to assume that the resolution of pictures is of no importance to crustaceans or insects. It must be of importance to flower visitors. From a distance of several meters the flowers may appear as colored specks; on approaching to within 1 cm the picture will fall on as many receptors as in man at a distance of 80 cm. The insects can thus orient and find the path between complex flower parts. The hermit crab *Pagurus* takes a transparent glass shell only after stripes have been painted on it.

Also many insects orient by using certain landmarks, houses, the forest edge and horizon. This is definitely known for bees and other Hymenoptera. For this only one example: the bee wasp *Philanthus triangulus* visits her burrows several times with a fresh supply of food. The burrow is found on the ground between stones or plants. If one moves some larger objects, the arriving wasp has to search before finding its burrow because its position in regard to surrounding objects has been changed.

Some mandibulates can use the sun (rarely also the moon) and the distribution of polarized light in a clear sky as a compass in the absence of land marks. The daily movement of celestial objects is considered. This was discussed in Chapter 11 and will be in the volume on Crustacea.

The optic centers in the protocerebrum are well developed, corresponding with the biological importance of compound eyes. They are so large that they extend, stalklike, on each side of the brain, and reach the proximal wall of the compound eyes. In malacostracans, myriapods, and insects there are three adjoining large optic ganglia (lamina ganglionaris, medulla externa, medulla interna), well developed and connected to each other by chiasmata. Both the lateral optic masses are connected by the large optic commissures as well as by association organs, the globuli and the central body. In other groups of Crustacea there are only two optic ganglia.

Relationships

The origin of mandibulates can only be discussed theoretically. Ancestral forms may be found among the early Paleozoic arthropods, some of which have characteristics found also in Recent Crustacea: for instance the carapace, two pairs of antennae, legs with two rami, divided as walking legs and swimmerets. The most distinctive mark of mandibulates, the mandibles, cannot be recognized because of their poor preservation. As carapace and epimeres are also found in trilobites, the possession of two pairs of antennae is the only specific character permitting us to relate the early Paleozoic arthropods to the Crustacea and thus also with the mandibulates.

Manton believes from studies of the anatomy and function of jaws that not only the chelicerates evolved separately, but also the Crustacea must have evolved separately from the group that would include Onychophora, Myriapoda and Insecta. The main argument is made that in Crustacea only the proximal endite (gnathobase) is used for biting, while in the myriapods, insects and also onychophorans a whole limb has became a jaw and the tip is used for biting. Also from these studies it has been concluded that the classes of myriapods as well as the insects, form a close group.

However the mandibles of insects are probably not the tips of appendages, but stiff endites, similar to those of Crustacea. Evidence for this might be the following.

1. The embryology indicates that distal leg articles are derived from unsegmented primordia that later constrict. In chelicerates the tip of the pretarsus is formed first with muscles (Vachon, 1947, Kaestner, 1952). If, as in the insect mandible, no further growth takes place, no appendage tip is formed. A similar condition is found in the germ band of woodlice, the mandibles of which resemble those of insects (in lacking mandibular palps).

2. The arthropod leg tip, the pretarsus, has characteristic muscles that insert on other leg articles. However, the mandibular endite lacks these muscles in both crustaceans and insects.

3. The distal article of the myriapod mandible, which is jointed, is provided with muscles for its function. These muscles originate from the tentorium and the head capsule. The endites of the insect maxilla (galea, lacinia) also have muscles that originate in a proximal maxillar article, and some that originate from the head. As any muscle in a pretarsus always originates in another leg article, the distal article of a myriapod mandible can only be compared with the endite of the insect maxilla, not with a pretarsus. (Fechter, 1961:497; Manton, 1965: 474–475, figs. 34, 35).

Manton (1964, p. 164, fig. 44) describes a distal appendage of the mandible in *Campodea staphylinus*. The muscle of this appendage originates also in the head capsule, not in a basal mandibular article as might be expected if it were a pretarsus.

4. These muscles are all comparable to those that insert in the galea and lacinia of insects. Also in their semitubular shape the basal articles of myriapod mandibles (Fig. 19–9) resemble the cardo and stipes of the insect first maxilla. And in its state of development the myriapod mandible resembles the insect first maxilla (Fechter, 1961).

The distal article of the myriapod mandible can thus be compared to the endites of the first insect maxilla, but not with the maxillary palp, which is a telopodite.

5. The embryological development of the insect mandible does not indicate that it arises as a telopodite from a leg primordium; the endite is an unsegmented median outgrowth. It is not the whole appendage in insects, as is assumed by Manton. Further research is probably desirable.

References

STRUCTURE AND EMBRYOLOGY OF MANDIBULATES

Bruckmoser, P. 1965. Embryologische Untersuchungen über den Kopfbau der Collembole *Orchesella. Zool. Jahrb. Abt. Anat.* 82:299–364.

Fechter, H. 1961. Anatomie und Kopfmuskulatur von *Cylindroiulus. Ibid.* 79:479–528.

Heymonds, R. 1901. Die Entwicklungsgeschichte der Scolopender. *Zoologica* 33:1–244.

Kaestner, A. 1952. Mundwerkzeuge der Spinnen. *Zool. Jahrb. Abt. Anat.* 72:106–116.

Manton, S. M. 1928. Embryology of a mysid crustacean, *Hemimysis. Phil. Trans. Roy. Soc. London* 216B:363–463.

———— 1934. Embryology of the crustacean *Nebalia. Ibid.* 223B:163–238.

———— 1964. Mandibular mechanisms and the evolution of arthropods. *Ibid.* 247B:1–182.

———— 1965. Functional requirements and body design in Chilopoda. *J. Linnean Soc. London* 46:251–501.

Schneider, F. 1952. Auftreten und Ovarialentwicklung der Maikäfer *Melolontha. Mitt. Schweizer Entomol. Ges.* 25:111–130.

Scholl, G. 1965. Die Kopfentwicklung von *Carausius. Verh. Deutschen Zool. Ges.* 28:581–596.

Siewing, R. 1960. Polyhylie der Arthropoda. *Z. Wiss. Zool.* 164:238–270.

———— 1963. Arthropodenkopfsegmentierung. *Zool. Anz.* 170:429–468.

Snodgrass, R. E. 1950. Jaws of mandibulate arthropods. *Smithsonian Misc. Coll.* 116:1–85.

Størmer, L. 1944. On the relationships and phylogeny of fossil and recent Arachnomorpha. *Skr. Norske Vidensk-Akad. Oslo* 5:1–158.

Tiegs, O. W. 1940. Embryology and affinities of Symphyla. *Quart. J. Microscop. Sci.* 82:1–225.

———— 1947. Development and affinities of the Pauropoda. *Ibid.* 88:165–267; 275–336.

———— and Manton, S. M. 1958. The evolution of the Arthropoda. *Biol. Rev.* 33:255–337.

Vachon, M. 1947. L'arthrogenèse des appendices. *Bull. Biol. France Belgique* 81:177–194.

Wada, S. 1966. Kopf-Hals-Region von *Tachycines* (Saltatoria) in morphogenetische Einheiten. *Zool. Jahrb. Abt. Anat.* 83:185–326.

Weygoldt, P. 1958. Embryonalentwicklung des Amphipoden *Gammarus. Ibid.* 77:51–110.

STRUCTURE AND FUNCTION OF ARTHROPOD EYES

Autrum, H. 1950. Belichtungspotentiale und Sehen der Insekten. *Z. Vergl. Physiol.* 32:176–227.

———— 1952. Zeitliches Auflösungsvermögen und Primarvorgänge im Insektenauge. *Naturwissenschaften* 39:290–297.

———— 1960. Vergleichende Physiologie des Farbensehens. *Fortschr. Zool.* 12:176–205.

———— 1961. Physiologie des Sehens. *Ibid.* 13:257–302.

———— 1961. Sehschärfe pigmentfreier Fazettenaugen von *Calliphora. Biol. Zentralbl.* 80:1–4.

———— and Burkhardt, D. 1960. Spektrale Empfindlichkeit einzelner Sehzellen. *Naturwissenschaften* 47:257.

———— and Seibt, U. 1965. Dunkeladaptation des Bienenauges. *Ibid.* 52:566.

———— and Stöcker, M. 1950. Verschmelzungsfrequenzen des Bienenauges. *Z. Naturforsch.* 5b:38–43.

———— and Wiedemann, I. 1962. Strahlengang im Insektenauge (Appositionsauge). *Ibid.* 17b:480–490.

———— and Zwehl, V. von. 1962. Empfindlichkeit einzelner Sehzellen der Drohne, *Apis. Z. Vergl. Physiol.* 46:8–12.

————— 1964. Empfindlichkeit einzelner Sehzellen des Bienenauges. *Ibid.* 48:357–384.

Bernard, F. 1937. La morphogénèse des yeux composés d'arthropodes. *Bull. Biol. France Belgique, Suppl.* 23:1–162.

Bernhards, H. 1916. Bau des Komplexauges von *Astacus*. *Z. Wiss. Zool.* 116:649–707.

Birukow, G. 1953. Photo-Geomenotaxis bei *Geotrupes*. *Naturwissenschaften* 40:61–62.

Buddenbrock, W. von. 1952. *Sinnesphysiologie, Vergleichende Physiologie* 1, Birkhäuser, Basel.

Burkhardt, D. 1960. Eigenschaften und Funktionstypen der Sinnesorgane. *Ergeb. Biol.* 2:226–267.

————— 1961. Allgemeine Sinnesphysiologie und Elektrophysiologie der Receptoren. *Fortschr. Zool.* 13:146–189.

————— and Autrum, H. 1960. Die Belichtungspotentiale einzelner Sehzellen von *Calliphora*. *Z. Naturforsch.* 15b:612–616.

————— and Wender, L. 1960. Die Fähigkeit einzelner Sehzellen des Insektenauges, die Schwingungsrichtung polarisierten Lichtes zu analysieren. *Z. Vergl. Physiol.* 43:687–692.

Dahl. E. 1954. Frontal organs in free-living copepods. *Kungl. Fysiograf. Sälskapets Lund Förhandl.* 23:32–38.

Danneel, R. and Zeutzschel, B. 1957. Feinbau der Retinula bei *Drosophila*. *Z. Naturforsch.* 12b:730–732.

Daumer, K. 1956. Farbensehen der Bienen. *Z. Vergl. Physiol.* 38:413–478.

————— 1958. Blumenfarben, wie sie die Bienen sehen. *Ibid.* 41:49–110.

Exner, S. 1891. *Die Physiologie der Facettierten Augen von Krebsen und Insekten.* Deuticke, Leipzig.

Friedrichs, H. F. 1931. Morphologie und Physiologie der Sehorgane der Cicindelinen. *Z. Morphol. Ökol.* 21:1–172.

Frisch, K. von. 1950. Die Sonne als Kompass im Leben der Bienen. *Experientia* 6:210–221.

————— 1952. Die Richtungsorientierung der Bienen. *Verh. Deutschen Zool. Ges.* 17:58–72.

————— 1965. *Tanzsprache und Orientierung der Bienen.* Springer, Berlin.

————— and Lindauer, M. 1954. Himmel und Erde in Konkurrenz bei der Orientierung der Bienen. *Naturwissenschaften* 41:245–253.

————— Lindauer, M. and Daumer, K. 1960. Die Wehrnehmung polarisierten Lichtes durch das Bienenauge. *Experientia* 16:289–336.

————— 1967. *The Dance Language and Orientation of Bees.* Harvard Univ. Press, Cambridge, Mass.

Gavel, L. von. 1939. Die "kritische Streifenbreite" als Mass der Sehschärfe bei *Drosophila*. *Z. Vergl. Physiol.* 27:80–135.

Goldsmith, T. H. and Philpott, D. E. 1957. Microstructure of compound eyes. *J. Biophys. Biochem. Cytol.* 3:429–440.

Hamdorf, K. and Kaschef, A. H. 1965. Adaptation beim Fliegenauge. *Z. Vergl. Physiol.* 51:67–95.

Hartline, H. K. and Ratliff, F. 1958. Spatial summation of inhibitory influences in the eye of *Limulus*. *J. Gen. Physiol.* 41:1049–1066.

Hassenstein, B. 1951. Ommatidienraster und afferente Bewegungsintegration. *Z. Vergl. Physiol.* 33:301–326.

————— 1954. Sehschärfe von Superpositionsaugen. *Pubbl. Staz. Zool. Napoli* 25:1–8.

Hoffman, C. and Langer, H. 1961. Spektrale Augenempfindlichkeit der Mutante "chalky" von *Calliphora*. *Naturwissenhaften* 48:605.

Homann, H. 1932. Die Optik der Facettenaugen im Versuch. *Z. Math. Naturwiss. Unterricht.* 63:13–18.

Horridge, G. A. 1966. Optokinetic memory in the crab *Carcinus*. *J. Exp. Biol.* 44:233–246.

Hundertmark, A. 1937. Helligkeits und Farbenunterscheidungsvermögen der Eiraupen, *Lymantria*. *Z. Vergl. Physiol.* 24:42–57.

Jander, R. 1957. Die optische Richtungsorientierung von *Formica rufa. Ibid.* 40:162–283.

——— 1963. Licht-und Schwereorientierung von Insekten. *Ibid.* 47:381–430.

——— and Voss, C. 1963. Formensehen der Roten Waldameise, *Formica. Z. Tierpsychol.* 20:1–9.

——— and Waterman, T. H. 1960. Discrimination between polarized light and light intensity patterns by arthropods. *J. Cell. Comp. Physiol.* 56:137–159.

Kampa, E. 1965. The euphausiid eye, a re-evaluation. *Vision Res.* 5:475–481.

Langer, H. 1965. Dichroitische Absorption des Sehfarbstoffes in den Rhabdomeren des Insektenauges. *Z. Vergl. Physiol.* 51:258–263.

——— 1966. Spektometrische Untersuchungen der Absorptionseigenschaften einzelner Rhabdomere im Facettenauge. *Verh. Deutchen Zool. Ges.* 29:326–338.

——— and Hoffman, C. 1966. Elektro-und stoffwechselphysiologische Untersuchungen über den Einfluss von Ommochromen und Pteridinen. *J. Insect Physiol.* 12:357–387.

Lindauer, M. 1963. Kompassorientierung. *Ergeb. Biol.* 26:158–181.

Lüdtke, H. 1953. Retinomotorik und Adaptationsvorgänge im Auge des Rückenschwimmers, *Notonecta. Z. Vergl. Physiol.* 35:129–152.

Magnus, D. 1953. Optische Schlüsselreize beim Paarungsverhalten des Kaisermantels *Argynnis. Naturwissenshaften* 40:610–611.

——— 1955. Überoptimale Schüsselreize. *Verh. Deutschen Zool. Ges.* 17:58–72.

Manning, A. 1956. The effect of honey-guides. *Behaviour* 9:114–139.

Miller, W. H. 1957. Morphology of the ommatidia of the compound eye of *Limulus. J. Biophys. Biochem. Cytol.* 3:421–428.

Möller-Racke, I. 1952. Farbensinn und Farbenblindheit bei Insekten. *Zool. Jahrb. Abt. Allg. Zool.* 63:237–274.

Moody, M. F. 1964. Photoreceptor organelles. *Biol. Rev.* 39:43–86.

Papi, F. 1960. Orientation by night: The moon. *Cold Spring Harbor Symp. Quant. Biol.* 25:475–480.

Pardi, L. 1960. Innate components in the solar orientation of littoral amphipods. *Ibid.* 25:395–402.

——— and Papi, F. 1953. Orientamento di *Talitrus* (Amphipoda). *Z. Vergl. Physiol.* 35:459–518.

Portillo, J. del. 1936. Öffnungswinkeln der Ommatiden, Krümmung und Gestalt der Insekten-augen, *Ibid.* 23:100–145.

Ratliff, F. and Hartline, H. K. 1959. Responses of *Limulus* optic nerve fibers. *J. Gen. Physiol.* 42:1241–1255.

Renner, M. 1956. Der Zeitsinn der Bienen. *Natur Volk* 86:185–196.

——— 1958. Zeitsinn der Arthropoden. *Ergeb. Biol.* 20:127–158.

——— 1959. Zeitsinn und Sonnenorientierung der Honigbiene. *Z. Vergl. Physiol.* 449–483.

Rutherford, I. and Horridge, G. A. 1965. The rhabdom of the lobster eye. *Quart. J. Microscop. Sci.* 106:119–130.

Satô, S. 1957. The compound eye of *Culex pipiens. Sci. Rep. Tohoku Univ.* (4) 23:83–90.

Schneider, D. 1956. Gesichtsfelder von *Bombina, Discoglossus* und *Xenopus. Z. Vergl. Physiol.* 39:524–530.

Schneider, G. 1956. Spektrale Empfindlichkeit des Komplexauges von *Calliphora. Ibid.* 39:1–20

——— 1964. Analyse der retinalen Flimmerpotentiale von *Carausius. Ibid.* 49:195–269.

—————— and Langer, H. 1966. Feinstruktur des Überganges zwischen Kristallkegel und Rhabdomeren im Facettenauge von *Calliphora*. *Z. Naturforsch*. 21b:196.

Stockhammer, K. 1956. Wahrnehmung der Schwingungsrichtung linear polarisierten Lichtes bei Insekten. *Z. Vergl. Physiol*. 38:30–83.

Thomas, I. and Autrum, H. 1965. Empfindlichkeit der dunkel-und hell-adaptierten Biene, *Apis*, für spektrale Farben. *Ibid*. 51:204–218.

Tinbergen, N. 1932. Orientierung des Bienenwolfes, *Philanthus*. *Ibid*. 16:305–334.

—————— et al. 1943. Balz des Samtfalters, *Eumenis*. *Z. Tierpsychol*. 5:182–226.

Waterman, T. H. and Horch, K. W. 1966. Mechanism of polarized light perception. *Science* 154:467–475.

Wehner, R. and Lindauer, M. 1966. Formensehens bei der Honigbiene: Winkelunterscheidung an vertikal orientierten Streifenmustern. *Z. Vergl. Physiol*. 52:290–324.

Wolken, J. J. et al. 1957. Photoreceptor structures, *Drosophila*. *J. Biophys. Biochem. Cytol*. 3:441–448.

17.

The Terrestrial Mandibulates

The mandibulate myriapods and insects are primarily terrestrial, though some have returned secondarily to water. They respire through ectodermal tracheae, have only 1 pair of antennae, and the midgut lacks long, branched ceca. The main excretory organs are Malpighian tubules that open into the hindgut. The myriapods and insects include an immense number of species compared to the 20 to 30 thousand Crustacea. The mainly marine and freshwater mandibulates (Crustacea) will be discussed in the next volume.

Not even among the fossil ancestors are there aquatic or marine representatives; the oldest, from the Devonian, are myriapod-like. Most of the characters that unite myriapods and insects, as opposed to Crustacea, are adaptations to a different habitat and mode of living.

RESPIRATORY SYSTEM. The tracheae are paired, originally metameric, branched respiratory tubes that arise as hollow or solid ectodermal invaginations, usually from the sides of the body. They form a large internal surface that permits gas exchange without excessive water loss. The openings, the spiracles, may be closed or partly closed. Almost always the tracheae bring oxygen directly to the tissues, either within the same somite as the spiracle (many myriapods and some insects, *Campodea*) or through anastomoses with tracheae of the neighboring segments, at times forming branches that run the length of the body.

Each trachea has epithelium that is continuous with the hypodermis and also forms a cuticle (the intima). Cuticle lines the lumen and is molted with the exoskeleton (Fig. 17–1). The thin cuticle consists of a basal procuticle and an epicuticle. Electron micrographs of insect tracheae indicate that the surface is papillose or has ridges. Also there is a strong spiral support, the taenidium, which prevents collapse. The tube can expand and can usually be pulled out to twice its length without tearing.

The delicate end branches continue as tracheoles. They have been studied in insects. Intracellular, tube-shaped cavities, with a diameter of 1 μm at most, they develop within tracheole cells. The tracheole cells may have pseudopod-like extensions into which branches of the tracheoles extend (Fig. 17–1). The inner lining of the tracheole is spiralled, like that of the tracheae, but is too small to be seen with the light microscope. Unlike the lining of the tracheae, that of the tracheole is smooth and is not molted. All tracheoles end blindly and give up oxygen to the surrounding tissues. Tracheole cells, with their fine extensions, push into and between tissue cells. Probably they live for the life of the animal and never transform.

Distribution of the tracheae depends on oxygen need. If a large trachea in the abdomen of the bug *Rhodnius* (Hemiptera) is cut, tracheole cells will immigrate from both neighboring segments. This happens even before the next molt and can be studied in tissues below the hypodermis. They move more than 1 mm, pulling tracheae along.

The stimulus, it can be demonstrated, comes from the area lacking oxygen. During the next molt the neighboring segments form more and longer tracheae and tracheoles than other segments. The growth of tracheae and new tracheole cells is limited to the period of cell division preceding the molt. During the same time new strings of cells, which hollow out later, grow from their ends. *Rhodnius* nymphs raised at low oxygen tensions form additional tracheae for the ventral ganglia and wing pads. The cross section of the main trachea grows in proportion to the diameter of the branches.

The lining of the tracheae and tracheoles is permeable to gas, water, fat and also to some dyes (indigo, carmine). Experimentally this has been demonstrated

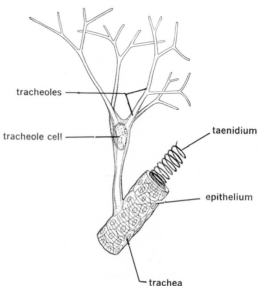

tracheoles

tracheole cell

taenidium

epithelium

trachea

Fig. 17–1.   Trachea with tracheole cell, diameter 0.5–0.2 μm. (From Weber.)

in very few insects. Their contents easily diffuse into neighboring tissues. The oxygen enters the surrounding tissues or hemolymph having a lower oxygen tension. It is replaced through the spiracle while CO_2 diffuses out. But a considerable amount of CO_2 carried in the hemolymph is removed through the exoskeleton. Oxygen diffusion is so strong it is sufficient for large larvae like *Cossus* moth caterpillars, *Dytiscus* and *Tenebrio* beetles. It is assumed that all insect larvae and pupae and also diplopods, geophilomorphs and scolopendromorphs, renew oxygen by diffusion through the tracheal system, and no ventilation movements have been noticed. However, higher insects (Pterygota) make ventilating movements, at least when active, by contraction and expansion of the abdomen. In this movement, which is usually dorsoventral, large tracheae and their air sacs, enlargements with flexible walls, are contracted and expanded.

Only rarely do the tracheae open on the body surface in a simple opening as in *Sminthurus* (Collembola). If the opening is in the same plane as the body surface, as it is in many Heteroptera or Orthoptera, it has lips and can be closed. In Chilopoda and Insecta it is generally below the body surface at the bottom of an atrium, the whole structure being considered the spiracle. The wall of the atrium has projections, spines and folds, which narrow the entrance and prevent the plugging of the tracheae. The efficiency of these spines has been examined in the honey bee, *Apis mellifera:* only the anterior spiracle was penetrated by particles of 5 μm diameter, the other spiracles even keeping out dust particles more than 2 μm in diameter. Most insects in addition can close the tracheae with muscles, thereby curbing further water loss.

Originally a pair of spiracles appears in each body somite. This condition is still found in geophilomorph centipedes, where each leg-bearing metamere (except the first and last) has a pair of spiracles. The distribution of spiracles is similar in diplopods. Among insects, there is great diversity, especially between nymphs and adults. There may be 10 pairs of spiracles in body segments 2 to 11 (none in the prothorax). A rare exception, probably of secondary nature, is the spiracle on the head in Symphyla (Fig. 21–4).

THE HEAD. The head has only one pair of antennae but in the embryo another metamere anterior of the mandibles corresponds to that bearing the second antennae in Crustacea and is called the intercalary or premandibular somite (Fig. 19–1). This always has a pair of ganglia which become the tritocerebrum (Fig. 4–8), and rarely has coelomic pouches (in *Scolopendra*) (Fig. 16–14), but usually only a solid mesodermal lining. Only rarely are there projections that can be considered the second antennae (Fig. 16–16a). In the course of development, the premandibular metamere moves forward, as it does in the Crustacea. Its ectoderm forms a part of the roof of the preoral space. Its ganglion attaches to the deutocerebrum and thus moves to the supraesophageal ganglion, the brain, and only its commissure is behind the foregut as in Crustacea

(Fig. 4–10). Strong connectives surround the foregut and go to the mandibular ganglion and a pair of nerves goes to the clypeus and labrum (Fig. 18–8).

As in other arthropods, the tritocerebrum is connected with the sympathetic nerves of the foregut, which in development arises from its ectodermal epithelium.

In insects in front of the brain the sympathetic system consists of a median frontal ganglion which is connected to the tritocerebrum by a pair of nerves and by a median nerve to the anterior of the protocerebrum. Anteriorly the frontal ganglion has a median nerve to the labrum; posteriorly there is a median nerve, the nervus recurrens, which passes through the gut passage space between brain and subesophageal ganglion and posteriorly enters the median hypocerebral ganglion. In insects this contains a nerve to the posterior of the foregut ending in the ventricular ganglia (median or paired) and also the endocrine glands, the corpora cardiaca or indirectly into the corpora allata.

The metameres following the intercalary metameres are part of the head and its appendages, the mouthparts. There are two pairs among the Diplopoda and Pauropoda and three among the Chilopoda, Symphyla and Insecta (Figs. 17–3, 19–1). Their paired ganglia fuse to form the subesophageal ganglion which shows a median break behind the first maxillary ganglion only in the Chilopoda, indicating that this region has to be considered an area of swollen connectives (Fig. 18–8). Their appendages are one pair of mandibles and, following these, one pair of maxillae, or two pairs in Chilopoda, Symphyla and Insecta.

The mandibles always lack palpi. In insects they consist of a single sclerite while in myriapods there are two or three segments connected by joint membranes (Figs. 16–6, 16–10, 19–8). The first maxillae of insects usually have a simple palp and endites (Figs. 16–6, 16–11); they enclose the space anterior to the mouth and extend medially where they fuse to form a plate-like labium; their endites (in myriapods the palps also) are very short (Figs. 18–4, 19–8).

If not fused to form a labium, the mouthparts of myriapods work against each other. This is not always the case in insects, where they may be transformed into biting or sucking mouthparts.

THE TRUNK. The trunk of myriapods consists of almost homonomous metameres. In diplopods two adjoining metameres grow together externally, forming diplosomites. In insects the head is always followed by two additional tagmata, the thorax and the abdomen. The thorax consists of three somites and bears the locomotor organs of the insect: legs and wings. The embryonic abdomen may have appendage primordia but they are only rarely retained after hatching (Fig. 17–3). The metameres of the insect abdomen are similar to each other except for the last, which may be modified for reproduction. There are 11 abdominal metameres in many embryos. Protura retain this number in the adult, but generally the number is reduced to nine.

In myriapods and most insect larvae the ganglia of the trunk segments, except for the last, are within their segments (Figs. 18–8, 18–9). In adult insects, however, most ganglia have migrated out of their metameres and have fused with others to form masses of various sizes.

The appendages of myriapods and insects are always uniramous. In contrast to chelicerates and Crustacea, it is most unusual for a myriapod or insect to have the end of an appendage transformed into pincers, and chelate mouthparts are unknown.

FAT BODY. The fat body forms lappets of large cells in the mixocoel on the sides of the gut. White, yellow, orange or sometimes green in color, they are more conspicuous than the rows of fat cells of Crustacea, though both are derived from coelom walls, as is the chloragogen tissue of oligochaetes and the large-celled connective tissue that surrounds the ceca of the chelicerates. All these tissues can store nutrients and some cells store excretory material. The physiology of the fat bodies is well known only for insects. Besides some cells containing uric acid and various fats and proteins, the fat body contains trophocytes, the main glycogen reserve of insects. The material comes from the gut but also from catabolic processes. The fat body gives up its stores during periods of starvation, overwintering, molt, metamorphosis and to provide eggs with yolk. Storage, however, is not its only function; it also can synthesize other materials.

If the intact fat body of the grasshopper *Schistocerca* is provided with C^{14} marked glycine, 36% C^{14} is later found in the incorporated protein portion, 24% in the lipid portion. The fat body works more or less as the mammalian liver.

CONNECTIVE TISSUE. The connective tissue of the few insects studied differs chemically from that of vertebrates. It encloses all organs in a layer 1 μm thick, and together with the basal membrane of the hypodermis and tracheae, it borders all tissue toward the hemolymph-filled mixocoel, forming an ionic barrier. This may be complex, as it has to permit passage of the large molecules of nutrients. The role of connective tissue in mechanical support is less in myriapods and insects than in other arthropods. This is easily seen in dissection as one has to separate the organs from their enclosures of tracheal branches.

EXCRETORY ORGANS. The original excretory organs of the metameric protostomes are nephridia. They are more reduced in myriapods and insects than in other arthropod groups and their function has changed in the highly developed flying insects. Excretory function, as in arachnids, is performed by thread-like Malpighian tubules, usually unbranched gut evaginations that reach far into the mixocoel (Fig. 18–9). In contrast to Crustacea there is no elimination of excretory material through the integument. That the excretory organs are derived from the gut is not surprising as the gut wall is more or less involved in excretion. Unlike those of arachnids, the Malpighian tubules of Myriapoda and Insecta are derived from the ectodermal proctodeum, from near the border of mid- and hindgut (Fig. 18–9). The myriapods have only a single pair of very long tubules;

insects have one to 75 pairs. Their one-layered epithelium, despite its ecto-dermal derivation, never secretes a chitinous cuticle against the lumen, but fre-quently develops a border with striations that are microvilli. Uric acid is the most important excretory product removed through the gut and anus.

Uric acid, like the guanin of arachnids, makes it possible to remove excretory material with little water loss, an adaptation of great importance to terrestrial animals. The alkaline materials are resorbed, then the water. Further water resorption takes place in the proctodeum before the uric acid is eliminated as a thick paste.

The nephridia open at the base of one or both maxillae. Some myriapods have 2 pairs, in the primitive wingless insects only one pair. Each maxillary gland consists of the remains of the coelom (the sacculus) and the more or less long excretory canal which widens to a bladder (Fig. 19–13). Morphologically the nephridia are distinct from the other cephalic glands by having a sacculus and having longitudinal bands (seen in sections) on the epithelial cells of the tubules (also known from coxal glands of arachnids). Physiologically these can be dis-tinguished by injecting dyes in the body cavity of the living myriapods. Sacculus and excretory canal take up the color and also excrete the dye. It is probable that the labial gland opening on the second maxilla of pterygote insects which secretes saliva or silk may be homologous to the gland of the apterygote insects which opens in the same place but has changed function.

As in other arthropods, nephrocytes are commonly found; also sometimes the gut functions as an excretory organ.

CIRCULATORY SYSTEM. As tracheae usually carry the oxygen directly to the tissues, there is little need for oxygen transport by the hemolymph and respira-tory pigments are usually absent. Hemoglobin is found only in some insect larvae, e.g., *Chironomus*, that live in almost anaerobic conditions.

A branched arterial system with a supraneural artery having branches to legs is thus found only in the large and probably primitive Chilopoda. The muscular dorsal vessel is always present and in primitive forms even has simple branch arteries. Only the dwarf Pauropoda and the strange scale insects, Diaspididae, lack a dorsal vessel. The dorsal vessel always traverses the whole body except for the last few segments. In the myriapods it also has in each metamere a pair of ostia and lateral arteries, probably a primitive feature. In insects it can always be divided into two parts: the heart with ostia and rarely with lateral arteries, and an anterior, tubular portion, an aorta, which brings blood to the head. In only a few primitive insects does the heart still reach the first thoracic somite: only in the few representatives studied of the Blattaria, Mantodea and Acrididae (Fig. 17–2). In other Orthoptera, Thysanura, Isoptera, Dermaptera and Plecop-tera there are ostia at least in the second and third thoracic segment. In the majority of insects (especially in the many Hemiptera, Coleoptera, Hymenoptera, Lepidoptera and Diptera) there are no ostia in the thorax. The abdomen still has the 9 pairs of ostia in primitive forms and Diplura. But in beetles and Odonata the heart extends through 8, in Lepidoptera through 7 or 8 abdominal segments, and in each segment has a pair of ostia. It is very short in Anoplura and many aphids.

Long metameric lateral arteries leading to the fat body are found in a few insects (e.g., Blattaria and Mantodea), but not in all somites (Fig. 17–2). In other primitive insects lateral arteries are very short, consisting only of a valve outside the heart.

The heart lies in a long dorsal pericardial sinus from which hemolymph moves through the ostia into the heart. A diaphragm separates the pericardial sinus from the body cavity. The pericardial sinus is formed by mixocoel, while in mollusks and deuterostomes it is a compartment of the coelom and never con-

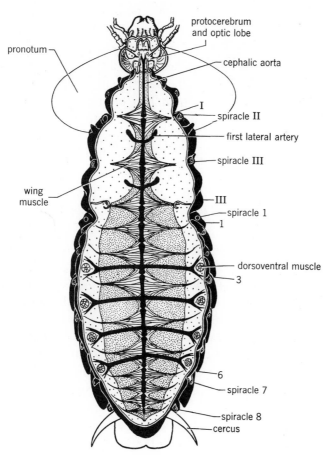

Fig. 17–2.   Circulatory system of the roach, *Blaberus trapezoideus*, ventral view. The injected vessels are black and are visible through the transparent dorsal diaphragm delimiting the pericardial sinus (stippled). Roman numerals give the posterior border of thoracic, Arabic the posterior border of abdominal segments; 3 cm long. (After Nutting.)

tains blood. Within the wall of the diaphragm are triangular thin muscles layers, the alary muscles, which move from the heart or its connective tissue laterally towards the thoracic wall. Their number corresponds to the number of ostia (Fig. 17–2). In a small number of insects it can be demonstrated that they take part in diastole. This is not the case in others. The diaphragm has various openings, permitting the up-take of blood which circulates through the body spaces. Contraction of the heart starts at the posterior end. In some species, contraction rapidly moves anterior almost giving the impression that it all contracts at the same time. Since the dorsal vessel is almost always closed posteriorly, the blood is pumped toward the brain especially in the many species lacking lateral arteries.

REPRODUCTION. The primordia of gonads are paired with two gonoducts. The gonoducts usually end secondarily in a median ectodermal duct or atrium. In most species of chilopods and insects the gonopore is in the last body segment. In Diplopoda, Pauropoda, and Symphyla, however, the gonopore is anterior, probably a secondary change. With the exception of the diplopod Chilognatha, the male myriapods lack copulatory organs. They deposit the sperm on the soil, usually on a web, from which it is picked up by the female. It is of interest that the up-take of sperm is similar in the few primitive apterygote insects. The chilognath diplopoda have one or both legs of the seventh ring transformed into gonopods with which the sperm is transferred into the female gonopore. The methods of direct insemination are diverse in pterygote insects. Usually there is an intromittent organ, a median penis (aedeagus) and paired complicated appendages in the last somites which may perhaps be derived from appendage primordia. Female insects, including Thysanura, often have ovipositors consisting of various parts not found in myriapods. Female chilopods have a small pair of gonopods (Fig. 18–13).

DEVELOPMENT. Usually the eggs of tracheates undergo superficial cleavage. Total cleavage is found in Pauropoda, Symphyla and some primitive insects (e.g., Collembola). The cleavage is never determined.

Anameric development is found in the young of Diplopoda, Pauropoda, Symphyla, many Chilopoda and also in Protura (Insecta). The young just hatched do not yet have all, usually not even half, their somites. In the course of development a preanal growth zone produces additional somites, which appear after each molt. The young always have the same habits as the adults, and many diplopods can reproduce even before they have the final number of body somites.

Epimeric development is found in some chilopods and all insects (except Protura). The young leave the egg with the final number of somites. The only change undergone is that during postembryonic development the epimorph chilopods and all apterygote insects produce genital organs. The pterygote insects in addition acquire wings, accompanied by changes in the thorax, sense organs, and often in the habits. Epimeric development is here combined with a metamorphosis to the adult, the imago.

Myriapods and the apterygote insect orders Collembola, Diplura, and Thysanura molt after becoming adult and after having reproduced. This never occurs in pterygote insects.

Relationships

The ancestory of the myriapods and insects can only be guessed as there are no fossils to tell of their origin. It is unlikely that they evolved from Crustacea. The idea of having evolved from Crustacea is based on their common possession of compound eyes, or the dubious interpretation of coxal styli of *Nesomachilis* (Thysanura) as expodites, and on certain resemblances between the mouthparts of insects and isopods. However, not all myriapods have one pair of mandibles and two pairs of maxillae, and there is no evidence or vestige of biramous appendages. The gut, lacking ceca, and the fat body are very different from the corresponding organs in Crustacea and never during the development of myriapods or insects are there larvae resembling nauplii.

The idea that myriapods and insects were derived from an Onychophora-like ancestor stands up better, supported by the simple structure of the onychophoran head which, except for the peculiar mandibles, would permit evolution of all the specialization found in myriapods and insects. In addition, Onychophora have a simple gut, produce uric acid, have a cephalic nephridium transformed into a salivary gland, have trunk musculature similar to that of Geophilomorpha, and similar formation of tracheae, as well as having ventral organs, primordia of ganglia, also found in myriapods.

Of course it should not be overlooked that we have only a small sample of the Paleozoic fauna for comparison. The likelihood is great that the myriapods and insects have come from ancestors that failed to leave fossil evidence. The myriapods display primitive, annelid-like ancestral characters in the homonomous metamerism of the body trunk, in their appendages, blood, and nervous and tracheal systems. The insects however are more specialized. Their development indicates that they have myriapod-like ancestors. Thus in the embryos of *Carausius* (Phasmida) and *Silpha* (Coleoptera) only the ventral or ventrolateral part of the somite of the second maxilla is part of the head, while the dorsal part stays outside of the head. It forms the membrane between head and thorax, including their sclerites, as well as the musculature which moves the head, and resembles the collum somite of diplopods, which follows that of their first maxilla. To prove that it gives rise to the membrane between the head and prothorax, the segment of the second maxilla in the germ band (of the orthopteran, *Tachycines*) can be destroyed with UV light: the membrane is not formed (Fig. 17–4). Also the germ band shows that the well differentiated insect body is derived from homonomous structures. Not only are the primordia of somites similar, but all bear appendage buds, as do those of myriapods (Fig. 17–3). These leg primordia are found even in specialized insects and are sometimes retained; they may be used in various ways, though never as walking legs. From them arise the cerci, the coxal plates, the furcula, larval gills of Ephemeroptera and Megaloptera, and parts of ovipositors. They are quite distinct in caterpillars and larvae of saw-flies, which still have stumps of eight or nine pairs of fleshy prolegs. They are useful as supports in peristaltic locomotion rather than in walking. The peristaltic movements start at the posterior, and push the prolegs forward.

Classification

A definitive arrangement of the five classes of terrestrial mandibulates, Chilopoda, Diplopoda, Pauropoda and Symphyla, is not possible. There are various conflicting alternatives.

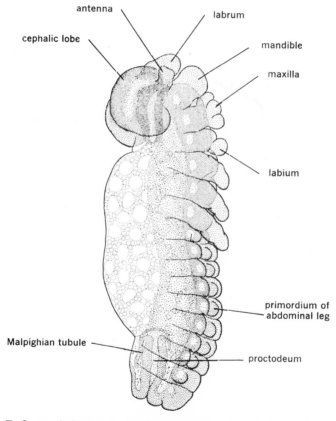

Fig. 17–3. Embryo of the sawfly *Pontania capreae*, lateral view. The acron with the protocerebrum has folded dorsally and the first antennae thus are anterior on the body, but still are at the level of the mouth. The neuropils are light spots in the densely stippled primordia of ganglia; 0.6 mm long. (After Ivanova-Kasas.)

1. The oldest grouping, based on body segmentation, still seems the most natural one. All groups with homonomous leg-bearing body somites are considered Myriapoda. These are further distinguished from the insects by lack of median eyes and of an abductor for their mandibular endites. The function of the abductor is taken over by a movable tentorium. In contrast the insects have legs on the thorax only and both the last thoracic somites may bear wings.

2. Another arrangement is based on the way in which appendages, through transformation of their basal articles into endites, have become mouthparts. There are three resultant groups.

In one group, sometimes called Dignatha, the head has just a mandibular and a maxillary somite. The hypophyarynx lies on the anterior side of the maxillae, which have fused to form a kind of labium. Diplopoda and Pauropoda (Fig. 19–8) are included here.

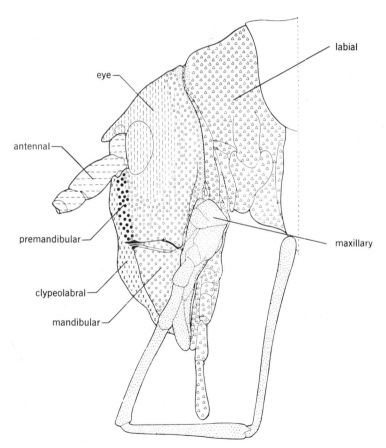

Fig. 17–4. Head of orthopteran *Tachycines* ready to hatch from egg, showing fate of various embryonic regions. (From Wada.)

Members of the next group, the Chilopoda, have four pairs of mouthparts. The true cephalic mouthparts are on three somites with the functional mandibles anterior, followed by the labium-like first maxillae behind the hypopharynx. The first maxillae enclose the preoral area. The following second maxilla has simple coxae and palps that can hold bits of food between its distal segments and move them totward the mouth Fig. 18–4). In addition the first trunk limbs, the maxillipeds, have on their basal articles labium-like coxal endites and have distal poison fangs, (Fig. 18–5).

The Trignatha have mouthparts with appendages on three somites. The second maxillae fuse in the midline and become a labium with the hypopharynx at its anterior face. Within the preoral cavity are the mandibles as well as the first maxillae. Included are the Symphyla and Insecta (Figs. 21–3, 21–4).

3. The position of the gonopore can be taken as a basis for grouping terrestrial mandibulates. One can separate the progoneates (Diplopoda, Pauropoda, Symphyla) from the opisthogoneates (Chilopoda, Insecta). In this grouping the chilopods are combined with the insects even though the first and second maxillae in these orders have a completely different developmental direction. Furthermore the specialization of the maxillipeds separates the chilopods and insects even though they may have had common ancestors. As Tiegs has pointed out, the progoneate condition can be explained by the fact that many diplopods and pauropods reproduce before all posterior segments (which in the Opisthogoneata bear the gonopore) are present. In Symphyla the normal oviducts are replaced by an ectodermal invagination which grows toward the ovaries indicating the secondary character of the gonoducts and gonopores.

The Myriapodous Arthropods

The myriapodous arthropods are all terrestrial. Their common character is a trunk made up of similar metameres, each of which almost always bears one pair of legs. In chilopods the first pair of walking legs is modified as a raptorial appendage; in other groups one or two pairs may be modified as gonopods. The number of species, about 10,500, is small compared with the number of insect species, probably 750,000.

Most myriapods usually prefer humid habitats. They lose water from the body surface and, as the spiracles cannot be closed, from the tracheal system. Some of the larger representatives, which have a relatively smaller ratio of surface to body volume, inhabit dry areas. Unlike the antennae of pterygote insects, those of myriapods have each article equipped with muscles. There are eyes only on the sides of the head; the median eyes typical of most other arthropods are missing.

MOUTHPARTS. The mandibular endites (gnathal lobes) lack abductor muscles, their function being taken over by the movable tentorium (Fig. 19–8d). The mandibles can be compared with the first maxillae of insects. The one- or two-articled base resembles the cardo and stipes of the first insect maxilla. It is a concave segment connected inside to the mixocoel of the head, permitting attachment of the full width of the head muscles. There is a median hinged endite, the distal end of which lies in front of the hypopharynx (Fig. 19–9). The endites meet in the median line. Adduction of the endite is caused by a strong muscle inserted on an apophysis. Abduction is caused not by muscles but indirectly by the motion of the tentorium, the internal skeleton of the head (Fig. 19–9). The tentorium of the myriapods consists of several arms (Fig. 19–8d). A transverse arm in the form of a rodlike thickening of the roof of the preoral chamber is usually attached to each side of the head on a hinge. A pair of ventral apophyses of the tentorium extend inside the hypopharynx toward the venter. If the transverse beam of the tentorium is rotated forward, the paired ventral branches are moved ventrally to the median corner of the endites and press both in abduction (Fig. 19–9).

The number of head metameres differs. Sometimes two gnathal segments are fused with the head behind the intercalary segment; in chilopods and Symphyla, however, there are three (see above, under classification of terrestrial mandibulates).

LOCOMOTION. Coordination of the numerous walking legs, to avoid getting legs entangled or working against each other, requires a certain rhythm of movement. The several basic gaits are determined by length of legs and body rings, and modified gaits permit rapid escape or slow penetration into the soil (Fig. 17–5). The legs not only push the body forward but lift it along its entire length above the ground, a task made possible by the metachronal wavelike rhythm of leg movements. But even the simple legs of Onychophora perform these functions, their movement resembling that of myriapods. The rapid walking movement of the many legs can be studied in slow motion pictures and by footprints on smoked paper. Several factors coordinate the various gaits and bring about different speeds:

1. The duration of a step partly determines the speed.

2. The relationship of the forward swing to the backward push can be expressed as a quotient whose denominator is the duration of the propulsive back stroke (period of contact).

During the forward phase the leg is lifted and swings (Fig. 17–5) until its tarsus touches a point far forward. Now the backward stroke begins; as the leg is moved posteriorly it pushes its insertion at the body forward (Fig. 17–5).

If the duration of the backward stroke is longer than that of the forward stroke, at a given moment more legs have contact with the ground than are in the air. The body thus has many supports, resulting in crawling motion. With the same muscular force, then, there is the possibility of much greater push than when only half of the legs are in contact, permitting a milliped to force itself through the soil. But if the forward stroke lasts longer than the backward stroke, fewer legs are in contact with the substrate than are raised (Fig. 17–6c). The animal "walks on stilts." Its speed increases with decreased duration of the backward stroke, partly because the length of the step increases. The length of the step is not identical with the span of the forward swing, but is increased as the segments whose legs are in the air are thrust forward by those whose legs push.

3. The distance covered by each step depends on factors mentioned above (no. 2) and on the leg length and size of the angle traveled during forward and backward strokes. With the increased leg length or angle of movement, the speed increases. But the angle of movement and leg length are limited by the length of the metameres as they must be able to avoid entanglement with neighboring legs. In some centipedes (e.g., Geophilomorpha) the distance between the coxae when running increases due to stretching of the joint membranes between tergites and sternites of adjacent segments. This is of great importance for rapid motion.

4. The difference in phase between two neighboring legs on the same body side influences the number and distance from each other of legs in the backward

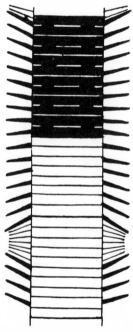

Fig. 17–5.   Diagram from moving pictures of running myriapods. The legs in the backward push are heavy; those in the forward swing fine. Extreme crawling motion of the soil diplopod *Spirostreptus*, whose body is pushed by the legs through the soil like a caterpillar tractor, by the long backstroke (fore to backstroke ratio 3 to 7) and the small difference in phase of successive legs (0.04) as well as by the large number of legs (more than 60). Length of legs, 2.5 mm; length of a step, 4 mm; speed, 2.5 mm/sec; step duration, 1.6 sec; body length, 38 mm. The black areas show the fusion of two leg carrying somites. (After Manton.)

stroke. This can be expressed as a fraction, easily determined by motion picture studies, that expresses the reciprocal value of the number of legs of one body side which are in the same phase up to the backward stroke (Fig. 17–5). In this fraction each leg moves in advance of its predecessor. For instance, if the difference in phase is ½, each odd-numbered leg is in the backward stroke phase, each even numbered is in the forward stroke (or the reverse). This difference of phase between successive legs is observed only in young diplopods having only three pairs of legs, in insects or arachnids. It follows that a six-legged animal always has three legs in contact. If the difference in phase is ⅓, each fourth leg is in the same phase. Rapidly running animals always have very low or very high difference in phase with a shortened backward stroke (Fig. 17–6).

5. The difference in phase of the two legs of the same metamere differs in various groups. In animals with few legs the difference may be ½. Each body ring can then be supported at each step on one side. This condition is found in six-legged diplopod larvae, insects and arachnids. Many legged animals may however shorten the backward stroke compared to the forward stroke without the hazard of falling over. Always near a segment that has its leg in the air there is one with its leg in contact. However, if both legs of a metamere are in

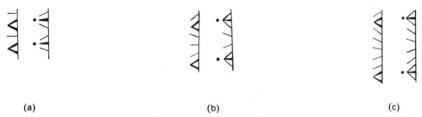

(a) (b) (c)

Fig. 17–6. Diagrammatic frames from moving pictures of running myriapods. The legs in backstroke are heavy; those moving forward fine. A geophilomorph centipede is shown changing rhythm from slow walk to flight; for each gait the most diverse phases are shown. The thick spots show the footsteps into which each leg steps; their spacing indicates the stride length: (a) slow gait (in crawling motion); (b) medium fast gait (stilted motion); (c) running motion of a *Cryptops*, 38 mm long, 2.4 mm leg length, with a speed of 29 cm/sec (see also Fig. 18–16, Tables 18–1, 19–1). Phase difference of successive legs: (a) 0.66; (b) 0.80; (c) 0.85. Ratio of fore to back stroke: (a) 5:5; (b) 6:4; (c) 7.2:2.7.

While the speed increases from (a) to (c), the angle of movement does not change. The increase of phase difference above 0.5 results in different distance of legs in backward stroke to each other, as would also a lowering of differences of phase to less than 0.5. The motion picture perceives a difference. One has the impression that the leg before the last in (a) is ⅓ ahead of the last. Actually it is ⅔ behind: it has just finished its backstroke and will be lifted immediately for the forward swing, already completed by the last leg. The last leg is starting its backward push and, as is necessary for stability, has contact with the substrate before the leg anterior is lifted. (After Manton.)

the same phase the forward swing can be at most 1.3 times as long as the backward stroke and the difference in phase is so low that the legs in backward push follow each other closely (Fig. 17–5).

Watching a milliped running one gets the impression of waves running over its legs, as wind runs over a grain field. This impression is due to convergence of the neighboring legs on each other, depending on difference in phase of successive legs. All legs in backward stroke are next to each other, as are all legs in the forward stroke (Fig. 18–16). Each of these two or three or more converging groups seems to move over the row of legs. If the phase difference is less than ½ it will move forward, otherwise back. Thus on Fig. 17–6a, the third leg is in the next phase; it reaches almost to the end of the backward stroke and is then directed posteriorly, at which point it forms a group with the leg posterior to it. The group has thus moved from the second and third legs to the third and fourth.

Of course, there are many interesting relationships between tergite length, the intersegmental membranes, the leg proportions and the gait. Thus the leg coxae of animals that move rapidly differ from those of animals that dig in the soil. The musculature also reflects difference in locomotion. Digging diplopods of the genus *Julus* have two insertions of very thick, short muscles from the trunk to the leg insertion. The fast *Scutigera* has at least 33 slender long muscles from trunk to leg. This corresponds with the fact that long muscles can contract rapidly, causing rapid motion, but cannot develop much force. The lack of force is compensated by the increased number of muscles.

References

(For Myriapoda see References for Chapters 18–21)

Butt, F. H. 1960. Head development in the arthropods. *Biol. Rev.* 35:43–91.

Clements, A. N. 1959. Metabolism of locust fat body. *J. Exp. Biol.* 36:665–675.

Connell, J. U. and Glynne-Jones, G. D. 1953. Entry of dusts into the respiratory system of the adult worker bee, *Apis mellifera*. *Bull. Entomol. Res. London* 44:291–298.

Denucé, J. M. and Vandermeerssche, G. 1954. Étude au microscope électronique des trachées des larves d'insectes. *Exp. Cell Res.* 6:76–78.

Dohle, W. 1965. Die Stellung der Diplopoden im System. *Vher. Deutschen Zool. Ges.* 28:597–606.

Edwards, G. A., Ruska, H. and deHarven, E. 1958. The fine structure of insect tracheoblasts, tracheae and tracheoles. *Arch. Biol. Liège* 69:351–369.

Ibrahim, M. M. 1958. Grundzüge der Organbildung im Embryo von *Tachycines* (Insecta, Saltatoria). *Zool. Jahrb. Abt. Anat.* 76:541–594.

Ivanova-Kasas, O. M. 1959. Die embryonale Entwicklung der Blattwespe *Pontonia capreae* (Hym., Tenthredinidae). *Ibid.* 77:193–228.

Locke, M. 1958. The coordination of growth in the tracheal system of insects. *Quart. J. Microscop. Sci.* 99:373–391.

Manton, S. M. 1959. Functional morphology and taxonomic problems of arthropoda. *Syst. Assoc. Public.* 3:23–32.

Nutting, W. L. 1951. The heart and accessory structures of the orthopteroid insects. *J. Morphol.* 89:501–597.

Richards, A. G. 1958. The cuticle of arthropods. *Ergeb. Biol.* 20:1–26.

_____ and Schneider, D. 1958. Über den komplexen Bau der Membranen des Bindegewebes von Insekten. *Z. Naturforsch.* 13b:680–687.

Roeder, K. D. (ed.), 1953. *Insect Physiology.* Wiley, New York.

Schneider, D. and Kaissling, K. E. 1959. Der Bau der Antenne des Seidenspinners *Bombyx mori.* Das Bindegewebe und das Blutgefäss. *Zool. Jahrb. Abt. Anat.* 77:8–132.

Sharov, A. R. 1966. *Basic Arthropodan Stock.* Pergamon, Oxford.

Smreczynski, S. 1932. Embryologische Untersuchungen über die Zusammensetzung des Kopfes von *Silpha. Zool. Jahrb. Abt. Anat.* 55:233–314.

Snodgrass, R. E. 1952. *A Textbook of Arthropod Anatomy.* Comstock Publ., Ithaca.

Tiegs, O. W. and Manton, S. M. 1958. The evolution of the arthropoda. *Biol. Rev.* 33:255–337.

Wada, S. 1966. Analyse der Kopf-Hals-Region von *Tachycines* (Saltatoria). *Zool. Jahrb. Abt. Anat.* 83:185–326.

Wessing, A. 1966. Die Exkretion der Insekten. *Naturwiss. Rundschau* 19:139–147.

Wigglesworth, V. B. 1953. Motility of insect tracheoles. *Nature* 172:247.

_____ 1954. Growth and regeneration in the tracheal system of an insect, *Rhodnius prolixus* (Hemiptera). *Quart. J. Microscop. Sci.* 95:115–137.

18.

Class Chilopoda, Centipedes

About 2800 species of centipedes are known. The largest is the South American *Scolopendra gigantea,* which can grow to a length of 26.5 cm.

Centipedes have the first walking leg modified into a clawlike maxilliped; opening near its tip is a poison gland. Each trunk segment, except for the last two, has one pair of legs. The gonopore is at the posterior end of the body.

Anatomy

Among the arthropods, the chilopods most resemble present day annelids with their homonomous metameres and serial appendages. This is especially true of the Epimorpha, most of which have uniform tergites. The Anamorpha exhibit variations in dorsal homonomy (also indicated in the epimorph Cryptopidae), short and long tergites alternating except at the middle of the trunk where tergites 7 and 8 are of similar length (Fig. 18–1).

The long tergites overlap the segment borders of the short ones and may telescope; probably this alternation of segment length facilitates stiffening of the trunk (Figs. 18–1, 18–2). The extreme is displayed by *Scutigera,* in which the short tergites are almost completely covered by the long ones (Fig. 18–10). The musculature corresponds. The long tergites of *Lithobius* are connected with coxae of three successive segments directly and with 5 sternites at least indirectly (Fig. 18–2). The body can thus resist the lateral pull of the propelling legs and prevent serpentine motion.

In motion pictures it can be seen that the trunk of *Scutigera,* in contrast to that of the Epimorpha, remains straight even when running rapidly, thereby avoiding entanglement of the long legs. Were the body to undulate, the long legs on the concave side would certainly interfere with each other.

The number of body segments bearing legs varies but is always odd. In the threadlike geophilomorphs, it is between 31 and more than 171; in the scolopendromorphs, 21 or 23. Adult lithobiomorphs and scutigeromorphs always have 15. The pregenital and genital segments are posterior, and with the telson can tele-

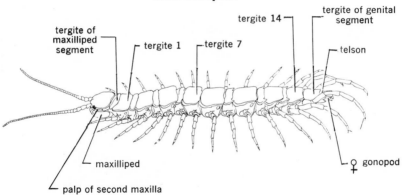

tergite of genital segment

tergite 14

tergite of maxilliped segment

tergite 1

tergite 7

telson

maxilliped

♀ gonopod

palp of second maxilla

Fig. 18–1. *Lithobius forficatus;* the spiracles can be seen on the sides; 3 cm long. (After Rilling.)

scope into the last leg-bearing metamere; the single pair of appendages of the genital segment may be reduced or modified or may be entirely absent (Fig. 18–13). In all species the last pair of walking legs is longest. In lithobiomorphs they are used for feeling and defense. Those of scolopendromorphs have heavy spines and spurs and are used for pinching in offense and defense. *Cryptops* can close the distal article (5th joint) against the 3rd joint with the 4th serving as a hinge. The distal end of the 5th comes to lie along the inner surface of the 3rd and teeth present may be used for holding prey.

The head of *Scutigera* is a spherical capsule (Fig. 18–3). But in all others, mostly inhabitants of crevices, the head as well as the trunk is flattened, the mouth has shifted posteriorly and ventrally (Figs. 18–4, 18–5), and the antennae arise at the anterior border of the head. All appear to be adaptations for living in fissures.

The next appendages behind the antennae are mouthparts (Fig. 18–4). The mandibles are semicircular in outline and are hinged by a basal article flat on the venter below the sides of the head. The basal articles are open toward the head and their full length attached by muscles. Anteriorly they bear endites, and these have sharp strong teeth below the mouth. The teeth work against one another (Fig. 18–4a). The endites are set off by a diagonal joint membrane from the basal article. The base of the succeeding two appendages lie transversely across the venter of the head, and in the midline the bases of each pair fuse (Fig. 18–4b), or rarely, as in *Scutigera*, they are slightly separated. The first pair of maxillae, in addition to endites, has a pair of palps with only two wide cone-shaped articles (Fig. 18–4b). Their surface toward the mouth is soft and they enclose the preoral area behind, containing the mandibles and the hypopharynx. Accordingly the second maxillae have no endites, only a palp that can hold pieces of food but cannot tear them apart (Fig. 18–4b). The 4th pair of mouthparts, the much stronger maxillipeds (forcipules, prehensors), are attached to the trunk (Fig. 18–5). Their huge coxae are fused with the first trunk sternite to form a

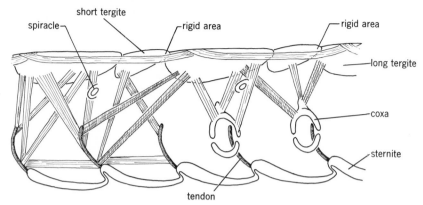

Fig. 18–2. *Lithobius forficatus:* **short segments and spiracle-bearing long segments, showing (left) muscles from tergites to metameric tendons and (right) muscles to coxae. Important muscles for the relationship of a long and short segment are crosshatched. Diagrammatic and simplified. (Modified after Manton and Rilling.)**

plate, the coxosternite, covering the mouthparts below and behind like a labium. These maxillipeds give the class its name, Chilopoda. The strong telopodites have a huge fang with the opening of a poison gland at its tip.

In *Scutigera,* with its spherical head, the second maxilla and the maxilliped resemble walking legs and like legs are on the sides of the head (Fig. 18–3). In all other chilopods, however, the number of maxilliped articles is reduced and the coxae are turned so that the telopodites are ventral and can move only in the plane of the sternum. This change in position contributes to the flatness of the head.

Chilopods are usually yellow or brown; some are reddish or green. Certain scolopendromorphs are olive or grass green, rarely blue. Some have a blue transverse band at the posterior end of each yellow tergite. The pigments are granules in the hypodermis and connective tissues. The procuticula of tergites and sternites consists of an inner lamella above which there is a hard exocuticle. In geophilomorphs and scolopendromorphs the mesocuticle in the elastic tergite and sternite borders does not form a thick layer but consists of many neighboring small cones which penetrate to the endocuticle. Epicuticle has been found in representatives of all orders, but there is disagreement as to its chemical nature.

The internal skeleton, which serves for muscle insertion (Fig. 18–2), is a kind of connective tissue, made up of intercellular collagen fibers. It is reduced in geophilomorphs and is most extensive in *Scutigera.*

SENSE ORGANS. Hairs and setae on the body and all appendages are the main sensory organs. Fast moving centipedes have many more than slow ones. The antennae also have sensory setae with complicated attachments and sensory pegs. Fields or rows of minute sensory hairs on certain areas of the anterior border of tergites, pleura and bases of antennal articles are probably proprioceptory.

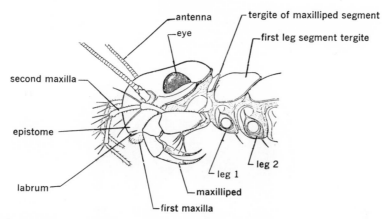

Fig. 18–3. Anterior of *Scutigera coleoptrata* in lateral view. Unlike centipedes that have the head flattened, this species has the mouthparts on the side; 6 mm long. (After Snodgrass.)

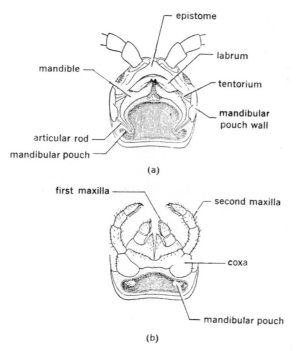

Fig. 18–4. (a) Ventral view of head of *Lithobius* after both maxillae have been removed. The mandibles are hinged anteriorly through a rodlike lateral projection of the tentorium to the head capsule; posteriorly they are attached to a rodlike swelling of the mandibular pouch. (b) Both maxillae of *Lithobius* with posterior of head capsule; coxae of second maxillae have a long oblique coxal ridge, an apodeme, which serves as muscle attachment; 2 mm wide. (After Snodgrass.)

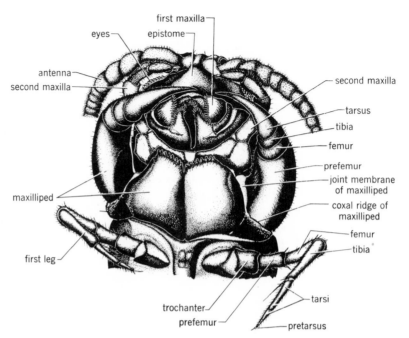

Fig. 18–5. Head of *Lithobius forficatus* from anterior and below; 2.4 mm wide. Leg articles are not necessarily homologous to those with the same name of other arthropods. (Illustrated by E. Popp.)

They are moved by movement of the joint membranes anterior to them, depending on the strength of contraction. Also under the joint membranes, mainly of the appendages, are sensory cells of constant position and number, that have branches ending in the membranes. Every leg joint, before its proximal end, has a small, non-sclerotized strip of cuticle that looks like a seam. Into this seam enter some branches of the nerve cells. These organs may correspond in function and structure to the slit sense organs of arachnids. Coxal joints and segmental membranes between tergites are connected by thin bands of muscles that have sense cells incorporated, as in the joints of decapods.

The organs of Tömösvary are found only in the Anamorpha. In *Lithobius* they appear anterior of the eyes as raised, bordered, thick, oval to round disks, each with a central pore. Below each is a group of large sense cells, their distal ends converging toward the pore and entering into its lumen, and their tips covered by cuticle. The distal section of each sense cell has an axon going to the protocerebrum.

The geophilomorphs and some scolopendromorphs lack eyes. Other centipedes have two very different kinds of eyes. The lithobiomorphs have a variable number of simple ocelli (*Lithobius* has up to 34 on each side or may lack eyes).

Under a biconvex lens is a very thin vitreous body, made up of hypodermis cells, which produces a new lens at each molt. Behind, the retinal cells are arranged around the sides of a cup. The rhabdoms are arranged radially, across the longitudinal axis of the eye, and fill up its middle (Fig. 18–6). In some species certain of the other eyes have a group of proximal retinal cells whose rhabdoms, facing the lens, lie between the lateral retinal cells. The fast moving Scutigeromorpha have compound eyes, *Scutigera* with 100 to 200, tropical *Thereuonema* to 600 ommatidia. These eyes presumably evolved independently from those of insects. Under each planoconvex lens there is a crystal cone consisting of 5 to 9 parts; its cells can be seen only early in development. The retinal cells are concentrated in a distal group of 9 to 12 and in a proximal group of 3 to 4 radially arranged cells. They resemble retinal cells of primitive insects (Figs. 16–18, 18–7). There are, in addition, 16 to 20 distal and 4 proximal pigment cells.

NERVOUS SYSTEM. The brain of the blind geophilomorphs is simpler than that of other chilopods, the globuli and central body being hardly distinguishable from other parts of the protocerebrum. The paired visual centers of other chilopods are composed of two masses. They are most differentiated in the Scutigeromorpha, as is to be expected in the presence of compound eyes.

The frontal ganglion of *Scutigera* is free as a separate ganglion anterior to brain and pharynx. In other chilopods, however, in which the mouth is far behind the anterior of the head, the frontal ganglion meets the tritocerebrum as in arachnids. It is joined with the tritocerebrum by a pair of nerves completely enclosed by ganglion cells of the tritocerebrum and gives the illusion of a tritocerebral commissure; it is called the stomodeal bridge.

The neuromeres of the three pairs of mouthparts fuse to a subesophageal ganglion, which also adjoins (except in geophilomorphs) ganglia of the maxillipeds (Fig. 18–8). The ganglia of all other segments form a long chain, which traverses the length of the body, with medially fused metameric pairs of ganglia. The pairs of ganglia are separated by paired connectives in all except the scutigeromorphs, in which the connectives are covered by a thin layer of ganglion cells.

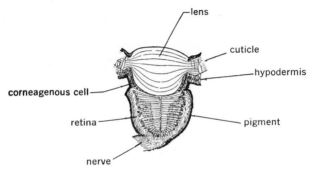

Fig. 18–6. Longitudinal section through eye of the scolopendrid *Ethmostigmus*, 0.26 mm long. (After Grenacher from Snodgrass.)

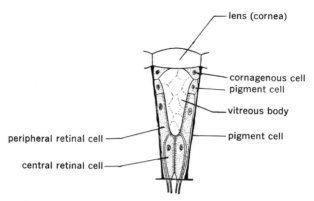

Fig. 18–7. **Longitudinal section through an ommatidium of the compound eye of** *Scutigera*, **0.2 mm long. (After various authors from Snodgrass.)**

Neurosecretory cells form a group on each side in front of the globuli of the protocerebrum. Their secretion flows posteriorly and ventrally toward the paired subhypodermal cerebral gland, located behind the eyes. This cell mass (formerly thought a frontal organ) contains secretions, but is probably a storage organ rather than a gland itself. There also are neurosecretory cells in the sub-esophageal ganglion and in the ventral nerve chain.

DIGESTIVE SYSTEM. The ectodermal foregut differs among the various families. In *Lithobius* it is one-seventh of the total gut length, in *Geophilus* almost half, and in *Cryptops*, two-thirds. In *Cryptops*, the lumen of the wide end of the foregut is filled with long forward-directed spines, continuations of the wall, which probably prevent rough food particles from entering the midgut. The midgut wall consists of columnar epithelium and between its cells are a few spherical glandular cells. The ectodermal hindgut is always short.

Multicellular ectodermal glands in *Scutigera* open near the bases of all three pairs of mouthparts and also on the maxillipeds and on the coxae of the first legs. In others they open only in the middle of the mandible and second maxilla (Fig. 18–9). In front of the labrum there are two pairs of buccal glands, the secretions of which emerge at the roof of the preoral area. There are poison glands in the maxillipeds.

EXCRETORY SYSTEM. There are Malpighian tubules and, in some groups, nephridia. Unlike Malpighian tubules of insects, those of *Lithobius* lack muscles and do not move. Fifty to 60% of the total soluble nitrogen in Malpighian vessels is in the form of ammonia, only 1–8% in uric acid. Anamorpha have maxillary nephridia, which are probably not of great importance for excretion. They consist of a sacculus whose lumen in the lithobiomorphs has deep villi with blood lacunae. The sacculus opens through two funnels into a labyrinth. The labyrinth in *Lithobius* is a single bladderlike organ; in *Scutigera*, it consists of anastomosing ducts. Two ducts start from the labyrinth, one of them opening mesally on the first maxilla, the other posteriorly on the second maxilla; the arrangement indicates that the maxillary gland is derived from the fusion of two neighboring nephridia.

CIRCULATORY SYSTEM. The circulatory system is much more elaborate in the scutigeromorphs, which have localized respiratory organs, than in other groups, in which the tracheae bring oxygen directly to the tissues. The heart lies in a peri-

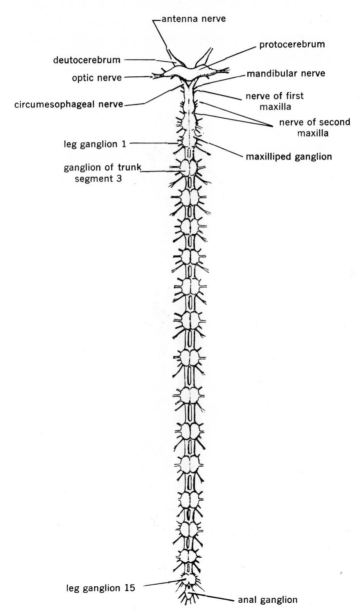

Fig. 18–8. Central nervous system of *Lithobius forficatus*, 2.5 cm long. (After Ivanov.)

cardial sinus (having ventrolateral muscles) and extends from the maxilliped metamere to the last leg-bearing segment. In each metamere it has one pair of ostia and one pair of lateral arteries. After branching extensively the lateral arteries open into the connective tissue on the sides of the gut. The anterior end of the heart extends into a head aorta that sends branches to the antennae and mandibles. It also sends a pair of semicircular branches ventrally, and these unite above the ventral nerve to form the supraneural vessel, which extends the whole length of the body, with a branch into every appendage. It also provides the ventral ganglia with blood. The blood from the open arteries returns via lacunae into the pericardial sinus.

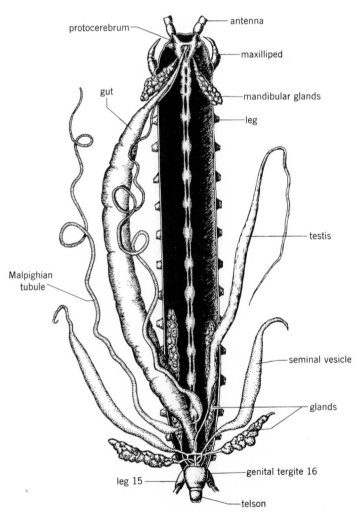

Fig. 18–9.   Internal organs of a male *Lithobius forficatus*, 2.6 cm long. (After various authors, illustrated by E. Popp.)

RESPIRATORY SYSTEM. In all centipedes except Scutigeromorpha there are branched tracheae, randomly arranged, that carry O_2 directly to the organs. The spiracles open on the sides of body segments but never on the head, maxillipeds or the somite of the last leg.

In lithobiomorphs the tracheae coming from spiracles are much branched, but do not connect with tracheae from other spiracles. In other orders there are longitudinal and transverse tracheae between body segments and the two sides of the body.

Localized respiratory organs in the form of tracheal lungs are found only in scutigeromorphs. They provide only the hemolymph with oxygen. In *Scutigera*, all long tergites have a median slit at the posterior border that leads into a respiratory atrium with perforated walls (Figs. 18–10, 18–11). From each perforation a tracheal capillary arises and branches once or twice before ending blindly without anastomosing with others. On each side about 600 such tubes form a kidneylike organ lying in a pericardial lobe. Similar organs are found in some spiders. These tracheal lungs inhale air, as can be demonstrated by placing a water droplet in front of the spiracle. Within 30–40 seconds it will be sucked into the tracheal capillaries. This suction may be caused by heart beat. In diastole the horizontal diameter of the heart expands to 2.7 times its width at systole. A strong suction thus produced in the pericardial sinus not only draws blood into the heart but also may affect the respiratory apparatus. Before entering the heart the blood has to flow over the bundles of tracheae.

In other centipedes no respiratory movements are noticeable. Tracheae are aerated by diffusion. But in transparent species the heart pulsation and movement of other organs can be seen to cause shifting of tracheal contents. Though they lie in an atrium filled by hairlike cuticular growths, there are no mechanisms or muscles for closing the spiracles.

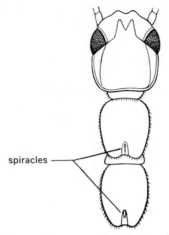

spiracles

Fig. 18–10. Anterior of *Scutigera coleoptrata,* dorsal view showing spiracle on posterior border of the long tergites; 6 mm long. (After Haase from Hennig.)

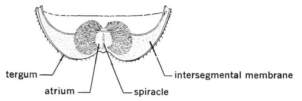

tergum —   — intersegmental membrane

atrium —   — spiracle

Fig. 18–11.   Tracheal lungs of *Scutigera coleoptrata*, 1.7 mm wide. (After Snodgrass.)

REPRODUCTIVE SYSTEM. The sexes are distinguished by secondary sexual traits, chiefly characters of certain appendages. Some species show greater sexual dimorphism than others. In Lithobiomorpha there is a long, median testis; in Scutigeromorpha and Geophilomorpha the testes are paired and tube-like; in the Scolopendromorpha there are 4–14 short testes in a row (Fig. 18–9). Two different sizes of spermatozoa have been described from *Scutigera*, *Scolopendra* and *Cryptops*. In *Scutigera* they are produced in different parts of the testis. From each testis a vas efferens leads to a median vas deferens. The vas deferens forks around the gut and rejoins on the venter and opens posteriorly into an ectodermal genital atrium (Fig. 18–9).

In the Epimorpha the spermatophores are formed in the very long, undulating vas deferens. In *Lithobius*, whose short vas deferens is just a fork of the ducts, the sperm is stored in two large seminal vesicles, which extend far anterior from near the end of the vas deferens (Fig. 18–9). The gonopore is anterior to the anus. The spinneret is found in all but the scutigeromorphs as a median hollow continuation in the wall of the genital atrium. At the tip of the spinneret opens a pair of large silk glands, and another pair of glands opens into the genital atrium.

The ovary is a long median tube above the gut which continues into a median oviduct. The oviduct forks posteriorly to surround the hindgut and each branch opens separately into the ectodermal genital atrium. In the scolopendromorphs one of the forks atrophies into a fine thin tube. Into the atrium opens one pair of slender ducts from the seminal receptacles and usually two pairs of glands.

Reproduction

The male deposits a spermatophore that is picked up by the female. The procedure is similar to that found in the apterygote insects, pselaphognath diplopods and by species of a number of arachnid orders. *Geophilus*, *Scolopendra* and *Lithobius* first spin a web in which the spermatophore is suspended, as in the Thysanura and pselaphognath diplopods.

Scutigera and *Lithobius* make the spermatophore outside the gonopore: first a secretion is produced from the gonopore and into it the sperm mass is deposited. In *Scolopendra* and *Geophilus* the spermatophores are formed within the long vas deferens.

In all species the two sexes engage in some courtship before mating. The male pats the female with his antennae. Then the partners stand next to each other, so that their bodies form a circle or oval, and with its antennae one animal pats the posterior of the other (Fig. 18–12a). After a few minutes or several hours the male deposits a spermatophore. Centipedes other than Scutigeromorpha first extend the spinneret out of the gonopore and make irregular silk threads either flat on the ground (*Lithobius*) or across the burrow in which they live (*Scolopendra, Geophilus,* Fig. 18–12b). During the spinning and construction of the spermatophore the female uses her antennae to maintain contact with the male, in *Lithobius* and *Scolopendra* with his hind legs, in *Scutigera* with the middle of his trunk. Only *Geophilus* leaves the female before completion of the web. The female remains someplace in the burrow system without further contact with the male, and three or four hours after their separation begins to run around. Eventually she finds the web left behind by the male. The females of *Scolopendra* and *Lithobius*, however, find the spermatophore by following the male's movements. *Lithobius* has a signal. After deposition of the sperm, the male turns and touches the female with his antennae. *Scutigera* pushes the female toward the spermatophore. The female extends her genital segment, feels with it and finally locates the spermatophore with her gonopore. The *Lithobius* female, with her long gonopods (Fig. 18–13), tears the spermatophore from its web and carries it off. *Thereuopoda decipiens* has been observed to pick up the spermatophore with his maxillipeds and first legs and push it into the genital pore of the female.

The epimorph centipedes differ from the anamorph species by taking care of their young. The anamorph centipedes (*Lithobius* and *Scutigera* have been observed) deposit their eggs individually, 2–4 days apart. The female of *Lithobius* with her gonopods carries the spherical egg, 1 mm in diameter, still hanging from

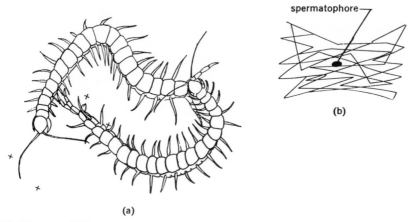

Fig. 18–12. (a) Male and female *Scolopendra cingulata* near their sperm web; limits of web indicated by + . Male is on left; female is 10 cm long. (b) Sperm web of *Scolopendra cingulata* containing the spermatophore; web 5 mm wide. (After Klingel.)

the gonopore. Later she lies flat on the ground and scratches the soil with her gonopod claws, covering the egg with fine soil while turning it. The egg thus becomes encrusted. The lens-shaped ootheca is carried with the gonopods for another hour before it is pushed between soil particles and abandoned. The protective value of the soil crust to the egg can be seen from the behavior of epimorphs.

The epimorphic *Scolopendra, Cormocephalus, Geophilus, Craterostigmus,* and *Pachymerium* may dig themselves into the ground, *Geophilus* to 40 cm, *Pachymerium* to 70 cm deep. Some are found under rocks and debris or tree bark. About 20–50 eggs are deposited there at one time. Then the mother wraps her body around the clump of eggs. In *Geophilus* the eggs are glued together as a mass and are surrounded by the mother backwards so that all sternites on which repugnatorial glands open are turned out. *Scolopendra* and *Cormocephalus* hold their eggs between their sternites using their legs to hold them together. All species watch and defend their broods until the young have molted three times. *Scolopendra* has been observed to take one egg after another between the mouthparts and "lick" them off, presumably removing fungal spores and supplying moisture. The mother does not feed during this brooding period, which lasts at least 5 weeks, 3 months in *Geophilus.* Eggs that accidentally fall to the side are not recovered and always die. Apparently the eggs are sensitive to the environment of the soil and the mother does not let the eggs come into contact with it. The eggs pass from the gonopore directly onto the mother's body. *Scolopendra,* to accomplish this, bends its body so that the posterior end is above the head. Within one hour, the first 20 eggs find space on the head and anterior tergites. Only then the animal pushes them to her venter. During the first 5–6 hours, *Geophilus* loops up the middle part of the trunk into an oval, taking an omega-shape, Ω. Then the viscid mass of eggs is transferred from the gonopore on her back to the place where the shanks of the oval meet. After all 12–70 eggs are deposited and glued together, the mother bends her trunk dorsally, spiralling around the eggs.

The length of brood-care appears to be determined by the developmental stage of the brood. With *Pachymerium* it has been possible to substitute a younger brood for an older one. The mother continued 20 days beyond the normal period of 40–50 days to care for the brood.

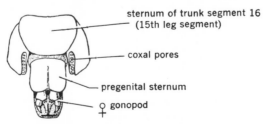

sternum of trunk segment 16
(15th leg segment)

coxal pores

pregenital sternum

♀ gonopod

Fig. 18–13. Posterior of female *Lithobius forficatus* in ventral view; telson stippled. (After Snodgrass.)

Development

The eggs have superficial cleavage and develop generally as do other arthropods.

The young of epimorphic centipedes, as hatched from the egg, have a full complement of segments, but can neither move about nor feed. Their appendages are at right angles to their plump, yolk-filled bodies. Central European *Geophilus* mature after about the ninth molt at the age of two years.

Anamorphic species at hatching cannot feed and have only a few segments; *Scutigera* and *Thereuonema* have four, *Lithobius* has 7 pairs of legs. After the preanal teloblastic zone has produced the remainder of the segments, the animal is still immature and undergoes additional molts before reaching sexual maturity. *Lithobius* probably matures after 3 years.

All chilopod species that have been successfully reared survive the reproductive period and continue molting.

In molting, first the dorsum of the head tears just behind the anterior border of the head. The tear continues along the joint membranes on the sides of the head to the pleura of the maxilliped somite. Anteriorly the antennae, eyes and mouthparts bend ventrally. The centipede now emerges from the slit between these parts and the dorsum of the head. The cast skin is compressed accordion-like into a wad only a small fraction of the body length while the animal emerges.

Preliminary experiments with injection of ecdysone into medium sized *Lithobius* indicate that it may cause molting. A trunk ligature between the first and second walking leg somites prevented or delayed the molt. Decapitation does not suppress molting. These observations suggest that between the head and the second walking leg somite there is a center that promotes molting. Also it is possible to conclude from these experiments that the subepidermal glandula cerebralis, behind the ocelli, is a storage organ for hormones that come from the protocerebrum through axons. These hormones do not cause the molt; however extirpation experiments in *Lithobius* suggest that this gland inhibits molting.

In molting, previously lost appendages are replaced, having been regenerated before the molt but rolled up within the surviving coxa. *Scutigera*, which very readily autotomizes its long legs, can completely regenerate them.

One individual regenerated 10 legs at the same time, and they had their full length. Other regenerations were observed in which the new legs were one-quarter to one-fifth shorter than the autotomized appendage. In *Scutigera* the autotomy takes place between the second and third leg articles (considering the coxa as the first) and as a reflex through the local segmental ganglion. The head ganglia influence only the muscle tonus. Loss of legs is compensated for by change of gait and by bending the body, both under control of nerve centers in the head. Even animals that have lost half their legs can move rapidly.

Habits

Although there are many chilopods in temperate zones, by far the majority of species live in subtropical and tropical areas. During the day they are found under stones, in leaf litter and loose bark. Geophilomorphs are usually deep in the soil to 20 cm or sometimes 40 cm below the surface. The flat body and head are adaptations to these habitats. At night they appear at the surface (geophilomorphs less often) and hunt. Scutigeromorphs, scolopendromorphs and even *Lithobius* may climb several meters up tree trunks. In warm countries scolopendromorphs are found in buildings. *Scutigera* is found in buildings, probably throughout the United States (except Alaska) and in summer can be found outside; it is also found in buildings in warmer parts of Europe. Caves are inhabited by lithobiids and cryptopids. While almost all chilopods avoid water, some geophilomorphs are found on ocean beaches.

Scolioplanes maritimus and *Hydroschendyla submarina* live on rocky coasts in Europe and go into the intertidal areas, where they are covered at high tide. They remain quietly coiled up under stones. In front of each spiracle, and at the mouth and anus, there remains an air bubble, which probably takes up CO_2, releases it into the water, and obtains O_2 from the water. The animals survive as long as 40 hours in ocean water.[*]

Hydroschendyla submarina also lives in the coralline algae areas of the Mediterranean, a 50 m wide band of the tidal zones of rocky coasts, where the lower areas remain flooded. It can stay 12–36 hours submerged in ocean water, *Strigamia maritima* 12–24 hours, the terrestrial *Stigmatogaster subterraneus* only 4–8 hours, although the osmotic pressure of geophilomorph hemolymph is only 45% of that of the ocean.

---

[*] But air is not the only important requirement for survival. *Lithobius* swells after 24 hours in fresh water; geophilomorphs do not, and therefore must have protection against the entrance of water, probably in the nature of the cuticle. In experiments with insects, if their bodies were dipped halfway into water, it could be demonstrated that smoothness and pubescence of the cuticle and its chemical nature produced different menisci. The meniscus is concave when the cuticle is wetted, convex when not.

Water resistance due to the chemical nature of the surface depends on the orientation of the molecules of the thin epicuticle in insects. If the cuticle below the epicuticle is tanned, the OH-groups of the paraffin chains of the epicuticle turn toward the substrate, turning the water repellant CH_3-groups to the outer surface (Holdgate, 1955; Beament, 1961).

In addition to preventing waterlogging in wet soil, the waxy epicuticle must be of importance to soil inhabiting animals in preventing desiccation when there is no water between the soil particles, considering that the water of adhesion of soil capillaries can produce suction of 12–31 atm, which dries plants to the wilting point. Thick hairs, strong club-shaped hairs (Fig. 19–4) and other raised areas of the cuticle hold the body surface away from the drying soil particles and protect it against abrasion of the waxy layers. Eggs of soil animals tend to be protected from soil particles by stalks, covers or thorns (Kühnelt, 1961).

Chilopods, usually geophilomorphs, rarely become accidental human parasites, invading nasal membranes or head sinuses, causing severe headaches. They probably survive long periods in such unusual habitats.

The places where centipedes rest do not show any particular structure, except that scolopendrids make a chamber for themselves. *Scolopendra cingulata,* among others, digs a flat chamber beneath a stone, and also a deep branched burrow system. Within two weeks in captivity, one excavated a flat cavity 10 cm long from which led a tunnel 50 cm long and another 45 cm long. The long tunnel has chamber-like enlargements 2 to 3 cm in diameter and 8 to 12 cm long. The tunnels are always vertical, never horizontal. A *Scolopendra* kept 4 months in a shallow container, 2 cm high and 0.25 m², built only a shallow cavity. When turned it started to dig a vertical burrow immediately. The location of the equilibrium organ is unknown.

In loose soil, *Scolopendra* just pushes its body into the soil, widens the hollow by contraction of longitudinal muscles, making its body short and wide and pulls its hind end in. In hard soils, stones and soil particles are picked up with the maxillipeds and the first 3–4 legs and the centipede pushes them in front or behind and out of the burrow, by stretching and contracting and using legs.

The chambers are probably used for several days. A *Scolopendra cingulata* throughout 4 months left only once in every 8 nights to wander about for 1–2 hours in its 0.5 m² terrarium. It had 4 glass plates 15 × 15 cm to hide under. After moving about it returned 4 times to the previously inhabited cover and 12 times under other plates. (Every evening all entrances below the plates were carefully covered.) The burrows thus may not be permanently inhabited.

There is almost certainly a relationship between the lack of protection against loss of moisture and nocturnal activity and searching for haunts. Adult *Lithobius* dry out in two days in soil of 73% relative humidity. Immatures of the large *Pachymerium* dry out even at 97% relative humidity. Thus the collecting places for *Lithobius* generally have at least 87% relative humidity and in experiments *Lithobius* and *Pachymerium* chose the area of highest humidity. Even inhabitants of arid areas (e.g. *Scolopendra*) do not have any protection against water loss. Their water loss increases proportionately to the lowering of relative humidity and increase of temperature. Their existence in arid areas is made possible by their seeking moist microclimates and limiting themselves to nocturnal activity on the surface.

At the same temperature and humidity *Scolopendra* was observed in an activity cage to be active only at night, even when left completely in darkness for several days (due to the endogenous rhythm). But if in constant darkness the temperature and humidity were changed, the activity was shifted to times of lowest temperatures—in arid areas this is the time of highest relative humidities. Loss of water can be replaced only by drinking dew. Central European species, and presumably North American species, tolerate cold during inactive periods; *Pachymerium* can tolerate −22 to −26°C for weeks.

LOCOMOTION. The gait is very different in families with 15 leg pairs and those with 21 or more leg pairs. The gaits also show interesting adaptations to the habits. The extremes are illustrated by the slow subterranean geophilomorphs with many short legs and the rapid, surface inhabiting *Scutigera*, which may run at speeds to 50 cm/sec (Table 18–1). In all, the coxae are attached laterally with a vertical axis and have a forward and backward swing so that the legs, if they are moderately long, have a large stride. This is in contrast to diplopods whose legs are adapted to digging rather than to rapid movement.

The epimorphic geophilomorphs (Fig. 18–14) and scolopendromorphs (e.g., *Cryptops, Cormocephalus, Geophilus, Stigmatogaster*) having more than 21 pairs of legs run "on stilts" (Figs. 17–6, 18–16a). Because of the large number of legs, some legs are in contact with the ground surface though more legs are in the air. Species with only 21 pairs of legs, however, have enough support along the trunk because here the two legs of each pair are in the opposite phase (Fig. 18–16a). After the first leg searches for a ground contact, all the legs on the same body side step in its track, one after another; obstacles are traversed by legs in forward motion in the air. Entanglement of legs is avoided because in locomotion the coxae are spread apart by stretching of the body. *Cryptops* stretches the body 22%, geophilomorphs 68%, from the resting position. This stretching and contraction of the trunk is made possible by the flexible jointed borders of tergites (except in Lithobiomorpha) and sternites (except in *Scutigera*). Their borders are sclerotized but elastic so that with contraction of the trunk they can bend inward, making possible a strong contraction of the body. Also in the geophilomorphs and Cryptopidae (less developed in other scolopendromorphs) there is

Table 18–1. Maximum speeds in short distances (after Manton). *Lithobius* and *Scutigera* do not use their last legs when running

Species	Number of legs	Body length in mm	Distance per sec in mm	Length of stride in mm	Duration of stride in sec	Relative duration of forward to contact phase	Difference in phase
Cryptops savignyi	20	38	290	12	0.04	7.2:2.7	0.85
Geophilus carpophagus	46	33	10	—	0.38	5.7:4.2	ca. 0.2
Geophilus longicornis	52	39	12	—	0.37	5.7:4.2	—
Lithobius forficatus	14	25	280	21	0.75	6.5:3.4	0.15
Scutigera coleoptrata	14	22	420 to 500	33	0.08	6.3:3.6	0.13

a short concave intercalary sternite or tergite in front of each tergite and sternite, facilitating change of body length.

In geophilomorphs with more than 41 pairs of legs, the two legs of a somite do not usually alternate. Even so there is sufficient stability. Leg movement here is independent of the subesophageal ganglion. Beheaded individuals or parts of the trunk can continue walking by themselves.

The anamorphic lithobiomorph and scutigeromorphs (Fig. 18–15) have a different gait. Their legs are longer than those of epimorphic centipedes, permitting longer steps that can be increased at greater speeds by increasing their angle of movement. This brings about a longer stride but with it the hazard that legs cross and trip. This is avoided by shortening the phase difference to less than 0.5. The legs in contact diverge (Fig. 18–16b). Also the legs increase in length from anterior to posterior, thus each leg steps slightly lateral of the preceding one.

The leg number never exceeds 15 pairs. That this is sufficient to support the body on both sides is made possible by a longer period of contact, and even in the most rapid gait does not lower to half the duration of the forward motion. As legs in contact diverge and alternate on the two sides, the footsteps on each side of the trunk are spaced closer than in *Cryptops* running with equal speed and the animal runs in the manner of a crawling gait (Fig. 18–16b). Although the duration of the step is twice as long as in *Cryptops*, the speed of *Lithobius* is comparable due to its longer legs and larger angle of movement. The long-legged *Scutigera* is even more rapid.

Speed in running is made possible in all chilopods by shortening the duration of the stride and the difference in phase (in epimorphs an apparent approach to the value one), as well as the shortening of the duration of the contact phase (the extreme in *Scolopendra* to one-seventh its walking gait, Fig. 17–6). Only lithobiomorphs and scutigeromorphs can also increase the angle of movement of legs, as do most other arthropods (Fig. 18–16).

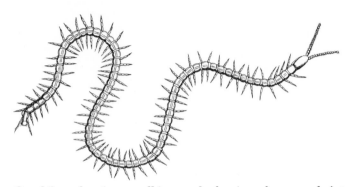

Fig. 18–14. *Geophilus electricus*, walking and showing the spread intersegmental membranes; 3.5–4.5 cm long. (After C. L. Koch.)

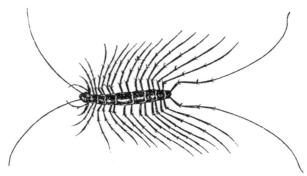

Fig. 18–15. *Scutigera coleoptrata*; tarsi may be one-third of leg length and have many secondary articles (like harvestmen). In contrast to other myriapods which walk on their claws, these walk with many tarsal articles in contact with the substrate. Body 2.4 cm long. (From Leunis.)

With little stimulation soil-dwelling geophilomorphs (and also *Cryptops*) can walk rapidly backwards for considerable distances, an ability of importance in getting about in narrow burrows and absent in most other terrestrial mandibulates. *Lithobius* can back up only a little.

Geophilomorphs (also commonly *Cryptops*) live in the soil, usually much deeper than *Lithobius*. The trunk muscles are used for penetrating the soil (as opposed to the burrowing of diplopods). By contracting the width of the segments, one after another, the hemolymph of the first third of the body is put under considerable pressure, causing the segments to become narrow and elongated. This is made possible by the structure of the segmental borders and intercalary plates (see above). When digging, *Orya*, with 105 pairs of legs, extends the first 11 body segments one after another by contracting the 3 layers of circular and diagonal muscles of the body wall. Since the remaining 94 leg pairs are in contact with the ground at the same time, the anterior part is pushed into the soil. Then, beginning at the head, the first 11 segments are widened by contraction of the longitudinal muscles and relaxing of body wall muscles. At the same time, each pair of legs of the anterior somite anchors itself. The burrow is thus widened and the remaining posterior segments can be pulled in. While pulling in they shorten one after another and push their legs into the soil. Then again the anterior 11 segments are extended by increasing the internal pressure of the anterior, and so on. The trunk behind the 35th leg does not take part in burrowing, but just walks after the other segments in the widened hole. The pressure of a 16 cm long *Orya* on its surroundings has been measured by placing a glass plate on the anterior trunk. Under a glass plate 28 mm long, *Orya* was still able to progress with 160 g weights on top; under a plate 42 mm long, it could progress with 230 g weights. It thus had a hydrostatic pressure of 2.3 g per mm^2. The greatest pressure might be 3.6–4 g per mm^2, considering that only the portion of the anterior legs was covered.

SOCIAL BEHAVIOR. We have observations only on *Scolopendra cingulata,* of which several may be found under a single stone. The observations were made in an artificial environment of tunnels in plaster of Paris in glass. If two animals meet on the surface they will throw their posterior ends against each other and attempt to embrace one another with the last legs. Then, clamped together, they may lie motionless for some time, later to let go and move apart. This happens

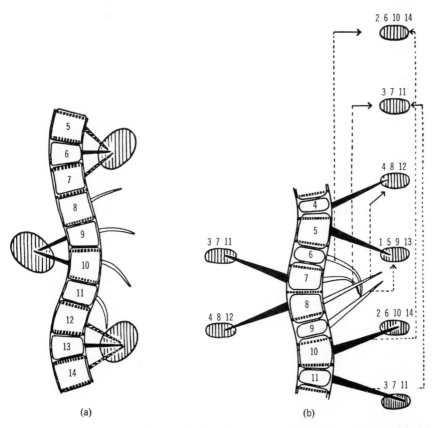

(a)   (b)

Fig. 18–16. Gaits of centipedes, diagrams from films. The legs in contact (black) are separated by a long row of forward moving legs, not in contact (white), forcing the serpentine movement of the animal. The dark (hatched) areas are footprints. The numbers within the tergites are walking leg segments; the dotted lines, borders of sternites, which in *Lithobius* are only partially beneath the tergite borders. (After Manton.) (a) Stilted gait of *Cryptops savignyi* at top speed; because of large phase difference, legs in contact with the ground converge. The legs directed anteriorly (striped) are just put down, those directly posteriorly (striped) are just being lifted; all legs on one side use same footprints. (b) Crawling gait of *Lithobius forficatus* at top speed; as result of low differences of phase the legs in contact with the ground diverge and step in different footprints; but in rapid motion several legs step almost into the same footprint. The numbers indicate which legs, one after another, step into the same footprints. The stippled lines connect the corresponding footprints and show the large stride, much larger than that of *Cryptops.*

immediately if one of the animals is ready to mate and the other pats its posterior, independent of the sex of the animals. If the animals meet in a burrow, one will back up, turn around and then run backwards with parted hind legs, into the other animal. They may then clamp together, or sometimes both animals push each other with open maxillipeds, but usually without biting. This avoids the hazard of decimating the population by many contacts. If strongly irritated, or if the head instead of the tail accidentally is clamped between the other's hind legs, the animal may bite. If the head or anterior end is bitten the wound is lethal.

PROTECTION. Their secluded habitats and ability to escape rapidly (except geophilomorphs) protect centipedes from enemies above ground.

The centipedes with large maxillipeds use them for defense. Lithobiomorphs and especially scolopendromorphs also use their hind legs to pinch. Geophilomorphs produce secretions from repugnatorial glands at their coxae and sternites.

Just below the tip of the maxilliped claw the large ectodermal poison gland opens. The gland is usually within the coxae, rarely elongated, reaching further back into the trunk. In *Chaetechelyne vesuviana*, it extends to the 12th or 18th segment. The glandular cells contain almost exclusively secretions. They are large and radially arranged around the gland lumen, which is lined with chitin. Each opens individually through a pore into the lumen and can be expressed by muscle fibers that lie between the individual cells. The bites of *Lithobius forficatus* and *Scutigera coleoptrata* are poisonous to flies. Even large bluebottle flies are immediately subdued. Only the first three or four bites of *Lithobius* are poisonous; later bites do not kill flies, the poison being rapidly exhausted. The maxillipeds can be used without injecting poison. The bite of the southern European *Scolopendra morsitans* is painful, the pain being strong for 2–3 hours and disappearing only after 2–3 days. Some patients have to be treated in the hospital for swelling at the site of bite, vomiting and fever. American and South Asiatic scolopendrids have painful bites. Usually the pain disappears after an hour. The poison of *Scolopendra* contains hemolytic phospholipase A and serotonin (5-hydroxytryptamine), a pain-producing substance.

Scolopendromorphs and lithobiomorphs can pinch with their spiny hind legs, facilitating defense from the rear in a burrow.

Repugnatorial glands are important to geophilomorphs. The glands are located inside the sternites, and sometimes also in the coxae. There are two kinds of gland cells, which open individually, forming sievelike areas. The gland cells are so lengthened that they extend into the body cavity beyond the hypodermis. Connective tissue holds them together in metameric clumps and striated muscles cause their contraction. If a geophilomorph meets an ant, it will ball up, turn its venter toward the insect and at the same time extrude droplets of liquid, causing the ant to leave.

A number of species, among them *Scolioplanes crassipes, Geophilus carpophagus* and *G. electricus,* produce a luminous secretion from the same glands when disturbed. Chloroform vapors also produce this reaction. The fluid luminates through the sternites while still within the cells. The glands are not in contact with tracheae and there are no bacterial symbionts. From August until October, during the reproductive period, one can see these luminous animals at night from a distance of 3–5 m. The biological significance of the light is not known.

Repugnatorial glands of a different kind have been found in *Lithobius* and *Bothropolys.* There are also individual gland cells found in large numbers on the last four legs, especially on the undersides of the femur, tibia and tarsus. There may be over 500 on the 15th pair of legs. They secrete a viscid substance if the *Lithobius* in a small container meets a wolf spider or ant. *Lithobius* turns its hind end toward the spider or insect and rapidly beats with its hind legs, throwing droplets some distance. They stick to the predator and impede him. If the 15th pair of legs is removed, the 14th does it. Perhaps coxal glands take part in producing this substance. An ant, *Formica rufa,* behaves as if all its legs were tied together. An ant with only two threads, one attaching a posterior leg to the substrate, the other a second leg to the antennae and substrate, needed an hour to free itself. The ant was able to move its own length away from the spot without tearing the threads. A 1 cm long wolf spider with both hind legs glued to the ground stretched the material 7 cm.

SENSES. Being nocturnal and living in dark places, the animals depend mainly on mechanical and chemical senses. That the most important receptors are the antennae has been shown in experiments. In *Scutigera* the legs are also important. The importance of antennae to *Lithobius* can be demonstrated by painting its eyes with lacquer and letting it run in a labyrinth. It will run against the walls when the antennae have been extirpated. For recognition of receptive sexual partners the antennae are necessary. Sponge or cotton touched by the antennae are dealt with differently than pieces of cork or glass of similar size, clearly differentiated by touch. The immediate recognition of prey leading up to the first bite is due mainly to chemical stimuli on contact.

Scolopendra and *Scutigera* bite glass beads, 2–3 mm in size, upon touching them with the antennae only if the beads are covered with extracts from flies, not if moistened with water. *Scolopendra* does not stop for meal worms cooked in alcohol, but immediately attacks cotton balls smeared with the alcohol extracts.

Only for *Lithobius* has chemical excitation at a distance been demonstrated. *Lithobius* was placed in the center of an area 22 cm in diameter, surrounded by a perforated wall and that in turn surrounded by 12 chambers with partitions 5 cm long. In 11 of the chambers, 2 cm beyond the wall, there was flesh-colored wood; in the 12th chamber, a piece of meat. In diffuse light, *Lithobius* went to the perforated wall with meat behind it three times as often as would be expected by chance and at times here tried to bite through the wall. Under different lighting conditions they also preferred this direction.

Differences in soil and air humidity are distinguished by *Lithobius*. Under experimental conditions the animal moves to the most humid places in the container. Finding the moist places is delayed by covering the antennae and tarsi; therefore it is assumed that the appendages carry the receptors. Experiments with *Geophilus* led to similar results. *Pachymerium* moves from an arid atmosphere to water drops 4.5 cm away within 3–11 minutes.

Lithobius responds to temperature differences. At high humidities in a 60 cm long runway with a temperature gradient ranging from 24 to −15°C, *Lithobius* shied away from the area below −2°C and returned to the warmer areas. All of thirty individuals with antennae removed moved into the cold areas where they froze to death. Partial amputation showed that temperature sensitivity is in the proximal half of the antennae.

Running *Lithobius* have been observed to respond to tones by stopping immediately or rapidly increasing speed. When the organs of Tömösvary were covered with nail polish, the number of responses reduced to 16–25% of the previous record, suggesting that these organs may have an auditory function. Though the response was tested for notes from 50–5000 Hz, only in the range of 500–2000 Hz were 73–80% of the tests positive. To avoid transmission through the substrate, the animals were kept in sponge rubber containers, suspended by rubber threads from the ceiling.

Scolopendra, *Lithobius* and *Scutigera* run toward black areas. The eyeless *Lithobius* and *Geophilus* find and rest in very small areas of shade. None of the three species with eyes reacted to moving black models 0.5–3 cm in diameter, on white background illuminated by 1, 10, 100, and 1000 lux at distances of 1–5 cm from the eyes. This corresponds to the observation that prey is taken only after having been touched. Even the compound eyes of *Scutigera* serve mainly to perceive the direction of light and dark.

FEEDING. In captivity, chilopods are predators. Chilopods generally take prey only after touching it with the antennae, *Scutigera* with the legs. After the antennae have been extirpated, *Lithobius* will not take food animals, not even flies sitting nearby, despite optical and auditory stimulation and vibration of substrate or air at 15, 25, 50, 100, 200, 500, 1000 Hz. *Fannia* (Diptera: Anthomyiidae), buzzing and held by forceps, was taken by *Scutigera* only after touching with the antennae. Most chilopods find their food by random movement. *Lithobius* lurks in the terrarium for a long time and attacks animals passing by. Only geophilids have been observed feeding in nature. They had killed earthworms to 5 cm long and soft insect larvae. *Strigamia acuminata* takes julid diplopods, whose hard exoskeleton is opened at the venter of the head. The shore-living *Strigamia maritima* has been observed to feed on *Sphaeroma* isopods, orchestiid amphipods, enchytraeids and even periwinkles (*Littorina*) and barnacles. Several *Strigamia* have been observed to feed on *Balanus balanoides* at the same time, but it could not be determined how they entered the animal.

In the gut of freshly collected *Lithobius* are found remains of spiders, mites, harvestmen, Collembola, Diptera, aphids, centipedes, oligochaete worms, mollusks, and nematodes, but often only detritus. Gut contents of *Lithobius forficatus* and *L. variegatus*, freshly caught in England, showed that they feed on detritus, *L. forficatus* during the whole year, *L. variegatus* during the cold season. The guts of large numbers of individuals did not contain remains of animals. In captivity, adult *Lithobius forficatus* feed on earthworms to 3.6 cm, julids of 2.3 cm, spiders, Diptera, thysanurans to over 0.5 cm. Young animals would take collembolans rejected by adults. *Scolopendra* has been kept on meal worms, *Scutigera* on *Fannia* flies.

Medium sized *Scolopendra* usually catch small or soft-skinned prey. They usually seize it with the maxillipeds and hold it with the distal segments of the second maxillae and some anterior legs. If the prey is heavily sclerotized, they press with the aid of the poison fang against the spines of the maxilliped coxae, which are much larger in *Scolopendra* than shown in Fig. 18–5. Moving the coxae toward the head at a plane parallel to the surface, they push the spines into the prey. Then from both sides the palps of the first maxillae are pressed into the wound, so that the soft tissues form a small cone. By lifting the first maxillae, the food is brought to the preoral area, where the tooth-armed mandibular coxae cut it off. Sometimes in biting with the mandibles the head is lifted and a piece of the food torn loose. *Lithobius* feeds the same way, but has not been observed to use the maxilliped teeth to cut prey open. The pieces bitten off and found in the gut are to 0.5 mm^2. Feeding this way can be done in narrow burrows. The mandibles are hinged below, parallel to the surface, and move in a deep ventral joint membrane groove of the head laterally bordered by a sclerotized wall.

The Scutigeromorpha have much more variable, more lateral and leglike maxillipeds and very sharp mandibles, whose abduction does not depend on the immovable tentorium. In catching a bluebottle fly, *Scutigera coleoptrata* uses head, maxillipeds, seven pairs of legs and body to overcome the prey, which is immediately killed, presumably by the poison. Though the centipede's legs embrace the fly, their distal segments do not lasso the prey as has been described of another species. In addition to the legs, the maxillipeds and the palps of the second maxillae, extending at right angles from the head, help to hold the fly while the mandibles bite a hole and cut the exoskeleton of the head. The first maxillae during this time are held so that their soft median palp surface is parallel to the long axis of the body. They are parted and in closing wipe over the surface of the food while pushing hemolymph, muscle pieces and other particles between the mandibles. Only the hardest part of the exoskeleton remains. If *Scutigera* is disturbed while feeding, it will run off with the prey carried between the maxillipeds.

Geophilomorphs, probably secondarily, have evolved simpler mandibles; their basal parts tend to be fused, and they are inserted directly. Such mandibles cannot move forward and backward and the endite is weakly armed. The tentorium does not take part in its movement.

Strigamia, for example, slits open the intersegmental membranes between two segments by pushing its maxillipeds laterally under the tergites of *Orchestina* (Amphipoda) before pushing in its head and anterior segments. Through the transparent cuticle of the prey it can be seen how the maxillipeds cut up the internal organs, permitting deeper and deeper penetration by the predator. At the same time one can see currents of fat droplets alternately flowing toward the mouth and away, suggesting the expulsion of enzymes. Absence of particles in the guts of 750 dissected animals, and the relatively small mandibles are other evidence that digestion takes place outside the digestive system.

Classification

The chilopod groups all display mixtures of ancestral and derived characters. Probably the exoskeletal structure and the trunk musculature are most useful characters. Thus the Geophilidae and *Cyptops* appear to be primitive, all lithobiomorphs and scutigeromorphs advanced, although some features are specialized. The trunk musculature of *Geophilus* and *Cryptops,* with three adjacent layers, each having many fibers going in the same direction, can perhaps be compared with the body wall of Onychophora and the polychaetes. These layers of muscles are not present in *Lithobius* and *Scutigera;* instead, there are individual muscle bundles. Also there is increased differentiation of longitudinal muscles from the simple *Geophilus* to *Scutigera.* While geophilomorphs have dorsal, pleural and ventral longitudinal muscles, the ventral muscles are weak in *Cryptops,* absent in *Lithobius* and *Scutigera.* Geophilomorphs have the strongest dorsal and ventral muscles attached in tendonous junctions to connective tissue of the muscles of the following somite. Such musculature, moving through the whole body as in the polychaetes, is believed primitive. In other chilopods there are only a few longitudinal muscles running the length of the body and most are attached to the exoskeleton.

In addition the homonomy of the many trunk segments and their musculature appears to be a primitive feature. In *Cryptops,* sclerites and muscles dorsal of the coxae show indications of the combination of one somite with and one without spiracles, a character very pronounced in *Lithobius* and *Scutigera.* In the lithobiomorphs and scutigeromorphs the dorsal homologous longitudinal muscles are repeated in every other somite and the tergites alternate in shape (Figs. 18–1, 18–2). Also the amount of connective tissue of the internal skeleton, on which muscles insert, as well as the number of muscles that go from the trunk into the legs, is least in geophilomorphs, greatest in scutigeromorphs. While the structure in *Scutigera* can conceivably be derived from that of the geophilomorphs, the structure of the geophilomorphs cannot apparently be derived from the lithobiomorphs or scutigeromorphs. The geophilomorphs thus seem the more primitive group.

SUPERORDER EPIMORPHA

The Epimorpha include two orders: the Geophilomorpha and the Scolopendromorpha. In both the young are born with the adult somite number. In all known species the mother broods the eggs and young. All lack organs of Tömösvary, and have a relatively primitive musculature. Other characters in common are that the maxilliped coxosternites are completely fused in the midline. Specializations are the extreme flattening in these two groups of head and mouthparts, the anastomosing tracheae, and the absence of maxillary nephridia in the adult.

In common with the anamorph Lithobiomorpha, both orders have spiracles on the sides of the trunk that open into tube tracheae. The tracheae in turn run as tracheoles to the various organs. Also in common with the Lithobiomorpha the Epimorpha have the maxillipeds flat against the underside of the head, their coxae fused and some of their telopodite articles, except for the proximal and distal ones, much shortened (Fig. 18-5).

Order Geophilomorpha

Included in the order are about 1000 described species.

Geophilomorphs lack eyes and have a thread-like body form (Fig. 18-14). The segment number is usually variable, even within species; it is often very large. The tergites and sternites of leg-bearing segments are alike. There are 31 to more than 181 pairs of short legs, the coxae of which have only a sickle-shaped sclerite. The many-legged species have most legs and leg articles similar, short and conical. The weak mandibles usually lack strong teeth. The maxillae are more diverse among the geophilomorph families than in other orders. Most sternites have areas of gland pores. Spiracles are found on all leg-bearing segments except the first and the last. Most species are slow moving and can burrow. Despite their primitive appearance, they are probably secondarily specialized for digging.

Himantariidae. The mandibles have a dentate lamella and several pectinate lamellae. The labrum is fused to form one piece. The antennae are short and flattened, making them appear thick at their base. *Himantarium gabrielis,* to 20 cm long, with more than 171 leg pairs, is palaearctic. *Stigmatogaster subterraneus,* 7–8 cm long, has 87–109 leg pairs. *Stenophilus* is nearctic; *Nothobius* is found in California.

Schendylidae. Mandibles have one row of simple teeth (pectinate lamella) and one dentate lamella. They are temperate and tropical. *Hydroschendyla submarina* is found in the intertidal areas chiefly of the Mediterranean. *Schendyla nemorensis* is 1.4–2.8 cm long, with 39 to 43 pairs of legs. *Nannophilus* and *Schendylurus* are neotropical. There are many New World genera.

Oryidae. The mandibles have several pectinate lamellae, no dentate lamella. The labrum is one piece. The coxae of the first maxillae are fused. *Orya barbarica,* to 22 cm long, is palaearctic; *Titanophilus maximus,* to 20 cm long, has 169 pairs of legs. *Orphnaeus* is pantropical, *Notiphilides,* neotropical.

Mecistocephalidae. As in the Oryidae, the mandibles have several pectinate lamellae, no dentate lamella. The labrum is tripartite and fused. The coxae of the first maxillae usually have a median suture. *Mecistocephalus* is pantropical, *Tygarrup* Asian and neotropical, *Arrup* Asian and nearctic.

Neogeophilidae. The mandible margin has one row of teeth (pectinate lamella). The coxae of the first maxillae are separated. The family is strictly neotropical in distribution. Some included genera are *Neogeophilus, Evallogeophilus* and *Cryptostrigla.*

Gonibregmatidae. The mandible margin has one row of teeth (pectinate lamella); the coxae of the first maxillae are fused. The labrum in some is a single piece. The coxae of the last pair of legs in some extend forward on the sides. *Gonibregmatus* occurs only on Southern Pacific islands.

Sogonidae. The mandible margin has one row of teeth (pectinate lamella). The coxae of the first maxillae are fused. The labrum is thought to be a single piece. The coxae of the last legs are not enlarged. The known genera are nearctic and neotropical.

Geophilidae. The mandible margin has a single row of small, simple teeth (pectinate lamella). The coxae of the first maxillae are often fused. The labrum consists of three pieces, the middle one smaller than the lateral parts. *Necrophloeophagus longicornis* (=*Geophilus longicornus*), of Europe, is 2–4 cm long with 49–57 leg pairs. It matures after 9 molts, in about 2 years, and produces 12–73 eggs. For molting it withdraws to a depth of 40 cm and makes a chamber. *Geophilus electricus,* 3.5–4.5 cm long, has at least 65 leg pairs; *G. carpophagus* of Europe, over 3 cm long, has 47 to 61 pairs. *Geophilus proximus* is found in Europe and North America. The North American *G. mordax* is bright red.

The European *Pachymerium ferrugineum,* 2–3.5 cm long with 41 to 47 leg pairs, produces 20–55 eggs, which are guarded by the mother for 40–50 days, until the young have sternites, glands, and tracheae. The eggs need a relative humidity of 100%. The largest individuals are probably several years old. While originally European, it is now widely distributed in North Africa, Asia, Japan, Hawaii and North America.

Dignathodontidae. This family has many of the characters of Geophilidae. The labrum is divided into a midpiece larger than either side piece, the latter may be rudimentary. (In Geophilidae the midpiece is smaller than the side piece.) The head is narrow anteriorly and noticeably small. *Strigamia acuminata,* to 3.4 cm long and with 39 or 41 leg pairs, is European. *Strigamia maritima,* which inhabits European tidal zones, is to 3.5 cm long. *Chaetechelyne vesuviana,* of Mediterranean region to British Isles, has recently been introduced into North America.

Soniphilidae. Has one row of teeth (pectinate lamella) on the margins of the mandibles. The coxae of the first maxillae are fused. The labrum has the median piece partly fused to the laterals. The known genera occur in the New World. *Soniphilus* and *Poaphilus* are included.

Order Scolopendromorpha

The approximately 550 described species include the largest centipedes.

Scolopendromorpha often have eyes. Either they have 25 segments with 21 pairs of legs or, rarely, 27 segments with 23 pairs of walking legs (Fig. 18-12). The exoskeleton is ring-shaped and the leg articles differ from each other. Spiracle distribution is similar to that of Lithobiomorpha. There are no grouped sternal glands.

Cryptopidae. Eyes are lacking. The sternites often have a single median groove and transverse grooves. *Cryptops hortensis,* to 3 cm long, from Europe, has become established in northeastern United States and Utah. Another species is *C. savignyi (=C. anomalans).* The North American *Theatops* is to 4.8 cm long; *Plutonium,* to 14 cm long. *Scolopocryptops* is North American, *Newportia* tropical American, and *Kethops* western North American.

Scolopendridae.° There are usually 4 ocelli on each side of head. Sternites in some forms have longitudinal grooves. *Scolopendra*° *cingulata* (Fig. 19-12), 6–17 cm long, of Mediterranean countries, is dark brown, rarely greenish, and is found under stones and logs. To deposit her eggs, numbering 15–30, the female crawls 3–8 cm deep into the soil. The mother defends her brood by pinching with the last legs and biting with the maxillipeds. Pantropical S. *morsitans,* up to 12 cm in length, is yellow-brown, olive or yellow with green transverse stripes. *Scolopendra gigantea* reaches a length of 26.5 cm in Brazil. *Scolopendra clavipes* is up to 6 cm long. *Scolopendra heros* with black head and posterior segments, up to 15 cm long, is found in the North American southwest; S. *viridis,* from southern United States to Brazil. *Hemiscolopendra (=Cormocephalus)* is another genus. *Cupipes* is up to 5 cm long. *Rhysida atra,* up to 6.5 cm long and deep blue, blue-green, dark green or violet with yellow legs, is neotropical in distribution. *Otostigmus* is tropical.

Craterostigmidae.† This family, which includes only one species, has six of its tergites elongated and divided by a joint membrane into a short anterior and long posterior plate, a modification of the structure that gives the trunk great flexibility. The female guards her eggs by twisting herself around them, impossible for a stiff *Lithobius.* The long segments permit a large difference in phase (0.75). The ratio of forward and backward motion duration is 5.5:4.5. Strongly illuminated, the animal begins to run, but cannot run long because its legs cross, forcing a serpentine motion. *Craterostigmus tasmanianus,* 4.6 cm long, occurs only in Tasmania and New Zealand. It is believed to feed on termites and seems somewhat specialized, having only 15 pairs of walking legs. It burrows, as do some geophilomorphs, in moist rotten wood.

SUPERORDER ANAMORPHA

This group includes the Lithobiomorpha and Scutigeromorpha, which have an anamorphic development, hatching with fewer than the adult number of segments and legs. The adult finally has 18 trunk segments and 15 pairs of legs. The mother does not take care of eggs or young. Organs of Tömösvary are present. The head is less flattened than in the Epimorpha.

Order Lithobiomorpha

This order includes about 1100 described species.

Lithobiomorph centipedes have spiracles on the sides of the trunk but only on

---

° The name Scolopendridae is on the *Official List of Family Group Names in Zoology,* Scolopendra on the *Official List of Generic Names in Zoology.*

† The placement of *Craterostigmus* in Epimorpha and Scolopendromorpha by S. M. Manton is very controversial. Evidence that they actually belong to the Anamorpha and closer to the Lithobiomorpha is abundant, e.g., anamorphic development, construction of the maxillipeds, and (according to R. E. Crabill, in letter) the heretofore overlooked organs of Tömösvary, which are always present in the Anamorpha but never in the Epimorpha.

segments with long tergites, not on every segment (Fig. 18-1). The tracheae do not anastomose. The maxilliped coxa is divided by a deep groove (Fig. 18-5), possibly a primitive feature. Maxillary nephridia are present in the adult. The female gonopods are leg-like (Fig. 18-13). Most short and long tergites alternate, the long tergites as in *Scutigera* are trunk segments 2, 4, 6, 8, 9, 11, 13 and 15, if one considers the first to be the maxilliped segment (Fig. 18-1). The trunk musculature is more differentiated; from the trunk there are 18 muscles into each leg, of which 15 go to the coxa. The connective tissue endoskeleton is well developed.

Lithobiidae.[*] There is a variable number of spurs present on tibiae and other leg articles. The coxal pores are in a single row. Female gonopods are usually armed with a serrate claw. *Lithobius*[*] *forficatus* (Fig. 18-1), to 3.2 cm long, brown, is found under stones and bark and is holarctic. All segments and leg pairs appear in the course of about 5 molts, but it takes another 5 before the reproductive organs mature at the age of 3 years. Most likely the animals live to be at least 6 years old. Smaller species may have fewer molts. Other genera are *Nampabius, Sonibius, Garibius, Nadabius, Neolithobius, Tidabius* and *Paitobius.*

Henicopidae. In most there is a distal spinous process outside on the tibiae of most legs, usually absent from the most posterior (legs 13, 14). In contrast to Lithobiidae, there are no spurs on the legs. *Lamyctes fulvicornis,* 0.7 to 1.1 cm long, is thought to be parthenogenetic in Europe; on the Canary Islands and the Azores there are males. Some other genera are *Zygethobius, Anopsobius* and *Paralamyctes.*

Cermatobiidae. The ocelli are distant from the head margin. There are no coxal gland openings through pores. The legs are without spurs. *Cermatobius* is found in India.

Watobiidae. The members of this family have a stout spur on the distal end of the tibiae of the first 12 legs but otherwise lack spurs completely. *Watobius* is found in North America.

Ethopolyidae. There is a variable number of spurs on tibiae and othe leg articles. The coxal pores are in several rows. *Eupolybothrus fasciatus* (*Polybothrus* of authors) to 4.5 cm long is the largest Central European centipede. The commonest genus in North America is *Bothropolys.*

Gosibiidae. There is a variable number of spurs on the tibiae and other leg articles. The coxal pores are in a single row. Males have the penultimate and usually last pairs of legs strongly modified. Female gonopod with a large unidentate claw. *Arenobius* is found in North America.

Order Scutigeromorpha

There are about 130 described species of Scutigeromorpha.

The Scutigeromorpha have large compound eyes. The respiratory system consists of tracheal lungs and 7 median spiracles at the posterior borders of the long tergites (Fig. 18-11). While these are specializations, there are a number of primitive features: the spherical head, the leg-like second maxilla and maxillipeds (Fig. 18-3). These leg-like maxillae, however, are longer than those of other groups and the tendons are more differentiated. The adult retains 2 pairs of fused maxillary nephridia.

---

[*] The name Lithobiidae is on the *Official List of Family Group Names in Zoology, Lithobius* on the *Official List of Generic Names in Zoology.*

The tarsi of the 15 pairs of long walking legs are divided into numerous pseudo-articles, sometimes more than 40. The dorsum consists of short tergites and long ones (segments 2, 4, 6, 8, 9, 11, 13 and 15). The 8th and 9th are fused. The trunk musculature consists of bundles. The internal connective tissue skeleton is strongly developed. Scutigeromorphs are very fast, insect-catching chilopods. There is only one family.

Scutigeridae. Scutigera coleoptrata, to 2.6 cm long, is generally absent from cold regions, though it winters in houses and in summer is found outside running about at dusk (in Wisconsin). The female of *S. mohamedanica* deposits individual eggs, one each day until she has laid 35, but does not guard them. The young at hatching are only 2 mm long, and have only 4 pairs of legs for about 18 days. After the 6th molt, about 58 days after hatching, all 15 leg pairs are present and the animal is 9 mm long. The animal becomes sexually mature after further molts. In captivity they live more than 1¼ years. Some other tropical genera are *Thereuonema, Thereuopoda.*

References

Applegarth, A. G. 1952. Anatomy of the cephalic region of a centipede, *Pseudolithobius. Microentomology* 17:127–171.

Attems, G. 1926. Chilopoda *in* Kükenthal, *Handbuch der Zoologie,* DeGruyter, Berlin, 4:239–402.

———— 1929. Geophilomorpha *in* Schulze and Kükenthal, *Das Tierreich,* DeGruyter, Berlin, 52:1–388.

———— 1930. Scolopendromorpha. *Ibid.* 54:1–308.

Auerbach, S. I. 1949. Ecological study of forest centipedes. *Amer. Midland Natur.* 42:220–227.

———— 1951. Centipedes of the Chicago area. *Ecol. Monogr.* 21:97–124.

Babu, K. S. 1964. Through-conducting systems in the ventral nerve cord in centipedes. *Z. Vergl. Physiol.* 49:114–119.

Bauer, K. 1955. Sinnesökologische Untersuchungen an *Lithobius forficatus. Zool. Jahrb. Abt. Allg. Zool.* 65:267–300.

Beament, J. W. L. 1961. Water relations of insect cuticle. *Biol. Rev.* 36:281–320.

Bennet, D. and Manton, S. 1963. Arthropod segmental organs and Malpighian tubules with particular reference to their function in chilopoda. *Ann. Mag. Natur. Hist.* (13)5:545–556.

Binyon, J. and Lewis, J. 1963. Physiological adaptations of two species of centipedes (Geophilomorpha) to life on shore. *J. Marine Biol. Ass.* 43:49–55.

Blower, G. 1951. Study of the chilopod and diplopod cuticle. *Quart. J. Microscop. Sci.* 92:141–161.

Blower, J. G. 1957. Feeding habits of a marine centipede. *Nature* 180:560.

Brocher, F. 1930. La ponte et les première stades du *Lithobius forficatus. Rev. Suisse Zool.* 37:375–383.

Brölemann, H. W. 1932. Chilopodes. *Faune de France* 25:1–405.

Cloudsley-Thompson, J. L. 1948. *Hydroschendyla submarina* with a historical review of the marine Myriapoda. *The Naturalist,* London 827:149–152.

———— 1950. Epicuticle of arthropods. *Nature* 165:692–693.

———— 1956. Studies in diurnal rhythms of centipedes, scorpions and beetles. *Ann. Mag. Natur. Hist.* (12)9:305–329.

———— 1958. *Spiders, Scorpions, Centipedes* and *Mites*. Pergamon Press, London.

Damaschun, G. and Füller, H. 1965. Chitintextur und Cuticula von Chilopoden, *Zool. Jahrb. Abt. Physiol.* 71:415–428.

Dawydoff, C. 1956. L'embryogénèse des Myriapodes Scolopendromorphes et Géophilomorphes indochinois. *Compte Rend. Acad. Sci. Paris* 242:2265–2267.

———— 1957. Mésoderme larvaire et postlarvaire chez les Myriapodes. *Ibid.* 244:1432–1434.

Demange, J. H. 1956. Biologie, en captivité, de *Lithobius piceus. Bull. Mus. Nat. Hist. Natur. Paris* (2)28:388–393.

———— 1967. Segmentation du tronc des chilopodes et des diplopodes chilognathes. *Mem. Mus. Nat. d'Hist. Natur. Paris* 44:1–188.

Dobroruka, L. J. 1962. *Die Hundertfüssler*. Neue Brehm Bücherei 285. Ziemsen Verl., Wittenberg-Lutherstadt.

Dubuisson, M. 1928. La ventilation trachéene chez les Chilopodes et sur la circulation sanguine chez les Scutigères. *Arch. Zool. Expér. Gén.* 67:49–63.

Eason, E. H. 1964. *Centipedes of the British Isles*. Warne and Co., London.

Fahlander, K. 1938. Anatomie und systematische Einteilung der Chilopoden. *Zool. Bidr. Uppsala* 17:1–148.

Füller, H. 1960. Bau der Stigmen bei Chilopoden. *Zool. Jahrb. Abt. Anat.* 78:129–144.

———— 1960. Chiasmen des Tracheensystems der Geophilomorphen. *Zool. Anz.* 165:289–297.

———— 1962. Helikoidstruktur der quergestreiften Muskeln bei Chilopoden. *Naturwissenschaften* 49:5.

———— 1963. Histologische, polarisationsoptische und histochemische Untersuchungen über das Innenskelett der Chilopoden. *Z. Wiss. Zool.* 168:184–207.

———— 1963. Skelettmuskelsystem der Chilopoden. *Abhandl. Deutschen Akad. Wiss Berlin, Klasse Chem. Geol. Biol.* 1962(3):1–98.

———— 1964. Struktur und Chemismus der Neurolamelle bei Chilopoden. *Z. Wiss. Zool.* 169:203–215.

———— 1965. Anfärbung von Chitin mit Thiazinrot, ein Chitinnachweis. *Zool. Anz.* 174:125–131.

———— 1965. Chitintextur der Chilopoden. *Ibid.* 175:173–181.

———— 1966. Elektronenmikroskopische Untersuchungen der Malpighischen Gefässe von *Lithobius. Z. Wiss. Zool.* 173:191–217.

Gabe, M. 1952. L'emplacement et les connexions des cellules neurosécrétrices dans les ganglions cérébroides de quelques Chilopodes. *Compte Rend. Acad. Sci. Paris* 235:1430–1432.

Görner, P. 1959. Optische Orientierungsreaktionen bei Chilopoden. *Z. Vergl. Physiol.* 42:1–5.

Hanström, B. 1934. Bemerkungen über das Komplex-Auge der Scutigeren. *Lunds Univ. Arsskr.* N. F. Avd. 2, 30, Nr. 6.

Holdgate, M. W. 1955. Wetting of insect cuticles by water. *J. Exp. Biol.* 32:591–617.

Holst, E. von. 1934. Das Laufen der Hundertfüszler. *Zool. Jahrb. Abt. Allg. Zool.* 54(2):157–179.

Hörberg, T. 1931. Der komparative Bau des Gehirns von *Scutigera coleoptrata. Acta Univ. Lund* (N.F.) 27(19):1–24.

Jangi, B. S. 1957. The reproductive system in the female centipede *Scolopendra morsitans. Ann. Mag. Natur. Hist.* (12)10:232–240.

Joly, R. 1961. Déclenchement expérimental de la mue chez *Lithobius. Compte Rend. Acad. Sci. Paris* 252:1673–1675.

———— 1964. Action de l'ecdysone sur le cycle de mue de *Lithobius. Ibid.* 158:584–550.

Kaiser, E. and Michl, H. 1958. *Die Biochemie der tierischen Gifte.* F. Deuticke, Wien.

Klingel, H. 1956. Indirekte Spermatophorenübertragung bei Chilopoden beobachtet bei *Scutigera coleoptrata. Naturwissenschaften* 43:311.

——— 1957. Indirekte Spermatophorenübertragung bei *Scolopendra cingulata. Ibid.* 44:338.

——— 1958. Indirekte Spermatophorenübertragung bei Geophiliden. *Ibid.* 46:632–633.

——— 1960. Vergleichende Verhaltensbiologie der Chilopoden *Scutigera coleoptrata* und *Scolopendra cingulata. Z. Tierpsych.* 17:11–30.

——— 1960. Die Paarung des *Lithobius forficatus. Verh. Deutschen Zool. Ges.* 23:326–332.

Lawrence, R. F. 1947. The post-embryonic development of the Natal forest centipede, *Cormocephalus multispinus. Ann. Natal Mus.* 11:139–156.

——— 1953. *The Biology of Cryptic Fauna of Forests.* A. Balkema, Cape Town.

Lewis, J. G. E. 1961. Life history and ecology of the littoral centipede *Strigamia maritima. Proc. Zool. Soc. London* 137:221–248.

——— 1965. Food and reproductive cycles of the centipede *Lithobius variegatus* and *L. forficatus. Ibid.* 144:269–283.

Lissmann, H. W. 1935. Körperhaltung und Bewegungsform eines Myriopoden im Zusammenhang mit seiner Autotomie. *Z. Vergl. Physiol.* 21:751–766.

Lorenzo, M. A. 1960. Cephalic nervous system of the centipede *Arenophilus* (Geophilidae). *Smithsonian Misc. Coll.* 140(4):1–43.

Manton, S. M. 1952. Locomotion of the Chilopoda and Pauropoda. *J. Linnean Soc. Zool.* 42:93–167.

——— 1958. Diplopoda and Chilopoda and limb structure of Diplopoda. *Ibid.* 43:487–556.

——— 1958. Habits of life and evolution of body design in Arthropoda. *Ibid.* 44:58–72.

——— 1964. Mandibular mechanisms and the evolution of arthropods. *Philos. Trans. Roy. Soc. London* (B)247:1–183.

——— 1965. Functional requirements and body design in Chilopoda. *J. Linnean Soc. Zool.* 46:251–501.

Meske, C. 1960. Schallreaktionen von *Lithobius forficatus. Z. Vergl. Physiol.* 43:526–530.

——— 1961. Studies on the sense physiology of Diplopoda and Chilopoda. *Ibid.* 45:61–77.

Palm, N. B. 1954. Elimination of injected vital dyes from the blood in Myriapods. *Ark. Zool.* 6:219–246.

Palmén, E. and Rantala, M. 1954. Life history and ecology of *Pachymerium ferrugineum* (Chilopoda, Geophilidae). *Ann. Zool. Soc. Zool. Bot. Fennicae Vanamo* 16:1–44.

Pflugfelder, O. 1933. Bau der Schläfenorgane der Myriapoden. *Z. Wiss. Zool.* 143:127–155.

Prunesco, C. 1964. Anatomie microscopique du système génital mâle des Lithobiides. *Rev. Roumaine Biol. Sér. Zool.* 9:101–107.

——— 1965. Abatomique et anatomo-microscopique du système génital femelle de Lithobiomorpha. *Ibid.* 10:11–16.

——— 1965. L'evolution des Chilopodes. *Ibid.* 10:89–102.

——— 1965. Système génital femelle du *Cryptops* (Scolopendromorpha). *Ibid.* 10:231–235.

Remington, C. L. 1950. The bite and habits of *Scolopendra subspinipes* in the Philippine Islands. *Amer. J. Trop. Med.* 30:453–455.

Rilling, G. 1960. Anatomie des braunen Steinläufers *Lithobius forficatus* (Chilopoda). Skelettmuskelsystem, peripheres Nervensystem und Sinnesorgane des Rumpfes. *Zool. Jahrb. Abt. Anat.* 78:39–128.

——— 1968. *Lithobius forficatus* in Czihak, G. ed. *Grosses Zoologisches Praktikum,* Fischer, Stuttgart, Heft 13b.

Scharmer, J. 1934 (1935). Die Bedeutung der Rechts-Links-Struktur und die Orientierung bei *Lithobius forficatus. Zool. Jahrb. Abt. Physiol.* 54:459–506.

Scheffel, H. 1961. Neurosekretion bei *Lithobius forficatus*. *Zool. Jahrb. Abt. Anat.* 79:529–556.

———— 1963. Häutungsphysiologie der Chilopoden. *Zool. Jahrb. Abt. Physiol.* 70:184–290.

———— 1965. Einfluss von Dekapitation und Schnürung auf die Häutung und die Anamorphose von *Lithobius*. *Ibid.* 71:359–370.

———— 1965. Larvenhäutungen bei *Lithobius*. *Zool. Anz.* 174:173–178.

Schubart, O. 1960. Die Zahl der in 200 Jahren zoologischer Forschung (1758–1957) beschriebenen Myriapoden-Arten. *Zool. Anz.* 165:84–89.

Seifert, G. 1967. Der Pharynxapparat von *Scutigera*. *Z. Morphol. Ökol.* 58:347–354.

Simon, H. R. 1960. Ernährungsbiologie von *Lithobius forficatus*. *Zool. Anz.* 164:19–26.

Snodgrass, R. E. 1952. *A Textbook of Arthropod Anatomy.* Comstock Publ. Assoc., Ithaca.

Sukla, G. 1963. Studies on *Scolopendra morsitans,* external features and skeleton. *Zool. Anz.* 170:131–149.

Verhoeff, K. W. 1902–1925. Chilopoda *in* Bronn's *Klassen und Ordnungen des Tierreichs,* Akad. Verlagsges., Leipzig, 5(2)1:1–725.

———— 1937. Biologie von *Scutigera coleoptrata* und über die jüngeren Larvenstadien. *Z. Wiss. Zool.* 150:262–282.

———— 1938. Die europäische Spinnen-Assel *Scutigera*. *Natur Volk* 68:442–448.

———— 1941. Der geographische Charaketer der Chilo- und Diplopodenfauna italienischer Mittelmeerinseln. *Z. Morphol. Ökol.* 37:83–104.

Weil, E. 1958. Biologie der einheimischen Geophiliden. *Z. Angew. Entomol.* 42:173–209.

Welsh, J. H. and C. S. Batty. 1963. 5-Hydroxytryptamine content of arthropod venoms. *Toxicon* 1:165–174.

19.

Class Diplopoda, Millipedes

About 7500 species of millipedes are known. The largest is the African spiro-streptid, *Graphidostreptus gigas,* to 28 cm long and 2 cm in diameter.

Millipedes have only two pairs of mouthparts. There are two pairs of legs on each body ring, except for the anterior four, and one or several at the posterior end. (Body rings 2, 3, and 4 have one pair of legs each.) The gonopores are anterior in the third trunk segment.

Millipedes are dignath, their mouthparts consisting only of mandibles and the first pair of maxillae. The maxillae form a kind of labium, the gnathochilarium (Fig. 19–8). The development of the diplopods and of the dignath pauropod, *Pauropus silvestris,* indicates that only the metameres bearing the mandible and the maxillae take part in the head formation (Fig. 19–1). The following segment, which carries the second maxillae of the trignath arthropods, becomes the first trunk segment, called the collum segment (Fig. 19–5). Therefore, the subeso-phageal ganglion, which innervates the mouthparts, contains the nerve cell bodies of only two segments.

Among the millipedes four different body shapes are found. Usually they are long with the trunk worm-like and cylindrical (juloid, Fig. 19–5), or ribbon-like with dorsolateral keels on the posterior of each diplosegment (polydesmoid, Fig. 19–2). Extremely flattened species are found among the Colobognatha. Besides these more common forms there are short, wide, armored forms (glomeroid, Figs. 19–3, 19–14) resembling woodlice but unlike woodlice they always have more than 7 pairs of walking legs. Most diplopods have few simple body setae or none and have the trunk strongly armored. The Pselaphognatha, however, have the body soft with numerous flattened, serrated, elaborate setae (Fig. 19–4).

Anatomy

The trunk consists of numerous rings, each consisting of two fused metameres (Fig. 19–5). Except for the first four and a variable number of posterior rings,

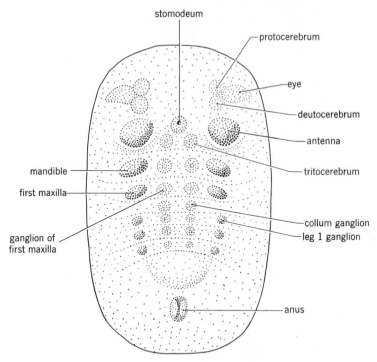

Fig. 19–1.   Germ disc of the embryo of a diplopod, *Dolistenus*; 0.6 mm long. (After Silvestri.)

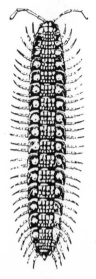

Fig. 19–2.   *Polydesmus angustus*; 2 cm long. (After Humbert from Brölemann.)

each has two pairs of legs and spiracles, internally two pairs of ganglia, ostia, and lateral heart arteries. The formation of these diplosegments, found in no other arthropod group, seems at first enigmatic. The key to the puzzle is in the movement of the diplopods, most of which live within the soil or in decaying wood, for fusion of segments gives advantages in penetrating soil or maneuvering in narrow crevices (see Locomotion).

The 2nd, 3rd, and 4th trunk rings differ from all the others in bearing only a **single pair of** legs and a single pair of spiracles (Fig. 19–5). The tergite of the first becomes the collum, and lacks spiracles or legs. The venter of these four rings is short, of advantage when the animal coils up, for the head and first rings form the innermost part of the coil. The four first rings also have only one pair of ganglia, one pair of ostia and one pair of lateral heart arteries. Recent embryological studies indicate that they are single metameres.

The diplosegments have the two tergites fused; sternites may be either separate or fused and are moveable. Pleurites are distinct sclerites only in the Pselaphognatha, Colobognatha, and among the Pentazonia (Fig. 19–6). In others they have been completely incorporated into the tergite to form a uniform exoskeletal sclerite that makes three-quarters of a ring (Figs. 19–5, 19–7).

On each diplotergite (except of the Pselaphognatha) two separate parts can be recognized, the anterior conical prozonite and the posterior cylindrical metazonite (Fig. 19–5). Whether the border between the two parts represents the area of fusion is not known.

The anterior part of the prozonite corresponds to the ball of a ball and socket joint, cupped as it is within the cavity of the previous metazonite (Fig. 19–5). The long transversely folded joint membranes facilitate strong, ventrally directed

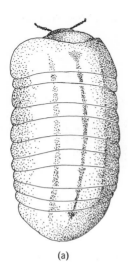

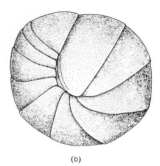

(a)   (b)

Fig. 19–3. *Glomeris conspersa:* **(a) 2 cm long (after Brölemann); (b) rolled up, diameter 6 mm (after Gruner).**

bending of the successive rings, important in coiling up, and also permitting rotation around the longitudinal axis. Burrowing species can turn one body part 180° from the rest of the trunk.

The sclerites around the anus consist of a telson, formed in the Chilognatha of three sclerites, two lateral paraprocts and one ventral hypoproct (Fig. 19–5). Between the last diplosomite bearing legs and the telson, the chilognaths usually have several rings without legs; ventrally these contain the growth area (see Development).

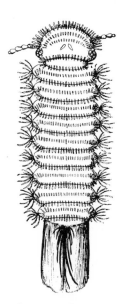

Fig. 19–4. *Polyxenus lagurus;* 3 mm long. (After Schubart.)

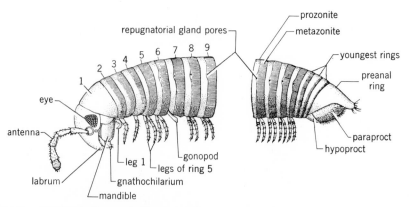

Fig. 19–5. *Schizophyllum sabulosum,* male, anterior and posterior body regions, lateral view; 1 to 4 are single segments, the others diplosegments; 1 is the collum segment, 7, the gonopod ring. Diameter of trunk rings, 3 mm. (After Ivanov.)

The head is usually large, an exception being the small conical head of colobognaths. The head capsule, which bears groups of ocelli and antennae (Fig. 19–8a), forms the dorsum and anterior; its anterior border is usually a dentate labrum (Figs. 19–8c, 19–10). Covering the venter of the head is the gnathochilarium, its anterior edge against the labrum (Figs. 19–8a, 19–8b). The basal articles of the mandibles are inserted on the venter of the sides, and have joint membranes on the lateral walls of the head capsule and also toward the gnathochilarium. The jointed endite of the mandible lies in a large preoral cavity bordered anteriorly by the labrum and epistome and posteriorly by the anterior of the gnathochilarium.

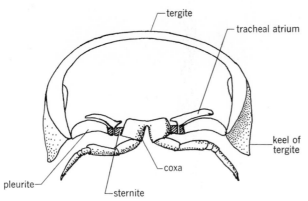

Fig. 19–6.   Cross section of the trunk of *Glomeris*; 7 mm wide. (Modified after Manton.)

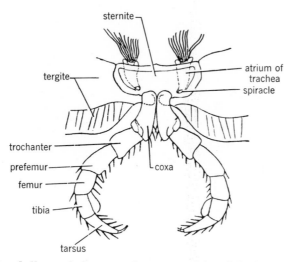

Fig. 19–7.   *Schizophyllum sabulosum*, male, venter of fourth body ring; the leg articles are not homologous to similarly named structures in other arthropods; leg length 2 mm. (After Ivanov.)

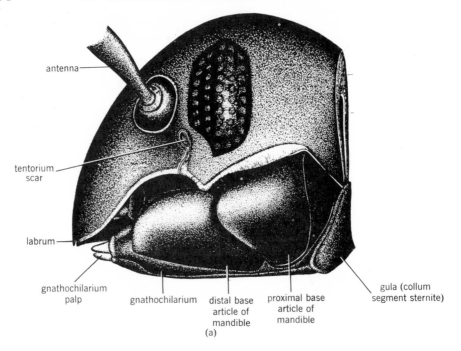

antenna

tentorium
scar

labrum

gnathochilarium
palp

gnathochilarium

distal base
article of
mandible

proximal base
article of
mandible

gula (collum
segment sternite)

(a)

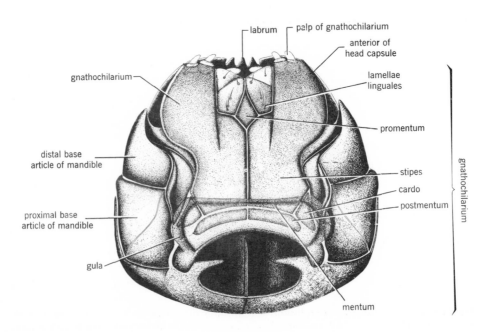

labrum

palp of gnathochilarium

anterior of
head capsule

gnathochilarium

lamellae
linguales

promentum

distal base
article of mandible

stipes

cardo

postmentum

proximal base
article of mandible

gnathochilarium

gula

mentum

(b)

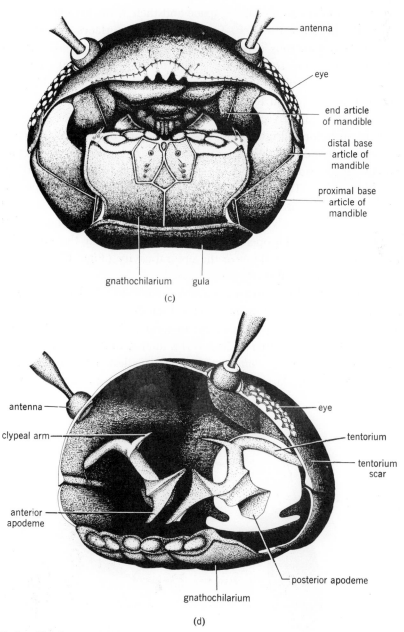

(c)

(d)

Fig. 19–8. Head of *Diploiulus caeruleocinctus*; 1.8 mm long. (The terms cardo, stipes, mentum, submentum, promentum are used by specialists of the group; these structures are not homologous to similarly named structures in insects.) (From Fechter.) (a) Lateral view; (b) ventral view; (c) anterior view, gnathochilarium bent back and open preoral cavity; behind labium the long transverse teeth of the mandibles can be seen; above the anterior border of the gnathochilarium, two dentate lamellae of its anterior surface; (d) endoskeleton of head capsule in anteriolateral view; clypeolabral part of the head capsule has been cut off.

The two mandibular endites fill the space and their wide, flat chewing surfaces meet in the middle (Figs. 19–8c, 19–9). The chewing surfaces consist of flexible material and have numerous parallel transverse rows of long rods and toothed files; anteriorly there are several long strong teeth (Fig. 19–8c). The tentoria whose function is described in the introduction to myriapods, Chpt. 17, is illustrated by Figs. 19–8d and 19–10.

The gnathochilarium corresponds to the first maxilla of trignaths and closes the preoral cavity posteriorly (Figs. 19–8b, 19–10). Its hard posterior wall, sclerotized and calcified, is divided by seams into different sized plates, of systematic importance. On its anterior border are three pairs of short, thimble-shaped appendages, possibly endites. The anterior wall of the gnathochilarium consists of flexible thin exoskeleton with many spines. The lateral borders of the gnathochilarium are connected only basally, by joint membranes, to the mandibles; thus the gnathochilarium can be opened down and out, while at the same time the mandible endites are extended out of the preoral cavity (Figs. 19–8c, 19–10). In the Colobognatha the mouthparts are modified.

The antennae generally consist of 8 articles, some of which may be reduced. The short distal article bears 4 or more conical, tactile sensory organs. The walking legs (Fig. 19–7) are usually short except in many polydesmids and lysiopetalids which run rapidly. The number of legs varies among different families and may be variable within a species. *Polyxenus* has the smallest number, only 13 pairs; glomerids, 17 pairs. The largest numbers are found in some Spirostrepida with

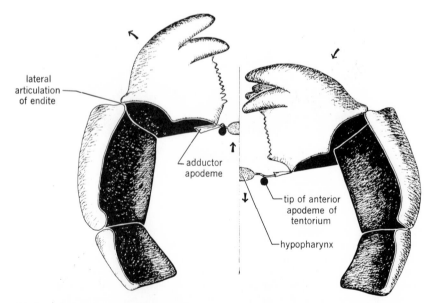

lateral
articulation
of endite

adductor
apodeme

tip of anterior
apodeme of
tentorium

hypopharynx

Fig. 19–9. Anterior view of mandibles of a spirostreptid millipede; the left mandible is abducted, the right adducted. (Modified after Manton.)

139 pairs, some colobognaths with more than 200 pairs, e.g., *Siphonophorella progressor* with more than 340.

In lysiopetalids and Colobognatha many coxae bear eversible coxal sacs, used for imbibing water. The sacs can be withdrawn with a muscle inserted at the blind end.

In small (3–10 mm when mature), litter-dwelling chilognaths, the exoskeleton is unpigmented, flexible and thin, and the animals are subject to desiccation. In larger Chilognatha the strong exoskeleton consists of three layers, like that of other arthropods. The soft epicuticle has no waxy layer; it is replaced by lipids embedded in the brown, polyphenol-tanned exocuticle. The distal layer of the endocuticle consists of parallel calcified lamellae which make the integument inflexible. (After treating it with HCl the exoskeleton becomes flexible.) The hypodermis has many glandular cells with ducts through all layers of the exoskeleton; probably, they secrete the lipids into the exocuticle. The exoskeleton of Pselaphognatha is flexible and not calcified.

The dry weight of the chilognath cuticle is about half that of the whole body. *Glomeris, Tachypodoiulus, Diploiulus* and *Polydesmus* have an exoskeleton con-

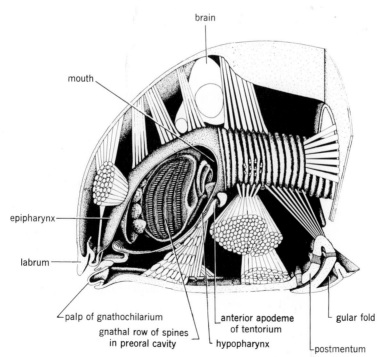

Fig. 19–10. Head of *Diploiulus caeruleocinctus*, in sagittal section; 1.8 mm long. (From Fechter.)

taining 72–78% dry weight of calcium salts, mainly as carbonate with very little phosphate. The calcium is obtained from plants, not directly from the soil.

The coloration of the diplopods is partly due to the brown color of the exocuticle and partly to the presence of pigments embedded in the hypodermis cells. While northern European species are dull in color, many North American and tropical species have bright red, green, or yellow coloration.

SENSE ORGANS. Besides innervated setae, diplopods have hypodermal knobs and sensory cones on the antennae as well as on the palps of the gnathochilarium. The Pselaphognatha have trichobothria on their heads.

The sensory nerves of the cones form several groups lying one behind another. Their distal dendrites enter the cones, sometimes several dendrites fusing into a terminal fiber. The terminal fibers end in pegs (which stain dark) underneath the opening of the cone. In the polydesmids, thimble-shaped projections of the cuticle contain sense cells with their dendrites also ending in pegs.

The organs of Tömösvary differ in various groups of diplopods. Usually each opening is circular; it may be shallow or may be a long tube with sense cells at the bottom (Fig. 19–11). In glomerids the lumen and also slit-shaped openings are horseshoe-shaped. Juloid millipedes and Colobognatha lack the organs. All of the Polydesmida and some members of some other orders lack eyes. When present they are composed of from one to many ocelli, arranged in rows, triangles or oval fields. The ocelli have a long cone-shaped lens and very few retinal cells (Fig. 19–12).

NERVOUS SYSTEM. The protocerebrum, in addition to the central body, has three pairs of globuli, and lateral projections that receive the nerves of the eyes and the organs of Tömösvary. The large blind species lack the large lateral lobes which are optic centers. The frontal ganglion is close to the tritocerebrum. The short subesophageal ganglion has a pair of nerves for the mandibles and a pair for the gnathochilarium. The ganglia of the trunk segments are in the midline of the body, fused into a single long cord which superficially does not show the presence of connectives. Each of the four anterior segments has one ganglion, indicated by a swelling; all displosegments have two ganglia per ring.

Neurosecretory cells are found in the brains of various diplopods. The course of the secretion-conducting fibers varies in different groups. A bundle of fibers from the brain goes to the lateral cerebral gland, which serves as a reservoir but also secretes its own hormone.

DIGESTIVE SYSTEM. The mouth is deep in the preoral cavity (Fig. 19–10) and opens into the ectodermal pharynx, the posterior portion of which extends into the trunk, in Julidae to the 7th trunk segment, in *Strongylosoma* to the 4th. There is a circular fold before it enters the long wider midgut (Fig. 19–13). The midgut has a uniform one-layered epithelium, the cells of which absorb and also secrete digestive enzymes by moving out of the cell layer and falling into the lumen. They are replaced by mitotic division of short cells of embryonic nature that are scattered between the epithelial cells. The proctodeum is also fairly long, extending through 7–10 diplosegments, and in the Julidae and *Strongylosoma* it consists of three different parts. The main portion, filled with fecal pellets, connects with a short, wide, eversible sac that opens at the anus.

The midgut musculature has an outer cell layer that stores nutrient material. These cells belong to the cellular connective tissue, the fat body that fills a large portion of the body cavity.

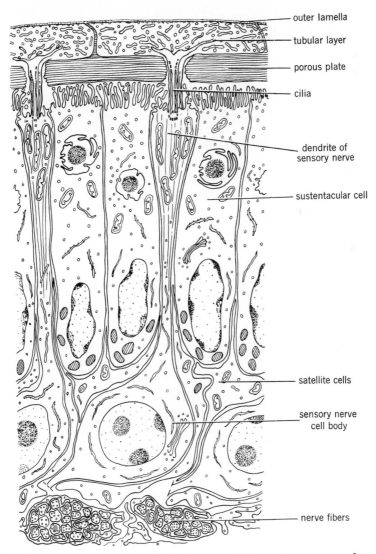

outer lamella

tubular layer

porous plate

cilia

dendrite of sensory nerve

sustentacular cell

satellite cells

sensory nerve cell body

nerve fibers

Fig. 19-11. **Structure of an organ of Tömösvary of *Glomeris romana*, after electron micrographs; width of dendrite is about 1-2 μm, the length of the subtentacular cells about 25-35 μm. (From Bedini and Mirolli, courtesy of the authors and P. Tongiorgi.)**

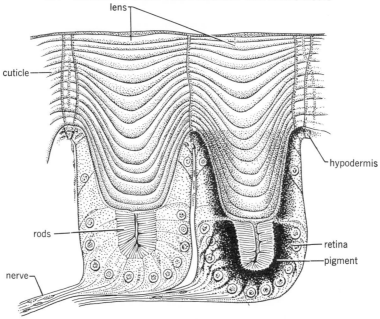

Fig. 19–12. Longitudinal section through two eyes of a julid; diameter of an eye, 0.05 mm. (After Grenacher.)

Into the preoral cavity open two compact glands, probably salivary glands (Fig. 19–13). The anterior one lies under the clypeus and frons, and opens into the roof of the preoral cavity. The posterior gland surrounds the foregut and opens anteriorly on the gnathochilarium (Fig. 19–13). *Strongylosoma* and *Polydesmus* also have a gland at the hindgut, which secretes into the lumen near the posterior constriction. Possibly the secretion is used to make the inner layer of molting chambers. Julidae lack this gland.

EXCRETORY SYSTEM. There is a single pair of Malpighian tubules (Fig. 19–13). The sacculus of the maxillary nephridia is in the head under the pharynx; its canal runs posteriorly, then turns toward the head before opening on the gnathochilarium between lateral and middle sclerites (Fig. 19–13).

CIRCULATORY SYSTEM. In contrast to that of chilopods, the circulatory system is not very developed; the lateral arteries do not branch, and there is no distinct supraneural artery. The thin-walled heart within the pericardial sinus extends from the first trunk segment to the end of the body. Posteriorly it is blind. The anterior segments, which have only one pair of legs, have one pair of ostia, lateral arteries, and alary muscles of the pericardial membrane; the diplosegments, with two pairs of legs, have two pairs of each of these structures. The lateral arteries on each side of the gut extend ventrally and open into the mixocoel. The head aorta pours blood into a wide sinus surrounding the foregut and is bordered posteriorly by a membrane-enclosed sinus surrounding the ventral nerve cord; in it the blood flows posteriorly. No leg arteries have been found.

RESPIRATORY SYSTEM. The tracheae are metameric, each sternite having a pair of narrow spiracles, covered in part by narrow folds in their walls, and leading into the atria. Usually there are two pairs of atria on the venter of double rings, a single pair on each of the four anterior rings. Only in some Colobognatha (*Polyzonium, Siphonotus*) are the atria thin-walled. In all others they consist of thick, stiff, sclerotized material and serve both as a respiratory atrium and as a hollow apophysis (tracheal apodemes) for muscle attachment, a double function otherwise found only in many spiders.

Various families have different arrangements of 1–3 bundles of tracheae (Figs. 19–6, 19–7) which bring oxygen directly to the tissues. In the Proterandria, the tracheae are unbranched and have normal spiral supports; only near the walls of spinning glands in Nematophora do they anastomose. However, the tracheae are branched in *Glomeris* and have irregular, anastomosing spirals that stiffen the structures. The tracheae in the Pselaphognatha are also branched.

REPRODUCTIVE SYSTEM. The gonads are ventral to the gut and extend from the second or third segment almost to the posterior end of the trunk. Their primordia are paired; in older individuals the ovaries are usually fused as a median tube, but the two germ cell strips remain recognizable. (*Strongylosoma* has the ovaries separate in the larva, the testes separate throughout the life of the animal.) In the third trunk ring the ovaries continue as a pair of short oviducts opening into a paired complex ectodermal atrium, the vulva, which can be evaginated from the cavity of the second coxae or from the folded joint membrane of the third trunk segment behind the second pair of legs. There is also a seminal receptacle in the atrium wall.

The testes are paired tubes in each double segment with two ladderlike connections or fused as a median tube as in the glomerids. Anteriorly a pair of vasa deferentia open on the coxae of the second walking leg or just behind it in a paired or median gonopore papilla of the third sternite. (The second pair of legs belongs to the third trunk segment.)

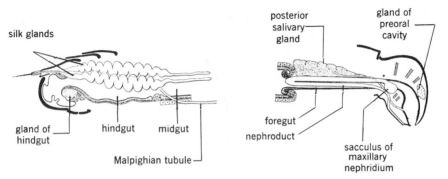

Fig. 19–13. Longitudinal section through parts of gut and glands of *Craspedosoma simile*. (After Wernitzsch.)

Reproduction

Most species of Helminthomorpha and Colobognatha (Proterandria) transfer the sperm with the aid of gonopods. In Pentazonia the transfer is accomplished by bringing the gonopores close to each other, and perhaps is aided by the use of mouthparts (Fig. 19–14). In Pselaphognatha lacking gonopods there is an indirect method of sperm transfer, as in other myriapod classes.

Helminthomorpha and Colobognatha have one or both legs of the seventh ring of the male transformed into gonopods (Fig. 19–15); rarely (in Colobognatha) are the posterior legs of the seventh and anterior legs of the eighth ring transformed. The gonopods may resemble walking legs or may be completely modified, resulting in a very useful systematic character for separation of species (Fig. 19–15). The gonopods may be external or may be carried completely or partly hidden in a pouch in the seventh ring. If there are two pairs of gonopods, usually one pair serves for the transfer of sperm and the other pair forms a shield around it. The gonopod consists of a coxa and telopodite; the telopodite is made up of a prefemoral region and the acropodite.

The gonopods are filled with sperm by rolling up the anterior part of the body so that the gonopores come to lie on top of the gonopods and the sperm is poured through a canal or groove into a sperm fovea at the base (except in Chordeumida). In copulation, male and female stretch out, venter to venter, after embracing with many legs (Fig. 19–16). Others spiral around each other (e.g., *Blaniulus*) while the male holds the female only with the posterior pair of gonopods. The position of the partners is such that the gonopods of the male are opposite the female gonopores. What causes the sperm to move from the gonopods to the gonopores is not completely known, but glandular secretions take part. The mating usually lasts several hours to 48 hours.

The Pentazonia lack gonopods, but the last legs of the male have been transformed to strong, thick clasping appendages (Fig. 19–14a). The male, walking backwards under the female, clasps her vulvae (Fig. 19–14b, d) on both sides, then rolls up ventrally, bringing his mouth and gonopore close to the female gonopore (Fig. 19–14e). The sperm is transferred with the aid of the mandibles and perhaps also with fused coxae of the telopodites. Sometimes the male and female have their venters adjacent, with the anterior of one close to the posterior of the other.

Pselaphognatha have an indirect method of sperm transfer. *Polyxenus lagurus*, on locating a suitable furrow or crevice, presses two genital appendages to the edge of the furrow and, with its hind legs at rest, moves the anterior part of the body to and fro. At the same time silk emerges from these two appendages which sit on the coxae of the second pair of legs and, by moving back and forth, the male constructs a silk bridge that covers the furrow. On one of the threads two sperm droplets are deposited. Then the male walks along the side of the groove and, first with the genital appendages, then with spinning glands of the legs of the seventh leg segment, places paired silk threads vertical to the bridge. These threads form a directional marker leading to the sperm. The whole procedure lasts barely a minute. When a female passes, she follows the 1.5 cm long threads, finds the sperm, extends her vulvae and picks the sperm up. There is no direct contact between the male and female.

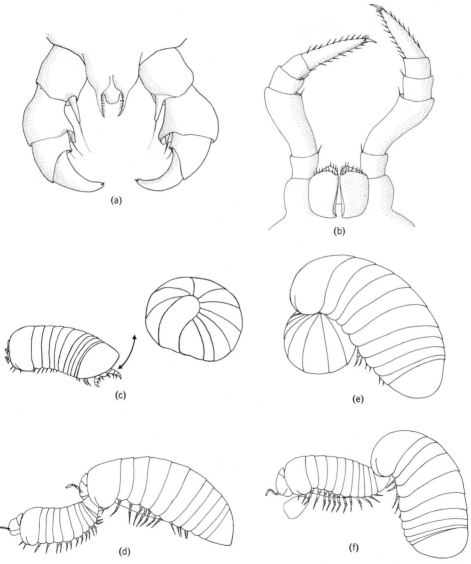

Fig. 19–14. *Glomeris marginata:* (a) male clasping appendages in anterior view; (b) second pair of legs and vulvae of female in posterior view, each leg about 1.1 mm long; (c) courting male, left; (d) male has backed toward female and with his clasping legs takes hold of her 2nd coxae and vulvae; (e) male rolls up while sperm is transmitted by mandibles; (f) after mating, the male takes a pellet of fecal matter and rolls it toward the female vulvae. Male left in (c–f), about 7 mm long. (From Haacker.)

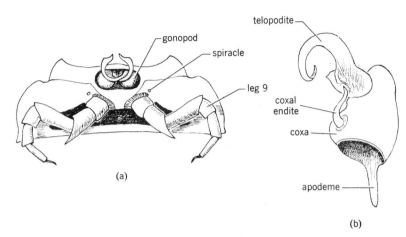

Fig. 19-15. Gonopods of *Apheloria coriacea* (Polydesmida): (a) ventral view of seventh ring; (b) left gonopod in posterior view. (Modified after Snodgrass.)

In the female Helminthomorpha and Colobognatha the vulvae are sometimes everted. In the Blaniulidae and the Lysiopetalidae they may be conspicuous, sometimes trailing to the middle of the body.

Development

Some diplopods deposit their eggs in clumps in moist humus. Many make egg chambers in which the eggs, surrounded by an air space, are protected from moisture extremes (Fig. 19-17).

Polyxenus lagurus makes the wall of chambers from the wide posterior setae. The female within the loose bark of a stump turns on her side and arches her body, venter concave. After depositing several eggs, she crawls a bit further in this position and deposits a few more, producing a disc-shaped spiral of eggs. Finally she walks around the egg mass with her tail setae pressed so firmly against the sticky mass that some setae break off and adhere to it, forming an efficient protective cover, with barbs on which mites and small beetles may become entangled without penetrating to the eggs.

A cocoon of white threads surrounds the egg mass of the Chordeumida. Its construction has been observed in *Polymicrodon polydesmoides*. The dimensions are 10 mm in diameter, 2 mm high, and the nests, made on the underside of wooden slats, were completed within a day. The silk appears to be drawn out from below the head; however, the threads almost certainly come from the silk glands at each side of the mid- or hindgut. The gland lumen, surrounded by a thick layer of gland cells, is lined by a sclerotized wall, indicating ectodermal origin. Both ducts fuse and enter a single spinneret, a transformed hollow seta directed posteriorly, near the dorsal midline of the preanal segment. There are from 1 to 3 pairs of spinnerets. The spinnerets produce a molting chamber composed of fibers and presumably also the egg cocoon.

In glomerids, polydesmids, julids, and spirobolids, constructions are made of earth, probably passed through the gut, deposited as clumps surrounded by secretion. The earth is placed by the evaginated hindgut, but judging by its texture and color it is certainly not simple fecal material. *Polydesmus* bends its body

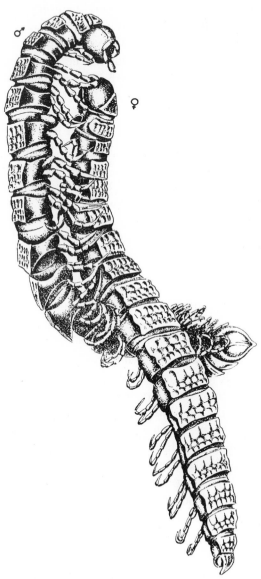

Fig. 19–16. *Brachydesmus superus,* mating. At anterior border of 7th ring of male, gonopods project ventrally, ready to attach to vulvae which female has evaginated at anterior border of 3rd sternite (visible as a black plate underneath first distinct tergite); 0.9 cm long. (After Seifert from Lang.)

laterally into a ring and, moving slowly and intermittently around a circle, places clumps of dirt next to each other to form a circular wall 6 mm in diameter. After the wall reaches a certain height, the female bends over and places 200 eggs into it. Then a dome, at places broken by a 3 mm long air duct, is built over the wall with more clumps of earth. The whole construction takes about 36 hours. Julids make similar egg cases, with or without a funnel (Fig. 19–17), and lay between 40 and 250 eggs. *Glomeris* forms small egg chambers 3–5 mm in diameter, each containing a single egg, rarely 2 or 3; the animal makes them with its last pair of legs while on its back. As the evaginated hindgut places new earth clumps, the legs are used to pat them together. The 16 cm long *Graphidostreptus* deposits a single egg within a capsule 6.5 mm in diameter. North American *Narceus annularis* (=*Spirobolus marginatus*) encloses each egg in a capsule, producing about 75–260 such capsules. The female bends her head and produces a small mass of regurgitated material which is taken up by the legs; the 8th to 11th pairs hold it while the front of the head flattens it to form a shallow disc. In the center, an egg is placed from the gonopores. Then the edges of the disc are bent up and kneaded together with the legs, the tip worked over by the head front or labrum, until it forms a sphere, the outside of which is rough. The completed capsule is passed posteriorly by the partly curled female, and is taken into the hindgut. Sometimes the capsule is reopened, turned, and taken back in. After 15–40 minutes the egg capsule, dried and smaller, is deposited among fecal pellets.

In the American colobognath *Brachycybe lecontei* the female transfers a clutch of eggs to the male, who coils about them while they are incubating.

Cleavage may be superficial or may give the first impression of total cleavage, without the appearance of a blastocoel. Soon there is a germ disk, which folds over in the middle so that part of the embryo is pressed into the yolk.

Most diplopods hatch with only 7 trunk rings, the second to fourth each with one leg while the fifth and sixth have two pairs of leg buds each (Fig. 19–18). The seventh ring has the posterior budding zone, behind which is the anus-bearing telson (Fig. 19–19). *Pachyiulus* may remain longer in the egg and has more segments when hatching; they may have as many as 17 developed leg pairs, acquired by members of related genera only after three molts. The embryo of *Narceus americanus* at hatching is short, white, indistinctly segmented, mouthless and legless. After probably only a few hours it molts to a larva. The larva, still

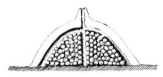

Fig. 19–17.   Egg mass and surrounding chamber of *Ophyiulus pilosus* cut open through its center. (After vom Rath from Schubart.)

enclosed in the pellet, has one ocellus on each side of the head. The anterior half of its body consists of six distinct segments; the first three rings each have a pair of segmented legs. The second larval stage is still white, has 3 ocelli on each side of the head, and the body is composed of 21 (sometimes 22) rings, with seven pairs of legs, the first five pairs on the first five trunk rings, the last two on the 6th ring. However, in Spirobolida the legs are pushed forward, making it appear that each segment has one pair of legs. Actually the first, the collum segment, has no legs, the fifth has two. There are now repugnatorial pores on the sixth ring. Near the end of the second larval stage, the diplopod chews its way out of the pellet into the damp soil. The next molts take place in cavities in the soil.

The embryonal region anterior of the anal segment produces a certain number of new double segments before each molt in families with constant segment number. Other diplopods may have a different number, depending on the species or sometimes even variable among individuals. In some families, the Glomeridae for instance, the animals may have all legs before sexual maturity, while in others, including the Julidae, new segments are added until maturity and even after mating and egg laying.

The new diplosegments in Julida are first without legs, but have leg buds within a posteriorly directed fold of the anterior and posterior border of each double sternite. Only after the following molt do the legs appear.

The embryonic zone in the preanal legless ring is first a slightly raised ventral hypodermal plate, its cells three to four times as high as most other hypodermal cells. Posteriorly it continues into the hypodermis of the telson, anteriorly into the hypodermis of the previous segment and also into the ventral cord (Fig. 19–19). New segments that are formed by this budding plate become many-layered, forming anteriorly median spherical cell groups, ganglia primordia. These separate from the peripheral layer, the future hypodermis. Both lateral regions of the plate form thimble-like outgrowths, later to become appendage primordia. The mesoderm of the new rings is formed by two thin cell layers on the dorsum of the plates. These become organized into paired, wide low coelomic pouches. The material comes from two neighboring cell rows which proliferate

Fig. 19–18. Julid just hatched from egg; ventrally on head are the mandibles and ganthochilarium; about 2 mm long. (After vom Rath from Krug.)

from the posterior edge of the budding plate. In all this, the development of the anterior end of the budding zone is ahead of the posterior. Only later are the lateral parts of the new rings formed. While the embryonic plate grows in length it forms folds, the valleys of which are the future segmental borders. The hypodermis of the dorsum and the sides of the last body segment separates and proliferates so that it forms the same folds as the other area. In this manner the sides and the dorsum of the new rings are formed. At the same time the coelomic pouches send branches into the appendages and just as in the embryo, grow up dorsally (Fig. 4–14). Finally the hypodermis folds under the old cuticle to form a new layer of sclerotized material. As the molt begins, the folds stretch and become new body rings. The gut, of course, has also increased in length.

The body of a growing diplopod thus consists of several areas. For example, a two and a half month old *Ophyiulus* has the following: 22 body rings with 41 pairs of complete legs; behind that, 8 newly formed rings with legs not visible from the outside; within the budding zone, as sectioning demonstrates, 3 double segments with minute leg primordia, and behind it 3 indications of diplosegments. After the next molt, the 8 posterior "legless" rings have legs and behind them the 3 anterior embryonic areas have moved out of the last ring as "legless" double segments.

In *Narceus americanus,* the third stage has 24 to 27 rings, with the last 5 to 7 legless; the sexes can now be separated, males lacking legs on the seventh body ring. After each succeeding molt, primordia of the gonopods grow a little larger and more like the adult. The animal now has 6 ocelli on each side and is brownish. The number of ocelli facilitates determining the stage, as the number

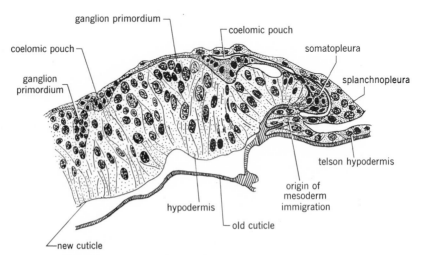

Fig. 19–19. Sagittal section through posterior growth area of young *Platyrrhacus amauros;* on the left the growth zone grades into ventral cord of last ring. (After Pflugfelder.)

of legs may now be variable. The larvae of the fourth stage have 29 to 33 rings, the last 5 or 6 legless, and have 10 ocelli. Adult animals appear after 12 molts, with from 47 to 53 rings in the third year. After the tenth stage no more rings may be added; the adult has about 40 to 50 ocelli in six rows.

The life span differs. *Glomeris* may reach 4–7 years in age; *Tachypodoiulus,* 2 to 6½; *Narceus,* 6 years. *Glomeris* becomes sexually mature after about 3½ years, *Tachypodoiulus* in about 1¾ years. Other species (*Strongylosoma pallipes*) are thought to live only 1 to 1¾ years. The polydesmid *Ampelodesmus iyonis* matures in the second year after 7 larval instars. Sexual differences are first seen in the fourth instar. Most julids continue to molt after maturity and add body rings. In males of some species, an unusual intermediate stage may appear in which the gonopods are reduced again and nonfunctional the gonopodal appendages lack an opening, before becoming functional again after another molt.

Molting starts with the solution of calcareous material from the exoskeleton. The animal becomes soft and cannot move its legs. The skin tears first behind the head and the trunk, by alternate stretching and contracting, moves out of the break, the legs held stiffly posteriorly. The freshly emerged animal is soft and frequently unpigmented. After about 24 hours, calcareous deposits stiffen and harden the exoskeleton. The molting, including the preceding stage of immobility, may take two to three weeks in older animals, in very young animals only 2.2 mm long, only three days. During this time the animals are defenseless, and withdraw into molting chambers. The molting chambers of polydesmids and chordeumids are similar to egg chambers. Glomerids and juliform millipedes excavate an earthen cavity, the walls of which are lined with pieces of fecal material and secretions from the anal flaps.

Habits

Most of the North American and Central European diplopods live in rotten logs, leaf litter, under stones and bark. Only a few species climb trees, shrubs and herbaceous plants, to 1 or 2 m *Schizophyllum sabulosum* of Europe, *Nemasoma varicorne* (=*Isobates*) of Europe and North America and *Polyxenus lagurus* to 20 m. Ribbon-shaped species enter leaf litter. Many juliform and glomerid millipedes dig into soil or use earthworm burrows. Such vertical migration may be caused by an approaching molt, need to deposit eggs, beginning drought and change of temperature. Also daily vertical movements due to an endogenous rhythm have been observed in *Diploiulus.* They will descend to 20 cm during the daytime. In Europe, Blaniulidae are found in caves. More than 4% of North American species are cave inhabitants, most of them chordeumids, except in Texas and New Mexico where polydesmids and cambalids predominate. Caves offer high humidity and continued darkness; obligate cave inhabitants have lost body pigment, and sometimes the exoskeleton is thin. A few have elongated legs and antennae. Members of some families and orders seem preadapted to cave life. Very wet habitats are generally avoided; however, *Thalassiobates littoralis* lives under kelp on ocean beaches in Europe.

Feeding on rotten vegetation and wood, many diplopods are found in places of high humidity and most have relatively little protection against desiccation. *Diploiulus caeruleocinctus* (=*londinensis*) at 15°C may become stiff within 13 hours, and dried out after 23 hours at low humidity as might be found in a house. Diplopods lack the waxy layer of the epicuticle. However, after the lipids of dead animals have been extracted with hot chloroform, water loss increases by four times. Most Colobognatha, also *Schizophyllum sabulosum*, live in dry places. in experiments, female *Schizophyllum*, during summer at 26°C, survived for 130 hours above silica gel, while *Julus terrestris* and *Oxidus gracilis* dried out within 10 hours. In fall, under similar conditions, females lose much more water per hour. There are hardly any differences, however, in water loss of recently molted animals and those that molted some time ago. Water can be replenished by drinking or through coxal sacs in Callipodidae (Lysiopetalida). If one experimentally offers the three above mentioned species a choice of different humidities, *Oxidus* moves toward moisture, *Schizophyllum* toward the dry area, while *Julus* is first indifferent, but then moves to the moisture. *Oxidus* at 98% separates small differences in humidity; *Schizophyllum sabulosum*, tested under other conditions, separates only differences of more than 10%. After the antennae have been extirpated, the animals barely react to moisture, even after being dried out over silica gel. One may assume, therefore, that humidity receptors are located in the antennae. Similar experiments with *Nemasoma* and *Polyxenus* support this assumption.

Because the place of hatching has abundant food, many species do not move more than a few meters away from it. If movement occurs, many individuals may migrate together. *Schizophyllum sabulosum* once crossed railway tracks in Alsace in such abundance that a train was stopped because the rails became too slippery from crushed millipedes. Mass migrations have been reported from all parts of the world. In recent migration of *Pseudopolydesmus serratus* in Ohio, densities up to 800 per m² were reported. It is assumed that the migration followed an extremely favorable period for reproduction, as the ratio of adults to immatures was 1:7. A *Chicobolus spinigerus* migration observed in southern Florida involved all mature individuals of rather small size. In Texas and Mexico species of *Orthoporus* are often seen moving in sunlight in large numbers after rains. Many climb desert shrubs.

PROTECTION. Mechanical protection of the Chilognatha is provided by the calcareous exoskeleton. Its pressure resistance is increased in many families by lobes or doming of the diplotergites. Between two glass panes, *Diploiulus caeruleocinctus*, 25 mm long, 1.7 mm in diameter, does not respond to pressure of 500 g. Only if the pressure is increased to 1 kg do the repugnatorial glands become active. Species that are not tube-shaped (e.g., *Glomeris*) can withstand only 500 g pressure without damage.

The delicate legs of most millipedes are well protected by their ventrolateral insertion and also by the lateral keels present in the rings of many species. If disturbed, many polydesmids and chordeumids stop and tuck their heads and the anterior part of the trunk under the wider diplotergites. Most juliform and many colobognath diplopods also bend the rest of the body rings and coil up, leaving only the most solid diplotergites exposed. If the spiral is flat, the leg attachments and sternites are protected by the tergites. If the spiral is raised they will be covered by the neighboring coil. The shortening of the venter of the trunk is made possible by the short sternites, or they can be turned dorsally (juliform millipedes) or pushed above each other. Experiments with *Diploiulus* and *Blaniulus* indicate that the coiling up is initiated by the nervous system of the head. After the head is removed, they cannot form a spiral. The ability to roll up, forming a hard little sphere, as do the pill bug isopods, has evolved several times in millipedes. It is seen in Pentazonia, pill millipedes, pill-forming polydesmids, and chordeumid Striariidae among others. The tergites cover all legs, sterna, head, preanal segment and telson. In the glomerids (Pentazonia), the last diplotergite is extended behind into a large cap which covers the head and wide tergites when coiled up (Fig. 19–18). Its border fits tightly against the collum. By raising and telescoping sterna, room is made for the flattened legs and head, a surprising evolutionary convergence with pill bugs.

In order to test the defensive value of the ability to coil, various predators were offered large, coiled African glomerids of the genus *Sphaerotherium*, which lack defensive glands. North American ants, a blue jay and a grasshopper mouse were unable to penetrate the armored sphere, but an African banded mongoose (*Mungos mungo*) smashed the millipedes by throwing them against a rock.

Pselaphognaths behave differently when disturbed. They shorten the trunk, so that the protective setae shift close together and the venter is appressed to the substrate.

Unlike centipedes, millipedes do not attempt to bite. Many have saclike repugnatorial glands, which open laterally in all segments from the 5th or 6th to the last or only in some (Fig. 19–5). The opening can be closed. The secretion in most slowly oozes out when the animal is disturbed; lysiopetalids and spirobolids can spray 10 to 30 cm. The pores are dorsal in the midline in *Glomeris marginata*, covering the largest possible area when *Glomeris* is coiled up.

The polydesmid *Apheloria corrugata* produces hydrogen cyanide when disturbed. Each gland has two fluid-filled compartments separated by a duct closed by a muscular valve. The inner, larger compartment contains a precursor, mandelonitrile, the second, an enzyme. When these fluids are mixed, benzaldehyde and hydrogen cyanide are produced. If only one leg of the polydesmid is disturbed, fluid is secreted only at the closest pore; only if the animal is handled do all glands discharge. Attacked by an ant, the millipede tucks his head in, whereupon the ant flees and stays away for 20 minutes. The residual benzaldehyde is also obnoxious and evaporates more slowly than the hydrogen cyanide. The millipede itself seems unaffected by the poison fumes.

The active principles of the glands of different millipedes are diverse. Julida, Spirostreptida and Spirobolida produce smarting p- benzoquinones, which also tan human skin, producing brown spots on the hands of the collector. The secretions of *Narceus americanus* will produce a blister on tender skin if applied freely. *Rhinocricus* produces an aldehyde, trans-2-dodecenal. The chordeumid, *Abacion*, produces p-cresol; its glands have only one compartment. Polydesmida produce HCN and benzaldehyde. The colobognath, *Polyzonium*, has a camphor odor; the chemical is still unknown. *Glomeris marginata* produces 1,2-dialkyl-4(3H)-quinazolinones, a heterocyclic compound close to the alkaloid arborine. Still unknown components, probably proteins, make this secretion sticky after exposure. Feeding of 20 milked glomerids each to test mice had no visible effect; feeding a few unmilked ones made the mice sick, caused them difficulty in walking, and two of five mice (*Apodemus*) died. That the millipedes give off secretions when blown at or on touching warm objects might suggest that the poison is directed against warm blooded predators. To humans the secretions taste bitter.

LOCOMOTION. Chilognaths walk on the tips of their leg claws and usually carry the body high above the substrate, keeping an air current on the ventral spiracles. Lysiopetalids, Colobognatha and Pselaphognatha can move upside down on the ceiling of a chamber by holding on with their claws. Chilognaths may be substrate or surface inhabitants, but the division is not clearcut. Substrate inhabitants may live in decaying logs, or among leaf litter, in soil, or under stones. They may come to the surface at night, but some of the small delicate thin-bodied chordeumids, polydesmids and julids may never leave the deep damp humus layer. The peculiar millipede structure is an adaptation to the habitat, and it probably is the habitat in which millipedes evolved.

Surface inhabitants live under overhanging cliffs or on loose bark. Examples are the lysiopetalids. Spirostreptida are sometimes conspicuous on the surface, but normally they live in burrows to 75 cm deep.

Inhabitants of the substrate must be able to exert a strong push forward. The forward push against a resistant medium is usually given by the legs, but in Colobognatha and Chordeumida the trunk musculature takes part. The force can be measured by harnessing millipedes to sledges, flatbottomed pans with variable loads. While surface dwelling lysiopetalids moved forward only reluctantly, the substrate inhabiting species are not inhibited. The maximal pull could be determined by adding weights (see Table 19–1). It corresponds with the possible pressure exerted by an animal pushing into the substrate.

The millipede's movement in the soil or narrow spaces is related to the following factors: long duration of the stride, small length of the stride, large number of legs taking part in a wave of motion (achieved by a very low phase difference; see Chapter 17), lengthening of the back stroke in relation to the forward swing, which results in having many legs in contact with the substrate simultaneously (Table 19–1). There are also anatomical adaptations such as the large number of legs that can push; attachment of legs on the venter medially, which prevents extension of the legs beyond the sides of the trunk while pushing; lateral keels on the tergites when long legs are present; very strong coxal-trunk joint; calcareous stiffening of the exoskeleton rings and diplosegments.

Three kinds of locomotion may be distinguished, although there are intermediates.

1. Most juliforms and glomerids can dig to 20 cm into the soil. The body is pushed only by the legs into the substrate, anterior first, bulldozer-like. Anterior is the collum; the head is bent down. In glomerids, the second large ring is anterior and both collum and head are tucked in. An important adaptation to these burrowing activities is the formation of diplosomites, which makes possible a large increase in number of legs without increase in body length; one diplosomite is shorter than two simple segments due to the lack of one set of joint membranes, insertion surfaces and trunk musculature. Thus, *Ophyiulus terrestris,* only 23 mm long, has 86 pairs of legs, and *Tachypodoiulus albipes,* 56 mm long, 123 pairs; centipedes of similar length have fewer legs. Also, because the number of body rings is almost half that of legs, the body is stiffer, facilitating the transmission of force. A sclerotized projection from the tergite and musculature into the body prevents telescoping of the rings. Other adaptations are the circular cross section of the diplosegments, the smooth surface and lack of hairs, and short, thick leg muscles which produce a powerful, though slow, movement.

2. Other diplopods dig by inserting the body as a wedge into a crevice and pushing against the substrate to widen the slit. The anterior segments are the most active. This type of motion is common in the Polydesmida, Chordeumida, and Colobognatha. Adaptations to this type of movement are the wide oval diameter of the rings, their lateral keels (Fig. 19–2), wedge-shaped anterior, the head and the collum being relatively narrow (Fig. 19–2). The push is brought about in various ways. Polydesmids use all of their long legs, which may project from the lateral keels into the sides of the slit. In extending, the millipede can push hard against the crevice, as the leg depressing prefemoris and femoris muscles are very strongly developed. With increased leg length, the diplosegments tend to be longer than in the soil-burrowing species, and the leg number less (19–22 body rings with 28–35 leg pairs). Colobognatha and Chordeumida exert force not only with their legs, but also with the trunk musculature. Motion picture studies show that trunk muscles pull forward a segment that has its legs up: as a wave of

Table 19–1. Comparison of gaits of

Species	Body length in mm	Body weight in g	No. of leg-carrying trunk rings	No. of pairs of active legs	No. of legs that participate in a wave of legs	
					fast gaits un-laden	slow gaits maximum load
Glomerida:						
Glomeris marginata	14	0.15	9	♀ 17	6–7	9
Polydesmida:						
Polydesmus angustus	20	0.08	18	♂ 30	7–9	26
Chordeumida:						
Craspedosoma rawlinsi	18	0.025	27	♀ 50	10–12	28
Callipus longobardius	42	—	61*	ca. 112	13–15	10–14
Julida:						
Diploiulus ceruleocinctus	38	0.34	46*	ca. 79	13	28
Blaniulus guttatulus	18	0.007	48*	ca. 83	8–10	—
Platydesmida:						
Brachycybe lecontei	14	0.019	41*	ca. 71	13	—
Dolistenus savii	34	0.019	91*	ca. 171	10	—
Polyzoniida:						
Polyzonium germanicum	11	0.018	36*	ca. 61	9	15
Siphonophora portoricensis	24	0.016	66*	ca. 121	10	—

* The number of diplosegments and legs varies within the species.

† These values can be used only for comparison, not as absolute measurements, since pull depends in part on nylon, silk, or cotton used to attach the sled.

contraction passes over the trunk, each segment with its legs lifted is pulled forward. Colobognaths thus have more force in pushing than juliform millipedes of the same size with legs of equal length. Some of these can pull the heaviest weights of all the diplopods (*Dolistenus, Brachycybe;* see Table 19–1). This form of burrowing is made possible by the telescoping body rings (a characteristic not shared by other millipedes), strong trunk musculature, movability of sternites and lateral keels (which strengthen the stiffening of the body).

But not all juliform millipedes burrow in soil; some have squared keels and look like polydesmids; some Polydesmida burrow and have a large collum.

Some Chordeumida with their long body setae and minute collum do not burrow but may move through passageways made by other soil animals. They rarely appear on the surface. If a digging chilognath walks on the surface in light, its speed of movement increases, but it cannot compete with that of a *Lithobius* of the same length.

different diplopods. (After Manton.)

Relative duration of forward to back strokes of legs		Maximal pull in g†	Maximal force exerted in g per mm² of body diameter	Shortest stride in sec	Maximal speed per sec in mm
slow gait un- laden	fast gait with load				
5.7:4.3	1:9	1.8	0.12	0.7	3.5
6.6:3.4	1.6:8.4	8.6	5.1	0.4	22
5.5:4.5	1.2:8.8	1.4	0.85	—	—
7:3	slow 5:5	—	—	0.2	80
6.3:3.7	2.6:7.4	5.0	0.66	0.5	4.5
6:4	—	0.3	0.76	0.6	—
7:3	—	—	6.3	1	1.3
6.5:2.5	—	—	8.95	1	2.7
6.4:3.6	2.6:7.4	0.4	0.35	1	1.7
5:5	—	—	1.8	1	—

3. Surface inhabiting millipedes (lysiopetalids) can run more rapidly than digging species. They have looser coxal-trunk joints, long thin leg muscles, and their leg excursions are as large as 90°. At its normal speed, *Callipus* moves 5.5 cm/sec.

sENSES. Chilognatha move their antennae continuously while moving, touching the ground with the sensory organs at the tip. At the same time, the short palps of the gnathochilarium are extended anteriorly and touch the ground when the head is bent. Presumably the area is examined chemotactically for food. *Blaniulus* responds to odors from a distance; it runs toward germinating beans, rotting fruit, and proteinaceous material from distances to 20 cm. Removing the distal antennal article with sensory pegs prevents the recognition of the odors.

The organs of Tömösvary of *Glomeris* have only recently been studied. The fine structure under the electron microscope (Fig. 19–11) is like that of the olfactory organs of other arthropods, especially the basoconic and coeloconic sense organs of insects, suggesting an olfactory function. Electrophysiological and behavior experiments have up to now not been successful.

All diplopods examined thus far, including eyeless *Polydesmus, Paradesmus,* and *Blaniulus,* respond to light. The light sense is not limited to certain areas, even though in *Polydesmus* an area of great light sensitivity was found on the seventh antennal article.*

Juliform millipedes may be blind or have 1–79 ocelli which apparently serve as direction finders. In horizontal illumination julids run in spirals or circles after one side of the head is covered with paint. From a distance of 40 cm they move toward large (7 × 10 cm) dark areas that contrast with the light background, behavior that presumably would lead the millipede toward cover. They certainly cannot see pictures.

Sounds of 500–1000 Hz (cps) cause *Polydesmus* and *Glomeris* to stop and pull in their antennae, while *Schizophyllum* reacts only after the sound (500–2000 Hz) stops. Sphaerotheridae can produce sounds.

LUMINESCENCE. Some southern California xystodesmids are continuously luminescent. The glow of *Amplocheir sequoia* (=*Xystocheir*) has a spectral maximum at 495 nm and is strongest at 31.5°C and high oxygen tension. The intensity of the green light, which comes from the entire integument, is variable.

FEEDING. Almost all diplopods feed on plants. Most feed on dead, decaying plant parts. In some central European lowland forests, diplopods are alleged to eat about one-fourth of the fallen leaves each year. They feed upon the middle layer of leaf litter, the moist decaying part, but not on the layer with fungal hyphae; in coniferous forests they consume the lowest parts of the litter. In North America, diplopods also inhabit fallen and decaying logs, a habitat completely absent in the carefully tended central European forests.

Diplopods which withdraw deeper into the soil (many juliform millipedes and Glomerida) also feed on soil, and their gut contains a mixture of plants and minerals. They thus contribute importantly to humus formation. They can live for periods in forest soil, and judging by the fecal pellets, feed on rotting roots and wood rather than on mineral particles. A number of julids (*Diploiulus boleti* and *D. luridus*) prefer wood already attacked by fungi, but they cannot digest the lignin. *Polyxenus* feeds on algae on bark, generally living plants. Fungal hyphae are rarely eaten by millipedes, but moss thalli and pollen are eaten by some species. *Blaniulus* feeds on fecal material and dead animals, as well as plant material. Certain lysiopetalids are the only predacious millipedes. Almost nothing is known about the food of subtropical and tropical species.

In feeding, the Helminthomorpha open the gnathochilarium down so that there is an opening between labrum and gnathochilarium to the mouth. As a

---

* It is striking that while spiders (except salticids), other arachnids and chilopods do not seem to notice the short flash of a stroboscopic photographic flashlight, many Chilognatha will stop and curl up. The flash duration is 1/1200 seconds.

result of pressure of the tentorium, the distal segments of the mandibles extend and spread. Biting into rotting leaf tissue, they cut off a piece with their strong anterior teeth. The mandibles are then withdrawn, forcing the piece of leaf toward the chewing surfaces. In withdrawing, transverse spines are turned toward the median and move against each other like the teeth of cogwheels, tearing the tissue. Most polydesmids rasp the surface of decaying vegetation with the serial rows of fine teeth on the mandibles.

DIGESTION. In the gut of the julids of central Europe, one finds pieces of leaves 3–10 mm long. They lie in the midgut within the peritrophic membrane. This membrane (also found in some insects and arachnids) is secreted from the midgut epithelium. Digestion and absorption by nonsecreting cells takes place in the midgut. A starch-splitting enzyme and fat-emulsifying materials have been found. Nothing is known about cellulose or protein digestion.

SYMBIONTS. Common parasites in millipedes are nematodes. Many millipedes are intermediate hosts of acanthocephalans. The gut of many millipedes contains acephaline gregarines.

Classification

The class Diplopoda is divided into two subclasses, Pselaphognatha and Chilognatha. The Chilognatha are grouped in 3 superorders: Pentazonia, Helminthomorpha and Colobognatha. Only the important families and those mentioned in the text are listed.*

SUBCLASS PSELAPHOGNATHA

There are only 60 species included. In contrast to other diplopods these dwarf forms have the integument soft, not calcareous. The 11–13 trunk rings have the tergite, pleurite and sternites separate (Fig. 19-4). From the padlike pleurites of the second ring to the one before the last, there are tufts of diverging, thick, tuberculate, blunt and hollow setae, deeply serrated. The posterior end has one or two thick posteriorly directed bundles of long, thin, barbed setae. The head bears some trichobothria. There are 13–17 pairs of legs, but no gonopods. The mandibles lack teeth. The soft gnathochilarium is indistinctly jointed. The tracheal atria are long and narrow, with relatively wide forked tracheae. The hindgut is uniform. Most are less than 4 mm long. Males are rare.

* The scientific names of millipede species are quite unstable compared with those of other invertebrate groups. Here the names of the useful Checklist of Millipedes of North America by R. V. Chamberlin and R. Hoffman (1958) have been used. This publication lists 749 species and subspecies in 200 genera of millipedes north of Mexico. One of the revisions (W. Keeton, 1960) reduced the number of species of *Narceus* from 14 in the checklist to only 4 (though probably not all groups have as many synonyms as the conspicuous *Narceus*). The number of species per genus is accordingly expected to be even smaller than in the checklist! Not only has this bewildering array of generic names become meaningless for indicating affiliation, but it will contribute to further instability unless a bold myriapodologist starts lumping genera.

Polyxenidae. The trunk has 11 rings and 13 pairs of legs. The European *Polyxenus*[*] *lagurus* is 2.1–4 mm long (Fig. 19-4); it inhabits leaf litter, especially rough textured tree bark, from the soil up to 20 m, and sometimes piles of stones bearing unicellular algae on which the animals feed. The algae are torn off by biting and tearing, and are crushed by the mandibles. Sometimes decayed bark is eaten. Walking on vertical surfaces is made possible by a pair of tarsal pads next to the leg claw. Usually *Polyxenus* rests in the space between bark and tree.

Because the coxae are immovable, the leg pivots on the joint between coxa and trochanter, so that the functional telopodite is more lateral than in the Chilognatha. Probably for this reason there is some similarity to the locomotion of centipedes. Each leg touches the substrate just before the previous one is lifted. When running, the right and left legs of a pair alternate. The ratio of forward stroke to back stroke is 0.5:9.5 if slowly walking; 4:6 if running; the difference in phase is 0.6 and 0.8. The angle of excursion is 80°, the shortest stride 0.2 second.

Corresponding with the few (13) legs, there are never more than 2 to 2½ waves over the legs; otherwise, the support for the trunk would be too small. Individuals barely 4 mm long run 5 mm in 1 second.

The parthenogenetic race of females can be recognized by the uniform dorsum. They will not respond to males, silk threads, or spermatophores. The bisexual females have three dark longitudinal dorsal stripes. The distribution of the two kinds of females within central Europe is not known. Transfer of sperm has been described above. After the egg membrane breaks, the larva is enclosed in still another embryonal cover, which is lost during the first molt, several days later. The first stage, 0.9 mm long, has five segments and three pairs of legs. In the course of seven molts, all rings and legs are acquired; the eighth stage is adult, 6 to 8 months having passed since hatching. The life span is at least two years. While adult it molts about three times a year. Removing the tail setae causes a molt; losing an antenna may also be followed by molting.

Although its eyes have only 8 ocelli, *Polyxenus* will run toward a tree 30 cm in diameter from a distance of 1.5 m. Not only the diameter of the tree, but also its height, seemed important in experiments. Odors are recognized by the last antennal digits, and there also are humidity receptors on the antennae. In experiments, more than half of the *Polyxenus* went first to areas of less than 50% relative humidity. After 3 days, 80% of them had moved to areas of 72–86% relative humidity. The trichobothria recognize air currents of only 1.65 cm/sec, which may be of importance in searching for crevices. *Polyxenus* reacts to vibrations even after the trichobothria are glued down.

Nothing is known about the American species. *Polyxenus lagurus* of Europe has been reported from Nova Scotia. *Polyxenus fasciculatus* is found in the eastern United States and Canada as far west as Texas. Its habits are similar to those of the European species. Other species have been described from the Pacific coast. *Lophoproctus* lacks pads on the tarsi.

Synxenidae. The trunk has 13 rings. The tergites are covered by scales. There are 17 pairs of legs. *Phryssonotus* (=*Synxenus*) is found in Africa.

---

[*] Application has been made to the Int. Comm. Zool. Nomencl. to place the name *Polyxenus* on the *Official List of Generic Names in Zoology.*

SUBCLASS CHILOGNATHA

The exoskeleton is stiff and calcareous. The hairs are short and few in number; there never are tufts of setae or posterior tufts. Mandibles usually have a large anterior outer tooth and a posterior internal tooth (Fig. 19-8c).

Superorder Pentazonia

Other names for this group are Oniscomorpha and Opisthandria. The male has the last leg, or sometimes the one before the last, transformed into clasping appendages that are used to hold the female while mating. The seventh ring has normal legs; there are no gonopods for sperm transmission. Every ring consists of a semicircular diplotergite and a flat ventral wall parallel to the substrate, made up of a pair of lateral and a pair of ventral plates one after another (Fig. 19-6). The preanal segment and the telson are very small and hidden by a large posteriorly projecting diplotergite. The tracheae have dichotomous branches and come from atria. About 500 species are included. They are rare in the Americas.

ORDER GLOMERIDESMIDA

There are about 35 species in the group, also called Limacomorpha. The body is long, flattened and cannot roll into a sphere. The trunk has 22 rings; the females have 36, the males 37 pairs of legs. There are no repugnatorial glands.

Glomeridesmidae. The family includes the genus *Glomeridesmus*.

ORDER GLOMERIDA

The order, also called Oniscomorpha, contains about 470 species. The trunk is short and can roll into a sphere. The tergites have lateral keels, protecting ventrally below the ventral sclerites. The venter is thus surrounded by the tergites, as in woodlice (Fig. 19-6). Each venter has one pair of pleurites connected by joint membranes to one pair of sternites. There are 15–17 trunk rings (including the collum), 12–14 tergites, 17–23 pairs of legs.

Sphaerotheridae. There are 13 tergites. Females have 21 leg pairs and males have an additional 2 pairs of posterior legs. There are 200 tropical species, including many very large ones that roll up to form a golfball-sized sphere. The last legs and also last tergites have stridulating organs which can make audible, moaning noises. They are found in Africa and India to the Philippines, Australia and New Zealand. *Sphaerotherium actaeon* is to 9.5 cm long, 5 cm wide.

Glomeridae. There are (including the collum) 11–12 tergites (Fig. 19-3). The tergite following the collum is very long. Females have 17, males 19 pairs of legs. The sides of the large shield behind the collum are smooth. Including the collum, there are 12 tergites. Species of *Glomeris* are common in southern to central Europe, usually shiny black with a colorful pattern. The larva has 3 pairs of walking legs and 5 pairs of leg primordia. There are 9 instars to adulthood, but after reaching the 6th instar, the animal has all of its tergites, including male clasping appendages (which change in appearance in the adult (Fig. 19-14a). It takes about 3½ years to mature. The animals molt after reaching maturity and probably live for 6 or 7 years. North American representatives are rare, small animals. The genus *Onomeris* is found in the southeastern United States; *Sonoromeris* occurs in California; *Glomeroides* is found in Mexico.

Gervaisiidae. There are 11 to 12 tergites including the collum. The tergite following the collum is very long. The sides of the large shield are depressed. Posteriorly the tergites have transverse ridges or longitudinal keels. *Gervaisia costata,* 2.5 to 5 mm long, is a whitish species living among rocks in Europe.

Superorder Helminthomorpha

Other names for this group are Eugnatha and Proterandria. The seventh ring of the male has at least one pair of legs transformed into sperm-transferring gonopods. The last legs of the male are never specialized. The preanal segment and the telson are well developed and visible from above (Fig. 19-5). The tracheae are not branched, except in the Chordeumida, where they supply the silk glands. The tracheae arise in bundles from a few tracheal atria.

The basal segments of the mandibles have wide cheeks and are visible on the sides of the head (Fig. 19-8a). The gnathochilarium is wide and its joints are visible. The trunk is formed from stiff rings. In cross section the rings cover at least three-quarters of a circle (Figs. 19-5, 19-7). There are no distinct pleurites, but the sternites are separate sclerites. The first pair of legs (and often also the second) of the seventh ring in the male has transformed into a gonopod (Fig. 19-15). The gonopods are of importance in separating species.

ORDER POLYDESMIDA

This order, also called Proterospermophora, includes about 2800 species, to 13 cm long. There are 18–22 trunk rings, usually 19 or 20; the number is usually constant within a species, but some sexual dimorphism is known in which males have 19, females 20. Of the second to last rings the sternite is always fused to the pleurite. The tergites usually have lateral keels, varying in width and height and slope from horizontal to vertical. Many species are ribbon-like and flat (Fig. 19-2), but a few are worm-like and cylindrical, having the keels reduced or absent. The tracheal atria are transverse, not forked. Repugnatorial glands are usually present, consisting of a gland and a vestibule, but never in all rings. The secretions are hydrogen cyanide, benzaldehyde and related compounds. The single pair of male gonopods is derived from the anterior leg of the seventh ring. There are no eyes. Organs of Tömösvary are present.

Polydesmidae. The small or large flat lateral keels are covered with tubercles. The gonopod coxae are enclosed and often immovable. Seminal canal of male gonopod has a vesicle near its distal end. *Polydesmus*° has 7 or 8 instars before the adult. *Polydesmus complanatus,* to 28 mm, is found in Europe and is introduced in eastern United States. *Brachydesmus superus* is introduced from Europe. North American genera include *Dixidesmus, Pseudopolydesmus* and *Scytonotus.*

Cryptodesmidae. The collum is very large, covering the head. Lateral keels are usually wide and flat. Genera include *Cryptodesmus* from South America and *Diaphanacme* from Central America.

° The name *Polydesmus* is on the *Official List of Generic Names in Zoology.*

Oniscodesmidae. Lateral keels are wide and bent ventrally; caudal margin of rings is sharply marked off into rectangular areas; they can roll up like *Glomeris. Oniscodesmus,* 1 cm long, occurs in South America.

Xystodesmidae. These are large bodied millipedes. The male gonopod coxae are freely movable; tergites are wide and sloping. Anal tergite is subtriangular. North American genera include *Amplocheir, Apheloria, Boraria, Brachoria, Chonaphe, Deltotaria, Fontaria, Harpaphe, Motyxia* with bioluminescent species, *Nannaria, Pachydesmus, Pleuroloma, Sigmoria,* and *Xystocheir.*

Euryuridae. This family has the characters of the preceding, but the anal tergite is almost square. Genera include *Euryurus, Auturus,* in eastern North America and *Pseudamplinus* in Central America.

Sphaeriodesmidae. Tergites are arched, keels almost vertical. Keels of the second segment are distinctly smaller than of the following. Male gonopod coxae are small and freely movable. Repugnatorial pores are usually on the upper surface of keels near the margin. These animals can roll in a sphere. *Sphaeriodesmus* is found in Central America, *Desmonus* in southern United States.

Stylodesmidae. The collum is large, sometimes covering the head, and the anterior margin is scalloped. Coxae of the gonopods are enlarged and not freely movable. Repugnatorial pores are on stalks. *Ilyma* and *Psochodesmus* are found in the southern United States. There are many genera and species in Central and South America. *Ampelodesmus* is found in Japan.

Vanhoeffeniidae. The family of delicate small-bodied millipedes has the characters of Polydesmidae but lacks a vesicle in the seminal canal. *Ophiodesmus* is found in northern Europe and is introduced to Newfoundland. North American genera include *Antriadesmus, Speodesmus* and *Speorthus.*

Nearctodesmidae. This has the characters of Polydesmidae but lacks a vesicle in the seminal canal, and the prefemur of the gonopod has two long slender processes. The family is found on the west coast of North America, *Nearctodesmus* is included.

Platyrrhacidae. These are tropical species with large keels. *Platyrrhacus pictus* reaches 130 mm long and 20 mm wide.

Paradoxsomatidae (Strongylosomidae). Male gonopod is complicated; the acropodite is set off from the prefemur. *Strongylosoma pallipes,* 23 mm long, has a cylindrical body and very small keels; it is found in Europe. The hothouse millipede *Oxidus gracilis* (=*Orthomorpha*) is pantropical, cosmopolitan in greenhouses, and is the most widely distributed and successful of all millipedes.

Eurymerodesmidae. Male gonopod is simple; the acropodite is continuous with the prefemur. *Eurymerodesmus* is represented by many species in the southeastern to central United States. *Paresmus* is another genus.

ORDER CHORDEUMIDA

This order, also called Nematophora, includes 740 species. On the posterior dorsal border of the preanal ring there are 1–3 pairs of posteriorly-directed hollow setae which function as spinnerets (Fig. 19-13). There are between 22 and 60 trunk rings, the number of which is not always constant within the species. The body is cylindrical or flattened if there are lateral keels or tubercles. The sternites are separated from each other and from the tergite by joint membranes. The tracheal atria are forked into a lateral and medial arm. There are repugnatorial glands from the 5th ring, one after another. Coxal sacs are present. Male gonopods are formed from the first and sometimes also the second legs of the 7th ring, but sometimes an anterior leg or one of the following rings may be specialized. Ocelli and organs of Tömösvary are present.

SUBORDER CHORDEUMIDEA (ASCOSPERMOPHORA)

The number of trunk rings is constant within a species; usually there are 30 but sometimes 26, 28, or 32. These are small or medium sized species, 4 to 25 mm long, which make a molting chamber and egg chamber of silk. The repugnatorial glands are absent. The male has a coxal sac in the 8th diplosomite. There are numerous American families.

Chordeumidae. Peculiar spermatophores are transferred. The viscous sperm from the gonopores, which are on the coxae of the 2nd walking leg, first is transferred to the coxal sacs of the posterior leg of ring 8. From here it is transferred into spermatophores made by coxal glands of the posterior gonopods. Then a secretion closes the spermatophore and later, in mating, it is pushed into the gonopores of the female with the gonopods. *Chordeuma* is found in Europe.

Craspedosomidae. Sternites of the anterior gonopods are small, of posterior gonopods large. There are 30 or rarely 28 rings, with lateral bosses or keels. *Craspedosoma alemannicum*, 11.5–17.5 mm long, of Europe, matures in 6–8 months; at the same time the number of legs increases from 3 to 48 in the male, 50 in the female. It lives 1 year.

Conotylidae. Telopodite of second leg of ring 7 is composed of 2 large thickened segments; the coxal segment bears a large endite. *Conotyla* is found in North America.

Cleidogonidae. Articles 1 to 3 of second legs of ring 7 are enlarged, and distal articles are either small or absent. *Cleidogona* is found from southeastern Canada to Central America. *Pseudotremia* is abundant in caves in the eastern United States.

Caseyidae. There are 30 trunk rings without shoulders. Leg pair 10 of the male consists of only 2 articles. *Caseya* is found in Oregon and Washington, others in Pacific coast states.

SUBORDER LYSIOPETALIDEA

There are more than 40 circular trunk rings with coxal sacs on the 3rd to 16th leg pairs. Long antennae and numerous ocelli are present. The legs have 2 tarsal articles. The known species run rapidly and are scavengers or sometimes predators. The repugnatorial pores of some species can spray 30 cm, and the hindgut can spray its contents. There are 60 species in the Mediterranean region north to southern Hungary, and about 30 species in the southern United States and California.

Lysiopetalidae. The collum is small, the body cylindrical, and the rings have numerous longitudinal crests and enlarged knobs bearing pores. *Abacion, Colactis* and *Delophon* are North American genera. *Tetracion* is found in caves. *Lysiopetalum*, 65 mm long, is European; *Apfelbeckia* is found in Yugoslavian caves.

Callipodidae. The 2nd pair of legs of the female is reduced to a vestige. *Callipus* is included.

ORDER JULIDA

There are about 1250 species of Julida. The Julida and the following 3 orders used to be combined as the Opisthospermophora or Juliformia. All 4 have the trunk cylindrical (juliform) and have tube-shaped rings. The number of rings is variable in all species (Fig. 19-5). The sternites are immovable, connected to the tergites. Tracheal atria are simple, with distal tracheae. The 7th ring of the trunk never has walking legs. If the anterior leg is a gonopod, the posterior one may be absent, or may also be a gonopod. The gonopods may be pulled back into a pouch. There are repugnatorial pores in all rings from the 5th. The gland has one chamber; its secretions are quinones. Eyes are usually present, but organs of Tömösvary are not. The mouthparts have visible joints (Fig. 19-8b). All four orders combined include about 3000 species.

The males of Julida have both pairs of legs on body ring 7 modified as gonopods, and the first pair of legs of the 2nd ring modified.

Blaniulidae. The gonopods cannot be withdrawn into a pouch. The family is cosmopolitan. *Nemasoma* is a North American genus. *Blaniulus guttatus,* the spotted wireworm, lives in cultivated areas of Europe and has been introduced into North America. It is 7.5–16 mm long, with 37–57 rings and 59–103 pairs of walking legs. There is a red spot on the side of each ring. It feeds on vegetable matter, feces, dead vertebrates or invertebrates, and has been found in broken coffins, 1 m deep, which had been buried 3–5 years previously. Lacking proteins, captive specimens will feed upon each others' legs. When very dry, they collect near roots, potatoes, bulbs, tubers and strawberries, and eat themselves a channel into the plant. This also happens when plant parts begin to rot, or are damaged by insects or rodents. Under these conditions, blaniulids may do damage, although healthy plants are not attacked. But wireworms help in aerating and mixing soil by burying organic material.

About 14 months after hatching, *Blaniulus* matures, having undergone 6 molts in summer, or 7 in other seasons. Within 3 months, males and females molt 8 times more. They live about 3 years. In building egg cocoons they use soil directly, but fecal pellets are used along with it, and the inner wall of the dome is covered by secretions. The nest is ready one or two weeks before it is needed for eggs. The eggs are deposited into the capsule with the evaginated genital atrium.

Paeromopidae. These are large bodied and have longitudinal striae. The anterior gonopods are connected along the median line. *Paeromopus* and other genera are found in western North America.

Paraiulidae. The first legs of the male are greatly enlarged and the 2nd legs of both sexes are much reduced. *Paraiulus* is found in Central America; *Litiulus* in Alaska; *Ptyoiulus, Uroblaniulus, Aniulus, Arvechambus, Ethoiulus, Bollmaniulus* and other genera in North America; *Karteroiulus* in Japan.

Julidae. The gonopods can be withdrawn into pouches. The family is Old World, but many members have been introduced into the United States. *Diploiulus* species are slow, *D. caeruleocinctus* (=*D. londinensis* = *Cylindroiulus teutonicus*), 18–37 mm long, with 38–53 rings and 63–97 pairs of legs, is found in unforested areas. It has caused damage by feeding on potatoes. *Ophyiulus pilosus* (=*O. fallax*), 16–45 mm long, with 49–63 rings and 85–117 leg pairs, runs rapidly and, if disturbed, will thrash about with its posterior end and slowly slip into a crack in the soil. The genera *Schizophyllum* and *Tachypodoiulus* belong here.

ORDER CAMBALIDA

Included are about 300 species. Cambalida are juliform millipedes (see above under the order Julida) having a large collum and some have longitudinal ridges on the body. Anterior and posterior gonopods are present. There are no obvious legs on the 4th ring. During development legs have moved forward. Thus the 3rd ring appears to have 2 pairs of legs.

Cambalidae. The promentum of the gnathochilarium is distinct. *Cambala* is found in southeastern United States. *Nannolene* is in California.

Leioderidae. There is no distinct promentum. *Leiodere* is found on the Pacific coast of North America.

ORDER SPIROBOLIDA

There are about 1150 species of Spirobolida. The Spirobolida are cylindrical juliform millipedes (see above under the order Julida) with copulatory legs hidden in a pouch. The fifth ring appears to have only one pair of legs. All legs during development move forward, making it appear that each of the first 5 rings, including the collum, has one pair of legs.

Spirobolidae. The second tergite extends below the level of the collum. *Narceus,* the large common "Spirobolus" of the eastern United States, is found in litter under rocks and loose bark. There are 4 species in North America: *N. americanus* (=*Spirobolus tinctorius*), to 13 cm, is found from Texas and Kansas to the Atlantic and Gulf Coasts and southeastern Canada; *Narceus annularis* (=*Spirobolus marginatus*), to 10 cm, is found from Quebec to North Carolina west to Kansas; *Narceus gordonus* and *N. woodruffi* of Florida prefer sandy soils. Other genera are *Hiltonius, Chicobolus,* and *Tylobolus* in North America; *Spirobolus* is found in China.

Atopetholidae. The 2nd tergite usually does not extend beyond the lateral edge of the collum. The anal valves are conspicuously rounded and have a thick row of setae along the mesal margin. *Atopetholus* and *Arinolus* are found in western United States in semiarid areas. They are desert millipedes. Others are found in Mexico.

Rhinocricidae. Prozonites of some rings usually have a pair of dorsal pits. *Rhinocricus* found along the Pacific coast of the United States and Canada, secretes an aldehyde besides quinones from its repugnatorial pores. Other genera are found in Mexico to South America and the Indo-Australian region.

ORDER SPIROSTREPTIDA

There are about 1300 species of Spirostreptida. The Spirostreptida are large cylindrical juliform millipedes (see above under order Julida) found in warm parts of the world. They have the posterior pair of male gonopods absent or rudimentary. The four families are separated by the structure of the male gonopods. Odontopygidae are African, limited to savannahs and relatively arid areas; Omopygidae are African; Harpagophoridae are South African and Indo-Australian; and Spirostreptidae are African and American.

Spirostreptidae. Scaphiostreptus seychellarum reaches 28 cm in length and 19 mm in diameter; the female has 139 pairs of legs. The African *Graphidostreptus gigas,* to 28 cm long, feeds on lettuce and carrots in captivity. *Orthoporus* has numerous species in the Americas, as far north as southern United States.

Superorder Colobognatha

There are about 270 species of colobognaths. The basal article of the mandibles and distal article are narrow and not visible from the side next to the gnathochilarium. In most species the mandibles are rod- or stylet-shaped and hidden under the small gnathochilarium.

In the Platydesmida the gnathochilarium still has middle and lateral parts; in Polyzoniidae it is a uniform triangular plate and, like the head, is pointed anteriorly. In the Siphonophoridae it is extended into a pointed tip (Fig. 19-20). Together with the labrum it forms a stiff proboscis-like preoral cavity that encloses the narrow mandibles. The labrum always lacks teeth. The rings differ in different groups. Unlike the Helminthomorpha, they can telescope into each other. Usually the tergites have wide lateral keels covering the legs completely, although the legs are not short. Most coxae have coxal sacs. Tarsal claws are long and strong. The posterior leg of the 7th ring and the anterior of the 8th are gonopods, but they still resemble walking legs. The tracheal atria are small and may serve only for respiration, not for muscle attachment as in other millipeds. Muscles insert on sternal apodemes. There are few ocelli if any. Organs of Tömösvary are lacking.

ORDER PLATYDESMIDA

The gnathochilarium has the usual parts; the tergites have a median dorsal groove and transverse rows of small tubercles.

Andrognathidae. Eyes are absent. The legs are covered by keels. *Brachycybe lecontei*, 1.4 cm long and pink, is found in southeastern United States in decaying wood.

Platydesmidae. Eyes are absent. Legs extend beyond lateral keels. *Platydesmus* is included. *Dolistenus* is yellow.

ORDER POLYZONIIDA

Eyes are present. The gnathochilarium is a single triangular plate. The tergites do not have a median dorsal groove.

Siphonophoridae. Eyes are absent, head is elongated into a long beak (Fig. 19-20). Dorsum is tuberculate or with hairs; trunk has regular constructions. *Siphonophora*

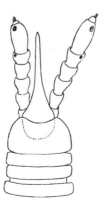

Fig. 19-20. *Siphonophorella ibis*, **dorsal view of anterior; the little head is prolonged into a "proboscis"; 1 mm wide. (After Attems.)**

portoricensis, 2.4 cm long and orange brown, is found on the surface of soil or below logs and bark. It can roll up. *Siphonophorella* is found in Europe.

Polyzoniidae. There are one or several ocelli. The head is not much drawn out. Dorsum lacks hairs or tubercles. Sternites and pleurites are movable. The trunk is without constrictions. *Polyzonium* is circumpolar with several North American species. The European *P. germanicum,* 1.75 cm long with 30–55 rings and 41–101 leg pairs, can coil up. The female coils around her eggs, of which there are about 65.

Siphoniulidae. The sternites, pleurites and tergites have fused, the trunk is cylindrical. *Siphoniulus* is found in Sumatra.

References

Attems, G. 1926. Diplopoda *in* Kükenthal, *Handbuch der Zoologie,* De Gruyter, Berlin, 4:129–238.

———— 1951. Revision systématique des Colobognatha. *Mém. Mus. Nat. Hist. Natur. Paris* N. S. Zool. 3:193–231.

Bedini, C. and Mirolli, M. 1967. The temporal organ of the pill millipede. *Glomeris. Monit. Zool. Ital.* (N.S.) 1:41–63.

———— 1967. Sensory cilia in the temporal organs of *Glomeris. Naturwissenschaften* 54:373–374.

Bower, G. 1951. Chilopod and diplopod cuticle. *Quart. J. Microscop. Sci.* 92:141–161.

Blum, M. S. and Woodring, J. P. 1962. Secretion of benzaldehyde and hydrogen cyanide by *Pachydesmus. Science* 138:512–513.

Brölemann, H. W. 1935. Diplopodes Chilognathes. *Faune de France* 29.

Buck, J. B. and Keister, M. L. 1950. *Spirobolus marginatus, in* Brown, F. A., edit., *Selected Invertebrate Types,* Wiley, New York, pp. 462–475.

Casnati, G. et al. 1964. Secretion of *Polydesmus. Experientia* 19:409–411.

Causey, N. B. 1943. Life history and ecology of the hothouse millipede *Orthomorpha gracilis. Amer. Midland Natur.* 29:670–682.

———— 1955. Life history of a spirobolid milliped. *Turtox News,* Genl. Biol. Supply Co., Chicago 33(10):200–203.

———— 1960. Speciation in North American cave millipeds. *Amer. Midland Natur.* 64:116–122.

Chamberlin, R. V. and Hoffman, R. L. 1958. Checklist of millipeds of North America. *Bull. U.S. Nat. Mus.* 212:1–236.

Cloudsley-Thompson, J. L. 1949. The enemies of myriapods. *The Naturalist,* London, 1949:137.

———— 1950. Water relations and cuticle of *Paradesmus gracilis* (Diplopoda, Strongylosomidae). *Quart. J. Microscop. Sci.* 91:453–464.

———— 1952. Responses to environmental stimuli. *Ann. Mag. Natur. Hist.* (12)5:417–434.

Davenport, D. et al. 1952. Biology of the Sierra luminous millipede, *Luminodesmus sequoiae. Biol. Bull.* 102:100–110.

Demange, J. M. 1959. L'accouplement chez *Graphidostreptus tumuliporus* avec quelques remarques sur la morphologie des gonopodes et leur fonctionnement (Diplopodes Spirostreptidae). *Bull. Soc. Entomol. France* 64:198–207.

———— 1967. Segmentation du tronc des chilopodes et des diplopodes chilognathes. *Mem. Mus. Nat. d'Hist. Natur. Paris* 44:1–188.

Dohle, W. 1964. Embryonalentwicklung von *Glomeris marginata*. *Zool. Jahrb. Abt. Anat.* 81:241–310.

———— 1965. Die Stellung der Diplopoden im System. *Verh. Deutschen Zool. Ges.* 28:297–606.

Dunger, W. 1958. Zersetzung der Laubstreu durch die Boden-Makrofauna im Auenwald. *Zool. Jahrb. Abt. Syst.* 86:139–180.

Eaton, T. H. 1943. Biology of a mull-forming millipede *Apheloria*. *Amer. Midland Natur.* 29:713–723.

Edney, E. B. 1951. Evaporation of water from woodlice and the millipede *Glomeris*. *J. Exp. Biol.* 28:91–115.

Eisner, T. and Davis, J. A. 1967. Mongoose throwing and smashing millipedes. *Science* 155:577–579.

———— et al. 1963. Cyanogenic glandular apparatus of a millipede. *Ibid.* 139:1218–1220.

———— and H. E. 1965. Mystery of a millipede. *Natur. Hist. Mag.* 74(3):30–36.

———— and Meinwald, J. 1966. Defensive secretions. *Science* 153:1341–1350.

Fahlander, K. 1940. Segmentalorgane der Diplopoda, Symphyla und Insekta Apterygota. *Zool. Bidr. Uppsala* 18:243–251.

Fechter, H. 1961. Anatomie und Funktion der Kopfmuskulatur von *Cylindroiulus*. *Zool. Jahrb. Abt. Anat.* 79:479–528.

Gabe, M. 1954. Emplacement et connexions des cellules neuro-sécrétrices chez quelques Diplopodes. *Compt. Rend. Acad. Sci. Paris* 239:828–830.

Gerhardt, U. 1933. Funktion des Gonopoden bei *Graphidostreptus*. *Mitt. Zool. Mus. Berlin* 19:430–438.

Gruner, H. E. 1953. Rollmechanismus bei kugelnden Land-Isopoden und Diplopoden. *Ibid.* 29:148–179.

Haacker, U. 1964. Paarungverhalten des Saftkuglers *Glomeris*. *Natur Mus.* 94:263–727.

———— 1967. Tagesrhythmische Vertikalwanderungen. *Naturwissenschaften* (in press).

Halka, R. 1958. Life history of *Schizophyllum sabulosum* (Diplopoda, Iulidae). *Ann Zool. Soc. Zool. Bot. Fennicae Vanamo* 19:1–72.

Hastings, J. W. and Davenport, D. 1957. Luminescence of the millipede *Luminodesmus sequoiae*. *Biol. Bull.* 113:120–128.

Keeton, W. T. 1960. Milliped family Spirobolidae. *Mem. Amer. Entomol. Soc.* 17:1–146.

Kinkel, H. 1955. Biologie und Ökologie des getüpfelten Tausendfusses *Blaniulus guttulatus*. *Z. Angew. Entomol.* 37:401–436.

Leiber, G. 1935. Vergleichende Anatomie des Gefäszsystems der Diplopoden. *Zool. Jahrb. Abt. Anat.* 59:333–354.

Loomis, H. F. 1933. Egg-laying habits and larval stages of *Arctobolus marginatus*. *J. Washington Acad. Sci.* 23:100–109.

Main, H. 1931. A millipede's tent. *Essex Natur.* 23:203–206.

Manton, S. M. 1952. The locomotion of the Chilopoda and Pauropoda. *J. Linnean Soc. London, Zool.* 42:93–167.

———— 1956. The structure, habits and evolution of the Pselaphognatha (Diplopoda). *Ibid.* 43:153–187.

———— 1958. Diplopoda and Chilopoda and limb structure of Diplopoda. *Ibid.* 43:487–556.

———— 1961. Functional requirements and body design in Colobognatha (Diplopoda). *Ibid.* 44:383–462.

———— 1964. Mandibular mechanisms and the evolution of arthropods. *Philos. Trans. Roy. Soc. London* (B)247:1–183.

Mason, B. and Gilbert, O. 1954. A peritrophic membrane in Diplopods. *Nature* 174:1022.

Meinwald, Y. et al. 1966. Defensive secretion of a *Glomeris*. *Science* 154:390–391.

Meske, C. 1961. Sense physiology of Diplopoda and Chilopoda. *Z. Vergl. Physiol.* 45:61–77.

Murakami, Y. 1965. Life history of *Ampelodesmus iyonis*. *Zool. Mag.* (*Dobutsugaku Zasshi*) 74:31–37.

Palm, N. B. 1954. Elimination of injected vital dyes from the blood in Myriapods. *Ark. Zool.* 6:219–246.

Perttunen, V. 1953. Reactions of Diplopods to the relative humidity of the air. *Ann. Zool. Soc. Zool. Bot. Fennicae Vanamo* 16:1–69.

———— 1955. Antennectomy and the humidity reactions of normal and desiccated specimens of *Schizophyllum sabulosum* (Diplopoda, Iulidae). *Ann. Entomol. Fennica* 21:157–162.

Pflugfelder, O. 1932. Mechanismus der Segmentbildung bei der Embryonalentwicklung und Anamorphose von *Platyrrhacus amauros*. *Z. Wiss. Zool.* 140:650–723.

———— 1933. Bau der Schläfenorgane der Myriapoden. *Ibid.* 143:127–155.

Ramsey, J. M. 1966. Migrating armies of *Pseudopolydesmus*. *Ohio J. Sci.* 66:339.

Roth, L. M. and Eisner, T. 1962. Chemical defenses in arthropods. *Ann. Rev. Entomol.* 7:107–136.

Sahli, F. 1955. Développement post-embryonnaire de *Cylindroiulus* (*Aneuloboiulus*) *silvarum*. *Ann. Univ. Saravensis Naturw.* 4:151–164.

Saundray, Y. 1953. La composition du tégument et ses modifications au moment de la mue chez les Myriapodes Diplopodes. *Compt. Rend. Acad. Sci. Paris* 237:1802–1804.

Schildknecht, H. et al. 1967. Wehrsekret der Diplopodengattung *Glomeris*. *Naturwissenschaften* 54:196–197.

Schmidt, H. 1952. Nahrungswahl und Nahrungsverarbeitung bei Diplopoden. *Mitt. Naturwiss. Ver. Steiermark*, Graz 81/82:42–66.

Schömann, K. 1956. Biologie von *Polyxenus lagurus*. *Zool. Jahrb. Abt. Syst.* 84:195–256.

Schubart, O. 1934. Tausendfüszler oder Myriapoda. 1. Diplopoda. in Dahl, *Die Tierwelt Deutschlands*, G. Fischer, Jena, 28:1–328.

———— 1960. Die Zahl der beschriebenen Myriapoden-Arten. *Zool. Anz.* 165:84–89.

Seifert, B. 1932. Anatomie und Biologie des Diplopoden *Strongylosoma pallipes*. *Z. Morphol. Ökol.* 25:362–507.

Seifert, G. 1960. Entwicklung von *Polyxenus lagurus*. *Zool. Jahrb. Abt. Anat.* 78:257–312.

———— 1961. *Die Tausendfüssler*. Neue Brehm Bücherei no. 273, Ziemsen Verl., Wittenberg Lutherstadt.

———— 1966. Das stomatogastrische Nervensystem der Diplopoden *Zool. Jahrb. Abt. Anat.* 83:448–482.

———— 1966. Häutungverursachende Reize bei *Polyxenus*. *Zool. Anz.* 177:258–263.

Shaw, G. G. 1966. Reproductive behavior in the milliped *Narceus annularis*. *Ecology* 47:322–323.

Silvestri, F. 1933. Sulle appendici del capo degli Japygidae e rispettivo confronto con quelle dei Chilopodi, dei Diplopodi e dei Crostacei. 5. *Congr. Internat. Entomol. Paris:* 329–343.

———— 1949 (1950). Segmentazione del corpo di Colobognatha. *Boll. Labor. Entomol. Agr. Portici* 9:115–121.

Stephenson, J. W. 1961. Biology of *Brachydesmus superus*, Diplopoda. *Ann. Mag. Natur. Hist.* (13)3: 311–319.

Thiele, H. U. 1959. Experimentelle Untersuchungen über die Abhängigkeit bodenbewohnenden Tierarten vom Kalkgehalt des Standorts. *Z. Angew. Entomol.* 44:1–21.

Toye, S. A. 1966. Activity of three species of Nigerian millipedes. *Entomol. Exp. Applied* 9:369–377.

———— 1966. Effect of desiccation on millipedes. *Ibid.* 9:378–384.

Tuzet, O. and Manier, J. F. 1954. Les organes hématopoiétiques et le sang des Myriapodes Diplopodes. *Bull. Biol. France Belgique* 88:90–98.

———— 1956. La spermatogenèse de neuf Myriapodes Diplopodes de l'ordre des Spirostreptida et des Spirobolida. *Bull. Inst. Roy. Sci. Natur. Belgique* 32:1–38.

Vannier, G. 1966. Loge de mue d'un nouveau type par un diplopode africain. *Rev. Ecol. Biol. Sol.* 3:241–258.

Verhoeff, K. W. 1932. Diplopoda, *in* Bronn's *Klassen und Ordnungen des Tierreichs* 5(2)2(12):1835–1962.

———— 1933. Wachstum und Lebensverlängerung bei Blaniuliden und über die Periodomorphose. *Z. Morphol. Ökol.* 27:732–749.

———— 1935. Biologie der Spirostreptiden. *Zool. Anz.* 109:288–292.

———— 1939. Wachstum und Lebensverlängerung bei Blaniuliden und über die Periodomorphose. *Z. Morphol. Ökol.* 36:21–40.

———— 1943. Diplopoden der Insel Ischia und über die Bedeutung des Mitteldarmturgors bei Häutungen. *Zool. Anz.* 141:214–231.

Wheeler, J. W. et al. 1964. Trans-2-dodecenal and 2 methyl-1, 4-quinone produced by millipede. *Science* 144:540–541.

Woodring, J. P. and Blum, M. S. 1963. Anatomy and physiology of repugnatorial glands of *Pachydesmus*. *Ann. Entomol. Soc. Amer.* 56:448–453.

———— 1965. Anatomy, physiology and comparative aspects of the repugnatorial glands of *Orthocricus arboreus* (Diplopoda: Spirobolida). *J. Morphol.* 116(1):99–208.

20.

Class Pauropoda

The Pauropoda include about 380 species, the largest being 1.9 mm long.

Pauropods are dwarf myriapods with two pairs of appendages transformed into mouthparts and 9 (rarely 8 to 11) pairs of walking legs. The antennae have 4 (rarely 6) articles and short branches as well as several long, multiarticulate flagellae.

Anatomy

The trunk of the primitive Hexamerocerata consists of 12 tergites and a posterior segment that probably corresponds to the telson. Eleven of the segments each bear one pair of walking legs. Most pauropods have only 6 tergites and a telson sclerite (Fig. 20–1). The first segment, and all even segments from the fourth on, are dorsally so reduced that they even lack a dorsal sclerite (Fig. 20–1). Each metamere, except the first and last, usually has a pair of walking legs.

The mouth, shifted slightly posteriorly, is covered anteriorly by a labrum. At its sides arise a pair of curved mandibles. In the Hexamerocerata the endite of the mandible is strong and diplopod-like; in others it is soft. By convention, the three articles of the first maxilla are called cardo, stipes and lacinia; there is no palp. The blunt triangular plate between the first maxillae (which together with the maxillae give the impression of a gnathochilarium) is derived from the sternite of the first maxillary segment.

The exoskeleton of most species is smooth, thin and barely pigmented. Only the Eurypauropodidae have strongly sclerotized and sculptured (granular or thorned) tergites. The diverse kinds of setae found in all species, sometimes annulate or club-shaped, are sensory organs of touch.

NERVOUS SYSTEM. The long trichobothria on or near the tergites possibly transmit vibrations. A large pseudoculus on each side of the head, probably corresponding to the organs of Tömösvary, consists of a domed, thin plate. Its hypodermis, innervated from the protocerebrum, probably contains sense cells. As in all small animals, the central nervous system is large in relation to the body volume. The small head has only enough space for the deutocerebrum; the protocerebrum extends posteriorly into the second trunk segment. Between the proto- and deutocerebrum the embryo has a small preantennal ganglion that, like the deuto- and tritocerebrum, develops in connection with a ventral organ. The tritocerebrum continues into the subesophageal ganglion, which consists of only two neuromeres (those of the mandible and first maxillae) and reaches deep into the first trunk segment adjacent to the first trunk ganglion (=collum ganglion). Posteriorly the medially fused ganglia of the remaining trunk segments form a thick cord that has segmental swellings but is not marked by free connective fibers. The ganglion of the preanal ring has moved anteriorly and is fused to the ganglion of the last leg-bearing segment. Detailed anatomy and embryology are known only for *Pauropus silvaticus*.

DIGESTIVE SYSTEM. The sclerotized ectodermal foregut has muscles for pumping and opens into the wide midgut in the third trunk segment. In the preanal metamere the midgut, lacking ceca, continues into the ectodermal hindgut, which divides into a narrow duct and a wide, sclerotized, rectal vesicle. There is a pair of Malpighian tubules.

The maxillary gland is derived from the coelomic pouch of the first maxillary metamere. The gland vesicle stores Trypan blue injected into the animal. The duct of the gland loops into the trunk; its walls are secretory, presumably functioning as salivary glands, and it opens between the maxillae. Near the mouth open two other pairs of salivary glands, both of which reach into the trunk. One is derived from the premandibular coelom pouch. The other gland, a much larger one, is derived from the ectoderm of the intermaxillary sternite.

RESPIRATORY SYSTEM. As in many other small animals there are no circulatory organs. Only the Hexamerocerata have respiratory organs. Their spiracles, on the coxae of the walking legs, usually open into a pair of very short tracheae; the first tracheae are long and extend into the head.

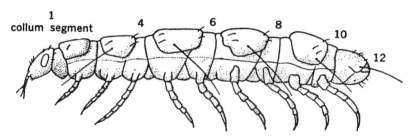

Fig. 20–1. *Pauropus silvaticus*, lateral view; numbers indicate segments which are narrow posteriorly and lack a tergite. Total length, 1.1 mm. (After Tiegs from Hennig.)

REPRODUCTIVE SYSTEM. The gonads develop ventral to the gut. The median, tube-shaped ovary remains in the same position throughout the life of the animal. From the sternum of the third trunk segment, a paired ectodermal invagination grows toward the ovary; one side of it remains rudimentary, the other forms the oviduct, a median atrium and a seminal receptacle. The male gonad pushes dorsally above the gut. In *Pauropus silvaticus* it constricts, forming four adjacent organs, each of which sends out a long vas deferens that widens into a seminal vesicle. These seminal vesicles unite into a median duct, then fork into paired ejaculatory ducts, which open between the 3rd walking leg coxae.

Reproduction

A spermatophore, consisting of a ball of sperm in a netlike cover, is deposited and attached by two threads to a crevice in the substrate. The presence of a female is not required.

Development

The eggs are only 0.1 mm in diameter, have much yolk, and are deposited individually in crevices in wood. In North Carolina most pauropod eggs were found in June and July. Only in *Pauropus amicus* is the female known to sit over a clump of eggs.

The eggs of *P. silvaticus* undergo total cleavage and even with 80 cells still form a blastula. Then one or two cells move into the blastocoel to become primary endoderm cells, a gastrulation by immigration. The nuclei of the blastula cells move slowly toward the periphery of the egg, and the central (=proximal) parts of the cells, the region that contains the yolk, fuse to each other so the egg resembles that of the other myriapods after having undergone superficial cleavage. Soon a typical germ band forms.

As the shell breaks, there hatches an immovable quiescent stage bearing long setae and primordia of the first antennae and of the first 2 pairs of walking legs. After a molt, a larva with 6 segments appears; the 2nd to 4th segments have legs, and the larva can take up food. In front of the telson is a growth zone that forms new segments and appendages, one after another, during the following molts (anameric development). *Pauropus silvaticus*, after successive molts, has 5, 6, and 8 pairs of legs. With the next molt, the 9th pair appears and the animal is sexually mature. Sexual maturity of all other Tetramerocerata studied seems to coincide with the appearance of the 9th pair of legs, even though some (*Polypaurus* and *Decapauropus*) grow an additional pair of legs in successive molts. Judging by the structure of a median male genital appendage, *Allopauropus*, like the Hexamerocerata, matures before its last leg pair appears. The embryonal development takes 13 days in *P. silvaticus;* the post-embryonal development, 14 weeks. In laboratory cultures, individuals lived for one year without molting again.

Habits

Pauropoda live in moist, not wet, decaying logs, leaf litter, compost, under stones, and soil crevices as deep as 5 cm. Below the high tide mark on the ocean shore, *Thalassopauropus remyi* and several species of *Allopauropus* live underneath stones partly covered by sand. Of 1800 specimens of myriapods collected in Duke Forest, North Carolina, 40.8% were pauropods. There were about 1,700,000 per acre (0.4 hectares) to 13 cm deep in clay soil, and 2,200,000 in sandy loam, more under oaks than pines. The thin cuticle and relatively large surface area permit *Pauropus* species to dry up rapidly; they survive only minutes at room humidity (in bright light only a few seconds, according to some authors).

LOCOMOTION. Compared with other dwarf arthropods living in the same habitat, the white pauropods move about rapidly. The strongly sclerotized *Eurypauropus* is slow. The gait pattern (forward stroke: back stroke) is from 6.6:3.4 to 7.2:2.5. Short distances are usually travelled in rapid motion (7.2:2.5) but the legs do not move as rapidly as in *Scutigerella*. In running, the body is kept stiff and straight and few legs touch the substrate at the same time (the contact phase is 0.28). The balance thus is not easily kept and blowing on them will readily unbalance the animals. This may not be a disadvantage for life in a crevice. As in centipedes the coxae are laterally attached to the body. The stiffness of the skeleton is due to heteronomous musculature of the sternites and tergites (as there are fewer tergites than sternites and no intercalary tergites). The smallness and stiffness of the hydrostatic skeleton permits penetration of crevices without digging.

FEEDING. Only *Pauropus lanceolatus* and *Allopauropus gracilis* have been observed feeding. Both bite into fungal hyphae with their mandibles and suck out the hyphae. Peristaltic motions are soon observed in the midgut, which may contract its diameter to one-half or one-third normal size, and produce strong suction without any mandibular action. The longest period of pumping observed was 50 minutes, but during this time the hyphae were bitten at several places. There may be some food selection, as sometimes *Pauropus* releases a hypha just bitten.

The gut content of *Millotauropus,* an animal having strong mandibles, was a homogenous mixture including also chewed hyphae, spores, and sometimes arthropod setae. Some observations indicate that semiliquid substances from the surface of dead earthworms are also taken up by pauropods.

Classification

Order Hexamerocerata

The order includes 5 known species. The antennae have articles that telescope into one another, and the penultimate and last articles bear flagella-like setae. The mandibles are strong like those of diplopods. There are 12 tergites plus telson, and 11 pairs of legs. There are spiracles on the coxae.

Millotauropodidae. This is the only family, and includes *Millotauropus*, to 1.8 mm long, known from the Congo, Angola and Madagascar.

Order Tetramerocerata

The order includes 375 species. The antennae have only 4 articles, which scarcely telescope into one another. The mandibles are soft. There are 11, rarely 12, trunk segments with 9, rarely 10, pairs of walking legs.

Pauropodidae. The trunk is whitish, soft, and has 11 segments and a telson (in the subgenus *Decapauropus*, 12 segments). There are 6 tergites. Usually metameres 2–10 (in *Decapauropus*, 2–11) each has one pair of walking legs. *Pauropus huxleyi*, to 1.5 mm long, is found in eastern and central United States and Europe; *P. silvaticus*, to 1.1 mm long, in Australia. In Europe and North America, *Allopauropus* includes some species in which the instar with 9 pairs of legs is followed by instars with 10 and 12 segments (in the subgenus *Decapauropus*). Other genera are *Stylopauropus* and *Polypauropus*.

Brachypauropodidae. This family contains 17 known species. The 2nd to 5th tergites are each divided by a transverse groove into an anterior and posterior portion. Each part has one pair of thick rectangular areas, giving the impression that there are 8 paired tergites. There are 9 pairs of walking legs on rings 2 to 10. *Brachypauropus*, 0.4 to 0.6 mm, is found in Europe and southeastern United States; *Aletopauropus* and *Deltopauropus* in North America.

Eurypauropodidae. The family contains 15 species. The 6 tergites are brown, sclerotized and sculptured. The first tergite covers the two anterior segments as well as the head; the last covers the telson. The body is relatively short and wide, and dorsoventrally flattened. There are 9 pairs of walking legs. *Eurypauropus spinosus*, 1.25 mm, is found in eastern and central United States and Europe. *Sphaeropauropus* can roll up.

References

Bagnall, R. S. 1935. *Thalassopauropus remyi*, an halophilous pauropod, and on the genus *Decapauropus*. *Scotland Natur.* 1935(213):79–82.

————— 1935. A classification of pauropods. *Ann. Mag. Natur. Hist.* 16:619–629.

Cloudsley-Thompson, J. L. 1948. *Hydroschendyla submarina* in Yorkshire, with an historical review of the marine Myriapoda. *The Naturalist*, London 827:149–152.

Hüther, W. 1959. Ernährung der Pauropoden. *Naturwissenschaften* 46:563–564.

Laviale, M. 1964, Présence de spermatophores chez *Stylopauropus*. *Compte Rend. Acad. Sci. Paris* 259:652–654.

MacSwain, J. W. and Lanham, U. N. 1948. Pauropoda from California. *Pan Pacific Entomol.* 24:69–84.

Manton, S. M. 1952. The locomotion of the Chilopoda and Pauropoda. *J. Linnean Soc. Zool.* 42:93–167.

————— 1966. Body design in Symphyla and Pauropoda. *Ibid.* 46:103–141.

Remy, P. A. 1936. Beitrag zur Fauna der Myriapoden Deutschlands. *Zool. Anz.* 116(11–12):310–320.

————— 1950. Les *Millotauropus*, types d'um nouveau groupe de Pauropodes. *Compte Rend. Acad. Sci. Paris* 230(5):472–474.

—————. 1953. Description de nouveaux types de Pauropodes: *Millotauropus* et *Rabaudauropus*. *Mém. Inst. Sci. Madagascar* 8A:25–41.

————— 1956. Pauropodes des Etats-Unis d'Amérique. *Mém. Soc. Nat. Sci. Natur. Math. Cherbourg* 47:1–48.

Starling, J. H. 1943. Pauropoda from Duke Forest. *Proc. Entomol. Soc. Washington* 45:183–200.

————— 1944. Ecological studies of the Pauropoda. *Ecol. Monogr.* 14:291–310.

Tiegs, O. W. 1947. The development and affinities of the Pauropoda, based on a study of *Pauropus silvaticus*. *Quart. J. Microscop. Sci.* 88(2–3):165–267; 275–336.

Verhoeff, K. W. 1934. Pauropoda *in* Bronn's *Klassen und Ordnungen des Tierreichs*, Akad. Verlagsges, Leipzig, 5(2)3:121–200.

21.

Class Symphyla

There are about 120 species of Symphyla, the largest, *Scutigerella immaculata,* being 8 mm long.

The Symphyla are myriapods with 3 pairs of mouthparts, 12 pairs of walking legs and a pair of spinnerets at the posterior. The gonopore is usually on the 4th trunk segment. In addition to the 12 leg-bearing segments, the trunk includes a preanal segment lacking appendages but with a pair of trichobothria, and a large sternite (the remainder of the growth zone) which extends below the telson. That the number of tergites is larger than the number of metameres is indicated by muscles, ganglia and appendages. Between the coxae on each sternite from segment 3 to 9 there is a pair of coxal sacs (Fig. 21–1). The exoskeleton, even of the tergites, is soft and colorless; the epicuticle is less than 1 μm thick.

This small group of myriapods is of general interest because its members display a number of characteristics found also in the apterygote insects: styli, coxal sacs, spinnerets, development by total cleavage and an embryonal dorsal organ. Although the pairs of ganglia and embryonal coelomic pouches correspond to the 12 pairs of legs, the dorsal region divides independently into a larger number of tergites (in some genera, up to 24), increasing the dorsoventral flexibility of the trunk. Presumably this adaptation is related to the habits of these animals, which live between soil particles (Fig. 21–1), compensating for their inability to dig.

Anatomy

The dorsal and ventral segmentation do not correspond; many dorsoventral, longitudinal and appendage muscles are not metamerically arranged but overlap the segmental borders. From the 4th segment on, the body can be divided into diplosomite areas, the ventral-dorsal and anterior-posterior borders of which match. But, from the dorsum it is impossible to recognize these diplosegments; they can be defined only by studying muscles and ganglia. Each of the new tergites that appears after the 3rd and 5th molts always includes two segments.

The posterior end of the trunk has a pair of spinnerets belonging to segment 13 and a pair of cones each tipped by a trichobothrium; the anus is under the tergite bearing the 12th pair of walking legs (Fig. 21–1). At the posterior end a large sternite represents the growth zone. It lacks borders and continues into the telson; whether it can be considered a metamere is doubtful.

Next to the coxae of at least 10 pairs of legs there is an unsegmented cone, the stylus, which in *Hanseniella* is constricted from the coxa. Next to the stylus is a pair of coxal sacs (Fig. 21–2), each consisting of a thin sclerotized membrane framed by thick sclerotized integument. These sacs can be everted by blood pressure and inverted by muscles. Although the coxal sacs arise from a cone which appears to be the subcoxa, embryology of *Hanseniella* shows them to be derived from the ventral organ (a metameric proliferation of the germ band giving rise to the segmental ganglion) in the area of the sternum.

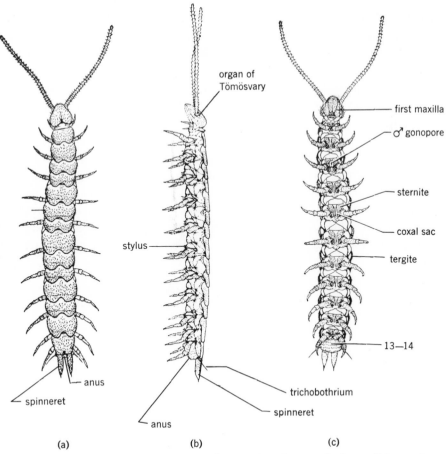

Fig. 21-1. *Scutigerella immaculata,* **dorsal, lateral and ventral views; 5.4 mm long. (After Michelbacher.)**

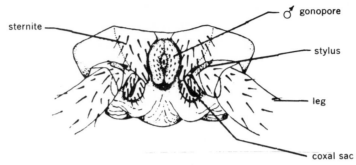

Fig. 21-2. *Scutigerella immaculata,* **venter of 4th segment of male; 0.54 mm wide. (After Michelbacher.)**

Held in the horizontal plane, parallel to the substrate, are 3 pairs of ventral mouthparts (Figs. 21-3, 21-4). Attached to the lateral walls of the head capsule, the mandibles, which resemble those of diplopods, have a single, one-jointed basal article. The endite has a strong adductor similar to that of the diplopods; abduction depends on the push of the tentorium. Apically the tentorium has a short lateral extension, the movement of which, transmitted to the apodeme of the endite, moves the endite laterally. Aiding this movement is a muscle that arises from the anterior end of the tentorium and attaches to the basal article next to its joint; contraction abducts the basal article and its movement is transmitted to the endite.

Although the musculature is different and Symphyla do not have a joint separating the cardo and stipes, the first maxilla is much like that of insects. It has two endites, lacinia and galea; the movable lateral tooth may be a vestige of a palp. The second maxillae, behind the first, fuse medially to form a plate, the labium (Fig. 21-4), the distal cones of which may be homologized with the glossae and paraglossae of the labium in insects. The large proximal part of the plate is open toward the body cavity; a wall anterior to (or above) the distal

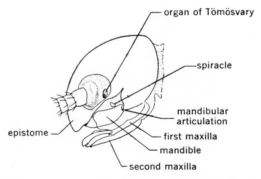

Fig. 21-3. Head of *Hanseniella agilis* **in lateral view; 0.5 mm long. (From Snodgrass after Tiegs.)**

portion forms the posterior (or lower) wall of the preoral cavity, enclosing the mandibles and maxillae. A soft tongue-like hypopharynx arises ventrally in the segment of the first maxilla, and in front of the second maxillae into the preoral cavity.

Spinnerets are present at the posterior border of the last tergite. At the top of the spinneret opens a mesodermal silk gland that, in the adult, may extend forward to segment 10 (or even 8). The non-functional silk gland and spinnerets present at birth are replaced at the third molt and again after the fifth. The old pair degenerates, but for a while in *Scutigerella* the old spinnerets are still visible on the posterior border of tergite 12 or 14. Because all 3 pairs of spinnerets appear on segments with legs, they cannot be considered transformed walking legs. In *Hanseniella* the cones (Fig. 21–4) bearing the trichobothria develop as do appendages and can be considered vestiges of them.

NERVOUS SYSTEM AND SENSORY ORGANS. Symphyla have innervated sensory setae and posterior trichobothria; there are usually no eyes. Organs of Tömösvary, just posterior to the antennae (Fig. 21–3), are formed of slightly domed cuticle with a small central pore. Each pore leads into a sclerotized capsule having a sievelike floor penetrated by the long rod-shaped ends of sensory cells. These rods, each containing a nerve fiber, fill a large part of the capsule cavity; each sensory cell has 6–15 of them.

The brain is relatively large. The protocerebrum, lacking globuli and an optic mass, receives the nerve fibers from the organs of Tömösvary. The subesophageal ganglion includes the neuromeres of the 3 sets of mouthparts.

DIGESTIVE SYSTEM. The foregut enlarges into the extendible midgut in segment 4 or 5; there are no ceca. At about segment 10 the midgut enters the ectodermal hindgut, which is differentiated into 4 parts, the most posterior widened.

EXCRETORY SYSTEM. There is one pair of Malpighian tubules. The maxillary nephridia, which open into the peroral cavity between the 2 pairs of maxillae, are derived from the coelom pouch of the first maxillary segment. Of these nephridia only the sacculus walls excrete; the long canal secretes saliva. A second pair, opening next to the first, has been noticed in *Scutigerella*.

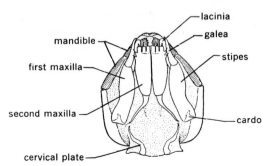

Fig. 21–4. Head of *Scutigerella immaculata* in ventral view; 0.5 mm long. (From Snodgrass.)

CIRCULATORY SYSTEM. The heart reaches from metamere 3 to 13, and ends blindly. Behind the posterior border of segment 5 it has 8 pairs of ostia. From the anterior of the heart arises a cephalic aorta. From near the base of the aorta arise a ventral artery and a pair of lateral cephalic arteries, which open near the maxillary gland sacculus. In the head a second pair of arteries leads toward the antennae. The ventral artery opens into the supraneural artery, which extends posteriorly above the ventral ganglion.

RESPIRATORY SYSTEM. There is a single pair of tracheae. The only spiracles are on the head near the base of the mandibles (Fig. 21–3), a rather unusual position. Each spiracle opens into a strong tracheal tube that supplies the anterior nervous system and head muscles with many branches and sends a few fine branches posterior toward the most anterior trunk segments.

REPRODUCTIVE SYSTEM. The paired ovaries, long lateroventral tubes from segment 4 to 12, continue into a pair of ectodermal oviducts that open through a median, dorsoventrally flattened atrium between the coxae of the 4th pair of legs. The testes, in the same position, are fused for some distance; the sperm traverses a pair of complex vasa deferentia and ectodermal vessels that open through a median atrium on sternite 4 (Fig. 21–2).

Reproduction

As in many myriapods and the lower insects, sperm transmission in *Scutigerella* is indirect. By placing his gonopore sternite on the substrate and contracting body rings 3 to 5, the male produces a droplet and pulls it out into a stalk by raising the anterior of his body (Fig. 21–5a). He remains in this position barely a minute, depositing a spermatophore at the tip of the stalk. Then, turning back like a hairpin, he walks several cm beyond the spermatophore and moves his spinnerets over the ground. Whether threads are attached is not known. In the absence of females, mature males will deposit spermatophores for most of the period (40 days at 20°C) between molts. Beginning when he resumes feeding, about 5 days after molting, each male deposits 150–450 spermatophores before halting about 10 days previous to the next molt.

The method used by the female to pick up the sperm is unusual. When she encounters a spermatophore as she runs about, she crosses her antennae behind it and folds them against her head, bending the spermatophore stalk down until it touches the front of her head. The female then bites off the spermatophore, leaving the stalk. In captivity, 18 sperm masses may be picked up in a single day, and this activity may be repeated a few days later.

As can be demonstrated by sectioning, the spermatozoa pass from the preoral cavity into one pair of spermathecae via a groove between hypopharynx and labium. (Swallowed sperm is digested.) Fertilization occurs at the time of egg deposition. As the egg emerges from the gonopore, the female, lifting her anterior 5 segments and bending her head, takes it with her mouthparts, deposits and cements it to moss (Fig. 21–5b). The mother then remains 1½ to 5 minutes with the egg, moving her mouthparts through the surrounding mucus as though chewing. As can be demonstrated with Feulgen stain if the egg is killed and fixed (Fig. 21–5c), it is during these motions that the sperm travels from the spermatheca to the egg. If a female is removed before she has had a chance to work over the egg, no sperm can be demonstrated on the egg and the egg dies. No sperm has ever been found in the female reproductive ducts.

Development

Scolopendrellids and *Hanseniella* deposit their eggs, 8 to 12 at a time, in crevices of moist soil and the female stays with the eggs but does not coil around them.

There is total cleavage and a true blastula. Primitive endoderm cells move into the blastocoel in different ways. In the Australian *Hanseniella* the cells delaminate; in Indochinese *Symphylella* there is a polar migration into the blastocoel; in Indochinese *Hanseniella* there is invagination by forming a true archenteron. The development of the head has been described above.

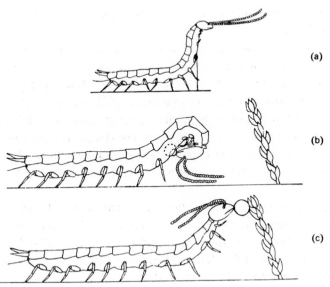

(a)

(b)

(c)

Fig. 21–5. Transfer of sperm by *Scutigerella immaculata*; body 5 to 6 mm long. (After Juberthie-Jupeau): (a) male has drawn out the spermatophore stalk and places sperm mass on its tip; (b) with her mouthparts, female takes egg emerging from gonopore; (c) female glues egg to a moss stalk and fertilizes it with sperm from the spermathecae in the preoral cavity.

Scutigerella hatches from the egg with 10 tergites and 6 free pairs of legs. Under the integument at the posterior of the body the primordium of the 7th pair of legs, already segmented, can be seen; the 8th pair is a simple bud. At the posterior end of the body, the large ventral organ and its two coelomic pouches develop as budding areas, anteriorly producing an additional segment and new functional leg pair with each molt. New tergites, however, are formed only at the 3rd molt (initiating the 9 leg pair instar) and the 5th molt (to the 11 leg pair instar); at each of these molts, *Scutigerella* develops a large tergite covering 2 future segments. One pair of legs appears on its venter; after the next molt a second pair appears under the tergite. Concurrent with these tergites new spinnerets appear and the old pair is lost.

After the 12th pair of legs appears, the animal has its adult shape, but it continues to molt, in the laboratory as many as 52 more times. In *Scutigerella*, molting begins as the cuticle of the head splits. The exuvia bends ventrally, permitting the body to push out anteriorly. The life span of *Scutigerella* may be more than 4 years.

Habits

Symphyla are found in moist habitats, such as between soil particles, in decaying leaf litter and wood, under stones and on ocean shores. Their soft integument is little protection against water loss. After 2 days at 70% humidity, Symphyla will shrivel to a fraction of their former size. Although the structure of the integument does offer some protection against waterlogging, *Scolopendrella* avoids ground water.

Symphyla move through the soil in response to changes in relative humidity. *Scutigerella* descends by using spaces between soil particles, rather than by digging; the body flexibility is advantageous in getting through the soil. Laboratory experiments show that *Symphylella* and *Scutigerella* move deeper in the soil if its air has less than 100% relative humidity. During humid weather they are found in the soil's upper layers, 2 to 10 cm deep, but during drouth they descend into the substrate; *Scutigerella* has been found as deep as 1.35 m. Even warm temperatures may cause vertical migrations from 7 mm down to 1.5 m below the surface.

The temperature optimum of *Scutigerella immaculata* is between 12 and 20°C. At lower temperatures the animals are lethargic, but they feed at 4.5°C and may produce eggs at this low temperature. Individuals acclimatized by 9 months at this low temperature could withstand 0°C for some months, indicating how it is possible for *Scutigerella* to live in the Alps at 3000 m elevation.

PROTECTION. The only protective adaptation known is the thrashing motion displayed by *Scutigerella immaculata* when its anterior is stimulated. It spins rapidly 180° around its last pair of legs so that the head faces away from, the spinnerets toward the possible predator. But it is not known whether the sudden turn only brings distance between the animal and predator or whether *Scutigerella* can use silk, as does *Lithobius*, to entangle and slow down the adversary. If touched with a fine brush, the spinnerets immediately secrete sticky silk.

LOCOMOTION. The soft Symphyla cannot dig. Movement in the soil is made possible by the very flexible trunk, which permits twisting the body and making hairpin turns. They can even bend 180° in the horizontal plane. This bending is made possible by the presence of several tergites above each soft sternite. The usual speed of a 5 mm long *Scutigerella* is about 20 mm/sec, but in flight, rapid motion is possible to 42 mm/sec, twice as fast as a 7 mm long second instar *Lithobius*. Undulation is avoided by using a gait in which many legs touch the ground at the same time. The coxae are attached laterally. In contrast to centipedes, only short lengths of the trunk are unsupported by legs at a given moment. The two legs of a pair are usually in the same phase. The backstroke of the legs lasts longer than the rapid forward swing. The forward stroke may take only 0.004 sec, the shortest backstroke 0.02 sec. (Backstroke in fast gait of *Cryptops* lasts 0.04 sec; of *Lithobius* 0.09 sec; in diplopods, about 0.5 sec, but in ants 0.08 sec.) The slow gait (relative duration of forward and back stroke) is 2.5:7.5, the fast gait, 5.2:4.8.

SENSES. Little is known of the senses. *Scutigerella* reacts immediately to vibrations, probably due to stimulation of the 2 posterior trichobothria. Also sensitivity to humidity and olfaction has been demonstrated by experiments using a smoked glass plate, 25 cm², over which small sacs are suspended every 2–30 mm. The sacs contain moist earth or moist glasswool. The animals used were 5 *Scutigerella immaculata*. When the air had only 70% humidity, the tracks under the moist sacs increased, especially those under the sacs containing earth, which provides certain chemical stimuli lacking in the glasswool. However, when the antennae were amputated, the preference for the earth was given up. It can be concluded that the antennae are necessary for olfaction.

In a second experiment, open-bottomed tubules containing glasswool and one containing moist soil were hung above the plate. The *Scutigerella* left the same number of tracks under tubes with soil as under those with glasswool. Then the coxal sacs of five animals were sealed with a droplet of rubber, and they were returned to the glass plate. Tracks then accumulated under the earth tube, but not under the glass wool tubes. This suggests that they were attracted again by the odor of the earth and the neglect of the glasswool tubes was due to loss of function of the humidity receptors, located in or near the coxal sacs.

FEEDING. Herbaceous plants form the main diet of *Scutigerella*, and the animals may do a great deal of damage to vegetables and flowers in gardens and greenhouses, preferring to feed on the smallest rootlets of young plants. In captivity, *Scutigerella immaculata* and *Hanseniella agilis* can be fed for years on soft tissued plants. Symphyla may be scavengers also, for they have been observed to feed on lettuce leaves touching the soil and also on dead Symphyla; arthropod remains have been found in the gut of *Hanseniella*.

Classification

Scolopendrellidae. The trunk has 17 distinct tergites, which, except for the last, have 1 pair of triangular posterior projections. The body is usually less than 4 mm long. The styli are small, sometimes reduced to small projections. The first leg pair is less than half the length of the second. Genera found in Europe include *Symphylella* and *Scolopendrellopsis*. Several species of *Scolopendrella* have been found in Texas.

Scutigerellidae. The trunk has 15 tergites, the posterior borders of which are at most slightly lobed. The body is usually more than 4 mm long. The styli are well formed. The first leg is more than half the length of the second. *Scutigerella immaculata,* called garden centipede in California, is up to 8 mm long (Fig. 21-1). Found all over Europe, North Africa, North America and Hawaii, it is reported to damage plants in gardens and greenhouses. At the age of 3 months, after the 7th molt, the female deposits eggs. *Hanseniella agilis* reaches 6.5 mm (Fig. 21-3); *H. nivea* is found in Europe and eastern United States.

Geophilellidae. The trunk has 21–24 tergites, the posterior borders of which may have paired sharp projections. *Geophilella, Symphylellopsis* and *Ribautiella* are common genera.

References

Dawydoff, C. 1943. Développement des Solopendrelles. *Bull. Biol. France Belgique* 77:1–28.

Edwards, C. A. 1959. Revision of the British Symphyla. *Proc. Zool. Soc. London* 132:403–439.

——— 1959. The ecology of Symphyla. *Entomol. Exp. Appl. Amsterdam* 2:257–267.

——— 1961. Factors controlling soil distribution of Symphyla. *Ibid.* 4:239–256.

Fahlander, K. 1938. Beiträge zur Anatomie und systematischen Einteilung der Chilopoden. *Zool. Bidr. Uppsala* 17:1–148.

Friedel, H. 1928. Ökologische und physiologische Untersuchungen an *Scutigerella immaculata*. *Z. Morphol. Ökol.* 10:738–797.

Hilton, W. A. 1931. Symphyla from North America. *Ann. Entomol. Soc. Amer.* 24:537–552.

Juberthie-Jupeau, L. 1956. Présence d'organes glandulaires céphaliques chez *Scutigerella immaculata*. *Compte Rend. Acad. Sci. Paris* 243:96–98.

——— 1959. Les phénomènes externes de l'émission des spermatophores chez les Symphyles. *Ibid.* 248:469–472.

——— 1959. La ponte chez Symphyles avec mes en évidence d'une fécondation externe des oeufs par la femelle. *Ibid.* 249:1821–1823.

——— 1960. Cycle d'emission des spermatophores et évolution des testicules et des vesicules séminales au cours de l'intermue chez *Scutigerella pagesi*. *Ibid.* 250:2285–2287.

——— 1960. Périod d'alimentation et évolution du tube digestif dans l'intermue chez *Scutigerella pagesi*. *Ibid.* 251:1241–1243.

——— 1965. Pontes et premiers stades chez deux espèces du *Symphylella*. *Rev. Ecol. Biol. Sol.* 2:53–64.

Manton, S. 1966. Body design in Symphyla and Pauropoda. *J. Linnean Soc. Zool.* 46:103–141.

Michelbacher, A. E. 1938. The biology of the garden centipede *Scutigerella*. *Hilgardia* 11:55–148.

———— 1939. Notes on Symphyla. *Pan Pacific Entomol.* 15:21–28.

———— 1949. The ecology of Symphyla. *Ibid.* 25:1–12.

Pflugfelder, O. 1933. Der feinere Bau der Schläfenorgane der Myriapoden. *Z. Wiss. Zool.* 143:127–155.

Ravoux, P. 1962. La segmentation des symphyles. *Ann. Sci. Natur. Zool.* (12)4:141–472.

Snodgrass, R. E. 1952. *A Textbook of Arthropod Anatomy.* Comstock Publ. Assoc., Ithaca.

Tiegs, O. W. 1940. The embryology and affinities of the Symphyla, based on a study of *Hanseniella agilis. Quart. J. Microscop. Sci.* 82:1–225.

22.

Class Insecta, Insects

There are about 750,000 species described, of which the walking stick, *Pharnacia serratipes* (Phasmida), 33 cm long, is the longest; the one with the largest body volume is the beetle *Titanus giganteus* (Coleoptera), 14 cm long.

Insects are mandibulate arthropods that have 3 pairs of appendages transformed into mouthparts. The trunk is separated into 2 tagmata: the thorax, which has 3 segments including all locomotory organs, and the abdomen. Usually there are both median and lateral eyes. Gonopores are located at the posterior end of the abdomen.

A huge number of species has evolved, the number being larger than those of all other animal classes combined. Insects have successfully invaded all terrestrial habitats and a large number of species, especially in the larval stages, have invaded freshwater. A few have invaded brackish water, but in the ocean there are only very few. In contrast to the myriapods, the insects have the mouthparts adapted and specialized in numerous ways, so that they have become tools for the utilization of varied new sources of food, and all possible ways of obtaining nourishment are employed by members of the class. The locomotory organs also have evolved drastically; in most of the insects the 3-segmented thorax, besides legs, has 1 or 2 pairs of wings. Flight has permitted development of modes of escape and searching for food and sexual partners otherwise developed only among birds and bats.

The concentration of organs of locomotion on the thorax made it possible to concentrate there all associated musculature. Especially in the winged forms, the sclerotized exoskeleton fuses and differentiates. The limitation to 3 pairs of legs made it possible for these to be very long without the danger of entanglement in movement. They are arranged fan-like and swing at a wide angle without overlapping.

There being only 3 pairs, the legs of each segment have to alternate and their forward phase cannot be longer than the period of contact. In the European ear-

wig, *Forficula*, walking slowly, the ratio is 3.5:6.5; running, it is 5:5. As the speed of walking increases, the angle of movement is increased and the pace duration shortened. Generally two legs on one side and one leg on the other side are in contact with the substrate.

The apterygote orders still transmit the sperm as do most centipedes by depositing free spermatophores. All other insects have evolved copulatory organs. Total cleavage is also found only among Collembola and is replaced in all others, with few exceptions, by superficial cleavage. During the development, except of the Protura, all segments are formed in the egg. The habits of the insect larvae often are very different from those of adults. This is especially marked in the highly specialized Holometabola, which includes most species.

It can be seen from a study of the comparative anatomy of the insect orders that from the primarily wingless orders with no metamorphosis to the Holometabola there is a steady decrease of homonomy of organs and increasing differentiation of the organs within certain segments. This progression is especially pronounced in the thorax, less so in the abdomen, with the exception of the genital segment.

Also there is a loss of abdominal appendages and nephridia, and a redistribution of spiracles and ganglia. With increasing complexity the dorsal heart loses its lateral arteries and the ostia of the anterior segments, so that in the area of the thorax the heart is represented only by the cephalic aorta; the heart itself is limited to several abdominal segments.

Relationships

The apterygote insects, belonging to several different lines of evolution, have a number of characters in common with the Symphyla. There are styli and cerci which may be connected with spinning glands. Also the coxal sacs common in both groups are found only in a few other diplopods: Lysiopetalidea and Colobognatha. The insects resemble the Symphyla also in respect to mouthparts which are enclosed in a preoral cavity, and the transformation of the second maxilla into a labium. In addition the gait of the Symphyla, despite their being many-legged, is more similar to that of the insects than to that of myriapods. It can therefore be assumed that the ancestors of insects resembled Symphyla.

References

Of the numerous good textbooks on insects only a few are listed here.

Borror, D. J. and Delong, D. M. 1965. *Introduction to the Study of Insects*, rev., ed., Holt, Rinehart and Winston, New York.

Brues, C. T., Melander, A. L. and Carpenter, F. M. 1954. Classification of Insects, 2nd ed. *Bull. Mus. Comp. Zool. Harvard* 108:1–917.

Comstock, J. 1940. *An Introduction to Entomology.* Cornell Univ. Press, Ithaca.

Farb, P. and the Editors of Life. 1962. *The Insects.* Time Inc., New York.

Grassé, P. P. (ed.), 1949–1951. Insectes, *in Traité de Zoologie,* Masson et Cie, Paris, vols. 9, 10.

Hennig, W. 1953. Kritische Bemerkungen zum phylogenetischen System der Insekten. *Beitr. Entomol.* 3 (Sonderheft): 1–85.

Imms, A. D. 1947. *Insect Natural History.* Collins, London.

———— 1957. *A General Textbook of Entomology,* 9th ed. Methuen & Co., London.

Klots, A. B. and E. B. 1959. *Living Insects of the World.* Doubleday, Garden City.

Rockstein, M. ed., 1964–1965. *The Physiology of Insecta.* Academic Press, New York, 3 vols.

Roeder, K. D. ed., 1953. *Insect Physiology.* Wiley, New York.

Snodgrass, R. E. 1935. *Principles of Insect Morphology.* McGraw-Hill, New York.

U.S. Dept. Agric. 1952. *Insects, Yearbook of Agriculture.* Government Printing Office, Washington.

Weber, H. 1933. *Lehrbuch der Entomologie.* G. Fischer, Jena.

———— 1954. *Grundriss der Insektenkunde.* G. Fischer, Stuttgart.

Wigglesworth, V. B. 1955. *Insect Physiology,* 5th ed. Methuen, London.

———— 1965. *The Life of Insects.* Weidenfeld & Nicolson, London.

SUBJECT INDEX*

A

Abacion, 412, 422

abdomen, 43, **45,** 63, 69, 83, **84,** 86, **210,** **293,** 342, 446, 447

abdominal ganglia, **46**

Acanthepedanus, **234,** 244

Acanthocephala, 417

Acanthoctenidae, 180, 195

Acanthoctenus, 195

Acanthophrynus, 122

Acari, 248

Acaridae, 269, 281, 282

Acaridei, 251, 252, 255, 256, 258, 259, 260, 261, 262, 264, 268, 281

Acarina, 248

Acarpis, 277

Acarus, 260, 262, **282, 283**

accessory claws, 171, **173**

accessory glands, **152**

accessory pigment cells, 316

Accola, 183, 207

accommodation, 167, 325

Aceria, 287

acetic acid, 119

acetylamine, 39

acetylcholine, 75

n-acetylglucosamine, 39

Achaearanea, 89, **90,** 153, 164, 169, 175, 187

Acherontia, 315

Achipteria, 286

aciniform glands, **144,** 146

acone, 315

Acrographinotus, **241,** 244

acron, 1, 4, **9,** 32, 42, 51, 53, 60, 63, 69, 84, 85, 309, 311, **313, 348**

acropodite, 402

Actinarctus, 26

Actinochaeta, 271

actinochitin, 271

Actinochitinosi, 271

Actinopodidae, 182

Actinopus, 182

Actinotrichida, 271

Aculus, 287

adaptations, 326

adenine, 141

adhesive gland, **3,** 9, 12

Admetus, 123, **124, 125,** 126

aedeagus, 346

Aedes, 279

Aeschna, 315, 316, 327, 328

Aganippe, 183

Agelena, 39, **95,** 164, 165, 166, 169, 190

Agelenidae, 156, 157, 169, 179, 180, 190

Agelenopsis, **151,** 156, 169, **170,** 190

aggregate gland, **144,** 146

Agkistrodon, 35

Agroeca, 192

alanine, 146

alary muscles, 346

albumin, 23

albuminoids, 16

Aletopauropus, 434

Allepeira, 189

Allokoenenia, 129

Allopauropus, 432, 433, 434

Allothrombium, 260

alveolus, **150**

Amaurobiidae, 181, 195

Amaurobioides, 157, 192

Amaurobioididae, 192

Amaurobius, **146,** 164, **172,** 195

Amblyomma, 248, 274

Amblypygi, 64, 122, 157, 215, 271, 297

ammonia, 48, 362

Ammothea, 300

Ammotheidae, 300

Ammotrecha, 225

Ammotrechella, 225

Ammotrechidae, 225

Ammotrechula, 225

Ammoxenidae, 194

Ammoxenoidea, 194

Ampelodesmus, 409, 421

Amphipoda, **48,** 303

*Boldface numbers refer to illustrations.

449